CONSTANTS

(See also Appendix I)

ELEMENTARY CLASSICAL PHYSICS

VOLUME 2

ELEMENTARY
CLASSICAL PHYSICS

VOLUME 2

(ELECTROMAGNETISM AND WAVE MOTION)

RICHARD T. WEIDNER

PROFESSOR OF PHYSICS
RUTGERS UNIVERSITY
NEW BRUNSWICK, NEW JERSEY

ROBERT L. SELLS

PROFESSOR OF PHYSICS
STATE UNIVERSITY COLLEGE
GENESEO, NEW YORK

ALLYN AND BACON, INC.   BOSTON

PRINTED IN THE UNITED STATES OF AMERICA

First printing . . . . July, 1965
Second printing . . . . December, 1965
Third printing . . . . . November, 1966

PREFACE

This is the second of two volumes in elementary classical physics. This volume treats electromagnetism and wave motion; the first volume treats mechanics, kinetic theory, and thermodynamics. Together with the authors' *Elementary Modern Physics*, these volumes constitute a series of introductory texts in college physics for students of science and engineering.

Again, our aim has been to be clear and rigorous and to concentrate on topics of fundamental importance. Wherever appropriate we have emphasized the atomic point of view. For example, we discuss Coulomb scattering in the chapter on electrostatics, emphasize the magnetic field produced by a moving point charge, and discuss polarization mainly in terms of the radiation from electric-dipole oscillators.

After the basic laws of electromagnetism have been developed in the usual sequence of electrostatics, currents, magnetic forces, and electromagnetic induction, and Maxwell's equations have been set down in Chapter 38, we turn to the basic ideas of wave behavior. This is illustrated first with mechanical waves propagated in one dimension. Chapter 39 is devoted entirely to transverse waves on a string; Chapter 40 mainly to longitudinal waves in elastic media. These two chapters on mechanical waves, including sound, may in fact be introduced at an earlier time by instructors who wish to take up mechanical waves immediately after mechanics. Our motivation for unifying wave motion, with both mechanical and electromagnetic waves discussed at one place, is simply that the basic wave effects are the same for all wave types. Interference and diffraction are illustrated not merely by visible electromagnetic waves; they are exemplified by sound waves through elastic media, as well as all types of electromagnetic waves.

Having developed the basic ideas of wave behavior in Chapters 39 and 40, we return to electromagnetism to derive the properties of electromagnetic waves from Maxwell's equations in Chapter 41. Then follow discussions of wave behavior in two and three dimensions. Included here are the Doppler effect for both mechanical and electromagnetic waves together with wave fronts, intensity variation, and the principle of reciprocity (or optical reversibility). This is followed by chapters on ray optics. We have included a brief treatment of the reflection properties of ordinary vectors and pseudovectors and have given more than the usual attention to Fermat's principle.

In introducing interference and diffraction phenomena, we have not placed sole, or even primary, emphasis on these effects as illustrated by incoherent visible light. Rather, we begin by considering coherent sources, such as radio or audio oscillators, derive the basic relations for interference and diffraction, and only then turn to the illustration of these effects by visible light.

Features of Volume 1 are continued here: numerous illustrative examples and problems (more difficult ones starred), thoroughgoing use of calculus and vector algebra (including the dot and cross products), secondary or optional material in small type, succinct summaries at the chapter ends. The rationalized mksa system of units is used exclusively. Appendix III gives a brief introduction to the Gaussian units, together with a conversion table. As in Volume 1, the historical development is largely omitted; a brief chronology to important advances in electromagnetism and wave motion is given, however, in Appendix V.

In addition to the material set in small type, the following chapters may be omitted without serious discontinuities: Chapter 36 on the electric and magnetic field vectors and para-, dia-, and ferromagnetism; Chapter 37 on electric oscillations and alternating-current circuits; Chapter 44 on lenses; and Chapter 47 on polarization.

Our thanks go to Professor Mason R. Yearian of Stanford University, who reviewed the manuscript; to Mr. Robert M. Wessely, who checked the answers to all problems and examples; to Mrs. Brenda W. Haywood, who assisted the authors in proofreading; to Mrs. Patricia B. Kinder, who typed the manuscript; and to the editorial and production staffs of Allyn and Bacon, who facilitated our efforts throughout.

Richard T. Weidner
Robert L. Sells

New Brunswick, New Jersey
Geneseo, New York

CONTENTS

TWENTY-EIGHT

ELECTRIC POTENTIAL

TWENTY-NINE

CAPACITANCE AND DIELECTRICS

THIRTY

ELECTRIC CURRENT AND RESISTANCE

THIRTY-ONE
D-C CIRCUITS

THIRTY-TWO
THE MAGNETIC FORCE

THIRTY-THREE
THE SOURCES OF THE MAGNETIC FIELD

THIRTY-EIGHT
MAXWELL'S EQUATIONS

THIRTY-NINE
WAVES ON A STRING

FORTY
ELASTIC WAVES

FORTY-ONE
ELECTROMAGNETIC WAVES

FORTY-TWO
WAVES IN TWO AND THREE DIMENSIONS

FORTY-THREE
REFLECTION AND REFRACTION

FORTY-FOUR
LENSES

FORTY-FIVE
INTERFERENCE

FORTY-SIX
DIFFRACTION

FORTY-SEVEN

ELEMENTARY CLASSICAL PHYSICS

VOLUME 2

T W E N T Y - F I V E

THE ELECTRIC FORCE
BETWEEN CHARGES

All the known forces in physics arise from four fundamental forces: the gravitational force, the nuclear force (or strong interaction), the weak interaction, and the *electromagnetic force*. The nuclear and the weak-interaction forces are of importance only within the atomic nucleus and in certain collisions between nuclei and decays of unstable elementary particles. The familiar gravitational force is important only when one of two inter-acting masses is comparable to that of a planet. This leaves the electro-magnetic force. With the exception of the force due to gravity, *all* of the forces of ordinary experience—the restoring force of a stretched string, the normal force of a floor acting upward on a person, the force between colliding automobiles—indeed, *all* of the forces acting between the atomic nucleus and its surrounding electrons, or between atoms in molecules, are ultimately electromagnetic in origin. The electromagnetic forces dominate all inter-actions from the size of atoms to that of planets.

We use the word *electromagnetism* to emphasize that electric and magnetic phenomena are not separate or unrelated. The word *electron* is the transliteration of the Greek word for amber, one of the materials used to produce electrical effects 2500 years ago, and the word *magnet* is derived from the name of the area in Asia Minor where the first natural magnets were found, Magnesia. Both electrical and magnetic effects are a consequence of a property of matter called electric charge. Although electromagnetic effects have a venerable history, we shall not chronicle the development of this important branch of classical physics, but a brief chronological outline of the important discoveries in electromagnetism is given in Appendix V.

25-1 Electric charge The distinctively new concept introduced in electromagnetism is that of *electric charge*. We know that when any two dissimilar nonmetallic objects are brought into intimate contact with one another—for example, by rubbing glass with silk—and then separated from one another, they show a mutual attraction (exceeding by far their gravitational attraction). Such objects are said to be electrically charged, and the presence of electric charge on each object is responsible for their interaction by an electric force. We assume that the reader is acquainted with this effect, and we shall not rehearse the many qualitative experiments which establish the following fundamental facts concerning these electric interactions: (a) there exist *two kinds of charge*, (b) *like charges repel*, and (c) *unlike charges attract* (Figure 25-1).

Figure 25-1. Like charges repel, unlike charges attract.

In this and the next several chapters we shall deal with electrostatics, the science of electric charges at rest. Strictly, we shall exclude situations in which interacting charged particles are in motion at speeds comparable to the speed of light (3.0×10^8 m/sec). Besides repelling or attracting by the electric force, charges in motion interact by the so-called magnetic force. Here we shall only deal with situations in which the charges' velocities are so small that the magnetic force between the charges is negligible compared with the electric force between them.

All electrical phenomena arise from the fact that the fundamental elementary particles of physics may have the property of electric charge. Thus, the electron has a negative charge, the proton a positive charge, and the neutron a zero charge. The use of the algebraic signs $+$ and $-$ to denote the two kinds of charge is appropriate, since combining equal amounts (soon to be defined precisely) of positive and negative charges results in a zero electric force acting on an object. As we know, the nucleus of an atom, consisting of protons and neutrons bound together within a volume never much greater than 10^{-14} m, is surrounded by electrons which are bound to and encircle it. An atom is electrically neutral as a whole when the number of electrons surrounding the nucleus equals the number of protons in the nucleus.

Atoms are closely packed in solids, their nuclei being separated from one another by a few times 10^{-10} m. In *conductors*, of which metals are examples, most of the electrons are bound to and remain with their parent nuclei, but approximately one electron per atom may be a *free electron*. A free, or conduction, electron wanders throughout the interior of a conducting material and it can easily be displaced within the conductor by external electric forces. In *insulating*, or *dielectric*, materials on the other hand, all atomic electrons are *bound*, to a greater or lesser degree, to their parent nuclei. Electrons are removed from or added to an insulating material only with the expenditure of energy. Examples of common conductors are metals, liquids having dissociated ions (electrolytes), the Earth, and the human body. Good insulators are very often transparent materials: plastics, glass, and a vacuum, which is a perfect insulator. The best electrical conductors are better than the worst conductors (or best insulators) by enormous factors, up to 10^{20}, which is a number that will be given precise quantitative meaning in Chapter 30. Lying between these extremes are the so-called semiconductors, whose conductivity is intermediate between conductors and insulators. Examples of semiconductors are germanium, silicon, and wood. In semiconductors only a very small fraction of the electrons are free; the number of conduction electrons in a semiconductor may be changed by heating the material, by shining light on it, or by applying a very strong external electric field.

Let us see how simple electrostatic effects are understood on the basis of the atomic model and of the properties of conductors and dielectrics. When two unlike dielectrics are rubbed together, some electrons at the interface between the materials will leave the material to which they would be less tightly bound for the material to which they would be more tightly bound, because systems always go to states of lower energy.

Upon separation one object now carries excess electrons and is negatively charged, while the other object has a deficiency of electrons and is positively charged. Hereinafter, when we refer to a large-scale object as being positively charged, we shall mean that its electrical neutrality is disturbed by its having lost electrons; similarly, a negatively charged object is an object with excess electrons.† Thus, the "charging" of an object consists simply of adding or subtracting electrons from it. When one type of charge is produced on an ordinary object, the other type must appear in equal amounts on a second object. The charging of any large-scale body results from the separation of charged particles (see Figure 25-2). When a body is charged, it has acquired or lost charged particles, namely electrons. For this reason we sometimes speak of the charge *on* a body, but of course the body acquires (or loses), not only the charge of electrons added to (or removed from) it, but also the mass of the added (or removed) electrons. The additional mass, however, is usually so trivial as to be negligible.

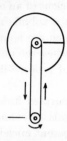

Figure 25-2. Schematic diagram for a Van de Graaff generator, a device for separating charge. The moving belt continuously carries charge from sharp points near it at the lower roller to points on the interior of a spherical conductor. In much larger versions the Van de Graaff generator is used to accelerate charged particles to very high energies (up to 20 Mev) for bombardment of targets in nuclear-physics experiments.

Whereas we may speak of the negative charge *on* a large-scale body—meaning the excess electrons on the body—it is not proper to speak of the charge *on* an electron (or on any other elementary particle for that matter). Electric charge is not something that can be added to or removed from an electron. An electron without charge is unthinkable; whatever it might be, it is certainly not an electron. Since electric charge is, like mass, an intrinsic property of an electron, we shall speak of the electric charge *of* an electron.

25-2 Coulomb's law Here we establish the quantitative aspects of the electric interaction between charges. Since the law for electric forces is known as Coulomb's law, after C. A. de Coulomb (1736–1806) who in 1785 found the electric force to vary as the inverse square of the separation distance, the electric force is often referred to as the Coulomb force.

We shall speak here of point-charges. By a point-charge is meant a group of one *or more* elementary charged particles confined to a region of space which is small compared with any other dimensions with which we might be dealing, such as the separation distance between two point charges. A single elementary particle best exemplifies the concept of point-charge, but

---

† In view of this it would, of course, have been far more convenient if Benjamin Franklin, who first introduced the + and − designations for the two types of charge, had assigned these labels such that the electron had a positive charge and the proton a negative charge, but it is obviously too late in the development of electromagnetism to have this convention reversed. We can be reasonably sure, however, that the inhabitants of one half of the populated planets call their electrons positive.

even here the charge has finite size. The stability of a charged particle of nonzero size against the strong mutual repulsion of its parts is not understood on the basis of present-day fundamental physical theory. We must simply say, for example, that the charge of an electron is confined to a very small, but not zero, volume, leaving the question of what holds it together as an important one not yet answered.

The electric force between point-charges is found to lie along the line connecting them. Thus, the Coulomb force is a *central force.* Indeed, it could not be otherwise, for between two points in empty isotropic space the only unique direction is the line between them.

The Coulomb force varies *inversely as the square of the distance r* between two point charges:

$$F \propto 1/r^2$$

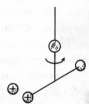

This was confirmed, at least approximately, in the experiments of Coulomb and, later, of Cavendish, who used a torsion balance (see Figure 25-3). The restoring torque of the twisted thin fiber is proportional to the angle of twist (see Section 17-1). Thus, one can measure the force of attraction or repulsion between these small charged objects of known separation by measuring the angle through which the rod attached to the fiber is displaced. Such ex-

Figure 25-3. Cavendish torsion pendulum for measuring the variation in the Coulomb force with distance between two charged bodies.

periments with charged objects are similar to the Cavendish experiment, in which the gravitational force between two small objects is measured (Section 16-2). Indeed, one of the trickiest difficulties in the Cavendish gravitational experiment is to eliminate the Coulomb force between the gravitationally interacting objects. Although experiments with a torsion balance can establish that the exponent of r in $F \propto 1/r^n$ is 2 to only within a couple per cent, other experiments (to be described in Section 27-5) show by indirect means that the exponent is precisely 2 (to within a few parts in 10^9).

Scattering experiments, in which positively charged particles are shot at atomic nuclei, show that the inverse-square Coulomb force holds down to dimensions of about 10^{-14}, the size of the very small, positively charged nuclei of atoms. Indeed, the Coulomb force operates between the protons *within* a nucleus. The electric repulsion between protons competes with the attraction between protons and neutrons. In the heavier atoms, in which there are many protons, the Coulomb repulsion is responsible for instabilities which can lead to the ejection of helium nuclei in alpha decay or the splitting of the nucleus in nuclear fission. Furthermore, indirect experiments involving the interaction of electrons and mu mesons with atomic nuclei, show that Coulomb's law is valid down to distances of about 10^{-16} m.

The Coulomb force is a *conservative* force (Section 12-2). It depends only on the separation distance between two charged particles, not on the time or on the velocities of the particles (provided the velocities are small compared with the velocity of light). An important consequence of this is, of course, that one may associate a potential energy with the electric interaction between charged particles.

The gravitational and electric forces are similar in several respects: both are *central, conservative, inverse-square forces*. Therefore, many of the concepts developed for gravitation—the gravitational field, gravitational potential energy, the energetics of particles interacting under the gravitational force (Chapter 16)—are equally applicable to the electric force. But there are also emphatic differences. For one thing, there are two types of electric charge, but only one type of gravitational charge (or gravitational mass). Electric charges may attract or repel; gravitational charges attract only. As a consequence, one cannot speak of a gravitational conductor or insulator, and certainly not of a gravitational shield. Another important difference is in the relative magnitudes of the electric and gravitational interaction. The electric force is immensely larger than the gravitational force; for example, between an electron and a proton the electric attraction is 10^{39} times greater than the gravitational attraction. The gravitational force is altogether trivial at the atomic level, because the electric force is overwhelmingly larger. And this is precisely why, paradoxically, the gravitational force can manifest itself. The electric force is so very strong and the amounts of negative and positive charge are so nearly equal in magnitude, that no ordinary object can easily avoid becoming electrically neutral. Thus, the electric force, operating internally, at the atomic scale, is not manifest but the gravitational force is.

The relative magnitudes of the electric and gravitational forces can be seen from other considerations. If all the electrons of the atoms in the Sun were somehow removed from the Sun and placed on the Earth, then the period of the Earth's orbit about the Sun would be 10^{-13} sec instead of one year. Similarly, if the electron and proton of the hydrogen atom were to interact by the gravitational force only, the period of the electron's orbital motion about the proton would be a couple of hours instead of 10^{-16} sec.

With only two point-charges one can learn how the electric force varies with distance, that it is an inverse-square force. On the other hand, we cannot determine with only two point-charges whether one charge is large and the other small. By Newton's third law, the electric forces on the two charges are equal in magnitude and opposite in direction. To learn something about the magnitudes of electric charge requires at least *three* charges. Suppose that charged bodies *1* and *2* are brought in turn to the same distance from charged body *3*. We find that the electric force on *1* due to *3* is F_1 and that on *2* due to *3* is F_2. Then, *by definition*, the relative magnitudes of the charges q_1 and q_2 are

$$q_1/q_2 = F_1/F_2 \qquad\qquad [25\text{-}1]$$

The ratio of the respective forces is the ratio of the charge magnitudes; see Figure 25-4. (This is, of course, precisely what is done in comparing gravitational masses, or gravitational charges: if two objects at the same location on Earth have weights in the ratio of 2 to 1, their respective gravitational masses differ by a factor 2.)

With the choice of some arbitrarily chosen standard electric charge, we can measure any other charge magnitude in units of the standard charge by means of Equation 25-1.

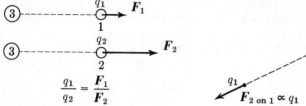

Figure 25-4. The relative magnitudes of two charges q_1 and q_2 is, by definition, the ratio F_1/F_2 of the respective forces arising from a third charged body.

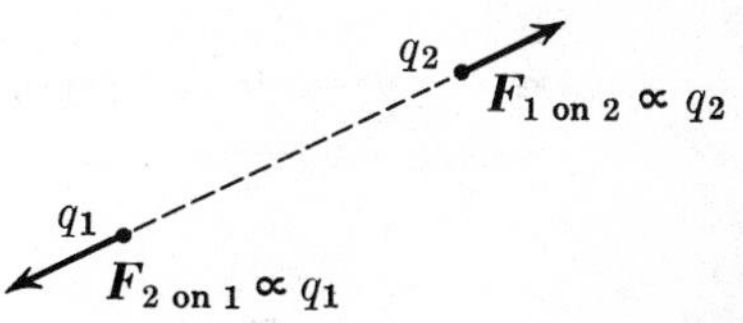

Figure 25-5. Two interacting charged objects. The force on each charged object is proportional to the magnitude of its charge.

There is a very simple procedure for dividing the charge on a conductor into halves. Suppose that one has two identical spherical conductors, one initially charged and the other uncharged. If the two spheres are brought into contact and then separated, after separation each will have exactly half the charge, by symmetry. This procedure can be extended, of course, to change the charge on a conductor by factors of 4, 8, ... It was used by Coulomb. The halving procedure cannot, however, be continued indefinitely; eventually one reaches that point where a single extra electron resides on a conductor, and the charge of one electron cannot be divided.

Equation 25-1 gives the charge ratio q_1/q_2 for two charges in terms of the force ratio F_1/F_2 for the two charges interacting, in turn, with a *third* charge. We determine thereby the charges q_1 and q_2. Now suppose that these two charges interact with one another only, as shown in Figure 25-5. From Equation 25-1 it follows that, when charges q_1 and q_2 interact, the force on q_1 is proportional to q_1. By the same token, the force on q_2 is proportional to q_2. Now, if the forces acting on the two interacting charges are equal and opposite, in accordance with Newton's third law, the magnitude of force, F, acting on either must be proportional to both q_1 and q_2 as well as inversely proportional to r^2; or,

$$F \propto q_1 q_2 / r^2$$

$$\boxed{F = k q_1 q_2 / r^2} \qquad [25\text{-}2]$$

where k is a constant whose value depends on the choice of units for charge.

If we use the radius vector r_{12} to designate the position of charge q_2 relative to q_1, then we may write Equation 25-2 in vector form as

$$F_{1\ on\ 2} = \frac{k q_1 q_2 r_{12}}{r_{12}^{\ 3}} = -F_{2\ on\ 1} \qquad [25\text{-}3]$$

See Figure 25-6. The separation distance r_{12} appears to the third power in the denominator to compensate for the magnitude of r_{12} in the numerator.

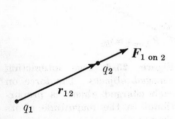

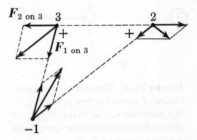

Figure 25-6. Relation between the force $F_{1\ on\ 2}$ on charge q_2 and the radius vector r_{12} from charges q_1 to q_2.

Figure 25-7. Three interacting point-charges. The principle of superposition applies for Coulomb forces.

Note that the direction of $F_{1\ on\ 2}$ is given correctly if we use the algebraic signs for q_1 and q_2: the force is positive (that is, repulsive) when both q_1 and q_2 have the same sign and it is negative (that is, attractive) when the signs are different.

Thus far we have treated the Coulomb force between only two interacting point-charges at rest. Suppose that a charge q_3 is in the presence of two other charges q_1 and q_2, as shown in Figure 25-7. Experiment shows that the force on q_3 is just the *vector sum* of the separate forces on it from q_1 and q_2. That is, the *superposition principle* of forces holds for the Coulomb force. Said differently, the force between any two charges is independent of the presence of other charges: to find the resultant force we merely add the individual forces as vectors. The superposition principle, although simple, is *not* self-evident; it is a result of observation for electric interactions. As we shall see, its consequences are many and important.

25-3 Electric units The numerical value of the constant k appearing in the Coulomb-law relation (Equation 25-2), depends, of course, on the units chosen for F, q, and r. In the *rationalized mksa* (meter-kilogram-second-ampere) *system of units*, which we shall use exclusively henceforth, the "mechanical" units are those of the mks system—meter for length, newton for force, joule for energy, etc.—and the unit of charge is the *coulomb* (abbreviated *coul*).

With F in newtons, r in meters, and q in coulombs, the constant k of Equation 25-2 has the value

$$k = 8.98755 \times 10^9 \text{ nt-m}^2/\text{coul}^2 \qquad [25\text{-}4]$$

Thus, two point-charges, each of 1 coul and separated by 1 m, exert an electric force of approximately 9.0×10^9 nt on one another. Therefore, one coulomb of charge is, as charges go, an enormous amount. One might find the net charge on a laboratory device of ordinary size to be 10^{-7} coul $=$ 0.10 μcoul. Two point-charges of this magnitude and separated by 1 cm repel one another with a force of about 1 newton.

The definition of the coulomb is a bit complicated. First, by definition, a net charge of 1 coul passes through the cross section of an electric conductor when an electric current of 1 amp exists in this conductor for 1 sec. The ampere is defined in turn by the magnetic force between two current-carrying conductors (Section 33-5).

For most computations it will suffice to round off the value for k, making it equal to 9.0×10^9 nt-m^2/coul^2. In the rationalized mksa system the constant k is written

$$k \equiv \frac{1}{4\pi\epsilon_0} \qquad [25\text{-}5]$$

where ϵ_0, the *electric permittivity of the vacuum*, has the value

$$\epsilon_0 = 8.85435 \times 10^{-12} \text{ coul}^2/\text{nt-m}^2 \qquad [25\text{-}6]$$

We may then write Coulomb's law in the form

$$F = \left(\frac{1}{4\pi\epsilon_0}\right)\frac{q_1 q_2}{r^2} \qquad [25\text{-}7]$$

In later sections we shall use both the constant k and ϵ_0 in equations, the choice of k or ϵ_0 being dictated by which of these will lead to the mathematically simpler relation.

In the *rationalized* unit system the factor 4π appears in Coulomb's law, as shown in Equation 25-7, but not in certain other fundamental relations, such as Gauss's law, Equation 27-3 (in the so-called nonrationalized systems it goes the other way: 4π does not appear in Coulomb's law, but it shows up in other relations). Unhappily, a large number of systems of electrical units exist. Other than the mksa system, the only system now in common use is the so-called *Gaussian cgs system*. The names of the electrical units, the forms of the fundamental laws of electromagnetism, and conversion factors for the Gaussian system are given in Appendix III.

The electron's charge, whose magnitude is that of any other charged elementary particle, is designated by $-e$; its magnitude is

$$e = 1.60207 \times 10^{-19} \text{ coul}$$

The direct measurement of the electronic charge e, as made in the Millikan experiment, is discussed in Section 26-5.

The electron's charge is small. For example, a charge of one microcoulomb, a typical charge by laboratory standards, corresponds to an excess or deficiency of 6×10^{12} electrons. Thus, we may ordinarily assume electric charge to be infinitely divisible and continuous and ignore its essential "graininess." We may, for example, imagine a negatively charged surface to have charge spread continuously over it, rather than concern ourselves with the actual finite number of electrons, acting as point-charges, which reside on it. We do the same thing in dealing with the mass of an ordinary object: we imagine it to be infinitely divisible, although the atomic nature, or graininess, of all matter implies that the mass is always an integral multiple of the mass of one atom or molecule.

When electrons are transferred to or from a laboratory object being charged, the difference in mass is trivial. Thus, when a body acquires charge of 1 μcoul (or 6×10^{12} electrons), its mass changes by only $(9.1 \times 10^{-31}$ kg/electron)$(6 \times 10^{12}$ electrons) $= 5 \times 10^{-18}$ kg $= 5 \times 10^{-9}$ μg.

The simplest device for detecting electric charge is the electroscope, in which the angular separation of light-conducting leaves, mutually repelled, is a measure of the charge on the electroscope (Figure 25-8). The electroscope is not, however, a precise or easily calibrated instrument. The electrometer, a refinement of the electroscope, is basically an electroscope that has been so calibrated that the angular displacement of a charged conductor suspended from a torsion fiber may be measured. Another way of measuring charge is to measure electric current over a period of time (the ballistic galvanometer, Section 34-6) or to measure the potential of a charged conductor of simple geometry (Section 29-2).

Example 1 What is the ratio of electric to gravitational attractive forces between a proton and electron?

The gravitational force (Equation 16-1) is $F_g = Gm_p m_e/r^2$ and the electric force is $F_e = ke^2/r^2$ where e is the charge magnitude of both particles. The ratio of the forces for *any* separation distance r is:

$$F_e/F_g = ke^2/Gm_pm_e$$
$$= (9.0 \times 10^9 \; nt\text{-}m^2/coul^2)(1.6 \times 10^{-19} \; coul)^2/(6.67 \times 10^{-11} \; nt\text{-}m^2/kg^2)$$
$$\times (1.67 \times 10^{-27} \; kg)(9.11 \times 10^{-31} \; kg)$$
$$F_e/F_g = 10^{39}$$

Figure 25-8. A simple type of electroscope.

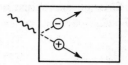

Figure 25-9. A photon enters a closed chamber and produces an electron-positron pair.

25-4 Charge conservation Electric charge is conserved. According to the law of conservation of charge, the net charge, or *algebraic sum of the charges, in any isolated system is constant.* This is illustrated very simply in the processes in which *two* objects are charged: electrons are transferred from one body to another, and the result is one body with positive charge and a second body with an equal amount of negative charge. No violation of charge conservation has ever been observed.

Electric charge conservation does *not* imply, however, that electric charge can be neither created nor destroyed, but only that the creation of positive charge must be accompanied by the creation of an equal amount of negative charge. An important example of the creation with equal but opposite electric charges of two charged particles is the phenomenon of *pair production.* When a sufficiently energetic photon, an electrically neutral particle of electromagnetic radiation, enters a closed container, as in Figure 25-9, it may be annihilated and in its stead appear two particles, an electron with charge $-e$, and a positron with charge $+e$. The *net* charge within the container has not changed.

The positron, which is identical with an electron in all respects except the sign of its charge (and the consequences of the difference in sign), is called the *antiparticle* of the electron. The electron and positron are but one example of a particle-antiparticle pair. Other examples are the proton and anti-proton, carrying charges of $+e$ and $-e$ respectively, and more exotic elementary particles such as the π^--meson and the π^+-meson. Just as particle-antiparticle pairs may be created, from photons (or by other means), a particle and its antiparticle may *annihilate* each other, producing two or more photons, or pairs of other particles. No matter what processes take place within a system—whether charge transfer between bodies in contact, nuclear transformations, creation of matter, or annihilation of particles—the total charge is always conserved. With the conservation of electric charge, the *classical* list of conservation laws is complete. They are: the conservation of linear momentum (Section 8-1), angular momentum (Section 15-4), mass (Section 7-4), energy (Section 12-3) and, now, electric charge.

25-5 Charge quantization The total electric charge of any object is just the algebraic sum of the charges of the elementary particles comprising it. *All* of the many elementary particles in physics now known, although they may differ greatly in mass and other properties, have just one of *three possible charge values:*

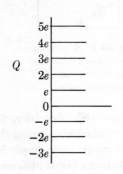

$$+e, \quad 0, \quad \text{or} \quad -e$$

where e is the magnitude of the charge of an electron. For example, the charges of the electron and positron are $-e$ and $+e$, respectively; the charges of the proton and antiproton are $+e$ and $-e$, respectively; and the charges of the three kinds of π-mesons, the π^+, π^0, and π^-, are $+e$, 0, and $-e$, respectively. The neutron and its antiparticle, the antineutron, have charges of exactly zero. Why the fundamental particles of physics, if they have any charge at all, have only the magnitude e, is not known on any more fundamental basis than that it is a well-established experimental fact.

Figure 25-10. Charge quantization. The only possible values of any charge Q are integral multiples of the electronic charge.

Since every charged object is nothing more than a collection of elementary particles, the only possible values of the total charge Q of any object are given by

$$Q = \pm Ne, \quad \text{where } N = 0, 1, 2, \ldots \quad [25\text{-}8]$$

Electric charge is *quantized*: it appears in *integral* positive and negative *multiples* of the charge of the electron, and no others; see Figure 25-10.

The discreteness, or granularity, of electric charge is not evident except through some rather subtle experiments, simply because most charged objects have a charge that is very much larger than e; that is, the integer N in Equation 25-8 is typically very much larger than 1. But the unique charge of the electron is shown directly in the fundamental experiments of Millikan (Section 26-5). Charge quantization is implicit in the chemical idea of atomic number, where this integer gives the total number of electrons (or protons) and, hence, the total negative (or positive) charge in a neutral atom. For example, the elements $_1$H, $_2$He, and $_3$Li have atomic numbers of 1, 2, and 3, respectively. Charge quantization is also implied in the chemical idea of valence, where again one assigns a positive or negative integer.

An atom with equal numbers of electrons and protons will be exactly neutral electrically only if the electronic and protonic charges are of *exactly* the same magnitude. How can one tell whether they are? In some recent precise experiments, presumably neutral atoms or molecules were subjected to intense electric fields. If the positive and negative charges were not of precisely the same magnitude, a resultant force would have acted upon the atoms or molecules. But no resultant force was found. If any difference at all exists between the magnitudes of the electronic and protonic charges, it is less than 10^{-20} e.

25-6 Coulomb scattering As an example of the Coulomb force between charged particles we consider the following. A positively charged particle is fired at a second positively charged particle of much greater mass, which can therefore be assumed to be remaining at rest. The light particle is, of course, deflected from a straight-line path, or scattered, by the repulsive Coulomb force. We wish to find the relationship between the angle of scattering, θ (the angle between the initial and final velocities of the scattered particle) and the so-called impact parameter, b, which is the closest distance the light particle would come to the massive particle if there were no force repelling it. See Figure 25-11a.

Since the Coulomb force falls off rapidly with distance, at great distances from the massive particle (called the scattering center) the incident particle of mass m travels in a (nearly) straight line at a (nearly) constant speed v, both before and after encountering the scattering center. The overall effect of the Coulomb force is to change the particle's direction but not its speed; that is, there is a change in the direction but not the magnitude of the particle's momentum.

The path of the particle, nearly straight at the start and finish, must be exactly *symmetrical* relative to the line OA, in Figure 25-11b, which bisects the angle $(\pi - \theta)$. This follows from the fact the Coulomb force between the particles depends only on their separation distance, not on the velocity or time. Said differently, if we imagine time to be run backward, the particle's velocity being reversed in direction at each point, then we must find the *same* path. Now it can be shown through a fairly complicated analysis that the path is, in fact, a hyperbola with the scattering center at one focus. We shall not have to avail ourselves of this information to relate b to θ, however. All that we need to know is that the force between the particles is *conservative* (already used in establishing the symmetry of the path), *central*, and *inverse-square*.

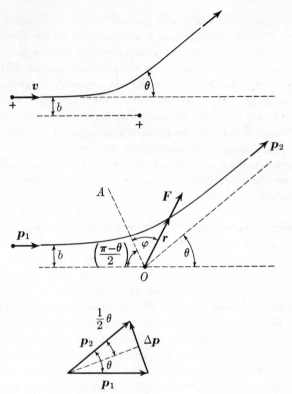

Figure 25-11. Coulomb scattering. (a) A particle with impact parameter b is scattered through the angle θ. (b) Geometrical details of the scattering; the initial and final momenta are p_1 and p_2. (c) Relation between p_1, p_2, and the momentum change Δp.

The change Δp in the scattered particle's linear momentum is found from the geometry of Figure 25-11c. Clearly,

$$\tfrac{1}{2}\Delta p = p \sin (\theta/2) \qquad\qquad [25\text{-}9]$$

where the magnitude of the initial (and final) linear momentum p is mv. The change in linear momentum can, in general, be written as

[9-11] $$\Delta p = \int F\, dt \qquad\qquad [25\text{-}10]$$

where the time integral of the force is known as the impulse. Since Equation 25-10 is a vector relation, the direction of the equivalent force producing the deflection is the same as that of Δp. Thus, only the *component* of the Coulomb force (magnitude, $F = kq_1q_2/r^2$) acting *along the direction of the line OA*, which is also the direction of Δp, will influence the overall change in linear momentum. The effects of the force components not along OA cancel; that is, the particle is slowed down by such a force component in approaching the scattering center, but is speeded up the same amount by an equal but opposite force component in receding from the center. We may then write

$$\Delta p = \int F \cos \phi \, dt = \int \frac{kq_1q_2}{r^2} \cos \phi \, dt \qquad [25\text{-}11]$$

Now we use a neat trick to avoid having to perform the complicated integration in Equation 25-11, an integration which is possible only if we know where the particle is at each instant of time. We make use of the fact that the Coulomb force is a central force, acting along the line joining the particles; therefore, the angular momentum L of the scattered particle, when measured relative to an origin at the scattering center, is constant (Section 15-3). In magnitude, we have

$$L = mvb = mr^2 \, d\phi/dt \qquad [25\text{-}12]$$

Here mvb represents the particle's angular momentum when it is far from the scattering center, while $mr^2 \, d\phi/dt$ can be recognized as the product of the particle's moment of inertia and angular velocity, both relative to an origin at the scattering center.

Eliminating r^2 between Equations 25-11 and 25-12 yields

$$\Delta p = \frac{kq_1q_2}{vb} \int \cos \phi \, \frac{d\phi}{dt} \, dt = \frac{kq_1q_2}{vb} \int_{-(\pi-\theta)/2}^{(\pi-\theta)/2} \cos \phi \, d\phi$$

The integral now involves only the angle ϕ between r and the line OA; its limits follow from Figure 25-11b. After integration, we have

$$\Delta p = \frac{2kq_1q_2}{vb} \cos \frac{\theta}{2} \qquad [25\text{-}13]$$

Eliminating Δp between Equations 25-13 and 25-9 and solving for b gives

$$b = \frac{kq_1q_2}{mv^2} \cot \frac{\theta}{2}$$

or, in terms of the particle's initial kinetic energy $K = \frac{1}{2}mv^2$,

$$b = \frac{k}{2} \frac{q_1q_2}{K} \cot \frac{\theta}{2} \qquad [25\text{-}14]$$

Equation 25-14 is the fundamental relation for Coulomb scattering. It shows that θ is large when b is small; that is, the more closely the incident particle is aimed to strike the scattering center, the greater is its deviation, as shown in Figure 25-12. In the extreme case, in which $b = 0$, we find

$\theta = 180°$; then the incident particle approaches the scattering center head on, is brought to rest momentarily, and is returned along the incident path.

The analysis we have just gone through has an important application: in the scattering of positively charged particles by the massive nuclei of atoms. In the historic experiments suggested by Lord Rutherford and carried out in 1911, highly energetic alpha particles (doubly ionized helium nuclei) were fired at thin gold targets. The alpha particles were scattered by the positively charged gold nuclei in the fashion shown in Figure 25-12. Indeed, these

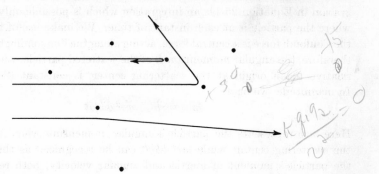

Figure 25-12. Charged particles scattered by nuclei.

experiments established that the positive charge and mass of an atom is confined to a very small region of space, the atomic nucleus, and that the Coulomb force holds with charge separation distances as small as 10^{-14} m. An alternative atomic model, that in which the positive electric charge was imagined to be distributed continuously throughout the atomic volume, was discarded because the distribution with angle of the scattered particles was interpretable only on the basis of the Rutherford model.

Example 2 An alpha particle (charge, $+2e$) with a kinetic energy of 8.0 MeV is scattered by a gold nucleus (charge, $+79e$). What is the scattering angle θ for impact parameters of (a) 1.0×10^{-14} m, (b) 1.0×10^{-13} m, and (c) 1.0×10^{-12} m?

From Equation 25-14 we have

$$\tan(\theta/2) = kq_1q_2/2bK = \frac{(9.0 \times 10^9 \text{ nt-m}^2/\text{coul}^2)(2)(79)(1.6 \times 10^{-19} \text{ coul})^2}{(2)(1.0 \times 10^{-14} \text{ m})(8.0 \times 10^6 \text{ ev})(1.6 \times 10^{-19} \text{ joules/ev})} = 1.4$$

With $b = 1.0 \times 10^{-14}$ m, we have $\theta = 110°$.

For such a small impact parameter, smaller than the distance between adjacent atoms in solid gold by a factor of more than 10,000, the alpha particle is strongly scattered. It is, in fact, turned back. For impact parameters larger by factors of 10 and 100, respectively, we have,

with $b = 1.0 \times 10^{-13}$ m, $\theta = 16°$
with $b = 1.0 \times 10^{-12}$ m, $\theta = 2°$

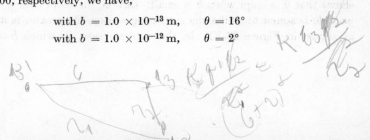

It is clear, then, that such highly energetic particles are appreciably scattered by gold nuclei only when they come very close, on an atomic scale, to hitting the nucleus head on. One cannot, of course, in a scattering experiment; aim any one alpha particle at a particular nucleus; one must direct a beam of particles at a collection of nuclei, usually in a thin foil. Since only very close encounters result in any substantial deviation of the incident particles, a very small fraction of the incident particles is found in the beam scattered from the forward direction. This small fraction is, however, highly significant. An atomic model in which the positive charge is imagined to be spread uniformly over a much larger volume would predict a still smaller fraction of particles scattered through large angles.

25-7 Summary The electric, or Coulomb, force between point-charges is given by

$$[25\text{-}2] \qquad F = kq_1q_2/r^2$$

where $k = 1/4\pi\epsilon_0 = 9.0 \times 10^9$ nt-m^2/coul^2. The unit of charge in the mksa system is the coulomb. The electric force is a central conservative force, and the superposition principle for forces applies to the Coulomb interaction.

Electric charge is conserved: in any isolated system, the net charge is constant. Electric charge is quantized: any observed charge is an integral multiple, positive or negative, of the electronic charge $e = 1.60 \times 10^{-19}$ coul.

PROBLEMS

25-1 Four charges, each of charge $+Q$, are placed at the four corners of a square of edge length L. Find the magnitude of the force on any one charge arising from the other three.

25-2 Three charges, each of charge $+Q$, are placed at the corners of an equilateral triangle of edge length L. What is the magnitude of the resultant electric force on any one of these charges rising from the other two charges?

25-3 Two point-charges of equal magnitude exert a force of 2.0 nt on one another. When their separation distance is decreased by 0.50 cm, the force increases to 3.0 nt. What is the magnitude of each charge?

25-4 A $+1.0\,\mu$coul point-charge is 5.0 cm from a point-charge of -2.0 μcoul and 10.0 cm from a point-charge of $+4.0\,\mu$coul. (a) Where must the two charges lie for the resultant force on the $+1.0\,\mu$coul charge to be a minimum? (b) What is this force? (c) How must the charges be arranged to give a maximum force on the $+1.0\,\mu$coul charge? (d) What is this force?

25-5 A charge of $+0.30\,\mu$coul is 6.0 cm from a charge of $-0.15\,\mu$coul. At what (noninfinite) point relative to the $+0.30\,\mu$coul charge can any third positive charge be placed so that the resultant electric force on it is zero?

25-6   Two spherical conductors, each of 5.0 gm, are hung from two insulated strings, each 50 cm long and attached to a common point at their upper ends. After the two conductors have been brought into contact, they repel one another and come to rest at a separation distance of 10 cm. What is the magnitude of the charge on each conductor?

25-7   Two charged objects are suspended from long insulating strings attached together at the top. The angle between the strings is θ. Show that, if θ is small, the electric force between the charged objects is proportional to θ.

25-8   A charge Q is placed midway between two negative charges of equal magnitude q. (a) For what value of Q will the resultant force on each of these three charges be zero? (b) Is this configuration one of stable or unstable equilibrium?

25-9   A positive charge Q is a distance d from an infinite line of positive point-charges, each of magnitude q and separated from one another by the distance d. Charge Q is directly above one of the charges in the line, as shown in Figure 25-13. Find the direction of the resultant force on Q and show that its magnitude is given by

$$(kqQ/d^2)\left[1 + \sum_{n=1}^{\infty} 2/(n^2 + 1)^{3/2}\right]$$

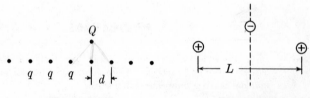

Figure 25-13   **Figure 25-14**

25-10 ★ A particle of mass m and charge $-q$ moves along the dotted line, Figure 25-14, midway between two fixed positive charges, each of magnitude q, separated by L. Show that for small displacements from the line joining the two positive charges, the particle oscillates in simple harmonic motion with a frequency $f = q/\sqrt{\epsilon_0 m \pi^3 L^3}$.

25-11 ★ A particle of mass m and charge q is located midway between two other fixed point-charges, each of charge q. When the particle in the middle is displaced by a small amount along the line on which the three charges lie, it oscillates in simple harmonic motion. Find the oscillation frequency.

25-12   Two identical spherical conductors initially are charged with *unlike* charges. When they are separated by a distance r, the force on each conductor is F. Then the two conductors are brought in contact, and separated again to r. The force on each is again found to have the magnitude F. What is the ratio of the two initial charges?

25-13 ★ A torsion pendulum has a horizontal rod of overall length L with a moment of inertia I relative to the axis of the fiber. When oscillating freely, the pendulum undergoes angular oscillations of period T. One end of the rod is charged and a second small charge is brought near this end, the electric force acting at right angles to the rod. The torsion fiber is then turned through the angle θ. Show that the electric force between the charges is given by $8\pi^2 I\theta/T^2 L$.

25-14 The plus and minus labels at the terminals of a certain battery are missing. How could you supply them?

25-15 When an electrically neutral insulated conducting body of nonzero size is brought near to a small charged object, the conductor is attracted, even though its net charge is zero. Explain.

25-16 An electron in a hydrogen atom orbits the proton in a circle of radius 0.53 Å. (a) What is the force on the electron? (b) What is the speed of the electron?

25-17 Two electrons rotate about a proton in the same circular orbit, the electrons being diametrically opposite each other. If the radius of the orbit is 5.3×10^{-11} m, what is the angular velocity of the electrons' orbital motion?

25-18 Find the Coulomb forces on each of two nuclear fragments of $_{56}Ba^{146}$ and $_{36}Kr^{90}$ formed in the nuclear fission of $_{92}U^{236}$ when, just after their formation, their centers are separated by 1.3×10^{-14} m.

25-19 The particles in atomic nuclei, protons and neutrons, attract each other by the very strong nuclear force. This force shows saturation; that is, any one nuclear particle will interact only with those neighboring particles lying within the range of the nuclear force. The Coulomb force, on the other hand, although it falls off with distance, has an infinite range; moreover, it acts between every pair of charged particles. In which type of nucleus, a light one or a heavy one, is the Coulomb repulsion more important relative to the nuclear attraction?

25-20 Two objects, each of 1.0 kg mass, attract each other by gravitational force. What equal and like charges must be placed on the two objects such that the gravitational force is neutralized by a repulsive Coulomb force of the same magnitude?

25-21 ★ (a) Confirm that, if all the electrons of the atoms in the Sun were somehow transferred to the Earth, the period of the Earth's orbit about the Sun would be 10^{-13} sec rather than one year. (Assume, for simplicity, that there is one electron for each proton and neutron; the neutron and proton masses are both approximately 1.7×10^{-27} kg). (b) Confirm that if the electron and proton of the hydrogen atom were to interact by the gravitational force only, the period of the electron's orbital motion would be a few hours rather than 1.4×10^{-16} sec.

25-22 What would the charge of a proton have to be if the electric repulsive force between two protons were to cancel exactly the gravitational attractive force between them?

25-23   It has been conjectured that the antiparticles, while gravitationally *attracting* one another, might be gravitationally repelled by particles. Why is it extraordinarily difficult to test this hypothesis by experiment?

25-24   (a) Suppose that overnight all positively charged particles became negatively charged particles and all negatively charged particles became positively charged particles. Could you tell? (b) Suppose that the magnitude of e changed overnight by a factor of 10^{10}. Could you tell?

25-25   An "atom" known as *positronium* having a transitory existence of 10^{-7} sec is formed by an electron and positron, moving in circular orbits about their common center of mass. If the electron and positron are separated by 1.0 Å, what must be the speed of each particle?

25-26   (a) How could you tell the difference between a hydrogen atom, comprised of an electron and proton, and an antihydrogen atom, comprised of a positron and an antiproton? (b) If some distant galaxy consisted exclusively of antimatter, would this be evident to us through the light captured in telescopes?

25-27   What evidence is there that the total charge in the universe, if not exactly zero, is only a small fraction of the total negative or positive charge?

25-28   The *faraday* is the name given to the charge of 1 mole of singly charged ions of any material. Show that the Faraday is 96,520 coulombs. (*Hint:* How many atoms are there in a mole?)

25-29   In an electrolysis experiment 2.0 gm of Cu^{++} (atomic weight, 63.6; valence, $+2$) are deposited on the negative electrode. How many grams of SO_4^{--} ions (atomic weight, 96.1; valence, -2) must have been neutralized on the positive electrode at this time?

25-30   In Section 25-6 we discussed the scattering of a charged particle by a fixed particle of *like* charge. What changes, if any, must be made in the analysis if the charges are of unlike sign?

25-31   An alpha particle (charge, $+2e$) having a kinetic energy of 6.0×10^{-13} joule is aimed so as to miss striking a gold nucleus (charge, $+79e$) by only 10^{-13} m. (a) Through what angle is the alpha particle scattered? (b) What is the scattering angle for an impact parameter of 10^{-14} m?

25-32   Energetic protons strike a target (paraffin) consisting mostly of unbound protons (strictly, the hydrogen nuclei in the paraffin are bound to the material with an energy that is so small compared with that of the incident particles that they may be considered to be effectively free). How can one tell, if at all, whether the protons emerging from the target are scattered incident protons or recoil target protons.

25-33   An incident proton encounters a free proton initially at rest and is thereby scattered through 45°. In what direction does the recoil proton move after the collision?

TWENTY-SIX

THE ELECTRIC FIELD

The electric field is a useful concept for computations involving the Coulomb force, and electric lines of force, which represent this field, are useful in visualizing the Coulomb interaction. In this chapter we compute the electric field for several simple charge distributions. The torque and electric potential energy of an electric dipole in a uniform electric field are derived.

26-1 Electric field defined Consider a number of point charges, such as q_a, q_b, and q_c in Figure 26-1, *fixed* in position. We introduce still another charge, q_t, a test charge, at position P and find the resultant electric force F_t acting on it by superposing as vectors the individual electric forces from the charges a, b, and c. Now suppose that we replace this test charge by another

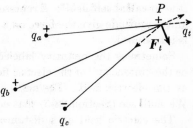

Figure 26-1. Test charge q_t is acted on by the resultant electric force F_t arising from the charges q_a, q_b, and q_c.

one of the same sign but twice its magnitude, again at the position P. We need *not* go through the whole computation again to find the resultant force on this charge: if the force is F_t with q_t at P, then the force on $2q_t$ at the same position is $2F_t$. Indeed, if we know the resultant electric force on a unit positive charge introduced into a collection of fixed charges, we know thereby the electric force on *any* other point charge at the same position. The force is proportional to the magnitude of the test charge; the direction of the force is reversed when a negative charge replaces a positive charge.

It is useful, then, to define the *electric field* E for any point in space as *the resultant electric force per unit positive charge*.

$$E = \frac{F}{q} \qquad [26\text{-}1]$$

Knowing E at some point we may then find the electric force F acting there on any charge q_t through the relation

$$F = q_t E \qquad [26\text{-}2]$$

It is essential that the charges which act as the source of the field (q_a, q_b, and q_c in Figure 26-1) remain fixed in position. Only then will the test charge, when introduced, not cause these charges to be displaced by the electric force it produces on them and thereby alter the field. This point requires emphasis because, in the case of an electrically charged conductor whose charges (free electrons) are easily displaced, introducing an additional charge may cause these charges to be redistributed. Thus, to compute E from one or more charges we imagine these charges to remain fixed in position; alternatively, we imagine the test charge q_t to be so very small that it will not appreciably affect the locations of the other charges. Furthermore, in computing E, we do not include the electric field of the test charge itself (the so-called self-field): E represents a vector field in space whose direction and magnitude give the force on a unit positive charge *before* any test charge is introduced.

Sometimes the quantity labeled E is called the electric field "strength" or the "intensity" of the electric field. We shall refer to it hereinafter simply as the electric field. The units of electric field are newtons per coulomb. We shall see (Section 28-5) that equivalent units are volts per meter.

The electric field at a distance r from a single point-charge q is easily found from Coulomb's law. The force between q and the test charge q_t is

$$F = k\,\frac{qq_t}{r^2}$$

Therefore,
$$E = \frac{F}{q_t} = \frac{kq}{r^2}$$
[26-3]

We may write this relation in vector form by using the radius vector r to denote the position of the test charge relative to the origin located at the charge q:

$$E = \frac{kq\mathbf{r}}{r^3}$$
[26-4]

The magnitude of the electric field from a single point-charge varies inversely as the square of the distance from it. The distance r appears to the third power in the denominator of Equation 26-3 to compensate for the additional factor r appearing in the numerator. Since electric forces superpose as vectors, the electric fields contributed by individual point-charges are added as vectors to give the resultant field.

Through the electric-field concept we associate a magnitude and a direction with each point in space. This gives a new way of looking at the interaction between two charges q_a and q_b. We can say that charge q_a acts as the source of, or creates, an electric field E_a which surrounds it and that the charge q_b, immersed in this field, is then subject to an electric force $F_{a \text{ on } b}$. That is,

$$E_a = \frac{kq_a\mathbf{r}}{r^3} \qquad \text{and} \qquad F_{a \text{ on } b} = q_b E_a$$

Similarly, we can interpret the electric force of q_b on q_a by saying that q_b generates the electric field $E_b = kq_b r/r^3$ and that q_a immersed in the field E_b then experiences the force $F_{b \text{ on } a} = q_a E_b$.

This two-stage process, the production of the field by one charge and the response to the field by the second charge, may seem at first sight to be a pedantic matter. But there is, in fact, real physical justification for the field concept, that is, for visualizing electric interactions as taking place *via* the electric field. For one thing, when q_a is moved, so that its separation distance from q_b is changed, q_b does *not* feel a different force *instantaneously*. Rather, q_b continues to experience the original force (therefore, electric field) for the time required for light to travel from a to b. That is, disturbances in the electric field arising from accelerated charges are propagated at the finite speed of light. This is no mere accident. As we shall see, light consists of electric (and magnetic) fields traveling through space. Thus, an electric field may become detached from the electric charge generating it. Such electric (and magnetic) fields, or electromagnetic waves, are physically real in the sense that one may attribute to them such "mechanical" properties as energy, linear momentum, and angular momentum.

Example 1 Two point-charges, one of $+36\,\mu$coul and one of $-36\,\mu$coul are separated by 8.0 cm. Find the electric field 6.0 cm from the positive charge, as shown in Figure 26-2.

We may compute the electric field arising from each of the two charges and add these fields to find the resultant by using Equation 26-3, or we may equivalently find the resultant electric force on a charge of $+1$ coul located at point P.

The magnitude of the electric field $\boldsymbol{E}_+$ originating in the positive charge is

$$E_+ = \frac{kq}{r^2} = k\,\frac{(36 \times 10^{-6}\,\text{coul})}{(6 \times 10^{-2}\,\text{m})^2}$$

$$= k\left(1.00 \times 10^{-2}\,\frac{\text{coul}}{\text{m}^2}\right)$$

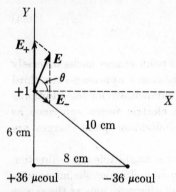

Figure 26-2

The direction of $\boldsymbol{E}_+$ is *away* from the positive charge along a line connecting point P with the charge. In like fashion, the magnitude of the field $\boldsymbol{E}_-$ from the negative charge is

$$E_- = \frac{kq}{r^2} = k\,\frac{(36 \times 10^{-6}\,\text{coul})}{(10 \times 10^{-2}\,\text{m})^2}$$

$$= k\left(0.36 \times 10^{-2}\,\frac{\text{coul}}{\text{m}^2}\right)$$

the direction of $\boldsymbol{E}_-$ being *toward* the negative charge.

We add $\boldsymbol{E}_+$ and $\boldsymbol{E}_-$ as vectors to find the resultant field $\boldsymbol{E}$ at P. We have

$$E_x = k\left(0.36 \times 10^{-2}\,\frac{\text{coul}}{\text{m}^2}\right)\left(\frac{8\,\text{cm}}{10\,\text{cm}}\right) = k\left(0.29 \times 10^{-2}\,\frac{\text{coul}}{\text{m}^2}\right)$$

$$E_y = k\left[(1.00 \times 10^{-2}) - (0.36 \times 10^{-2})\left(\frac{6\,\text{cm}}{10\,\text{cm}}\right)\right]\left(\frac{\text{coul}}{\text{m}^2}\right) = k\left(0.78 \times 10^{-2}\,\frac{\text{coul}}{\text{m}^2}\right)$$

The magnitude of $\boldsymbol{E}$ is

$$E = \sqrt{E_x{}^2 + E_y{}^2} = k\left(0.83 \times 10^{-2}\,\frac{\text{coul}}{\text{m}^2}\right)$$

$$= \left(9.0 \times 10^9\,\frac{\text{nt-m}^2}{\text{coul}^2}\right)\left(0.83 \times 10^{-2}\,\frac{\text{coul}}{\text{m}^2}\right) = 7.5 \times 10^7\,\frac{\text{nt}}{\text{coul}}$$

and its direction θ relative to the X-axis is

$$\theta = \tan^{-1}(E_y/E_x) = \tan^{-1}(0.78/0.29) = 70°.$$

Example 2 Two charges, each of magnitude q but opposite sign, are separated by a distance d. Find the direction and magnitude of the electric field at a large distance r from the charges in a plane perpendicular to the line connecting the two charges.

The two charges and the fields $\boldsymbol{E}_+$ and $\boldsymbol{E}_-$ which they produce respectively at point P are shown in Figure 26-3. In magnitude,

$$E_+ = E_- = kq/r^2$$

the distance r being the distance from P to either of the charges.

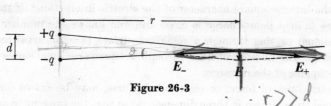

Figure 26-3

$E \propto \dfrac{1}{r^3}$ for dipole resultant

The resultant field **E** is parallel to the line connecting the charges. From the geometry of Figure 26-3, its magnitude is

$$E = E_+ \frac{d}{r} = \frac{k(qd)}{r^3}$$

The field at large distances in the equatorial plane varies inversely as the *cube* of the distance from the two electric charges. It can be shown, in fact, that *E* varies as $1/r^3$ in *any* direction. Such a pair of equal and opposite charges is known as an *electric dipole*. The quantity *qd*, equal to the product of either charge and their separation distance, is known as the *electric dipole moment*.

26-2 Electric lines of force One may use a number of vectors, as in Figure 26-4a, to represent the electric field of a point-charge (taken to be positive in this example). The vectors are all radially outward, and their magnitude is chosen to be inversely proportional to the square of the distance from the charge. An equivalent way of mapping this electric field is shown in Figure 26-4b, where a number of uniformly spaced, outwardly directed, *electric lines of force* are shown radiating from the point-charge. Clearly, the direction of the continuous lines corresponds to the direction of **E**; moreover, the number of such lines passing through a small area of fixed size oriented at right angles (transverse) to the electric field lines varies inversely as the square of the distance from the point-charge. This follows

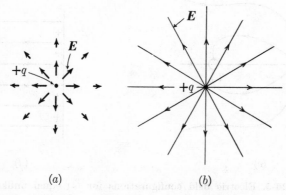

(a)   (b)

Figure 26-4. The electric field of a point-charge represented (a) by **E** vectors and (b) by electric lines of force.

from the inverse-square character of the electric interaction: if the number of lines from a point-charge is fixed and one knows the number (in three dimensions) passing through a spherical surface ($4\pi r^2$ in area) centered at the charge, the number of lines through a transverse area varies inversely as the square of the distance.

Electric lines of force, or electric-field lines, may be drawn (or, strictly, imagined to be drawn in three dimensions) so that the tangent to an electric-field line at any point gives the direction of the electric force on a positive charge and so that the number of lines through a small area transverse to the electric-field lines is proportional to the magnitude of the electric field at that point. Certainly, one may always draw lines to give the *direction* of **E**; it is *not* obvious, however, that the density of lines gives the magnitude of the field *in general*, not only for the rather simple case of a single point-charge but for *all* possible charge distributions. That this is indeed the case will be

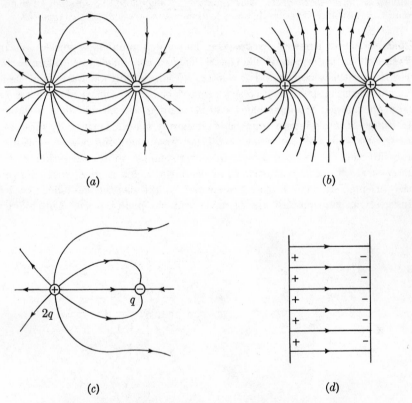

(a)   (b)

(c)   (d)

Figure 26-5. Electric field configurations for (a) equal unlike point-charges, (b) equal like point-charges, (c) unequal unlike point-charges, and (d) two parallel, uniformly charged plates of opposite sign.

proved in the next chapter. At the moment we shall merely note that lines of electric force are a very useful means of visualizing the electric field. The electric *field* is real, or as real as any other physically measurable property; the *lines* which represent the field are a useful *fiction*.

Several charge configurations and their associated electric fields are shown in Figure 26-5. Electric lines originate from positive charges and terminate on negative charges. Where the lines are crowded together the field is strong. Where the lines are equally spaced and parallel the field is uniform, or constant. Any object carrying charge of a *single sign* will, when viewed from a great distance, have the field of a point-charge; that is, $E \propto 1/r^2$. This is *not* the case for an object carrying separated charges of unlike sign. Recall that in Example 2 we found that for an electric field from an electric dipole $E \propto 1/r^3$.

It must be emphasized that the electric-field lines give the *force* acting upon a unit charge introduced into the field: the force is *in* the direction of the lines for a *positive* charge and *opposite* to their direction for a *negative* charge. The field lines do *not* portray the *paths* of a charged particle released in an electric field. One can, of course, find the paths of charged particles if one knows the electric field: knowing E one finds the force on the particle, knowing the force one finds the particle's acceleration, and knowing the acceleration and initial velocity of the particle one finds the particle's displacement at all times. This is, of course, a basic reason for being interested in the electric field; one may compute in detail the motions of a charged particle in the presence of other charged particles through a knowledge of the electric field.

26-3   Electric fields for three simple geometries   Except for some rather special geometries, the matter of computing the electric field from a collection of charges is tedious, mathematically complicated, or both. There are, however, three simple geometries, a point-charge, a line of charge, and a surface of charge, for which one can readily find how E varies with position. Since more complicated distributions can frequently be thought of as superpositions of a number of simple distributions, knowing the electric-field configurations for these three cases permits one to know, at least qualitatively, the fields for such complicated charge distributions. Below we take up the three simple geometries separately and determine the electric field of each.

POINT-CHARGE   We have already solved this problem. The electric field is radially outward from a positive point-charge and varies with the distance r from the charge, following Equation 26-3:

$$\text{point-charge:} \qquad E \propto 1/r^2$$

Here we imagine electric charge to be distributed uniformly along the length of an infinitely long wire, a cylinder of negligible cross-sectional area. We designate the charge per unit length the linear charge density (in coulombs per meters). Of course, any charge distribution can never actually be truly continuous inasmuch as the particles at the atomic level are discrete, each with a charge of e. Therefore, we shall assume that we view the distribution of charges along the wire from a distance which is always large compared with the distance between charges, so that the charge distribution is effectively continuous. At the same time, we recognize that a line of charge can never actually be infinitely long, so that what we

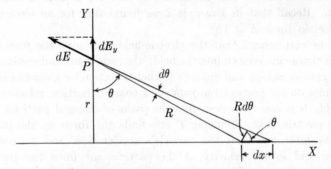

Figure 26-6. The electric field dE contributed by the element dx of an infinite, uniformly charged wire.

find is the electric field for a finite length of charged wire (whether a conductor or a thin dielectric rod) at points which are much closer to the wire than its finite length.

It is easy to establish the direction of the electric field from symmetry considerations alone: E must be radially outward (inward) from a line of positive (negative) charge, the electric lines of force being straight and lying in a plane perpendicular to the line. Only such a direction is consistent with the fact that the infinite line is symmetrical to the left and right at any point. If E made some angle other than 90° with the wire, there would be a difference between left and right.

To find the magnitude of E at a distance r from the wire in terms of the linear charge density λ we consider Figure 26-6. The wire lies along the X-axis. In dealing with a continuous charge distribution the strategy is always to subdivide it into small elements, each effectively equivalent to a point-charge, and then add, as vectors, the contributions of all such elements to the resultant electric field. We are interested in the contribution to the electric field at point P a distance r from the wire by the charge dq lying within the length element dx, where $dq = \lambda \, dx$. This element is a distance R

from point P, and it produces an electric field dE along the line of R, whose magnitude is

$$dE = k\, dq/R^2 = k\lambda\, dx/R^2$$

The outward component of dE is dE_y where

$$dE_y = dE \cos \theta$$
$$= \frac{k\lambda\, dx \cos \theta}{R^2} \qquad\qquad [26\text{-}5]$$

Only the component dE_y will contribute to the final field, since we can choose a symmetrically placed charge element to the left whose X-component exactly cancels that of the one to the right. Similarly, there is no Z-component, either out of or into the paper. The existence of such a component would imply that one can tell the difference between the upper and lower "side" of the wire, a possibility again ruled out by symmetry.

The integration we are about to perform is done most simply if we choose the angle θ as variable. From the geometry of Figure 26-6, we see that

$$R = \frac{r}{\cos \theta} \quad \text{and} \quad dx = \frac{R\, d\theta}{\cos \theta}$$

Using these relations in Equation 26-5 we have

$$dE_y = \frac{k\lambda \cos \theta\, d\theta}{r}$$

To find the resultant field E we integrate θ from $-\tfrac{1}{2}\pi$ to $\tfrac{1}{2}\pi$:

$$E = \int dE_y = \frac{k\lambda}{r} \int_{-\pi/2}^{\pi/2} \cos \theta\, d\theta$$

$$\boxed{E = \frac{2k\lambda}{r}} \qquad\qquad [26\text{-}6]$$

The electric field is proportional to the linear charge density and falls off with r to the *first* power:

line of charge: $E \propto 1/r$

Curiously, we find that the electric field from an infinite line of charge, one having an *infinite* total charge, is *finite*.

Example 3 An electron is to be projected to move in a circle about a uniformly and positively charged wire. What is the required speed?

See Figure 26-7, which shows the negatively charged particle acted on by a radially inward electric force $F_r = eE = 2ek\lambda/r$, from Equation 26-6. (Note

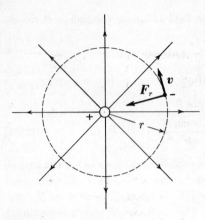

Figure 26-7. Charged particle circling a charged wire in a transverse plane.

that the electric-field lines *cannot*, in this *two*-dimensional figure, be distinguished from those of a point-charge.) The electron of mass m moves at a constant speed v in a circle of radius r. Therefore, from Newton's second law,

$$\Sigma F_r = ma_r$$
$$2ek\lambda/r = mv^2/r, \quad \text{or} \quad v = \sqrt{2ek\lambda/m}$$

There is a *single* speed v, independent of the distance r, for *all* the orbiting electrons. This is in contrast to the case of a charged particle orbiting a fixed point-charge in a circle, in which the speed is proportional to $r^{-1/2}$. This reflects the fact that in the one case the field varies as $1/r$ and in the other as $1/r^2$.

INFINITE SURFACE OF CHARGE Here we consider the electric field produced by a uniformly charged infinite plane surface. The constant *surface charge density*, the charge per unit area (in coulombs per square meters) is represented by σ. We can immediately, on the basis of symmetry considerations alone, say that the electric field must be *perpendicular* to the surface. It is outward along the normal for a positively charged sheet and inward along the normal for a negatively charged sheet. This follows from the fact that there is but one direction for a plane, that of the normal.

To find the magnitude of the resultant field at a point P a distance D from the surface in terms of the surface charge density σ, we first concentrate on the contributions to E from a circular ring of radius r and width dr whose center lies beneath P; see Figure 26-8. All charges on this ring are the same distance R from P. The charge on some one small portion of the ring

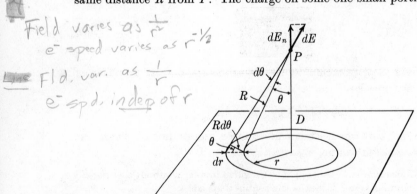

Figure 26-8. A ring of charge from a uniformly charged infinite plane.

charged parallel plates. After leaving the region between the plates, the electrons move in free flight and strike a distant screen; see Figure 26-10. Show that the amount of deflection, y, of the electron beam on the screen (from its position when the field is zero) is directly proportional to the magnitude of the electric field.

The arrangement is that used in a cathode ray (electron beam) oscilloscope or in a television picture tube. The position at which the electrons strike the sensitive screen is controlled by two pairs of deflecting plates, one pair, as in Figure 26-10, for vertical deflection and the other for horizontal deflection. Since the electric field from a single plane, uniformly charged surface is uniform, the electric field between the two oppositely charged parallel flat plates is also uniform. This means that the electric force on any charged particle within the

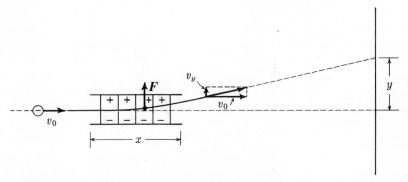

Figure 26-10. A charged particle shot at right angles through a uniform electric field.

region between the plates is constant, in the same fashion that the gravitational force on any projectile in the uniform gravitational field near the Earth's surface is constant. Consequently, the most general path traced out by a charged particle in a uniform E field is a parabola, the axis of the parabola lying along the direction of the electric field. The motion is that of constant acceleration, both in magnitude and direction, and the kinematic relations (Equations 2-7, 2-8, 2-10, and 2-11) apply.

Since, in Figure 26-10, the electron has a negative electric charge and the electric field is downward, the electric force on the electron is upward and has the magnitude

$$F = eE$$

The constant upward acceleration a is, then,

$$a = eE/m$$

where m is the electron mass.

Only the Y-component of the electron's velocity changes. During the time t that the electron is between the plates, the vertical component of the velocity goes from zero to

$$v_y = at = (eE/m)t$$

During this same time the electron travels horizontally a distance x with the constant velocity component v_0 where

$$x = v_0 t$$

whence $$v_y = (eE/m)(x/v_0) = eEx/mv_0$$

The direction in which the electrons leave the charged plates is determined by the relative magnitudes of v_0 and v_y. Once launched into the region beyond the charged plates, the electrons coast in a straight line and then strike the distant screen a distance y from the undeflected path (strictly, one ought to add the very small vertical displacement which the electrons undergo while they are between the plates). The displacement y consequently is proportional to v_y; or,

$$y \propto eEx/mv_0$$

The deflection y is proportional to the electric field E between the deflecting plates. Moreover, the deflection is inversely proportional to the initial linear momentum mv_0 of the electrons.

Example 5   A beam of electrons, each having an energy of 10 electron volts, enters the region between two oppositely charged parallel plates separated by 10 cm. The electrons enter through a hole in one plate and travel initially along the direction of the electric field; see Figure 26-11. What is the minimum magnitude of the electric field which will stop the electrons before they hit the second plate?

The electric force on the electrons is opposite to their initial velocity. The electrons are therefore, subject to a constant retarding force which can bring them to rest and then accelerate them backward toward the hole. In bringing particles of initial kinetic energy K to rest in a distance d, a constant electric force F does work in the amount Fd. Therefore,

$$K = Fd = eEd$$

or $$E = \frac{K}{ed} = \frac{(10 \text{ ev})(1.6 \times 10^{-19} \text{ joule/ev})}{(1.6 \times 10^{-19} \text{ coul})(0.10 \text{ m})}$$

$$= 100 \text{ nt/coul}$$

Note that we had to convert the units for kinetic energy from electron volts to joules, using the conversion factor 1.60×10^{-19} joule/ev. Since the magnitude of the charge of the electron is the same number (not by accident, as we shall see), the computation is rendered particularly simple. Note, further, that the mass of the charged particle does *not* enter. A 10 ev chlorine ion, Cl^-, would be stopped by the same electric field. Of course, such an ion initially would be traveling at a much lower speed.

26-4   Electric fields and conductors   For a conductor in electrostatic equilibrium the electric field, both within the conductor and at its exterior, is very simple: at any point inside the conductor's surface, $E = 0$; at the conductor's surface, E is always perpendicular to the surface; see Figure 26-12. Let us prove these assertions.

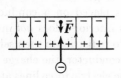

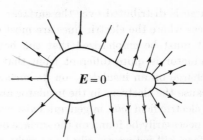

Figure 26-11. Electron acted upon by a retarding force in a uniform electric field.

Figure 26-12. Electric field for a charged conductor. Within the conductor $E = 0$; at the outer surface E is perpendicular to the surface.

Imagine that a net charge is somehow placed on the interior of a solid conductor. Then an electric field is established momentarily within the conductor. This field acts on the free electrons within the conductor, and they redistribute themselves throughout the conductor's volume until they are no longer acted upon by a resultant electric field and finally come to rest. Since the conduction electrons are highly mobile, the state of electrostatic equilibrium is achieved very rapidly indeed. Now if an electron in the interior of the conductor is subject to *no* net electric force, the electric field on the conductor's interior must be exactly *zero*. This means that there can be no net charge within the conductor. Where has the net charge added to the conductor gone? It must, of course, be found residing on the conductor's surface.

For electrostatic equilibrium the net charge on a conductor appears at rest on the conductor's outer surface. If any one charge on the surface is at rest, there can be no electric force acting on it along the surface, inasmuch as such a force would cause the charge to move along the surface. Thus, the electric field at the conductor surface must be perpendicular to the surface at all points. In terms of electric lines of force we can say that (a) there are no electric force lines within a conductor and (b) electric lines originate from charges at the surface and are always perpendicular to the surface (Figure 26-12).

Recall that the electric field of any uniformly charged infinite plane is perpendicular to the plane and proportional to the surface charge density σ (Equation 26-8). Any very small portion of a conductor's surface closely approximates a flat plane and, as we have seen, the electric field is perpendicular to its surface. Since $E \propto \sigma$, the charge on a conductor's surface is most dense at those points where the electric field is large. Thus, the electric field lines emanating from a charged conductor indicate how the charge is distributed over the surface: the charge is concentrated at those places where the electric lines are most dense.

It must be emphasized that the behavior of charges placed on a non-conductor is quite different from that of charges placed on a conductor. A charge on an insulator—on its surface or in its interior—does *not* move, because the electrons in the insulator are *not* free to redistribute themselves. An electric field *will*, in general, exist within a nonconductor, the charge will *not* necessarily be found on the surface only, and the electric force lines at the surface will *not* necessarily be at right angles to the surface. The effects of charge on an insulator are further complicated by the fact that the added charge and its attendant electric field, acting on the bound electrons in the insulator, will create an additional electric field having its origin in the slightly displaced bound charges (more on this in Section 29-4).

26-5 The Millikan experiment The charge of the electron was first measured directly in the historic experiments of R. A. Millikan (1868–1953) beginning in 1909. These experiments involve observations of electrically charged oil drops in a uniform electric field. The strategy of the experiment is this: one balances the force of an electric field on a single electron, or a small number of electrons residing on the droplet with a second force, the weight of the very small droplet of oil (oil does not evaporate readily).

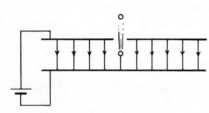

The essential parts of the experimental arrangement are shown in Figure 26-13. Oil droplets enter the region between two horizontal parallel plates by a hole in the top plate. If the plates are uncharged, no electric field exists between them. One always observes one specific oil droplet. The drop initially accelerates downward but very quickly reaches a *constant*

Figure 26-13. Essential parts of Millikan oil drop experiment.

terminal speed because it falls under the influence of *two* forces, its weight F_g, downward and a resistive force F_r upward. The resistive force, which arises from the molecular bombardment by air molecules, is proportional to the speed v_0 of the oil drop; this speed may be measured by timing the fall of the oil drop viewed through a microscope. Thus, in the absence of an electric field,

$$F_g + F_r = 0, \quad \text{where} \quad F_r = -Kv_0$$

The droplet is too small to permit its weight to be measured directly, but by measuring v_0 and knowing the constant K the droplet weight F_g can be determined.

Now with the vertical electric field turned on, the oil droplets, if charged, are subject to an additional electric force $F_e = qE$, where q is the charge on the drop and E is the constant electric field acting either up or down (we shall later see that, for a uniform field, $E = \Delta V/d$, where ΔV is the easily measured potential difference between the charged plates and d is their separation distance). Again, if the charged droplet is initially subject to an unbalanced force, it very quickly reaches a constant terminal velocity under the influence of the resistive force F_r. When this terminal velocity is achieved, the resultant force on the droplet is again zero, so that

$$F_g + F_r + F_e = 0$$

where $$F_e = qE \quad \text{and} \quad F_r = -Kv \qquad [26\text{-}9]$$

One can measure the magnitude and direction of the droplet's constant velocity v. The constant K is known, E is easily measured, and F_g was determined in the observations without the electric field. Thus, one can determine the magnitude and sign of the charge q by using Equation 26-9. Moreover, by exposing the drop to a short burst of ionizing x-rays one can change the charge q on the drop (without, of course, having changed the drop's weight F_g).

The results of experiments involving many different droplets and charges are these:

$$q = ne$$

where $n = 0, 1, 2, \ldots,$ and $e = 1.60 \times 10^{-19}$ coul

Electric charge is quantized. The Millikan experiment showed that the only observed charge is always an integral multiple of nature's basic quantum of charge, the elementary charge e.

26-6   An electric dipole in an electric field   An electric dipole consists of two point-charges of equal magnitude separated by a distance d. As a whole the dipole is electrically neutral. It is useful to define the *electric dipole moment* p as:

$$p = qd \qquad [26\text{-}10]$$

where q is the magnitude of either of the two charges and d, a vector, is the displacement of the positive point-charge relative to the negative point-charge; see Figure 26-14. The magnitude of the electric dipole moment is simply qd, the magnitude of one charge multiplied by the charge separation distance.

We wish to find the torque τ acting on an electric dipole placed in a uniform electric field E. Figure 26-15 shows an electric dipole whose axis is at an angle θ with respect to that of the electric-field lines. Each of the two

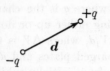

Figure 26-14. An electric dipole.

point-charges is acted on by an electric force of magnitude qE. Since the two forces are in opposite directions, the *resultant* force on the dipole is zero. Consequently, the dipole is not displaced translationally in a *uniform* electric field.

We compute the torque τ from the general relation

$$\tau = r \times F \qquad [14\text{-}2]$$

or, in magnitude,

$$\tau = r_\perp F \qquad [14\text{-}1]$$

It is convenient to choose the origin of the vector d as the axis for computing torques (actually, we get the same torque for any choice of axis). Then,

$$\tau = r_\perp F = (d \sin \theta)(qE) = pE \sin \theta \qquad [26\text{-}11]$$

This can be written more compactly in vector form as

$$\tau = p \times E \qquad [26\text{-}12]$$

The torque on the dipole is zero when it is aligned with the uniform field and a maximum when it is at right angles ($\theta = 90°$) to the field. Clearly, if the dipole is initially aligned with the field, work must be done on it to turn it. Thus, we can associate an electric potential energy U with a dipole in an external field. The potential energy is equal to the work done in reorienting the dipole. In general, the work done by the torque is

$$W = \int \tau \, d\theta \qquad [14\text{-}11]$$

Using Equation 26-11 we have

$$U = \int_{\pi/2}^{\theta} pE \sin \theta \, d\theta = -pE \cos \theta \qquad [26\text{-}13]$$

The lower limit of the integral was chosen as $\tfrac{1}{2}\pi$ to give a simple final result.

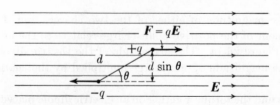

Figure 26-15. An electric dipole in a uniform electric field is subject to a resultant torque.

This amounts to choosing the zero for the potential energy to correspond to the angle $\theta = 90°$. We may write Equation 26-13 using the dot product:

$$U = -\boldsymbol{p} \cdot \boldsymbol{E}$$ [26-14]

The potential energy is a minimum ($U = -pE$) when the dipole is aligned with the field and a maximum ($U = +pE$) when $\theta = 180°$.

The cross and dot products of $\boldsymbol{p}$ with $\boldsymbol{E}$ give, respectively, the torque and potential energy of an electric dipole in an electric field. We may, in fact, regard Equations 26-12 and 26-14 as *defining* an electric dipole moment. Thus, we attribute an electric dipole moment to *any* object which is subject to a torque and which has potential energy of orientation in a uniform electric field. For example, a neutral molecule has an electric dipole moment if it is reoriented in an electric field. Here there are *not* two separated *point-charges* of equal magnitude and opposite sign; a neutral molecule has an electric dipole moment because its "centers" of positive and negative charge do not coincide. The molecule NaCl, for example, has a permanent electric dipole moment, and it is said to be a polar molecule, because the end of the molecule with the sodium atom has a net positive charge while the end with the chlorine has a net negative charge. It is not necessary to specify the charge separation distance d for a polar molecule; indeed, it is not possible to give q and d separately, since it is their product, qd, which enters into the torque and potential-energy relations.

When an electric dipole is in a *nonuniform*, or inhomogeneous, electric field, the forces acting on the two opposite charges are *not* of equal magnitude,

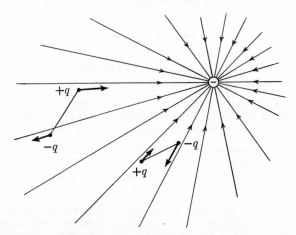

Figure 26-16. In a nonuniform, or inhomogeneous, electric field, electric dipoles are subject to a resultant *force*.

and the dipole is subject to a resultant force which may displace it translationally; see Figure 26-16.

26-7 Summary The electric field E at any point in space is the resultant force per unit positive charge:

[26-1] $$E = \Sigma \, F/q$$

The charges which are the source of the electric field must remain fixed in position when the test charge used to measure the field is introduced. One may map the magnitude and direction of an electric field with electric lines of force. The electric field varies with position for three simple geometries, as follows:

[26-3]   point-charge: $E = kq/r^2 \propto 1/r^2$

[26-6]   line of charge: $E = 2k\lambda/r \propto 1/r$

[26-8]   surface of charge: $E = \sigma/2\epsilon_0 \propto$ constant

The linear charge density is λ; the surface charge density is σ.

The charge on a charged conductor resides on the conductor's surface. The electric field is perpendicular to the surface outside the conductor and zero within the conductor.

The torque τ and potential energy U of an electric dipole of dipole moment $p = qd$ in a electric field E are:

[26-12] $$\tau = p \times E$$

[26-14] $$U = -p \cdot E$$

PROBLEMS

26-1 A charge of -10 μcoul is subject to an electric force of 0.20 nt east. What are the magnitude and direction of the electric field at this point?

26-2 Two point charges, one of $+20$ μcoul and the other of $+40$ μcoul, are separated by 10 cm. Find the three (!) locations at which the electric field is zero along the line joining the charges.

26-3 The magnitude and locations of three point-charges are as follows: $+Q$ at $(0, 0)$ cm, $+2Q$ at $(0, 4.0)$ cm, and $-2Q$ at $(0, -4.0)$ cm. What are the direction and magnitude of the electric field at the point $(4.0, 4.0)$ cm?

26-4 A square of edge length L has charges of $+q$, $-q$, $+q$, and $-q$ on its northeast, northwest, southwest, and southeast corners, respectively. (a) What are the direction and magnitude of the electric field at the center of the square? (b) What is the field at the center with the two first-named charges interchanged?

26-5   Sketch electric lines of force for the following configurations: (a) an equilateral triangle with charges $+q$, $+q$, and $-q$ at its corners, (b) a negative point-charge close to a uniformly and positively charged surface, (c) two oppositely charged parallel wires, and (d) a positively charged wire parallel to a uniformly and negatively charged surface.

26-6   Prove that electric-field lines can never cross.

26-7   A point-charge $-q$ is located at $x = -\frac{1}{2}d$, $y = 0$, and a point-charge $-3q$ is located at $x = \frac{1}{2}d$, $y = 0$. E_x and E_y represent the X- and Y-components of the resultant electric field along the axis. Sketch the following graphs: (a) E_x as a function of x, (b) E_x as a function of y, and (c) E_y as a function of y. (d) At what point along the Y-axis is E_y a maximum?

26-8   In Example 2 we found that the electric field from an electric dipole (two opposite charges, each of magnitude q, separated by d) at large distances from the dipole and at right angles to the axis of the dipole was $E = kqd/r^3$. Show that the electric field *along* the dipole axis is given for large distances by $E = 2kqd/r^3$.

26-9   (a) An electron initially traveling east with a speed of 6.0×10^5 m/sec is to be brought to rest in a distance of 3.0 cm by a uniform electric field. (a) What are the required direction and magnitude of the field? (b) What is the required field if the electron is replaced by a hydrogen ion H$^-$ moving with the same initial velocity?

26-10   How far will a singly charged ion travel from rest before acquiring a kinetic energy of 10 ev when in an electric field of 20 nt/coul?

26-11   In a certain linear accelerator employing a constant electric field, a proton acquires a kinetic energy of 10 Mev in traveling a distance of 15 m. What is the magnitude of the electric field?

26-12   An electron enters a uniform electric field of 40 nt/coul with an initial speed of 3.0×10^6 m/sec. Its initial velocity makes an angle of 30° with respect to the electric force lines. (a) What is its displacement, measured perpendicular to the electric force lines, when its speed is again 3.0×10^6 m/sec?

26-13   A hydrogen atom is located between two oppositely charged parallel plates which produce a uniform electric field of 10,000 nt/coul. (a) Assuming that the electron circles about the proton in a radius of 5.3×10^{-11} m, compare the electric field due to the parallel plates with that due to the proton which acts on the electron. (b) How large would the surface charge density on the plates have to be for the two fields to be equal?

26-14   An electron gun shoots a narrow beam of electrons horizontally into the region between two oppositely charged horizontal parallel plates. The uniform electric field produced by the parallel plates is 800 nt/coul, and the average distance between neighboring electrons in the beam is 10^{-5} m. Compare the force between two neighboring electrons with that between an electron and the electric field of the plates.

26-15 ★   (a) How does the magnitude of an electric field vary with distance along the axis of a uniform ring of charge for distances large compared with the radius of the ring? (b) Suppose, now, that one half of the ring is uniformly positively charged and the other half of the ring is uniformly negatively charged; how does the electric field vary with distance along the ring's axis, again for distances large compared with the radius of the ring?

26-16 ⋆ A thin uniformly charged dielectric rod is bent into a circular arc of radius R which subtends an angle θ at the center of the circle. The total charge on the rod is Q. Find the direction and magnitude of the electric field at the center of the circular arc in terms of R, θ, and Q.

26-17 ⋆ A uniformly charged ring of radius r has a total charge q. (a) Show that at a distance x along the symmetry axis of the ring the magnitude of the electric field is $kqx(r^2 + x^2)^{-3/2}$. (b) Sketch the electric lines of force for a uniformly charged ring.

26-18 An electron travels in a circle around a uniformly charged wire at a speed of 2.0×10^4 m/sec. What is the linear charge density of the wire?

26-19 The electric field at one point close to an infinitely long, uniformly charged, straight wire is 20 nt/coul. At a point 2.0 cm closer to the wire the electric field is 25 nt/coul. What is the linear charge density of the wire?

26-20 When moving close to a single uniformly charged flat surface a hydrogen ion H^+ is subject to a constant force of 4.0×10^{-15} nt. What is the magnitude of the surface charge density?

26-21 A proton is subject to a constant force of 2.0×10^{-16} nt in the uniform electric field between two parallel oppositely charged plates. What is the magnitude of the surface charge density on either of the two plates?

26-22 In Figure 26-10 an electron enters the region between the plates with an initial horizontal velocity of 3.0×10^5 m/sec. The electric field between the horizontal plates is 0.50 nt/coul, and the horizontal distance along either plate is 3.0 cm. The distant screen is 20 cm from the nearest ends of the plates. (a) What is the electron's vertical displacement y upon leaving the plates? (b) What is the direction of the electron's velocity at that time? (c) What is the displacement of the electron on the screen relative to its position when the electric field between the parallel plates is zero?

26-23 Two sheets, one conducting and the other dielectric, are charged with the same constant surface charge density. Hence, the electric field for both configurations is the same. When a charged object is brought to the same distance from first one surface and then the other, it is found that the electric force on the object is *not* the same in the two cases. Explain.

26-24 In a Millikan experiment it is observed that an oil droplet is balanced and at rest between the plates when an electric field of 1.0×10^5 nt/coul exists and there is an excess charge on the droplet of $+1.6 \times 10^{-19}$ coul. (a) What is the direction of the electric field? (b) What is the mass of the oil droplet?

26-25 Refer to Problem 26-24. When there is no excess charge on the droplet, it is observed to fall at the constant speed of 0.10 mm/sec. (a) Determine the value of the resistive constant K. (b) With what velocity (magnitude and direction) does the droplet move when it has an excess of 5 electrons? (c) When it has a deficiency of 50 electrons?

26-26 Refer to Problem 26-24. When there is no excess charge on the droplet it falls at the constant speed of 0.10 mm/sec. With what velocity will it move if it is deficient in one electron and the electric field is 2.0×10^5 nt/coul?

26-27 An electric dipole makes an angle of 30° with the lines of force of a uniform electric field of 1.0×10^5 nt/coul when a torque of 3.0×10^{-4} m-nt acts on it. (a) What is the electric dipole moment? (b) If the dipole is released from rest and then turns freely, what is the kinetic energy of the dipole when it is aligned with the electric field lines?

26-28 An electric dipole, originally aligned with an electric field, is turned through 180° by doing 0.040 joule of work on it. What torque must be applied to this dipole to hold it oriented at right angles to the field?

26-29 An electric dipole is free to swing about a vertical axis through its center. The dipole oscillates in an electric field when displaced slightly from alignment with the field. (a) Show that the oscillations are angular simple harmonic. (b) Show that the magnitude of the electric field is proportional to the square of the dipole oscillation frequency.

26-30 ★ An electric dipole is projected horizontally into the region between two parallel horizontal oppositely charged plates. Assume that the initial angle between the dipole moment p and the direction of the constant electric field E is so small that $\sin \theta \simeq \theta$. The mass of each charge is m. (a) What is the path of the center of mass of the dipole as it moves between the plates? (b) What type of motion do the charges make with respect to the center of mass? (c) Calculate the period of oscillation of the dipole in terms of m, d, q, and E.

26-31 ★ Two small bodies are connected to the opposite ends of a light rigid rod of length d. One body has charge $-q$ and mass $2m$; the other body has charge $+2q$ and mass m. This system of charges is projected into a uniform electric field E with an initial velocity v which is perpendicular to E. The rod makes a small angle θ with respect to E (the positive charge being toward E) and is not initially rotating. (a) Describe the motion of the system while it is in the uniform electric field. (b) What perpendicular distance with respect to E does the system's center of mass move during the first quarter-cycle of oscillation of the system about its center of mass? (c) If the electric field were turned off at the instant the system had rotated one quarter-cycle, what would be the velocity of the center of mass and the angular velocity about the center of mass from then on?

TWENTY-SEVEN

GAUSS'S LAW

Gauss's law is an alternative formulation of Coulomb's law; it expresses in a simple and altogether general way the fact that the electric force between point-charges is strictly inverse-square. Through Gauss's law one may readily find, for simple geometries, the electric field produced by distributions of charges. Conversely, knowing the electric field emerging from any closed surface, one may deduce the net charges within the surface. When applied to an electric conductor, Gauss's law implies that the net static charge on any conductor must lie completely on the outside. The experimental observation that this is indeed the case is the most precise demonstration of the Coulomb-force law.

27-1 Electric flux Since Gauss's law is a statement about electric flux, we first define this quantity. We shall be concerned with an imaginary *closed* surface of arbitrary shape (a so-called *Gaussian surface*) and with the electric field penetrating this surface. We consider the small surface element of area dS shown in Figure 27-1. The area is sufficiently small to be considered perfectly flat. The orientation of this surface element is defined by the direction of the *outwardly* drawn normal. Then the vector dS is assigned a direction along the outward normal to the surface element, its magnitude being the area of the element. (We shall never be in doubt as to which direction is outward from the surface since we always deal with completely closed surfaces.)

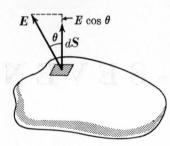

We may assume that the electric field E at the location of the surface element dS is constant over this very small area. The angle between E and dS is θ. The field E may arise from one or more point-charges or from a continuous charge distribution. By definition, the electric flux $d\phi_E$ through this surface element is

$$d\phi_E = E \cos \theta \, dS$$

Figure 27-1. Computing the electric flux through the element of surface dS, whose direction is that of the outward normal to the surface.

That is, the electric flux is the component, $E \cos \theta$, of the electric field perpendicular to the surface (or parallel to dS) multiplied by the area dS. We may express this more compactly by using the dot product (Section 11-4) of the vectors E and dS. Then we have:

$$d\phi_E = \mathbf{E} \cdot d\mathbf{S} \qquad \text{[27-1]}$$

If the electric field is directed outward from the Gaussian surface, that is, if the angle θ is less than 90°, the flux $d\phi_E$ is positive. On the other hand, if the angle θ is between 90° and 180°, the electric field penetrates the Gaussian surface in the inward direction and the flux is negative. When the electric field lies in the plane of the surface element, $\theta = 90°$ and the flux through the surface is *zero*. Since the Gaussian surface may be chosen, as we shall see, to be of any shape, we will often so choose the shape that either E is perpendicular to the surface (parallel to dS) and the flux is simply $d\phi_E = E \, dS$ or E is along the surface (perpendicular to dS) and the flux is $d\phi_E = 0$.

To find the *total electric flux* ϕ_E over an entire closed Gaussian surface we merely sum up the contributions from all surface elements, taking into account, of course, the variation in E both in magnitude and direction from one point on the surface to another.

$$\phi_E = \oint d\phi_E = \oint \mathbf{E} \cdot d\mathbf{S} \qquad \text{[27-2]}$$

total flux

The flux is called the surface integral of E over the closed Gaussian surface.

The circle in the integral sign reminds us that the integration is to be taken over the entire Gaussian surface. Although such an integral might, at first sight, appear formidable to evaluate, we shall see that computing the electric flux in situations of high geometrical symmetry can be remarkably simple.

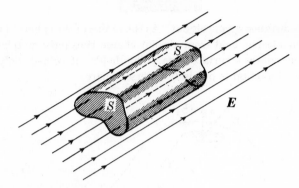

Figure 27-2. The total electric flux through a closed surface in a uniform electric field is zero.

Example 1 Compute the electric flux through a closed surface in a uniform electric field, the surface being that of a cylinder whose axis is the electric-field direction, as shown in Figure 27-2.

There is *no* contribution to ϕ_E along the curved surface, since E is there perpendicular to dS. The electric-force lines go in one end of the cylinder and out the other, and are perpendicular to both of these surfaces. The inward lines produce a flux $-ES$; the outward lines, a flux $+ES$. The total flux $\oint E \cdot dS$ is *zero*.

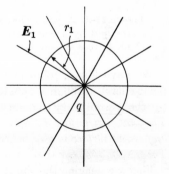

Figure 27-3. The electric field E_1 at a distance r_1 from a point-charge q.

27-2 Gauss's law First consider a single point-charge q (assumed positive for definiteness) surrounded by a spherical Gaussian surface of radius r_1 centered at the point-charge; see Figure 27-3. We can easily find the total electric flux through this surface, since the electric field, radially outward, is perpendicular to the surface at all points. The magnitude of the electric field E_1 at a distance r_1 from a point-charge is given by

[26-3] $$E_1 = kq/r_1{}^2$$

The surface area of the sphere is $4\pi r_1^2$. Therefore, the electric flux is

$$\phi_E = \oint E \cdot dS = (kq/r_1^2)(4\pi r_1^2) = 4\pi kq$$

$$\boxed{\phi_E = q/\epsilon_0} \qquad\qquad \epsilon_0 = \frac{1}{4\pi k} \qquad \text{[27-3]}$$

Note that the distance r_1 cancels out. As the radius of the sphere is increased, dilution of the electric field from a point-charge is exactly matched by the dilation in the sphere's surface area. This holds, of course, only because the Coulomb interaction is precisely inverse-square.

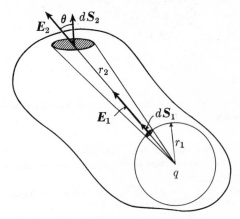

Figure 27-4. A point-charge q surrounded by a volume of arbitrary shape and by a concentric sphere. The electric flux through the two shaded areas is exactly the same.

We have found, following Equation 27-3, that the electric flux from a point-charge through a sphere encircling it is simply the charge q divided by the permittivity constant ϵ_0. This simple relation holds in general: *The total electric flux ϕ_E arising from any number of electric charges through any closed surface is q/ϵ_0, where q is the net charge enclosed by the surface.* This is Gauss's law. Let us prove it.

First we imagine the single point-charge q to be surrounded by a surface of arbitrary shape, as shown in Figure 27-4. We concentrate on the flux through the surface element dS_2 at a distance r_2 from the point-charge. The electric field here is

$$E_2 = kq/r_2^2 \qquad\qquad \text{[27-4]}$$

The surface element is so chosen that it subtends the same solid angle as does the surface element dS_1 lying on the concentric sphere of radius r_1; that is, a single cone drawn outward from the charge intercepts the surface elements

dS_1 and dS_2. We wish to show that the flux is the same through these two surface elements.

First, we note that E_2 and dS_2 are not parallel in general. Therefore the flux through this surface element is

$$d\phi_2 = E_2 \cdot dS_2 = E_2 \cos \theta \, dS_2 \qquad [27\text{-}5]$$

The area dS_2 is larger than dS_1, not only because it lies farther from the charge q but also because dS_2 is inclined relative to E_2. In fact,

$$\frac{dS_2 \cos \theta}{dS_1} = \left(\frac{r_2}{r_1}\right)^2 \qquad [27\text{-}6]$$

The factor $(r_2/r_1)^2$ arises from the difference in distances, and the factor $\cos \theta$ arises from the inclination of dS_2.

Substituting Equations 27-4 and 27-6 in Equation 27-5 yields

$$d\phi_2 = (kq/r_2{}^2)(\cos \theta)\left[\frac{(r_2/r_1)^2 \, dS_1}{\cos \theta}\right] = \frac{kq}{r_1{}^2} dS_1$$

But the electric flux $d\phi_1$ through the surface element dS_1 is

$$d\phi_1 = E_1 \, dS_1 = \frac{kq}{r_1{}^2} dS_1$$

and therefore $\qquad\qquad\qquad d\phi_2 = d\phi_1$

The electric flux through the two matched surface elements is the *same*.

To find the flux through the surface of arbitrary shape we merely extend this procedure, choosing matched pairs of surface elements, until all of the arbitrary surface (and, therefore, all of the spherical surface) is accounted for. It follows that the total electric flux through an arbitrary surface is precisely the same as the electric flux through a sphere centered on the point-charge, and therefore Equation 27-3 applies to any point-charge and any closed arbitrarily shaped Gaussian surface surrounding the charge.

$\phi_E = \dfrac{q}{\epsilon_0}$

When the Gaussian surface encloses a positive charge, the electric flux is positive and the electric lines of force pass outward through the surface. On the other hand, an enclosed negative charge gives a negative flux, the electric lines of force passing inward through the Gaussian surface.

One special case is worthy of note, that in which the point-charge is *outside* the closed surface, as in Figure 27-5. The total flux through the surface is then zero. Said differently, as many electric-force lines penetrate into the surface as emerge outward from it.

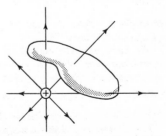

Figure 27-5. The total electric flux through a closed surface *not* enclosing a net charge is zero.

Thus far we have dealt with only a single point-charge. Now suppose that we have two or more charges, $q_a, q_b, \ldots$. We compute the electric flux for each charge through the *same* arbitrarily shaped closed surface. Writing Equation 27-3 for each charge separately, we have

$$\oint E_a \cdot dS = \frac{q_a}{\epsilon_0} \quad \text{and} \quad \oint E_b \cdot dS = \frac{q_b}{\epsilon_0}$$

Adding these two relations into a single equation gives

$$\oint (E_a + E_b + \cdots) \cdot dS = \frac{(q_a + q_b + \cdots)}{\epsilon_0} \qquad \text{[27-7]}$$

This addition (*under* the integral sign) *is* permitted. Recall that the surface was assumed to be the same for each of the point-charges. Moreover, we know that electric forces follow the superposition principle. Equivalently, electric fields add as vectors; thus, the resultant electric field is $E = E_a + E_b + \cdots$. Similarly, from the right-hand side of Equation 27-7, the total *net* charge q enclosed by the surface is $q = q_a + q_b + \cdots$. Equation 27-7 may then be written as

[27-3] $$\phi_E = q/\epsilon_0 \qquad \frac{1}{4\pi k}$$

We have proved Gauss's law: the total electric flux ϕ_E through *any* closed surface is simply the *net* charge q *enclosed* by the surface divided by ϵ_0.† There were two crucial assumptions in the proof: (a) the electric force varies as $1/r^2$ and (b) electric forces follow the superposition principle.

Applied to charge distributions in general, Gauss's law involves a surface integral which may be difficult to evaluate. But for charge distributions of high geometrical symmetry—a line of charge or a surface of charge, for example—it is a simple, almost trivial, matter to compute the integral. The key is this: since we are free to choose a Gaussian surface of any shape, we choose a shape which matches the symmetry of the charge distribution within.

Example 2   Find the electric field about a uniformly charged infinite wire, using Gauss's law.

We have already solved this problem (Section 26-3) by summing the contributions to the resultant electric field of all charge elements. We found that the magnitude of E is given by

[26-6] $$E = 2k\lambda/r = \lambda/2\pi\epsilon_0 r$$

where λ is the constant linear charge density.

Let us now use Gauss's law to find E. We can assert that the electric field for this simple geometric configuration is radially outward (for a positive charge)

† Since the constant in Coulomb's law was chosen to be $1/4\pi\epsilon_0$, we avoid the appearance of a factor 4π in Gauss's law. In an *unrationalized* system of units, such as the Gaussian cgs system, 4π appears in Gauss's law but not in Coulomb's law.

and lies in a plane perpendicular to the wire. This is the only possible direction for E that would not violate the requirements of symmetry. Since we know the direction of E, we so choose our Gaussian surface that it will be simple to find the electric flux through it. Its shape is a right circular cylinder of radius r and length L whose axis coincides with the wire, as shown in Figure 27-6. The flux through the ends of the cylinder is zero, since the electric field is in the plane of the ends, and the flux through the cylindrical surface of total area $2\pi r L$ is $E(2\pi r L)$. Therefore, the *total* flux through the Gaussian surface is

$$\phi_E = \oint E \cdot dS = E(2\pi r L)$$

Note that the magnitude of E is the same for all points on the cylindrical surface. From Gauss's law,

$$\phi_E = E(2\pi r L) = q/\epsilon_0 = \lambda L/\epsilon_0$$

We have used the fact that the total charge q enclosed by the cylinder is λL, where λ is the linear charge density. Finally, $E = \lambda/2\pi\epsilon_0 r$, in agreement with our earlier result.

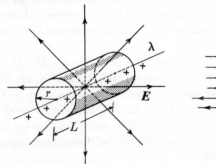

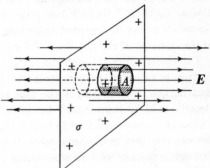

Figure 27-6. A cylindrical Gaussian surface used for computing the electric field from an infinitely long line of charge.

Figure 27-7. The cylindrical Gaussian surface used for computing the electric field from a uniformly charged sheet.

Example 3 Find the electric field from a uniformly charged infinite plane sheet, using Gauss's law.

This problem was also solved earlier (Section 26-3). There we found the field to be independent of the distance from the surface and to have the magnitude

[26-8] $$E = \sigma/2\epsilon_0$$

where σ is the constant surface charge density.

Now we use Gauss's law. From symmetry alone we know that the field must be perpendicular to the surface on *both* sides. Note that our surface is imagined to be an infinitesimally thin sheet of charge, *not* a conductor. We again choose the Gaussian surface as a cylinder, this time with the axis perpendicular to the surface, as shown in Figure 27-7. As before, the electric-force lines lie parallel to the curved surface, and there is no flux through this surface. The electric field is perpendicular to and outward from the ends; the flux through each end is EA, where A is the surface area of an end. The *total* charge enclosed by the Gaussian surface is σA (we count the surface area only *once*, since the charges lie on an infinitesimally thin sheet). Therefore, from Gauss's law we have

$$\phi_E = q/\epsilon_0$$
$$2EA = \sigma A/\epsilon_0$$
$$E = \frac{\sigma}{2\epsilon_0}$$

in agreement, of course, with our earlier result.

27-3 Electric lines of force   In Chapter 26 it was asserted that one may map the electric field of a charge distribution with electric lines of force which originate on positive charges, terminate on negative charges, and are continuous in between. Furthermore, the electric-field lines denote the direction of the electric field at any point by their tangent and denote the magnitude of the electric field by their number through an area held perpendicular to them. Gauss's law gives us proof of these assertions. Indeed, Gauss's law may be regarded as nothing more than a mathematical statement of the concept of electric lines of force.

The electric flux through the surface element dS is $d\phi_E = \mathbf{E} \cdot d\mathbf{S}$. If this surface is oriented perpendicular to the electric field, then $E = d\phi_E/dS$; that is, the electric field is the flux per unit transverse area. Now, if the electric field is represented by force lines such that an electric field of 1 nt/coul is represented by 1 electric line per unit transverse area, we see that the electric flux is nothing more than the number of force lines passing through a transverse Gaussian surface.

We may always so construct the Gaussian surface that electric lines entering or leaving it do so at right angles to the surface. Then the total flux ϕ_E is simply the net number of lines of force leaving the Gaussian surface. If no charge is enclosed by the surface, $q = 0$ and hence $\phi_E = 0$, by Gauss's law; then the net number of lines into the Gaussian surface equals the number out. Inasmuch as the closed Gaussian surface can be made as small as we wish, in a region where there are no electric charges the electric lines are continuous. If, on the other hand, a net charge is enclosed by the Gaussian surface, the net flux through it is not zero, and the number of force lines, $\phi_E = q/\epsilon_0$, is directly proportional to the charge which acts as the source of the field. That is to say, the electric-force lines originate and terminate on charges, the number of lines being directly proportional to the charge.

Given the electric-field lines at any point on any closed surface, we can immediately say something about the charge within: if the same number of lines go in as come out, there is no net charge inside; if more lines emerge from the surface than go in, the surface encloses positive net charge (and

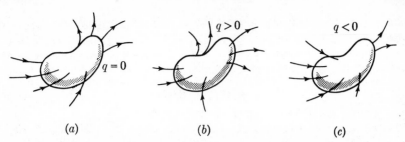

Figure 27-8. By counting the net number of electric force lines out of a closed surface one may deduce the net electric charge q within the surface: (a) $q = 0$, (b) $q > 0$, (c) $q < 0$.

conversely for negative charge); see Figure 27-8. We cannot say how the charge is distributed within the surface or how the charge is located outside the surface; we can only say what the net enclosed charge is.

27-4 Spherically symmetric charge distributions We wish to find the electric field from a spherical shell of charge. Since the charge is assumed to be spread uniformly over the spherical surface, there can be no preferred direction in space. Consequently, the electric field outside the shell must be radial (outward for positive charge, inward for negative charge). To find the external electric field we apply Gauss's law to a spherical Gaussian surface surrounding the charged shell and concentric with it, as shown in Figure 27-9a. By symmetry, the electric field has constant magnitude at every

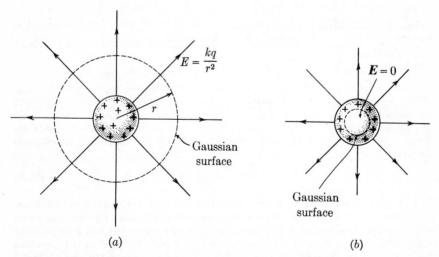

Figure 27-9. Spherical Gaussian surface used to compute the electric field (a) outside and (b) inside a spherical shell of charge.

point on the Gaussian sphere, and the electric flux through the spherical surface is

$$\phi_E = E(4\pi r^2)$$

By Gauss's law we know that this flux is q/ϵ_0; or,

$$E(4\pi r^2) = q/\epsilon_0 \qquad [27\text{-}8]$$

where q is the total net charge on the interior shell.

The electric field is radial and has, from Equation 27-8, the magntiude

$$E = \frac{q}{4\pi\epsilon_0 r^2}$$

We recognize this equation as being identical with that found earlier for the electric field at a distance r from a *point-charge* (Equation 26-3). Thus, the electric field on the *exterior* of a spherically symmetric shell of charge is precisely the same as that produced by the same total charge located at the center of the shell.

What about the field on the interior of the shell? We find this easily by taking the Gaussian surface to be a concentric spherical surface *inside* the shell of charge, as in Figure 27-9b. Since no charge is enclosed by this surface, the electric flux through it must be zero. But if the shell is truly spherically symmetric, the electric field must be radial and of the same magnitude at all points on the Gaussian surface. Equation 27-8 then gives $E(4\pi r^2) = 0$, which gives $E = 0$ at all points within the shell. The only spherically symmetric electric field consistent with the requirement of zero net flux is *zero field*. Thus, there is no electric field in the interior of the spherical shell of charge, and there is no electric force on any test charge placed within the shell. A spherical shell of charge is, from an external point of view, electrically equivalent to a point-charge; from an internal point of view, it is electrically nonexistent.

The results are reminiscent of those found in Section 16-8 for the gravitational effects of spherical shells of mass. There the computation of the resultant gravitational force, however, was considerably more complicated, since we did not invoke Gauss's law. The gravitational force is, like the Coulomb force, an inverse-square force, and one may write Gauss's law for gravitational interactions as follows:

$$\phi_G = \oint \mathbf{g} \cdot d\mathbf{S} = -4\pi Gm \qquad [27\text{-}9]$$

The gravitational flux ϕ_G is defined as the integral over a closed Gaussian surface of the gravitational field $\mathbf{g}$, the gravitational force per unit gravitational mass. On the right-hand side of Equation 27-9 appear the universal gravitational constant G and the mass m representing the entire mass enclosed by the Gaussian surface. The minus sign appears in Equation 27-9 because the gravitational force is always attractive.

It is a simple matter to find the electric field for a dielectric solid sphere (*not* a conductor), if one knows the results for a single shell. If the distribution of charges throughout a dielectric sphere depends only on the distance to the center (that is, if the charges have spherical symmetry relative to the center), then one simply imagines the solid sphere to consist of a series of closely fitted shells. From the outside, the electric field is just that due to a point-charge at the center whose magnitude is the net charge of the sphere. From the inside at a distance r from the center, the resultant field at any point is that due only to those shells whose radius is less than r. At the center, the electric field is zero.

One interesting case is that in which a sphere has constant charge density, the charge per unit volume ρ (in coul/m³) being the same at all points throughout the sphere. Take the radius of the sphere to be R, We know that for any distance $r > R$, the electric field is that of a point-charge at the center. What is the interior electric field with $r < R$? The only charge that matters is the charge *inside* the radius r. The total charge within r is $\rho(\frac{4}{3}\pi r^3)$ and the electric field of this charge is like that due to a point-charge at the center. Therefore,

$$E = kq/r^2 = k\rho(\tfrac{4}{3}\pi r^3)/r^2 = (\tfrac{4}{3}\pi k\rho)r$$

The resultant field within the sphere of charge is proportional to the distance r. If the shell has a positive charge, the field is radially outward, if negative, inward.

The electric field for a uniformly charged sphere is shown in Figure 27-10. Outside the surface, $E \propto 1/r^2$; inside the surface, $E \propto r$.

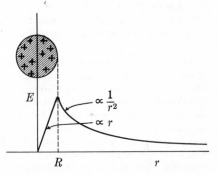

Figure 27-10. Electric field as a function of distance from the center of a uniformly charged dielectric sphere.

Example 4 Compare two frequencies: the frequency of an electron orbiting a positive fixed point-charge, or nucleus, in a circular path and the frequency of an electron oscillating in simple harmonic motion, traveling diametrically through a uniform spherical charge of the same magnitude, and having a radius equal to that of the orbiting electron. These two situations correspond, respectively, to the nuclear atomic model confirmed by the Rutherford scattering experiments (Figure 27-11a) and the Thomson atomic model (after J. J. Thomson) in which the positive charge of an atom is imagined to be distributed continuously throughout the atomic volume (Figure 27-11b).

It is a simple matter to show that in the second case the electron oscillates in simple harmonic motion. We imagine a thin hole to be drilled diametrically through the sphere of positive charge of radius R. Anywhere within this hole the electron is subject to an inward force whose magnitude varies with its distance r from the center: $F \propto r$. Since the electron is subject to a restoring force proportional to its displacement from the equilibrium position (at the sphere's center), the electron must execute simple harmonic motion. At the amplitude position, that is, at the sphere's surface, the force on the electron is simply that due to a point-charge Q. This is just the constant magnitude of the force acting on the orbiting electron in Figure 27-11a. Now we recall that simple harmonic motion is the projected motion along a diameter of uniform circular motion. It follows, therefore, that the two frequencies are exactly the same.

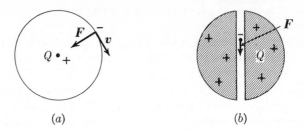

(a)   (b)

Figure 27-11. (a) Electron orbiting a point-charge in uniform circular motion. (b) Electron moving through a uniform spherical charge distribution in simple harmonic motion.

The results just found had an interesting implication at the time the Thomson atomic model was being seriously considered as the basis of atomic structure. One *cannot* tell the difference between the two models on the basis of the electron frequencies (which would also, in terms of classical electromagnetism, be the frequency of the light emitted by atoms). If the electron radius for hydrogen is taken to be 0.5 Å in the nuclear model, the frequency is found to be 7×10^{15} sec^{-1}; precisely the same frequency, lying in the ultraviolet region of the electromagnetic spectrum, is found when the electron is imagined to move through a uniformly distributed positive charge of radius 0.5 Å. The Rutherford scattering experiments discussed in Section 25-6 were not merely confirmations of a reasonable and almost self-evident nuclear model; they were necessary and decisive in ruling out a reasonable and appealing alternative.

27-5 Gauss's law and conductors In what follows we shall have occasion to speak of the electric field *within* a conductor. Let us first be clear about what this means. We *cannot* mean the electric field measured over a volume of space which is small compared with the distance between particles on an atomic scale. At the atomic level we see nothing but point-charges, so the electric field within any material, whether conductor or nonconductor, changes rapidly as we approach and recede from these point-charges. Therefore, by the electric field within a material we shall mean the *average* force acting on a unit positive charge over a volume that is large enough to include many charged particles, but small enough to allow us to speak of the electric field at a "point."

What, then, is the electric field within an insulated charged conductor that has reached static equilibrium? It is exactly zero! To see that this must be the case, let us suppose that the field is not zero. Then free electrons within the conductor, of which there are always approximately one per atom, would be subject to an unbalanced force, and these electrons would move until they finally came to locations where the resultant electric force on any free electrons within the conductor was zero. That is, free electrons move about within the conductor until electrostatic equilibrium is achieved. Since we are considering only static charge distributions on a conductor insulated from the rest of the universe, at any point *within* the conductor $E = 0$.

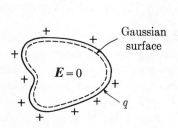

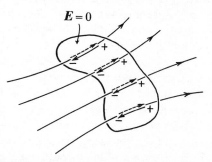

Figure 27-12. Electrical conductor with a Gaussian surface chosen to lie just inside the conductor's outer surface.

Figure 27-13. The electric field on the interior of any conductor is zero, whatever the external electric field and the charges on its outer surface.

We can immediately deduce an important consequence by using Gauss's law. We imagine a Gaussian surface to be located just inside the outer surface of a charged conductor of arbitrary shape, as shown in Figure 27-12. The conductor may be a solid piece of metal or one with interior cavities. Since the boundary of the Gaussian surface lies on the interior of the conductor, the electric field at every point on the Gaussian surface is zero; consequently, the electric flux through the surface is zero. From Gauss's law, if $\phi_E = 0$, then $q = 0$. There is *no* (net) charge inside the surface of a charged conductor. All the net charge must be on the outside surface. Thus, atoms within the interior of the conductor are neutral, while any excess or deficiency of electrons occurs in a thin layer of atoms at the conductor's surface. We saw earlier that the electric field within a *spherically symmetric* shell of charge is zero. Our present result for *conductors* is more general: the interior field is zero for *any* shape and for *any* charges on the exterior surface.

Figure 27-13 gives an interesting illustration of this rule. Here a conductor carrying no net charge is immersed in an external electric field. This field redistributes the charge on the conductor, positive charge appearing at one portion of the outside surface and negative charge of the same magnitude appearing on the opposite side. The interior field is exactly zero. There is another way of looking at this. We can say that the external electric field is exactly annulled by the field arising from the positive and negative charges on the outer surface of the conductor: the two fields when combined produce a resultant $E = 0$ within. Note that the electric-force lines are perpendicular to the conductor's surface at all points. This is always the case for a conductor in electrostatic equilibrium; for, if the electric field were not along the normal to the surface, there would be a component lying along the surface. This component would then act on free electric charges at the surface of the conductor and change the charge distribution. Since the charge distribution on a conductor in equilibrium is fixed, the electric field is always normal to the surface.

The assertion that the net electric charge within a conductor, quite apart from external electric fields or charges on the surface, is always zero, is a consequence of Gauss's law. If we test this assertion by experiment, we test the correctness of Gauss's law, which is to say that we test Coulomb's law and the inverse-square variation in the electric interaction between point-charges. If the net charge within a conductor were found to be just slightly different from zero, the exponent of r in Coulomb's law would differ from 2 by some very small amount. Such experimental attempts at seeking a net charge inside a conducting shell, which are the most sensitive tests of the exponent in Coulomb's law, have been made by many physicists including Benjamin Franklin, Michael Faraday, and Henry Cavendish. The most recent and precise tests, made by Plimpton and Lawton in 1936, show that in the relation $F = kq_1q_2/r^n$, the exponent n differs from 2 by no more than 1 part in 10^9.

The essential steps in Faraday's famous ice pail experiment are shown in Figure 27-14. The conductor is an ice pail, and the charge on its outer surface is indicated by the charge on the attached electroscope. A positively charged object is introduced into the interior of the conductor. Negative charges appear on the inner surface, and positive charges of the same magnitude on the outer surface. We may say that the charged object "induces" charges on the inner and outer surface of the conductor. Then the object is touched to the conductor's inner surface, and thereby becomes, so to speak, a part of the conductor. Finally, when the object is removed, the electroscope shows no change: the charge on the exterior of the conductor has not changed. The object itself is found to have *zero* charge. The experiment shows that the charge induced on the inner surface is of exactly same magnitude as that of the charge carried by the object. The charge originally carried by the object has been transferred entirely to the exterior of a conductor. Any

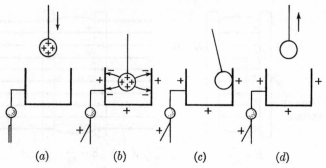

Figure 27-14. Stages in the transfer of charge from a charged object to the outside of a hollow conductor, whose state of charge is indicated by the attached electroscope. (a) The charged object is outside. (b) The charged object is within the conductor, and equal and opposite charges are found on the inside and outside of the conductor. (c) When the object is touched to the conductor's inside, it annuls the charge on the conductor's inner surface and the exterior charge is unchanged. (d) The object, now electrically neutral, is removed.

static electrical effect on the exterior of a conductor is not felt by charges within the conductor. A closed conductor (or one with only small holes leading to the interior) acts as a perfect electric shield. The perfect shielding by a conductor is of practical importance. Thus, electrical apparatus placed within a metallic screen, which is effectively a closed conducting surface, is screened from external electrical influence.

Example 5 What is the electric field near the surface of a conductor having a surface charge density σ?

We first consider a charged conducting surface of arbitrary shape, as shown in Figure 27-15, and concentrate on a portion of the surface so small that it can be regarded as flat. We know already that the electric field on the outside surface is perpendicular to the surface and that the electric field within the

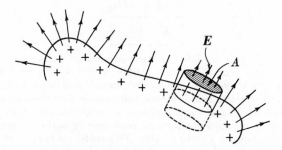

Figure 27-15 A charged conductor with a Gaussian cylindrical surface.

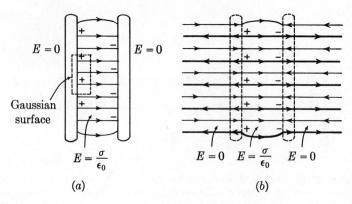

Figure 27-16. (a) Two oppositely-charged parallel conductors and a Gaussian surface for evaluating the electric field between the plates in terms of the surface charge density. (b) The electric fields from two oppositely-charged parallel infinitesimal sheets. Note that the superposed fields are equivalent to the field shown in part (a).

conductor is zero. We choose as a Gaussian surface a small cylinder whose axis is parallel to the normal to the surface and whose ends lie, respectively, within the conductor and just outside the conductor. The electric field E can be considered to be constant in both magnitude and direction over the chosen surface area of magnitude A. The surface charge density σ is also constant over the small surface within the Gaussian cylinder.

The total charge enclosed by the Gaussian surface is $q = \sigma A$; therefore, from Gauss's law we have

$$\phi_E = q/\epsilon_0$$

$$\oint \boldsymbol{E} \cdot d\boldsymbol{S} = \frac{\sigma A}{\epsilon_0}$$

The electric flux is zero within the conductor, since E is zero there. The flux is also zero along the curved surface of the cylinder, since the electric lines lie in this surface. The only contribution to ϕ_E is through the outside end of the cylinder, where $\phi_E = \oint \boldsymbol{E} \cdot d\boldsymbol{S} = EA$. Therefore, the relation above becomes

$$EA = \sigma A/\epsilon_0$$

$$\boxed{E = \sigma/\epsilon_0} \qquad\qquad [27\text{-}10]$$

The electric field just outside the conductor's surface is proportional to the surface charge density at this point. Although the electric field E and surface charge density σ vary along the conductor's surface and depend on the curvature of the surface, the electric field is strong and electric-field lines are closely spaced at those regions where the electric charge is concentrated. Now consider two parallel oppositely charged conductors, each having surface charge density of magnitude σ, as shown in Figure 27-16a. This is the configuration of a so-called parallel-plate capacitor, of which we shall have more to say later (Section 29-2). At any point not close to the edges of the plates, where a "fringing" of the electric field occurs, the electric field will, by symmetry, be uniform and perpendicular to the charged surfaces.

We choose a Gaussian surface just like that in Figure 27-15, with one end inside the conductor and the other end outside the charged surface. The magnitude of the electric field E outside the conductor's surface and, in fact, at any point between the two oppositely charged conducting plates, is given by Equation 27-10,

[27-10] $$E = \sigma/\epsilon_0$$

where σ is the charge density on *one* of the two conducting plates. Note that the electric field at the surface of a conductor is *twice* that found near the surface of a uniformly charged sheet of infinitesimal thickness (Example 3). To see that there is no contradiction here, consider Figure 27-16b, where the electric fields are produced on both sides of two sheets of charge of opposite sign. The field from *one* sheet is $E = \sigma/2\epsilon_0$. In the region between the two sheets both fields act to the right, giving a resultant field $E = \sigma/2\epsilon_0 - (-\sigma/2\epsilon_0) = \sigma/\epsilon_0$ in agreement with our result above for a conductor. Moreover, to the left of the left sheet and to the right of the right sheet the resultant field is zero, just as required for the interior of a conductor.

Example 6   A hollow conductor initially carries a charge $+3Q$. Then an object carrying a charge $-2Q$ is introduced into the interior of the conductor. Finally, another object of charge $-4Q$ is brought close to the outside of the conductor. Find the net charge on the inner and outer surfaces of the conductor in each instance. See Figure 27-17.

Initially, the charge of $+3Q$ is found on the outside surface of the conductor with zero charge on the inner surface. Since no charged object touches the conductor at any later stage, the *net* charge on the conductor must always remain $+3Q$.

To find the charge on the inner surface after the $-2Q$ charge is brought inside, we choose a Gaussian surface which lies within the conductor (we may

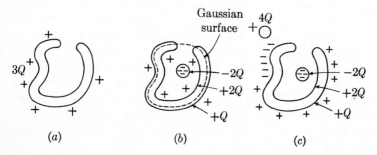

(a) (b) (c)

Figure 27-17. (a) A hollow conductor having a net charge $+3Q$. (b) With an object of charge $-2Q$ on its interior, a charge of $+2Q$ appears on the inner conductor surface and a charge of $+Q$ on the outer surface. The Gaussian surface is shown dotted. (c) The situation is as shown in part (b) but a charge of $+4Q$ is brought close to the outside of the conductor. The *net* charge on the outer conductor remains $+Q$, although the distribution of this charge changes.

ignore the hole of negligible size). Within any conductor, $E = 0$. Therefore, $\phi_E = 0$, and the *net* charge within the Gaussian surface is zero. Since a charge of $-2Q$ is inside the conductor, the inner conductor surface must have a charge $+2Q$. (The induced charge is, from this argument, always equal in magnitude to the inducing charge.) The total charge on the conductor is $+3Q$; therefore, with $+2Q$ on the inner surface, the outer surface must have a charge $+Q$.

When the charge of $+4Q$ is brought near the conductor, nothing changes in so far as the *net* charges are concerned. Our earlier argument with Gauss's law is unaffected, since it involved only those charges *within* the Gaussian surface. The net charge on the outer surface is still $+Q$. Of course, the external charge will influence the *distribution* of charges over the outer surface. There may, in fact, be portions of the outer surface carrying a negative charge, but the net charge remains unaffected.

27-6 Summary The electric flux $d\phi_E$ through an outwardly directed surface element dS is defined as

[27-1] $$d\phi_E = \boldsymbol{E} \cdot d\boldsymbol{S}$$

According to Gauss's law, which is an alternative formulation of Coulomb's law, the total electric flux ϕ_E through any closed surface is proportional to the net charge q enclosed by the surface:

[27-3] $$\phi_E = \oint \boldsymbol{E} \cdot d\boldsymbol{S} = q/\epsilon_0$$

Gauss's law justifies the use of electric lines of force to represent the magnitude and direction of the electric field.

In so far as the external electric field is concerned, a spherically symmetric charge distribution is equivalent to a point-charge of the same magnitude at its center.

When applied to conductors, Gauss's law implies that no net charge will be found within a conductor, all the net charge residing on the outside surface. The experimental observation that the charge is indeed on the surface of a conductor confirms Gauss's law; that is, it shows that the electric force between point-charges is strictly inverse-square. A closed conducting shell, or screen, produces perfect electrical shielding on its interior; the electric field within is always exactly zero, quite apart from the external electric fields or the electric charges on the surface.

The electric field just outside a conductor's surface is proportional to the surface charge density at that point:

[27-10] $$E = \sigma/\epsilon_0$$

PROBLEMS

27-1   A constant electric field of 2.0 nt/coul exists in the direction 30° above the X-axis, the electric-force lines lying in the XY-plane. What is the magnitude of the electric flux through a 1.0 m^2 area lying in the XZ-plane?

27-2 Three point-charges, $+2Q$, $-3Q$, and $+1Q$, are placed at three different points in space. Find the total electric flux across a Gaussian surface which (a) encloses only the $-3Q$ charge, (b) encloses the $2Q$ and $-3Q$ charges, (c) encloses all three charges. (d) Could one use Gauss's law to find E due to these three charges?

27-3 A charge Q is located at the center of a cube of edge-length L. (a) Find the electric flux through any one face. (b) If the charge Q is located inside the cube but not at the center, how would this affect the total flux through the cube's surface? (c) The flux across each face?

27-4 The term *flux* implies the flow of something. (a) Show that when the vector electric field is replaced by the vector velocity field v arising in streamline flow in hydrodynamics (Section 18-5), the flux $\phi_F = \oint v \cdot dS$ is, in fact, the volume flux equal to the net volume of fluid flowing through a closed surface per unit time. (b) How does one write Gauss's law for incompressible fluids, assuming that there are no sources or sinks of fluid within the Gaussian surface?

27-5 Show that Gauss's law for gravitational interactions is written $\oint g \cdot dS = -4\pi Gm$.

27-6 If an electric field of 1 nt/coul is represented by one electric-force line per square meter, how many electric lines of force originate from a charge Q?

27-7 A nonconducting sphere of radius R is in a uniform electric field of magnitude E. What is the electric flux through the spherical surface?

27-8 An infinitely long dielectric solid cylinder with radius R has a constant volume charge density ρ (coul/m^3). What is the electric field as a function of the distance r from the axis for (a) $r < R$ and (b) $r > R$?

27-9 A particle of mass m and charge $-q$ moves diametrically through a uniformly charged sphere of radius R with total charge Q. Find the frequency of the particle's simple harmonic motion.

27-10 A thin metallic spherical shell 50 cm in radius has a charge of $4.0 \text{ } \mu\text{coul}$. What is the electric field at the following distances from the center of the sphere: (a) 25 cm, (b) 50 cm, and (c) 100 cm?

27-11 Two concentric cylindrical dielectric shells have radii of 5.0 cm and 10.0 cm and respective charges of $+2.0 \text{ } \mu\text{coul}$ and $-4.0 \text{ } \mu\text{coul}$. Find the electric field at the following distances from the center of the cylinders: (a) 2.5 cm, (b) 7.5 cm, and (c) 20.0 cm.

27-12 A hollow dielectric sphere has inner and outer radii of R_i and R_o. The total charge carried by the sphere is $+Q$, this charge being uniformly distributed throughout the dielectric. Find expressions giving the electric field for (a) $r < R_i$, (b) $R_i < r < R_o$ and (c) $r > R_o$.

27-13 $\star$ A solid charged dielectric sphere has a spherically symmetric charge distribution; that is, the volume charge density ρ is a function only of the coordinate r measured from the center of the sphere. How must ρ vary with r if the electric field at every point within the sphere is to be of the same magnitude?

27-14 An electron is subject to a constant force of 3.0×10^{-15} nt when it moves between two parallel oppositely charged conducting plates. What is the surface charge density on either plate?

27-15 A uniform electric field exists between two parallel, oppositely charged conducting plates. A third conducting plate is placed between the two charged plates and oriented parallel to the other two plates. Show that the electric field is zero in the interior of the third conducting plate and that the opposite sides of the plate carry charges of opposite sign but equal magnitude (a) by Gauss's law and (b) by applying the relation $E = \sigma/2\epsilon_0$ giving the electric field from an infinitesimally thin sheet of charge.

27-16 Three concentric, conducting, spherical shells carry charges $+2Q$ (on the smallest), $-Q$, and $-3Q$ (on the largest). Find the charges on the inner and outer surfaces of each of these three spherical shells.

27-17 A hollow conducting spherical shell having zero net charge is placed in a uniform electric field. (a) What is the electric field within the shell? (b) Sketch the electric field lines within and around the conducting shell.

27-18 A charge Q is introduced into the interior of an initially uncharged spherical hollow conductor of radius R. (a) Plot the electric field as a function of distance from the center of the sphere. (b) Now a second charge, $-Q$, is placed outside the conductor; what part of the field, if any, is affected? (c) Does the charge on the interior experience a force arising from the charge on the outside? (d) Does the charge on the outside experience a force arising from the charge on the inside? (e) Is there a violation of Newton's third law?

27-19 ★ An electron is released from rest at a distance of 15 cm from the center of a spherical conducting shell 10 cm in radius carrying a total positive charge of 2.0×10^{-7} coul. Two small holes are made in the shell to allow the electron to pass in and out. (a) Describe the motion of the electron. (b) Find the upper and lower limits on the period of the electron.

TWENTY-EIGHT

ELECTRIC POTENTIAL

In this chapter we exploit the fact that the Coulomb force is a conservative force in that it depends only on the separation distance between point-charges. Consequently, we can define an electric potential energy and utilize the conservation law of mechanical energy.

We first find the potential energy between a pair of point-charges, and then extend this to a system of interacting point-charges. Then we define the electric potential as a scalar quantity whose magnitude at each point in space surrounding the charges permits us to solve easily problems involving changes in the energy of a charged particle. We derive the general relations between the electric potential and the electric field, and discuss their graphical representation through equipotential surfaces and electric field lines. Finally, we consider electric potential as related to conducting objects.

28-1 Electric potential energy of two point-charges We can, of course, solve all problems involving electric forces simply by knowing the Coulomb force and applying Newton's laws, but this is neither necessary in all problems nor desirable. Because the Coulomb force is a conservative force (Section 12-2), one depending only on the separation distance between interacting charges, we may associate an electric potential energy with the Coulomb interaction. In introducing the potential-energy concept, we deal with a *scalar* quantity rather than a vector quantity, and the powerful conservation of energy principle applies. We have already seen the utility of the potential-energy concept and the conservation law of mechanical energy in dealing with such conservative forces as the gravitational force and the elastic force of a deformed body.

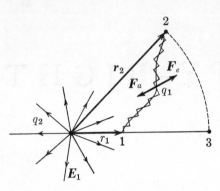

Figure 28-1. Charge q_1 is moved from point 1 to point 2, so that its separation distance from charge q_2 goes from r_1 to r_2. The series of small radial and circular segments is equivalent to the continuous path, and we can imagine the charge q_2 to go from point 1 radially outward to point 3 and then to point 2 along the circular arc.

We first find the electric potential energy U associated with two interacting positive point-charges q_1 and q_2. We imagine q_2 to be fixed in position while the charge q_1 is moved from point 1 to point 2 at separation distances r_1 to r_2 respectively, as shown in Figure 28-1. (We could, of course, do this in reverse: keep q_1 fixed and move q_2.) Recall that the difference in potential energy,

$U_f - U_i$, between some initial and final states is given, in general, by

[12-12] $$U_f - U_i = -W_{i \to f} \text{ (by } F) = -\int_i^f F \cdot ds$$

That is, the change in potential energy is simply the negative of the work $W_{i \to f}$ done *by the interaction force*. Since the two charges are imagined to be of like sign, they repel one another and the electric force F_e on charge q_1 is radially outward. If we are to find the system's change in potential energy we must imagine the charge q_1 to be transported from 1 to 2 at *constant* speed, so that kinetic energy is unchanged. We must, therefore, apply a radially inward force F_a whose magnitude at each point just matches that of the outward Coulomb force. Then the charge can move at constant speed, and the work $W_{1 \to 2}$ done by the electric force F_e is, from the equation above, given by

$$U_2 - U_1 = -W_{1 \to 2} = -\int_1^2 F_e \cdot ds \qquad [28\text{-}1]$$

Although the path shown in the figure is quite general, evaluating the integral of Equation 28-1 is easy. For one thing, we can imagine the complicated path to be replaced by a series of small segments which closely approximate the actual path, these segments lying either radially outward or along circular arcs centered at charge q_2. No work is done along the circular segments, since the force F_e is perpendicular to the displacement ds there. Only the radial displacements contribute. This is equivalent to saying that we can imagine the charge to be moved radially outward to point 3 at the same distance r_2 as point 2, and then moved, with no expenditure in energy, from point 3 to point 2 along the circular arc. Therefore, Equation 28-1 becomes

$$U_2 - U_1 = -\int_{r_1}^{r_2} \frac{kq_1q_2}{r^2}\,dr = kq_1q_2\left(\frac{1}{r_2} - \frac{1}{r_1}\right) \qquad [28\text{-}2]$$

Note that in taking the outward route from point 1 to point 3, the vectors F_e and dr are in the *same* direction.

Equation 28-2 gives the *difference* in potential energy for two different separation distances of the point-charges. This is all it can give, since choice of the zero of potential energy is always arbitrary. It is customary to choose the zero of potential energy to correspond to that configuration in which the force between the interacting particles is zero. Thus, we shall take U to be zero when particles are infinitely separated, putting

$$U_2 = 0 \quad \text{when} \quad r_2 = \infty$$

Then Equation 28-2 becomes, without the subscript,

$$\boxed{U = kq_1q_2/r} \qquad [28\text{-}3]$$

We will have to bear in mind that electric potential energy, unless otherwise noted, is always zero for infinite charge separation.

Equation 28-3 is the basis of *all* further considerations in this chapter, and it shall be important to understand its implications. First, we can speak of electric potential energy only because the Coulomb force is <u>conservative</u>. Said differently, the *work done* in taking a charge around any *closed loop in an electrostatic field is zero:*

[12-13] $$\oint F \cdot ds = 0$$

In returning a charge to its starting point we restore the system to its initial state, doing no net work. Equivalently, the *work done* in moving one charge relative to another is *independent of the path* and *depends only on the end points*.

Whenever one can associate a potential energy with an interaction, as in the case of the gravitational force, the spring force and, now, the electric force, the *conservation of mechanical energy principle* applies. That is, if the system is isolated from external work-producing forces, the total mechanical energy E_m, comprised of the kinetic energies of the particles and the potential energy between the particles, is constant. For two particles a and b, we may write

$$E_m = K_a + K_b + U_{ab} = \text{constant} \qquad [28\text{-}4]$$

where U_{ab} is the potential energy *of the system* (not of one or the other particles).

We see from both Equations 28-2 and 28-3 that the potential energy associated with two positive charges is *positive*. This is as it should be, since two such particles repel each other. If one brings the positive charges together from infinity, one *increases* the potential energy (over zero). The same remarks apply when one has two negative charges: U is again positive.

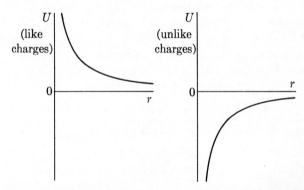

Figure 28-2. Electric potential energy as a function of the separation distance between two like point-charges and two unlike point-charges.

On the other hand, if a positive and negative charge interact, the force is attractive and the potential energy is negative. See Figure 28-2. This follows directly from Equation 28-3 (q_1 is $+$ and q_2 is $-$, hence U is $-$). It follows also from a simple physical argument. Suppose the two unlike charges are far separated and initially at rest. The total energy of this isolated system is initially zero and must remain so. If the charges are released and move toward one another, they gain kinetic energy and, since the total energy E_m remains zero, the potential energy must become *negative*. Or, try it in reverse. If the unlike charges are to be pulled apart at constant speed, work must be done on the system and its potential energy must increase (become less negative) until it reaches zero and the charges are infinitely separated. The matter of signs will arise often in this chapter. One can always deal properly with this tricky matter by scrupulously assigning the right signs to q and to U. Still better, physical arguments will always determine whether the signs have been correctly assigned.

Now, all of our arguments on electric potential energy have paralleled exactly those used earlier (Sections 16-5, 16-6) for the gravitational force, a result which is not very surprising, since both are inverse-square forces. Because of this, we may immediately appropriate some earlier results concerning the energetics of gravitational interactions. We assume, for simplicity, that one of two interacting charged particles is very massive, so that the total mechanical energy of the system consists of the system's potential energy U and the kinetic energy K of the light particle only. Then, the path traced out by the light particle is a conic section and depends on the total energy $E_m = K + U$ as follows:

$$E_m < 0, \text{ an ellipse}$$
$$E_m = 0, \text{ a parabola}$$
$$E_m > 0, \text{ a hyperbola}$$

If two charges of like sign interact, as in the case of an alpha particle scattered by a nucleus or an electron scattered by a negatively charged ion, the total energy E_m must be positive (both U and K are never less than zero), and the path is hyperbolic. On the other hand, when a positive and negative charge interact, the particles may be *bound*, one particle moving in an elliptical path, but only if $E_m < 0$.

Energy conservation results from the fact that the Coulomb force is conservative. *Angular momentum* is also conserved in electric interactions. This follows from the fact that the Coulomb force is *central* (Section 15-3), lying along the line connecting the charges. When one measures the angular momentum of a particle $L = r \times p = r \times mv$ relative to an axis passing through the force center, the angular momentum of this particle, whatever the details of its path, remains constant. One may exploit angular momentum conservation as well as energy conservation, as we saw earlier in the discussion on Rutherford scattering (Section 25-6), in treating the motions of charged particles.

A word on units for electric potential energy. Since we will use only mks units, U carries the unit joules (newton-meter) with electric charges in coulombs. A more convenient energy unit for systems of atomic particles is the electron volt, where by definition, 1 ev $= 1.6 \times 10^{-19}$ joule (we shall very shortly see how this definition arises). The electron volt is a particularly convenient energy unit because two electrons (or any other two charged particles with charge magnitude e) when separated by atomic distances (10^{-10} m $= 1$ Å) have electric potential energies of the order of a few electron volts, as one can easily verify from Equation 28-3.

Example 1 In the classical planetary model, an electron in a hydrogen atom moves in a circle of radius r about the proton. (a) What is the total energy of the system? (b) What is the binding energy of the system if the radius of the orbit is 0.53 Å? See Figure 28-3.

(a) Taking the proton mass to be infinite (relative to the much smaller electron mass), we have for the total energy

$$E_m = U + K = kq_1q_2/r + \tfrac{1}{2}mv^2$$

Here q_1 and q_2 are the proton and electron charges, m is the electron mass, and v is the electron speed. We take $q_1 = +e$ and $q_2 = -e$. Then,

$$E_m = -ke^2/r + \tfrac{1}{2}mv^2 \qquad [28\text{-}5]$$

Note that the potential energy is negative because the two particles attract one another.

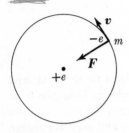

Figure 28-3. An electron orbiting a proton in the classical planetary model of the hydrogen atom.

We can eliminate the speed v by applying Newton's second law, noting that a radial Coulomb force of magnitude ke^2/r^2 causes the electron to travel in a circle at constant speed v:

$$\Sigma\, F_r = ma_r$$

$$ke^2/r^2 = mv^2/r$$

$$\tfrac{1}{2}ke^2/r = \tfrac{1}{2}mv^2$$

For a circular orbit, the kinetic energy is just half the *magnitude* of the potential energy. Using this result in Equation 28-5 yields

$$E_m = -ke^2/r + \tfrac{1}{2}ke^2/r$$
$$E_m = -\tfrac{1}{2}ke^2/r \qquad [28\text{-}6]$$

The *total* energy E_m is negative. The electron is *bound* to the nucleus.

(b) Suppose that one removes the electron from the proton. Then one must do work on the particles to separate them and bring them to rest at infinite separation. One must raise the system's energy up to zero by adding the so-called *binding* energy E_b. From Equation 28-6 it follows that

$$E_b = \tfrac{1}{2}ke^2/r$$

Taking $r = 0.53$ Å $= 0.53 \times 10^{-10}$ m, we have

$$E_b = \frac{\tfrac{1}{2}(9.0 \times 10^9 \text{ nt-m}^2/\text{coul}^2)(1.6 \times 10^{-19} \text{ coul})^2(1 \text{ ev}/1.6 \times 10^{-19} \text{ joule})}{(0.53 \times 10^{-10} \text{ m})}$$

$$E_b = 14 \text{ ev}$$

The binding energy of this atomic system is the *ionization energy* of hydrogen, since it is the energy required to change the neutral atom into an electron and positively charged ion (proton).

Example 2 An electron passes close to a helium nucleus (charge, $+2e$), at a speed of 3.00×10^6 m/sec when separated from it by 4.00 Å, as shown in Figure 28-4. (a) In what sort of path does the electron travel? (b) What is the electron's speed, Figure 28-4, at point 2 at a distance of 8.00 Å from the nucleus? (c) What is the electron's velocity at this point?

(a) The question concerning the path is answered simply by finding whether $E_m > 0$ or $E_m < 0$. The total energy of the system at the initial point 1 is

$$E_m = K_1 + U_1 = \tfrac{1}{2}mv_1{}^2 + \frac{kq_1q_2}{r_1}$$

$$E_m = \tfrac{1}{2}(9.00 \times 10^{-31}\ \text{kg})(3.00 \times 10^6\ \text{m/sec})^2$$

$$+ \frac{(9.00 \times 10^9\ \text{nt-m}^2/\text{coul}^2)(-2)(1.60 \times 10^{-19}\ \text{coul})^2}{(4.00 \times 10^{-10}\ \text{m})}$$

$$= (+4.10 \times 10^{-18}\ \text{joule}) + (-1.15 \times 10^{-18}\ \text{joule}) = 2.95 \times 10^{-18}\ \text{joule} > 0$$

The electron travels in a *hyperbolic* path. Despite the fact that the electron is attracted by the nucleus, the electron's kinetic energy is too great for it to be bound
to the nucleus.

(b) Since $r_2 = 2r_1$,

$$U_2 = kq_1q_2/r_2 = \tfrac{1}{2}U_1 = -0.58 \times 10^{-18}\ \text{joule}$$

Therefore, at point 2 its kinetic energy is

$$K_2 = E_m - U_2 = 2.95 - (-0.58)$$

$$\times 10^{-18}\ \text{joule} = 3.53 \times 10^{-18}\ \text{joule}$$

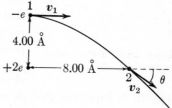

Figure 28-4. An electron being scattered by a helium nucleus.

and its speed is

$$v_2 = \sqrt{2K_2/m} = \sqrt{2(3.53 \times 10^{-18}\ \text{joule})/(9.1 \times 10^{-31}\ \text{kg})} = 2.8 \times 10^6\ \text{m/sec}$$

(c) We find the direction of v_2 by applying angular-momentum conservation, choosing the nucleus, which acts as the center of the central force, as axis:

$$L = mr_1v_1 = mr_2v_2 \sin \theta$$

$$\sin \theta = r_1v_1/r_2v_2 = (4.0\ \text{Å})(3.0 \times 10^6\ \text{m/sec})/(8.0\ \text{Å})(2.8 \times 10^6\ \text{m/sec})$$

$$\theta = 32°$$

28-2 Systems of interacting charged particles

We have found that the electric potential energy of two point-charges separated by r is kq_1q_2/r. What is the potential energy for a system of three (or more) interacting charges, such as that shown in Figure 28-5? It is easy to show that the total electric potential energy U of the system is simply

$$U = U_{12} + U_{23} + U_{13}$$

$$= kq_1q_2/r_{12} + kq_2q_3/r_{23} + kq_1q_3/r_{13} \qquad [28\text{-}7]$$

First suppose that only the charges q_1 and q_2 are brought together until their separation is r_{12}. The work required, and hence the potential energy of the system thus far, is given by the first term in Equation 28-7. Now charge q_3 is brought from infinity toward the charges q_1 and q_2, these latter charges being assumed fixed in position. Imagine, for the sake of argument, that the electric force on q_3 from q_1 is "turned off." Then only charge q_2 acts on q_3, and the potential energy between these charges is given by the second term in Equation 28-7. Now imagine just the reverse situation: q_3 is brought toward q_1 while the electric force from q_2 is "turned off." The last term in Equation 28-7 represents the potential energy between q_1 and q_3. In assuming that first one then the other electric force was inoperative, we implied, in effect, that the two forces could be thought to act independently of each other. Said differently, we assumed that the resultant force on charge q_3 was the vector sum of the electric forces from q_1 and q_2 separately. But this is just the principle of super-position for electric forces! Thus, since electric forces obey the superposition rule, the total electric potential energy of a system of charges, as given in Equation 28-7 (or its extensions to four or more charges), is simply the sum of terms, each term giving the potential energy between the two charges of a pair.

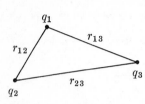

Figure 28-5. Three inter-acting point-charges.

The total potential energy U of the system is independent of the way in which the system is assembled. One may bring charges together in any order or by any route. The potential energy is always the same. It is a property of the system, not of any one charge, and it depends only on the separation distances between the charged particles.

Example 3   Three charges, $+Q$, $+Q$, and $-Q$, are brought to the corners of an equilateral triangle of side L; see Figure 28-6a. What is the total energy required to assemble these charges?

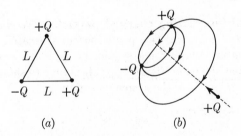

(a)   (b)

Figure 28-6. (a) A system consisting of three point-charges at the corners of an equilateral triangle. (b) No work is required to bring the third charge toward the other two charges (constituting an electric dipole) along the dotted path, or along any other path.

The work W done in assembling the system equals the system's total potential energy. Therefore, from Equation 28-7,

$$W = U = +kQ^2/L - kQ^2/L - kQ^2/L = -kQ^2/L$$

The total energy is negative. This means that the three charges form a bound system. That the total U is just equal to that of a single pair of unlike charges can be arrived at from another angle. Imagine that first the charges $+Q$ and $-Q$ are separated by L and therefore have a potential energy $-kQ^2/L$. Then the third charge is brought to its final position along a line which is perpendicular to the line joining the first two charges; see Figure 28-6b. Since this charge is acted on by the electric field of the first two charges (an electric dipole) and this field is always perpendicular to its displacement, no work is required to move the third charge to its final location along this or any other route!

28-3 Electric potential defined The concept of electric potential energy leads us naturally to that of the *electric potential*, a quantity which is extraordinarily useful in treating problems involving electric charge distributions.

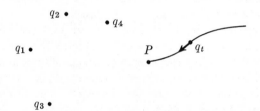

Figure 28-7. Test charge q_t brought from infinity to point P in the vicinity of other charges held fixed in position.

Suppose that we have a collection of charges *fixed* in position and that still one more charge, q_t, a test charge, is brought from infinity at constant speed to point P; see Figure 28-7. We can readily compute the work required to do this: it is simply the electric potential energy of the system after q_t has been brought to its final position at P less the potential energy of the same charges with q_t infinitely far away. Note that we need *not* specify the route followed by q_t. Suppose, now, that we take the charge q_t away and bring, instead, another charge $2q_t$ to the same position P as that at which we had earlier placed q_t. Again, we wish to know the total work required. There is no need to go through the whole computation again; we know that in the second instance the work is just twice that in the first. Thus, if we know the work required to bring a *unit* positive charge from infinity to some location, we know at once the work required to bring any other charge there. Note that the assembly of charges into which we introduce the additional charge must be such that these charges remain fixed in position; equivalently, we may imagine the test charge to be so small that it does not affect the charge distribution.

The work W required to bring a unit positive charge from infinity to some position is defined as the *electric potential* V of that point. In symbols,

$$V = W/q$$ [28-8]

where W is the work done by the *external* force and V is the corresponding *increase* in potential. We have assumed, of course, that the electric potential energy of any pair of charges is chosen to be zero when the charges are infinitely separated. Given a fixed distribution of charges we can then associate an electric potential, a scalar quantity, with every point in space.

The electric potential can be measured in units of joules per coulomb A special name, the *volt*, is given to this ratio:

$$\text{1 volt} = \text{1 joule/coul}$$

The volt is named after A. Volta (1745–1827) who developed a rudimentary battery. Units related to the volt (abbreviated v) are the microvolt ($1 \ \mu v = 10^{-6}$ v), the millivolt ($1 \ mv = 10^{-3}$ v), and the kilovolt ($1 \ kv = 10^3$ v). If we have a positive charge of 1 coul initially far from some charge distribution and then bring this charge to a point P_1 and find that the total work done was 10 joules, the potential assigned to P_1 is $+10$ v. By the same token, we know at once that to bring a charge of -4 coul from infinity to P_1 will require, from Equation 28-8, work in the amount

$$W = qV = (-4 \text{ coul})(+10 \text{ v}) = -40 \text{ joules}$$

That is, rather than our actually having to do work in bringing the negative charge to P_1, negative work, -40 joule, is done by the fixed charges on the negative charge brought near. Here we see the motivation for introducing the concept of electric potential: if this quantity is known or can be readily calculated for a given charge distribution, we can at once find the work done in moving any charge along any path from one location (with one potential) to a second location (with, possibly, another potential), and we can do all of this without (explicitly) having to deal with the rather complicated problem of finding the electric force acting on the charges at each point.

Our concern from now on will be primarily with potential *differences*. If point 1 has the potential $V_1 = +10$ v and point 2 the potential $V_2 = +2$ v, then the work required to transport a charge of $+1$ coul from point 2 to point 1 is $W_{2\to1} = qV_{21} = (+1 \text{ coul})(10 - 2) \text{ v} = 8$ joules. By the same token, to move a charge of -1 coul from point 2 to point 1, the work required is -8 joules. The *sign* of the potential difference is important but, when we deal with potential differences, the choice of zero for potential is not. It is often convenient to specify potentials relative to that of the Earth (a reasonably good conductor), in which case we take "ground" to be zero. Electric potential or potential difference is sometimes referred to loosely as "voltage."

The *electron volt* (ev) is an energy unit chosen so that the work done in moving a particle with charge e (1.60×10^{-19} coul) across a potential difference of 1 volt is, by definition, 1 electron volt = 1 ev. Thus, with $q = e = 1.60 \times 10^{-19}$ coul and $V = 1$ v,

$$W = qV = (1.60 \times 10^{-19} \text{ coul})(1 \text{ v}) = 1.60 \times 10^{-19} \text{ joule} = 1 \text{ ev}$$

For example, if an electron is accelerated through a potential difference of 100 v, its kinetic energy changes by 100 ev; similarly, a singly charged chlorine ion, Cl^-, falling through the same potential difference changes its kinetic energy by 100 ev (the change in speed is, of course, not the same). Units related to the electron volt are the kilo electron volt (1 kev $= 10^3$ ev), the million electron volt (1 Mev $= 10^6$ ev), and the billion electron volt (1 Bev $= 10^9$ ev).

A familiar device which maintains an essentially constant potential difference across its terminals is the cell, which changes internal chemical potential energy into electrostatic potential energy at its terminals. The common automobile battery consists of three (or six) lead cells, each maintaining a potential difference of approximately 2.0 v across its terminals (when "charged"). That the potential difference across cell terminals is typically a few volts is no accident. It is a direct consequence of the fact that the electric potential energy of ions separated by atomic distances is also a few electron volts.

Potential differences (or "voltages") may be measured by a voltmeter. An electroscope is one very simple (but not very useful) form of voltmeter. The divergence of the similarly charged leaves is a measure of the potential of the leaves relative to the shielding case. A voltmeter of the more familiar variety, one involving a moving coil in a magnet, is usable only when one measures potential differences across devices carrying an electric current.

28-4 Electric potential of point-charges The electric potential energy U_1 of a charge q_1 and a test charge q_t at a distance r_1 from it is given by

[28-3] $$U_1 = kq_1q_t/r_1$$

It follows that the electric potential V_1 at the location of the test charge is

$$V_1 = U_1/q_t = kq_1/r_1 \qquad \text{[28-9]}$$

Now, if one has a number of point-charges, $q_1, q_2, q_3, \ldots$, at the respective distances $r_1, r_2, r_3, \ldots$ from the test charge q_t, it follows that the total potential V is simply the scalar sum of the potentials contributed by each charge separately (electric potential energies add as scalars). That is,

$$V = V_1 + V_2 + \cdots = k(q_1/r_1 + q_2/r_2 + \cdots)$$

$$\boxed{V = k\Sigma \, q_i/r_i} \qquad \text{[28-10]}$$

Equation 28-10 gives the potential for *any* charge distribution, since we can regard even a continuous distribution of charge as arising from a large number of point-charges. The procedures for finding (easily) the potential from a continuous charge distribution are treated in the next section.

Example 4   Charges of $+24$ μcoul and -30 μcoul are placed at $(0, 0)$ and $(4.0, 0)$ cm, respectively, as shown in Figure 28-8. (a) Find the electric potential arising

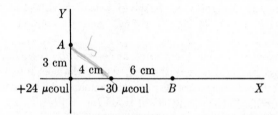

Figure 28-8.

from these charges at points A, $(0, 3.0)$ cm, and B, $(10.0, 0)$ cm. (b) What is the work required to move an electron from A to B? (c) What is the work required to move a Zn^{++} ion from A to B?

(a) Using Equation 28-10, we find the potentials at points A and B to be the following:

$$V_A = 9.0 \times 10^9 \text{ nt-m}^2/\text{coul}^2 \left(\frac{+24 \times 10^{-6} \text{ coul}}{3.0 \times 10^{-2} \text{ m}} \right.$$
$$\left. + \frac{-30 \times 10^{-6} \text{ coul}}{5.0 \times 10^{-2} \text{ m}} \right) = 1.8 \times 10^6 \text{ v}$$

$$V_B = 9.0 \times 10^9 \text{ nt-m}^2/\text{coul}^2 \left(\frac{+24 \times 10^{-6} \text{ coul}}{10.0 \times 10^{-2} \text{ m}} \right.$$
$$\left. + \frac{-30 \times 10^{-6} \text{ coul}}{6.0 \times 10^{-2} \text{ m}} \right) = -2.3 \times 10^6 \text{ v}$$

Therefore, $V_{AB} = V_A - V_B = [(+1.8) - (-2.3)] \times 10^6 \text{ ev} = 4.1 \times 10^6 \text{ v}$.

(b) The potential goes "downhill" from point A to point B. Therefore, the work done by an external agent in moving an electron with charge $-e$ from A to B is

$$W_{A \rightarrow B} = -qV_{AB} = -(-e)(4.1 \times 10^6 \text{ v}) = +4.1 \text{ Mev}$$

(c) To take a doubly and positively charged Zn^{++} ion from A to B the work required is

$$W_{A \rightarrow B} = -(+2e)(4.1 \times 10^6 \text{ v}) = -8.2 \text{ Mev}$$

28-5 Relations between V and E   Given the electric field E as a function of position for a known charge distribution, how does one find the corresponding electric potential V as a function of position?

The potential energy U and conservative force F are related in general by

[28-1] $$U_2 - U_1 = -\int_1^2 F_e \cdot ds$$

Dividing both sides of this equation by the charge q_t gives

$$U_2/q_t - U_1/q_t = -\int_1^2 (F_e/q_t) \cdot ds$$

The left side above represents the electric potential difference $V_2 - V_1$. The electric field $E = F_e/q_t$ appears on the right. Therefore, we have

$$V_2 - V_1 = -\int_1^2 E \cdot ds \qquad \text{[28-11]}$$

The potential difference is the negative of the line integral of the electric field between the end points. If we are able to choose $V = 0$ for an infinitely distant point (say, point 1), this reduces to

$$V_p = -\int_\infty^p E \cdot ds \qquad \text{[28-12]}$$

Where V_p is now the potential at point p.

Example 5   Find the electric potential as a function of the distance r from an infinitely long and uniformly charged wire.

In Section 26-3, we found that the magnitude of the electric field for this configuration is given by

[26-6] $$E = \lambda/2\pi\epsilon_0 r$$

where λ is the constant linear charge density.

We find the potential difference between two points r_1 and r_2 from Equation 28-11:

$$V_2 - V_1 = -\int_{r_1}^{r_2} E \cdot dr$$

We take the wire to be positively charged. Then the outward electric field E is in the same direction as dr, and the above relation becomes

$$V_2 - V_1 = -\int_{r_1}^{r_2} \frac{\lambda}{2\pi\epsilon_0} \frac{dr}{r} = -\frac{\lambda}{2\pi\epsilon_0} \ln \frac{r_2}{r_1} \qquad \text{[28-13]}$$

We *cannot*, for this configuration, take $V = 0$ for $r = \infty$, for then Equation 28-13 would lead to an infinite potential for all finite r (the physical reason for this mathematical difficulty is that an *infinitely* long wire would always look infinite in length, even if viewed from an infinite distance away). This is not troublesome, however, inasmuch as we always deal with potential differences. We simply make V equal to zero for some arbitrarily chosen finite r.

The electric potential varies logarithmically with distance in all charge configurations having cylindrical symmetry, such as a wire surrounded by a cylindrical tube or two coaxial cylindrical shells.

Let us find how the electric potential is related to E for the simplest possible geometry, that of a constant, or uniform, electric field. We imagine that a charge q_t is moved along the direction of the uniformly spaced and parallel electric field lines a distance d, as shown in Figure 28-9. The potential difference V between two points separated by d is, by the definition of V, given by

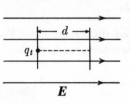

[28-8] $$V = W/q_t$$

We can also write the work W as the negative of the product of the *constant* electric force $F_e = Eq_t$ and the displacement d along the direction of E:

$$W = -q_t E d$$

Figure 28-9. A test charge q_t moved along the lines of force of a uniform electric field.

Eliminating W between the last two equations yields

Uniform E: $E = -V/d$ [28-14]

We could, of course, have obtained Equation 28-14 directly from Equation 28-11.

The magnitude of the electric field is simply the potential difference divided by the displacement along the direction of field lines. We see, then, that the electric field may be expressed in volts per meter as well as in newtons per coulomb. Note the minus sign in Equation 28-14. It corresponds to the fact that, when we travel *along* the direction of the electric force lines, we move to points of progressively *lower* electric potential.

28-6 Equipotential surfaces Through the concept of electric potential we associate a number (positive or negative) with every point in space surrounding a charge distribution. Through the electric-field concept we associate a vector (with three scalar components) with every point in space. We can map the electric field with electric lines of force. Similarly, we can map the electric potential with *equipotential surfaces*.

Consider the simple case of a single point-charge q. The electric field is radial, and the potential V at any point r from the charge depends only on this distance ($V = kq/r$). Therefore, for a given radial distance r, *all* points on the sphere of radius r have the *same* potential. Indeed, we can imagine the point-charge to be surrounded by a number of concentric spherical surfaces, each point on a given sphere having the same potential and each spherical equipotential surface differing from its neighboring surfaces in potential by a constant amount (of course, in a two-dimensional figure the equipotential surfaces are represented as equipotential lines); see Figure 28-10a. The electric force lines, radially outward for a positive charge, are perpendicular to the equipotential surfaces.

One may represent the relationship between V and E for a single positive point-charge by a diagram in which V is plotted as an elevation against r,

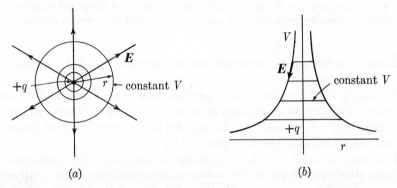

(a)   (b)

Figure 28-10. (a) Electric force lines and equipotential surfaces (in two dimensions) for a point-charge. (b) Electric potential plotted against distance from a point-charge; the electric field at any point is the negative gradient of the potential hill.

as in Figure 28-10b. Constant elevation now corresponds to constant electric potential (just as constant elevation corresponds to constant gravitational potential energy for an actual hill), and the electric field is a measure of the *gradient*, that is, the *steepness* of the grade. A model of this sort is useful for visualizing the interaction between two point-charges. If a small object is rolled up the potential hill, its path, when viewed from above, corresponds to the path of the scattered charge; it is a hyperbola. By the same token, the potential hill of a negative charge is represented by a hole; a small object rolled toward such a hole may, when viewed from above, trace a hyperbolic, parabolic, or elliptical path, depending on the total energy.

Three-dimensional models of the electric potential are of practical use. One may construct them from sheets of rubber, raising or lowering points to represent point-charges. Then the path taken by small balls rolled over the surface are those taken by point-charges moving in the corresponding electric field configuration. In this way one may find the paths of charged

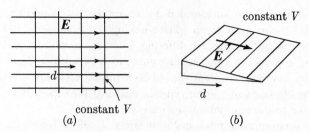

Figure 28-11. (a) Electric force lines and equipotential surfaces (in two dimensions) for a uniform electric field. (b) Electric potential plotted as a function of the distance d along the electric force lines; the electric field is again the negative gradient of the potential hill (here an inclined plane).

particles in complicated charge distributions for which detailed computation is not practicable.

The equipotential surfaces in a uniform field consist of parallel plane surfaces, these surfaces again being at right angles to the field lines, as shown in Figure 28-11a. The model for the uniform electric field is—of all things—an inclined plane, as shown in Figure 28-11b.

It is easy to show that for *any* charge configuration the equipotential surfaces are always normal to the corresponding electric field lines. Suppose, for the sake of argument, that E did *not* lie perpendicular to constant V surfaces. Then there would be a component of the electric force acting along the equipotential surface. But, by definition, a charge can be moved over an equipotential surface without doing work on it. Therefore, E lines must be normal to constant V surfaces; see Figure 28-12. Moreover, the direction of E is always toward surfaces of *lower* potential.

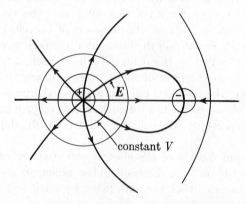

Figure 28-12. Electric force lines and equipotential lines for two unlike charges of different magnitudes.

We have found the general relation which gives V, knowing E (Equation 28-11). We wish now to find the inverse relation, E in terms of V. Let the vector $d\mathbf{s}$ represent the small displacement made when one moves *along the direction of* E between two neighboring equipotential surfaces differing in potential by dV. Since $d\mathbf{s}$ is parallel to $\mathbf{E}$, that route has been taken which involves the *largest* potential difference for a given path length ds. The electric force does positive work on the charge q,

$$dW = F_e \, ds = qE \, ds$$

thereby leading to a decrease in potential energy dU of

$$dU = q \, dV = -dW = -qE \, ds$$

$$E = -\frac{dV}{ds} \qquad [28\text{-}15]$$

The electric field is the negative of the spatial derivative of the electric potential *taken along that direction for which V changes most rapidly with position* (note that in Figures 28-9b and 28-10b the electric field is represented as the steepest downward slope, or *gradient*, of the potential). It is clear that in the case of a constant $\mathbf{E}$, we have $E = -V/d$, as found earlier.

When the electric potential is given as a function of the space coordinates $V(x, y, z)$, the rectangular components of the electric field are given by

$$E_x = -\partial V/\partial x, \qquad E_y = -\partial V/\partial y, \qquad E_z = -\partial V/\partial z \qquad [28\text{-}16]$$

Example 6 Given that the electric potential of a point-charge is $V = kq/r$ (Equation 28-9), find the electric field.

Using Equation 28-15 we have

$$E = -dV/dr = -d/dr[(kq/r)] = kq/r^2$$

which is exactly the relation for the electric field of a point-charge (Equation 26-3).

Example 7 Find the electric potential as a function of r for a uniformly charged spherical shell of radius R.

We found earlier that a uniformly charged spherical shell produces an electric field which is equivalent to that of a point-charge at its center for all points *exterior* to the shell, and that the electric field is *zero* for all points within the shell. It follows that the potential exterior to the shell is just like that of a point-charge, namely $V = kq/r$ where q is the total charge on the shell. On the interior, $E = 0$. Since $E = -dV/dr$, from Equation 28-15, V must be *constant* at all points within the shell. But what constant? The potential cannot change in going from the exterior to the interior of the shell, for then an electric field would exist inside the shell. Therefore, the potential at all interior points must

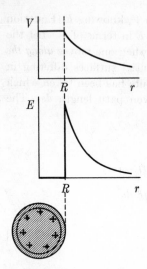

Figure 28-13. Electric potential and electric field as a function of the distance r from the center of a spherically symmetrical shell of charge of radius R.

be just the potential at the surface, $V = kq/R$; see Figure 28-13. Any charge placed within the shell is not subject to an electric force and can be moved about without work being done on it.

28-7 Electric potential and conductors

Let us recall some important results (Section 27-5) for all electric conductors: (a) even if a conductor of arbitrary shape carries a net charge, there is *no charge inside* the outer surface of the conductor, all of the net charge residing on the outer conductor surface; (b) the *electric field inside* any conductor (within solid metal or within a hole in a conductor) is exactly *zero*; and (c) at the surface the *electric field lines* are always *perpendicular* to the exterior conductor *surface*.

Since $E = 0$ inside a conductor, we know at once that the *electric potential* at all points *within a conductor*, charged or uncharged, in electrostatic equilibrium is *constant*, quite apart from the shape of the conductor; thus an equipotential volume. A closed conductor is a perfect electric shield, since a charge can be moved around in the interior without experiencing a change in potential.

The surface of any conductor in equilibrium is an *equipotential surface*. If it were not, any difference of potential over the surface would correspond to an electric force acting along the surface. The electric force lines, however, are normal to a conductor's surface and the free charges do *not* move over the surface when the conductor has reached equilibrium. It follows that the constant electric potential at all locations within a conductor is just the electric potential at the surface.

Suppose that two or more metallic objects are connected by a conducting wire and electrostatic equilibrium has been achieved. Then we no longer have a number of separate conductors, but really just a *single* conductor. This means that any conducting objects connected together with a conducting wire will, when the free charges no longer move, be at the *same* electric potential.

As an example, consider an initially charged hollow spherical conducting shell

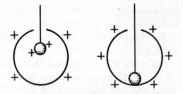

Figure 28-14. Any charge brought to the interior of a conductor goes to the conductor's outside surface.

into which a second smaller charged conducting sphere is introduced while attached to an insulating thread as in Figure 28-14. The small sphere is made to touch the interior of the large shell. Where is the small sphere's charge after this? Once the two objects are brought in contact, we have, in effect, a *single* conductor. Therefore, all points on the interior of the shell will achieve a single potential, and all of the net charge will be found on the *outside* of the shell, no matter how much charge was originally on the exterior of the shell.

Example 8   How is the charge distributed over the surface of a conductor carrying a net charge?

Of course, for a sphere the surface charge density is constant. We wish to show that for a nonspherical surface the charge is concentrated at regions of

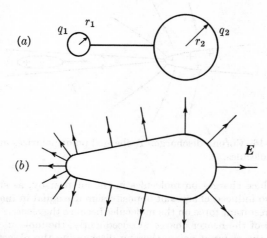

Figure 28-15. (a) Two spheres connected by a conducting wire. (b) A charged conductor. Note that the electric field is strong at points of small radius of curvature.

small radius of curvature, or points, on a conductor. Let us first consider the situation shown in Figure 28-15a, that in which two spheres of radii r_1 and r_2 and carrying charges q_1 and q_2, respectively, are connected by a conducting wire. We wish to find the charge densities σ_1 and σ_2 on the two spheres.

Since the spheres and connecting wire comprise a single conductor, the potential is the same for both spheres. Therefore,

$$V_1 = kq_1/r_1 = kq_2/r_2 = V_2$$
$$q_1/q_2 = r_1/r_2 \qquad\qquad [28\text{-}17]$$

Most of the charge is on the *larger* sphere.

By definition,

$$\sigma_1 = q_1/4\pi r_1^2 \quad \text{and} \quad \sigma_2 = q_2/4\pi r_2^2$$

Therefore,

$$\sigma_1/\sigma_2 = (q_1/q_2)(r_2/r_1)^2$$

Using the relation for q_1/q_2 given above, we have

$$\sigma_1/\sigma_2 = r_2/r_1$$

The *charge density* is greatest on the *smaller* sphere. Since the electric field near any conducting surface is proportional to the charge density $E = \sigma/\epsilon_0$ (Section 26-4), the electric field is strong at the surface of the small sphere, compared with the field at the surface of the larger sphere.

The two connected spheres in Figure 28-15a may be thought of as approximating a single conductor of the shape shown in Figure 28-15b. Therefore, the charge is concentrated mostly at the pointed end, and the electric field is greatest there. The very strong electric fields produced at sharp points on charged

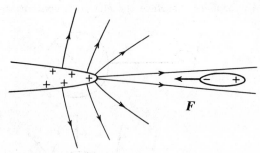

Figure 28-16. Corona discharge. A charged point polarizes and attracts neutral molecules.

conductors induce charges on molecules in the air near-by, as shown in Figure 28-16. The two induced charges of opposite sign are equal in magnitude; there is, however, a resultant force on the molecules because the electric field is stronger at the location of the nearer charge. Consequently, the molecules are attracted to, and touch the charged point, thereby discharging the object. In addition, strong electric fields can cause ionization of neutral molecules. For example, with air at standard temperature and pressure, an electric field of about 3×10^6 v/m will cause electric breakdown. The phenomenon is known as *corona discharge*.

Example 9 In the Van de Graaff electrostatic generator, an important type of particle accelerator, a moving charged belt is brought inside a large spherical shell. The charge is removed from the belt by conducting needles connected to the sphere, as shown in Figure 28-17. The electric potential of the sphere relative to ground can reach such high values as *millions* of volts, and this high potential can be used to accelerate charged particles to relatively high energies (up to 10 Mev). (a) Why is a *sphere* used? (b) Why a *large* sphere? (c) Why is the charge introduced through the *inside* of the sphere?

(a) The sphere is that closed shape which, for a given volume, has the smoothest surface. Corona discharge is minimized by using this shape.

(b) Corona discharge eventually limits the charge that can be accumulated on the sphere. Let E_m represent that electric field at the spherical surface for which corona discharge first occurs. The electric field at the surface of a sphere

of radius R is $E = kq/R^2$ and the potential there is
$V = kq/R$. Therefore, $E_m = V/R$. For a given high
potential V, the least electric field at the surface is
achieved through the use of a large R, hence a large
sphere. For example, for air at STP, $E_m = 3 \times 10^6$ v/m.
To obtain a potential V of, say, 3×10^6 v would require a
sphere of radius $R = V/E_m = (3 \times 10^6 \text{ v})/(3 \times 10^6 \text{ v/m})$
$= 1$ m. The charge on the 1 m sphere would then be
more than 300 μcoul.

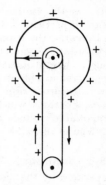

(c) The charge is brought to the hollow sphere through
the inside because, once there, the charge is *not* repelled
by charge already on the outside of the sphere. All
charge coming in contact with the interior surface then
goes at once to the outside.

The Van de Graaff electrostatic charged-particle accelerator is used to accelerate charged particles to high
energies by having the particles travel across a very
high potential difference. Corona discharge is suppressed
by surrounding the spherical shell by gas under high

Figure 28-17. Sche-
matic diagram of a
Van de Graaff ac-
celerator.

pressure, and the sphere may then be raised to a potential of up to 10 million
volts above ground. Protons or other singly charged particles, accelerated from
rest across this potential difference, acquire a kinetic energy of 10 Mev. These
highly energetic particles may then be used in nuclear-physics experiments

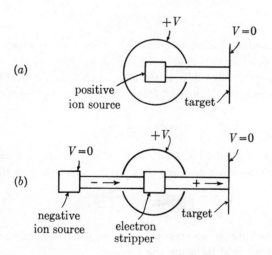

Figure 28-18. (a) A Van de Graaff generator accelerates positive ions
from a high potential to ground potential. (b) A tandem Van de Graaff
accelerates particles *twice* with a single high potential by changing the
charge of the particles. Negative ions are first accelerated from ground
potential to a high positive potential; their charge is changed in sign;
then the positive ions are accelerated again from the high potential to
ground potential.

such as the Rutherford scattering experiments (Section 25-6), in which the beam of particles is directed at a target; see Figure 28-18a.

Recently, the maximum energy of particles accelerated by a Van de Graaff electrostatic generator has been *doubled* through a remarkably simple procedure. Singly charged *negative* hydrogen ions (H⁻) are first accelerated, for example, from ground potential to the positive potential of the sphere; then the two electrons are stripped from the highly energetic hydrogen ions to produce *positive* protons, which are accelerated a second time, now from the high positive potential to ground. Such a device is called a tandem Van de Graaff accelerator; see Figure 28-18b.

28-8 Summary The electric potential energy U of two point-charges separated by the distance r is

[28-3] $$U = kq_1q_2/r$$

For more than two point-charges the total electric potential energy of the system, which represents the total work required to assemble the charges in the system, is the sum of the potential energies between pairs of point-charges.

The electric potential V at any point P is equal to the total work W required to move a unit positive charge from infinity to P while all other charges remain fixed in position:

[28-8] $$V = W/q$$

Electric potential and electric potential difference are measured in volts. The electron volt (1 ev = 1.60×10^{-19} joule) is the energy acquired by a particle of charge e which falls across a potential difference of 1 v.

The electric potential V arising from a collection of point-charges is given by

[28-10] $$V = k\Sigma \, q_i/r_i$$

Knowing the electric field E as a function of position, one can derive the potential difference between two points from it according to the relation

[28-11] $$V_2 - V_1 = -\int_1^2 E \cdot ds$$

Conversely, knowing the electric potential as a function of position one can derive the electric field by using the relation

[28-15] $$E = -dV/ds$$

where the displacement ds is taken along that direction in which V changes most rapidly with position. For a *uniform* electric field,

[28-14] $$E = -V/d$$

An equipotential surface is the locus of points, all of which are at the same electric potential. Electric lines of force intersect equipotential surfaces at right angles. The surface of a conductor, charged or uncharged, is always an equipotential surface. The electric field and charge density at the surface of a charged conductor are greatest at regions of small radius of curvature.

PROBLEMS

28-1 An electron (charge, $-e$) and a positron (an electron with charge $+e$) are initially separated by 10.0 Å and at rest. The two particles are released simultaneously and approach one another. What is the kinetic energy of the electron when it is 2.0 Å from the positron?

28-2 An alpha particle (charge, $+2e$) of 8.0 Mev kinetic energy approaches a gold nucleus (charge, $+79e$) head on. The gold nucleus may be assumed to remain at rest. What is the minimum separation distance between the two particles?

28-3 An electron passes a helium nucleus (charge, $+2e$) at a distance of 4.0 Å. What is the minimum kinetic energy, for the electron at this position, which will permit it to avoid being bound to the nucleus?

28-4 ★ An alpha particle (charge, $+2e$) of 8.0 Mev kinetic energy approaches a gold nucleus (charge, $+79e$) such that the alpha particle would miss striking the nucleus by 2.0×10^{-14} m if it were not for the Coulomb force between them. Assume the gold nucleus to remain at rest. (a) What is the closest distance between the two particles? (b) What is the alpha particle's kinetic energy at this point? (*Hint:* Conserve angular momentum and energy.)

28-5 ★ A charge of 2.0×10^{-2} μcoul is located at $x = 0$; a charge of 1.0×10^{-2} μcoul is located at $x = 10$ cm. What is the minimum speed with which an electron must be projected to the right from $x = 2.0$ cm to reach the point $x = 8.0$ cm?

28-6 An electron and a positron (positive electron) rotate in a circle about their center of mass, the radius of the circle being 1.1 Å. (a) What is the ratio of the total kinetic energy of this system to the electric potential energy between the two particles? (b) What is the binding energy of the system?

28-7 Four charges, each of magnitude Q, are placed at the corners of a square of edge length L, as shown in Figure 28-19. (a) What is the electric potential at the center? (b) How much work must be done in bringing a charge $-q$ from infinity to the center of the square?

Figure 28-19

28-8   Four charges, two of $+Q$ and two of $-Q$, are to be brought to the corners of a square of edge length L. (a) How should the charges be placed on the corners if the work done in assembling this system is to be a minimum? (b) Find this minimum electric potential energy.

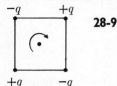

28-9   Each of the charges in Figure 28-20 has a mass m; the mass of the square is negligible. At what angular speed must the system be rotated about an axis through the center of symmetry and into the paper so that the total energy of the system is zero?

Figure 28-20.

28-10 ★ (a) Graph the potential energy between a point-charge q and two fixed point-charges, each of charge q, as a function of position along the line joining the two fixed charges. (b) Show that for small displacements from the midpoint the potential energy between the charge q and the two fixed charges is parabolic. (c) Is the charge q in stable or unstable equilibrium with respect to a small displacement along any direction?

28-11   Plot the electric potential as a function of x for the following configuration of electric charges: $+2.0 \,\mu\text{coul}$ at $x = 0$, $-3.0 \,\mu\text{coul}$ at $x = 4.0$ cm, and $+1.0 \,\mu\text{coul}$ at $x = 6.0$ cm.

28-12   At a point midway between two point-charges separated by 10 cm the electric field is 10 v/m and the electric potential is zero. What are the two charges?

28-13   Points A, B, and C have the following electric potentials: $V_A = -50$ v, $V_B = +20$ v, and $V_C = -70$ v. Compute the work required to transport the following charges at constant speed between the end points indicated: (a) $+2.0$ coul from A to C, (b) -2.0 coul from C to A, (c) -2.0 coul from B to C, (d) -2.0 coul from B to A, and (e) $+4.0$ coul from B to C.

28-14   Two "cells," each assumed to consist of two equal but opposite point charges of magnitude $2.0 \,\mu\text{coul}$, are initially arranged as shown in

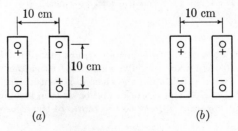

Figure 28-21.

Figure 28-21a. Then one cell is turned through 180° so that it is arranged as shown in Figure 28-21b. How much work is required?

28-15 The stopping potential (the electric potential difference which brings charged particles to rest) for a beam of electrons is found to be 60 v. What is the initial speed of the electrons?

28-16 A potential difference of 2.0 kv accelerates doubly ionized atoms from rest. What is the final kinetic energy of the particles?

28-17 What potential difference must be applied across two oppositely charged parallel plates separated by 1.0 cm, so that an electron starting from rest at one plate will reach the other plate in 10^{-7} sec?

28-18 A negatively charged particle of initial speed v is just brought to rest when it travels a distance d parallel to the electric field lines between two parallel oppositely charged insulated conducting planes separated by the distance d. The plate separation is now increased to $2d$. What is the maximum speed of particles that will now be stopped in traversing the distance $2d$?

28-19 The potential difference between two coaxial cylindrical conductors is 100 v. The outer conductor has a radius of 4.0 cm, and the conductors have a linear charge density of 4.0×10^{-9} coul/m. What is the radius of the inner conductor?

28-20 At a distance of 5.0 cm from a long straight uniformly charged wire the electric potential is 50 v. At 2.5 cm the potential is 40 v. What is the linear charge density of the wire?

28-21 ★ Show that the total energy necessary to distribute a total charge q uniformly throughout a sphere of radius R is $\frac{3}{5}kq^2/R$. (*Hint:* Find the work required to bring the charge dq from infinity to the spherical shell of radius r and thickness dr against the charge already present within the sphere of radius r. Integrate from zero to R to find the total potential energy.)

28-22 ★ Two charges, each of magnitude q, are imagined to be spread uniformly throughout a sphere of radius R. Show that the electric potential energy due to the interaction of the two charges is given by $6kq^2/5R$. (*Hint:* First assume one charge to be spread uniformly throughout a spherical volume. Find the electric potential as a function of distance r from the center for this first charge alone. Then imagine the second charge to be added. Find the electric potential energy between a spherical shell of the second charge and the sphere of the first charge. Integrate to find the total electric potential energy.)

28-23 ★ Show that the potential at any distance r $(r < R)$ from the center of a dielectric sphere of constant charge density ρ is given by $V = kqr^2/R^3$, where R is the radius of the sphere. (*Hint:* Use Equation 27-8, giving the electric field as a function of r. Note that the potential at the surface of the sphere must be $V = kq/R$.)

28-24 Calculate the work necessary to charge a conducting sphere of radius R to a total charge Q.

28-25 ⋆ (a) Graph the electric potential energy as a function of the distance between a point-charge $-e$ and a spherical charge distribution composed of a point-charge $+2e$ at the center surrounded by a uniform distribution of negative charge $-e$ spread throughout the sphere of radius R. (b) Compare this graph with that between a point-charge $-e$ and a point charge $+e$, and give the binding energy of the point-charge $-e$ to each system when the $-e$ charge is at rest and at a distance $R/2$ from the center of the other charge distribution.

28-26   Sketch the equipotential lines for a point-charge placed close to an initially uncharged conducting plane.

28-27   A 6.0 v battery consists of three 2.0 v cells arranged as shown in Figure 28-22. Sketch the electric field lines and the equipotential lines for this configuration.

Figure 28-22.

28-28 ⋆ A point-charge is brought close to an initially uncharged flat conducting surface. The electric field E, as shown in Figure 28-23a, is perpendicular to the plane surface, which itself is an equipotential surface. Figure 28-23b shows the electric field arising from two charges of equal magnitude but opposite sign. It is clear that Figure 28-23a and the right half of Figure 28-23b are alike, both having a plane equipotential surface at the same distance from the positive charge. Thus, one can imagine an "image charge" of opposite sign lying behind the conductor surface. Consequently, a charge brought close to an initially uncharged conductor is attracted to the surface by the electrical image.

A charge of 1.0 μcoul is placed 10 cm from a flat conducting surface initially uncharged. What is the force on this charge?

28-29   A point-charge of $+4.9 \times 10^{-7}$ coul is brought to a distance of 5.0 cm from a plane conducting sheet originally having a uniform surface charge density of $+5.0 \times 10^{-7}$ coul/m². What is the ratio of the force on the point-charge, arising from the real surface charge, to the force

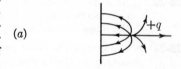

(a)

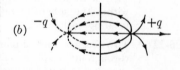

(b)

Figure 28-23. (a) Electric force lines for a point-charge near an initially uncharged plane conducting surface. (b) Electric force lines for two unlike point charges of the same magnitude. Note that the right halves of parts (a) and (b) are identical. Therefore, the point-charge in part (a) may be thought of as acted upon by an "image charge" of opposite sign lying an equal distance behind the conducting plane.

on the point-charge arising from surface charge induced by the point-charge. See Problem 28-28.

28-30   An infinite conducting plane has a uniform charge distribution of $+\sigma$ coul/m². (a) At what distance from the conducting plane will a point-charge $+q$ experience *no* electric force? (b) Explain why this is a point of unstable equilibrium. See Problem 28-28.

TWENTY-NINE

CAPACITANCE AND DIELECTRICS

In this chapter we deal with capacitors, the devices for storing separated charges and electric potential energy. We find the capacitance for some simple geometries, and set down the rules for combining capacitors in series and in parallel. We relate the qualitative behavior of conductors and dielectrics in an external field to the polarization properties of these materials. We define the dielectric constant. Finally, we find the energy of a charged capacitor and the energy density of the electric field.

29-1 Capacitance defined To charge a conductor requires work. After the first electron has been placed, for example, on a spherical conducting shell, other electrons brought to the conductor are repelled. Then, after the conductor has acquired a total charge Q, it can be thought of not only as a device which stores this charge but also as one which establishes an electric field around it; that is, it has an electric potential V representing the storage of electric potential energy.

We have seen (Example 7, Chapter 28) that, when a spherical conductor of radius R acquires a charge Q, its electric potential V (relative to zero potential at infinity) at the conductor is given by

$$V = kQ/R \qquad [29\text{-}1]$$

For this simple geometrical configuration the conductor's potential is directly proportional to the charge on it and inversely proportional to the conductor's radius. Thus, for a given potential, the larger the radius the larger the stored charge. This behavior is seen for conductors of other shapes: [the stored charge is always proportional to the potential and also to a characteristic dimension of the conductor]

Of course, if one places a negative charge on one conductor, some other object must acquire a positive charge of equal magnitude. In what follows we shall always be concerned with two conductors (plates) carrying opposite charges of equal magnitude Q and having a potential difference V between them, as shown in Figure 29-1. Since all points on the surface and interior of any one conductor, charged or uncharged, are at a single potential, V represents the potential difference between *any* two points, one on one conductor and the other on the other conductor. Such a pair of oppositely charged conductors are said to constitute a *capacitor* (or, in an older terminology now passing out of use, a *condenser*). The electrical property one ascribes to a capacitor is *capacitance C*, where, by definition,

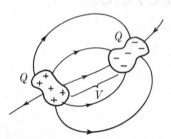

Figure 29-1. Most general form of capacitor: two conductors carrying equal but opposite charges of magnitude Q and having an electric potential difference V between them.

$$\boxed{C = Q/V} \qquad [29\text{-}2]$$

the capacitance being the charge magnitude (on *either* of the two oppositely charged conductors) per unit potential difference between the conductors. The capacitance C of a given configuration of conductors is a constant, independent of Q and V. Thus, a capacitor's capacitance is a quantitative measure of the conductor's capacity for storing separated charges and thereby for storing electric potential energy. A capacitor is symbolized in an electric circuit diagram by ─┤├─ or by ─┤(─.

Capacitance has the units of coulombs per volt. A special name, the *farad*, (after the famed experimentalist in electromagnetism, Michael Faraday), is given to this ratio:

$$1\ \mathrm{f} = 1\ \mathrm{coul/v}$$

As we shall see shortly, a capacitance of one farad is enormous; that is, the dimensions of a capacitor carrying charges as large as one coulomb on each of its two plates when a potential difference of only one volt exists between the plates, are extraordinarily large. More commonly used units for capacitance are the microfarad ($1\mu f = 10^{-6}$ f) and the micromicrofarad ($1 \mu\mu f$, or pf, $= 10^{-12}$ f).

Capacitors are commonly found in electrical circuits, such as radios, the ignition systems of gasoline engines, and telephone cables and other coaxial cables. Besides storing electric charge and electric potential energy, capacitors have interesting properties when the potential difference across the plates varies with time (Sections 30-8 and 37-5).

29-2 Capacitance for some simple configurations

Any two oppositely charged conductors comprise a capacitor. A practical capacitor, however, is small, has its oppositely charged plates easily insulated from one another, and is so arranged that external fields will not disturb the distribution of charge on the plates. These requirements are met by capacitors with parallel plates or with coaxial cylindrical conductors, and the symmetry of these geometries allows the capacitance to be computed easily.

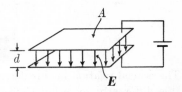

PARALLEL-PLATE CAPACITOR   A capacitor with two parallel plates, each of area A and separated by a distance d, is shown in Figure 29-2. The plate separation d is small compared with the size of the plates, so that

Figure 29-2. A parallel-plate capacitor with plate area A and plate separation distance d.

the electric field E is uniform and confined almost entirely to the region between the plates, fringing of the electric force lines at the boundaries being negligible. The two plates must be held apart by an insulating material, not only to prevent charges from going from one plate to the other but also to hold apart the oppositely charged plates under the action of the attractive force between them. The insulator may be a dielectric material sandwiched between the plates, in which case the capacitance is enhanced over its value when a vacuum exists between the plates. In what follows here we shall assume the plates to be immersed in a vacuum; the effect of dielectric, or insulating, materials will be treated in Section 29-4.

One may charge a capacitor by carrying electrons from one plate to the other against the opposing electric force produced by the field between the plates. Alternatively, one may charge a capacitor very simply by connecting the capacitor plates with conducting wires to the terminals of a battery. (The charging or discharging of a capacitor does *not* take place instantaneously; rates of charge and discharge are treated in Section 30-8.) Since the potential difference between the terminals of a (charged) battery is constant, the capacitor plates acquire the same potential difference V as that of the battery. Furthermore, the chemical potential energy of the battery is reduced as the electric potential energy of the capacitor is increased.

Let us find the capacitance C of a parallel-plate capacitor. From the definition of C, Equation 29-2, we must know the charge Q on either plate in terms of the potential difference V. The link is the electric field E. Since the field is uniform over the plate separation distance d,

[28-14] $$E = V/d$$ [29-3]

We found that the electric field between two uniformly charged plates, each carrying a surface charge density of $\sigma = Q/A$, to be

[26-8] $$E = \sigma/\epsilon_0 = Q/\epsilon_0 A$$ [29-4]

Therefore, from Equations 29-2, 29-3, and 29-4, we have

$$C = \frac{Q}{V} = \frac{Q}{Ed} = \frac{Q}{(Q/\epsilon_0 A)\,d}$$

$$\boxed{C = \epsilon_0 A/d}$$ [29-5]

The crucial relation in this derivation was Equation 29-4. Let us arrive at this differently by using Gauss's law. We choose a cylindrical Gaussian surface as shown in Figure 29-3; one end lies *within* the conductor, the other end is perpendicular to the electric field lines between the plates, and the sides are parallel to E. Since the electric field within any conductor is zero, the only contribution to the electric flux comes from the electric lines penetrating the area A_1. The charge enclosed by the Gaussian surface is Q_1. Therefore,

[27-3] $$\phi_E = \oint E \cdot dS = q/\epsilon_0$$

$$EA_1 = Q_1/\epsilon_0$$

[29-4] $$E = (Q_1/A_1)/\epsilon_0 = \sigma/\epsilon_0$$

As Equation 29-5 shows, the capacitance is (a) proportional to the plate area and (b) inversely proportional to the plate separation. Both make sense on the basis of simple physical arguments: (a) the larger the plate area (for a given V and d) the larger the amount of charge which can be stored on the plates; (b) when Q and A are fixed (and E thereby constant), bringing the plates closer together reduces the distance over which this field exists and hence reduces V.

Notice that according to Equation 29-5, C equals the constant ϵ_0 multiplied by the ratio A/d, which has the dimensions of length. This was also the case

for a single spherical conductor, where we found, from Equations 29-1 and
29-2, that

$$C = Q/V = R/k = 4\pi\epsilon_0 R.$$

That the farad represents, in fact, an enormous capacitance follows directly
from Equation 29-5. Suppose that we have two large plates, each with an
area of 1.0 m² separated by 1.0 mm = 10^{-3} m. Then, with this arrangement
$C = \epsilon_0 A/d = (8.85 \times 10^{-12}$ coul²/nt-m²$)(1.0$ m²$)/(10^{-3}$ m$) = 8.85 \times 10^{-9}$ f, or
somewhat less than $\frac{1}{100}$ μf. One would need a plate area of 10^8 m² with this
separation distance to have a capacitance of 1 f.

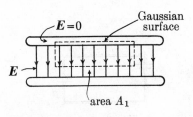

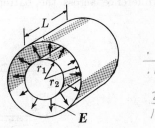

Figure 29-3. Gauss's law applied to
a parallel-plate capacitor. The
cross section of the Gaussian surface
is shown with dotted lines.

Figure 29-4. A coaxial
cylindrical capacitor.

COAXIAL CAPACITOR A coaxial capacitor consisting of two concentric
cylindrical conductors of radii r_1 and r_2 is shown in Figure 29-4. The two
cylindrical surfaces are equipotential surfaces between which there exists a
potential difference, $V_1 - V_2$. We recall another arrangement, in which the
equipotential surfaces were coaxial cylinders: that of an infinitely long
charged wire having a linear charge density $\lambda = Q/L$, where Q is the magnitude of the charge on the conductor of length L. We found earlier that

[28-13] $$V_1 - V_2 = \frac{\lambda}{2\pi\epsilon_0} \ln\frac{r_1}{r_2} = Q\left(\frac{1}{2\pi\epsilon_0 L}\right) \ln\frac{r_1}{r_2}$$

We may now take Q to represent the charge per length L on each of the two
capacitor plates. The capacitance is then given by

$$C = \frac{Q}{V_1 - V_2} = \frac{2\pi\epsilon_0 L}{\ln(r_1/r_2)} \qquad [29-6]$$

The radius r_1 is always to be taken as that of the outer conductor, to insure
that C in Equation 29-6 is positive.

The capacitance of a coaxial capacitor can also be derived directly through Gauss's law. The reader is urged to carry out such an exercise.

29-3   Capacitor circuits   Electric circuits comprised entirely of capacitors are neither very interesting nor useful. They are worthy of attention, however, because they illustrate some fundamental concepts common to all circuits. Furthermore, one may use the rules for combining capacitors in series and in parallel combinations to advantage in computing the capacitance of capacitors filled entirely or partially with dielectric materials.

Consider the simple circuit shown in Figure 29-5a, a single capacitor connected across the terminals of a battery. We say at once that the potential difference across the battery V_b is equal in magnitude to the potential

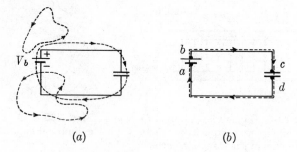

$$(a) \hspace{5cm} (b)$$

Figure 29-5. Circuit consisting of a battery and capacitor. (a) For electrostatic equilibrium, the net change in electric potential around any closed loop (shown with dotted lines) is zero. (b) A loop *abcda* around the circuit passing along the conducting wires.

difference V_C across the charged capacitor: $V_b = V_C$. Let us see how this is justified according to fundamental physical laws. First suppose that electrostatic equilibrium has been achieved and all of the charges on the circuit elements are at rest. Then, if we imagine a single point-charge to be moved at constant speed in a closed path so that it returns to its starting point, we know that the total amount of work done on this point-charge by the electric forces is *zero*. In mathematical terms,

$$\oint \mathbf{F} \cdot d\mathbf{s} = q \oint \mathbf{E} \cdot d\mathbf{s} = 0$$

since

[28-11] $$\oint \mathbf{E} \cdot d\mathbf{s} = 0$$

The electric field $\mathbf{E}$ is produced by the conservative Coulomb forces of the charges residing on the circuit elements. Now, if the total work done on a unit positive charge about any closed loop is zero, then the *total electric*

potential difference around any closed loop is zero. From the definition of
potential difference (Equation 28-11), $V = -\int E \cdot ds$, we have

$$\oint E \cdot ds = -\oint dV = 0$$

$$\Sigma V = 0 \quad \text{(closed loop)} \qquad [29\text{-}7]$$

For example, the net change in electric potential is zero for any of the three
loops shown in Figure 29-5a.

Equation 29-7 is simply the conservation of energy principle applied to
electric charge distributions. The second fundamental principle we shall
use in analyzing circuits is the law of electric charge conservation.

Consider the loop in Figure 29-5b, which passes along the connecting wires
starting at point a, the negative terminal of the battery. Going from a to b,
from the negative to the positive battery terminal, the potential rises by
V_b, where V_b is the constant potential difference maintained across the
battery terminals. Going from b to c along the connecting wire to the positive
capacitor there is *no* potential change, since all points on a conductor in
electrostatic equilibrium have the same potential. Across the region between
the capacitor plates, from c to d, the potential falls by V_C, the potential
difference across the capacitor. Finally, there is no potential difference
between points d and a, since again the route is along a single conductor.
Therefore, the total potential drop around the loop ($-V_b$ across the battery
and V_C across the capacitor) is

$$\Sigma V = -V_b + V_C = 0$$

$$V_b = V_C$$

The potential differences between the battery terminals and between the
capacitor plates *are* the same.

CAPACITORS IN SERIES   Suppose that several capacitors, C_1, C_2, C_3, are
connected in series and attached across battery terminals as shown in
Figure 29-6a. We wish to find the value C of the single capacitor which is
equivalent to this group of capacitors.

We see from Figure 29-6a that the *net* charge on the single conductor
shown within the dotted loop must remain zero, since this section is isolated
electrically from everything else. The battery serves only to separate the
charges on this conductor, equal amounts of positive and negative charge
appearing on the plates of adjoining conductors. Thus, all capacitors in
series have the *same charge:*

$$Q_1 = Q_2 = Q_3$$

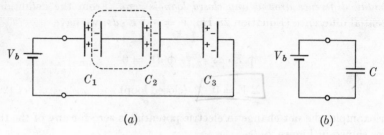

(a) (b)

Figure 29-6. (a) Capacitors in series; the net charge within the dotted loop is zero. (b) The equivalent single capacitor.

Choosing the route along the wires connecting the capacitors, we see that

$$V_b = V_1 + V_2 + V_3 \qquad [29\text{-}8]$$

where V_1, V_2, and V_3 are the respective potential drops across the capacitors. By definition, $V_1 = Q_1/C_1$; similarly for the other two capacitors. Using these relations in Equation 29-8, we have

$$V_b = Q_1/C_1 + Q_2/C_2 + Q_3/C_3 = Q(1/C_1 + 1/C_2 + 1/C_3)$$

where we have used Q to represent $Q_1 = Q_2 = Q_3$. Now, if a single equivalent capacitor C, as shown in Figure 29-6b, were connected to the battery terminals, its effect on the rest of the circuit would be the same as that of the capacitors in series. That is, its potential difference, $V = Q/C$, would equal V_b. Therefore,

$$Q/C = Q(1/C_1 + 1/C_2 + 1/C_3)$$

$$\boxed{\frac{1}{C} = \frac{1}{C_1} + \frac{1}{C_2} + \frac{1}{C_3}} \qquad [29\text{-}9]$$

In general, for capacitors in series the reciprocal of the single equivalent capacitance is the sum of the reciprocals of the individual capacitances. As a consequence, the equivalent capacitance is always less than the smallest of the series capacitors. For example, with four capacitors, each 20 μf and connected in series, the equivalent capacitance is 5 μf.

CAPACITORS IN PARALLEL The circuit arrangement for capacitors connected in parallel is shown in Figure 29-7a. What single capacitor, as in Figure 29-7b, can replace them while removing the same charge from the battery? The charges and potential differences for C_1, C_2, and C_3 are again designated respectively Q_1, Q_2, Q_3 and V_1, V_2, V_3. By taking potential differences along the routes shown by dotted lines in the figure, we establish that the potential difference across each capacitor is the same as that across the battery terminals. *Parallel capacitors have the same potential difference;* that is,

$$V_b = V_1 = V_2 = V_3$$

Since the circuit contains only two conductors attached to the battery terminals (the upper plates with their connecting wires and the lower

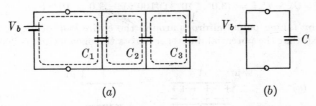

$$(a) \qquad\qquad\qquad (b)$$

Figure 29-7. (a) Capacitors in parallel; the net potential difference around any dotted loop is zero. (b) The equivalent single capacitor.

plates with theirs), the total charge Q held on a single capacitor equivalent to those in parallel is given by

$$Q = Q_1 + Q_2 + Q_3$$

or $\qquad\qquad Q = C_1V_1 + C_2V_2 + C_3V_3 = V_b(C_1 + C_2 + C_3)$

But $\qquad\qquad\qquad\qquad C = Q/V_b,$

Therefore, $\qquad\qquad\boxed{C = C_1 + C_2 + C_3} \qquad\qquad$ [29-10]

In general, for parallel capacitors the equivalent capacitance is the sum of their several capacitances. The equivalent capacity always exceeds that of the largest capacitor in parallel. The rule for combining parallel capacitors is evident from an examination of Figure 29-7 where it is seen that three parallel capacitors with the same plate separation are effectively the same as a single capacitor with a plate area equal to the sum of the three plate areas in parallel.

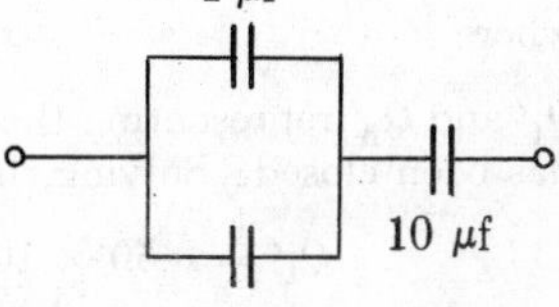

Example 1 What single capacitance is equivalent to the capacitors shown in the circuit of Figure 29-8?

The 4 μf and 6 μf capacitors are in parallel because they have a common potential difference. Therefore, they are equivalent to a single capacitance of 10 μf, by Equation 29-10. The equivalent 10 μf capacitor and the original 10 μf capacitor are in series because they have the same charge; thus, by Equation 29-9, the equivalent capacitance of all three capacitors in Figure 29-8 is 5 μf.

4 μf

10 μf

6 μf

Figure 29-8

Example 2 A 1.0 μf capacitor and a 3.0 μf capacitor are connected in turn to a 100 v battery. Then the two charged capacitors are connected as shown in Figure 29-9a. What is the charge on (one plate of) each capacitor (a) before the switch is closed and (b) after the switch is closed?

(a) We have immediately that

[29-2]

$$Q_1 = C_1 V = (1.0 \times 10^{-6}\,\text{f})(100\,\text{v}) = 1.0 \times 10^{-4}\,\text{coul}$$

$$Q_3 = C_3 V = (3.0 \times 10^{-6}\,\text{f})(100\,\text{v}) = 3.0 \times 10^{-4}\,\text{coul}$$

Note that by taking potential drops around the entire loop of Figure 29-9a we can establish that the potential difference across the open switch is 200 v.

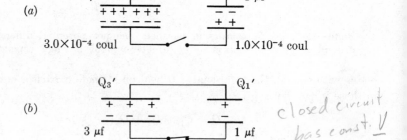

Figure 29-9

(b) After the switch has been closed, as shown in Figure 29-9b, there is a redistribution of charge on the plates. The *net* charge on the upper two plates must be, by the law of conservation of charge, $(3.0 \times 10^{-4}) + (-1.0 \times 10^{-4}) = +2.0 \times 10^{-4}$ coul. Rather than spend time trying to decide whether the two capacitors in Figure 29-9 are connected in series or in parallel, we can proceed most directly by recognizing that, after the switch has been closed, the potential differences across the two capacitors are the same:

$$Q_1'/C_1 = Q_3'/C_3, \quad \text{or} \quad Q_1'/1\,\mu\text{f} = Q_3'/3\,\mu\text{f}$$

where

$$Q_1' + Q_3' = +2.0 \times 10^{-4}\,\text{coul}$$

Q_1' and Q_3' representing the charges on the respective capacitors after the switch has been closed. Solving the two equations above we find

$$Q_1' = 0.50 \times 10^{-4}\,\text{coul} \quad \text{and} \quad Q_3' = 1.5 \times 10^{-4}\,\text{coul}$$

Moreover, the common potential difference is now

$$V_3' = V_1' = \frac{Q_1'}{C_1} = \frac{0.50 \times 10^{-4}\,\text{coul}}{1.0 \times 10^{-6}\,\text{f}} = 50\,\text{v}$$

29-4   Polarization in conductors and in dielectrics As a preliminary to finding how a dielectric material introduced between the plates of a capacitor affects its capacitance (it increases C), we first consider from an atomic point of view the behavior of the charges induced on a conductor and on a dielectric placed in an external electric field. Consider the situation shown in Figure 29-10, where a conductor and a dielectric are placed in turn between the charged plates of a parallel-plate capacitor.

As Figure 29-10a, b, and c shows, when a conductor is brought between the plates of a charged capacitor (without touching these plates), the free charges within the conductor redistribute themselves under the influence of the charges on the capacitor plates until the *resultant* electric field within the

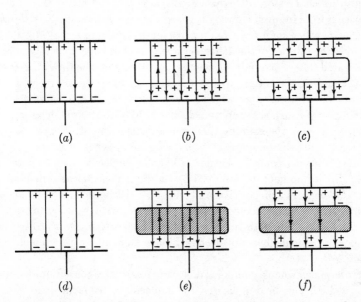

(a) (b) (c)

(d) (e) (f)

Figure 29-10. A conductor and a dielectric placed between the plates of a charged capacitor. Conductor: (a) electric field produced by the charges on plates, (b) electric fields produced by induced charges and charges on plates, and (c) resultant electric field for part (b). Dielectric: (d) electric field produced by charges on plates, (e) electric field produced by induced charges and charges on plates, and (f) resultant field for part (e).

conductor is zero. The charge $+Q$ on a capacitor plate faces an equal charge $-Q$ on the neighboring conductor surface. One may regard the electric field within the conductor itself as consisting of two contributions, the external field established between the capacitor plates and the electric field resulting from the separation, or polarization, of an essentially unlimited number of *free* charges within the conductor. These fields, of equal magnitudes but opposite directions, give a resultant $E = 0$. Said differently, the polarization of the conductor by the external electric field is *complete*, the charges induced on the opposite faces of the conductor being just equal in magnitude to the respective inducing charges. The induced charges also contribute to E outside the conductor. (After the conductor has been introduced one may regard the composite arrangement as that of two capacitors in series.)

The situation is different when a dielectric, or nonconducting material, is introduced between the capacitor plates; see Figure 29-10d, e, f. Net charges again appear on the surfaces of the dielectric, and the electric field produced by charges on the capacitor plates is again opposed by the electric field arising from induced charges appearing on the dielectric. Now, however, with *bound* rather than free charges displaced by the external electric field, the field in the interior of the dielectric is reduced but *not* completely annulled. By the same token, the induced charges appearing on the dielectric surfaces are *not* equal in magnitude to the inducing charges. In short, when a dielectric is placed in an external field, the material becomes polarized, charges appearing on its surfaces, and the electric field within is reduced, although never to zero. Let us examine this from an atomic point of view.

First, we must distinguish between two general types of molecules, polar molecules and nonpolar molecules. A polar molecule has a permanent electric dipole moment (Section 26-6); although electrically neutral as a whole, its "centers" of positive and negative charge do not coincide. For example, in the polar molecule NaCl, the end with the sodium atom is positive while the end with the chlorine atom is negative. On the other hand, a nonpolar molecule has no electric dipole moment *in the absence of an external field*.

What happens when a nonpolar dielectric material is placed in an external electric field? The field polarizes the molecules, displacing the electrons (on the average) in the direction opposite to that of E, as shown in Figure 29-11. That is to say, the external electric field induces electric dipole moments in the molecules. This polarization is manifest only at the surface of the dielectric. As the figure shows, for any small volume lying entirely *within* the dielectric material the positive and negative charges, although not coincident, appear in equal magnitudes. This is not the case, however, when we choose a small volume which encloses one external surface of a dielectric. A net charge appears at the surface. The degree of polarization, as measured by the amount of induced charge at the dielectric surface, is, for small external fields, proportional to the magnitude of the field (this is equivalent to saying that the molecular restoring forces are, for small displacements, proportional to the displacement).

A polar dielectric, one having molecules each with a permanent electric dipole moment p, shows no *net* polarization in the absence of an external electric field. By virtue of the thermal agitation within the material, the

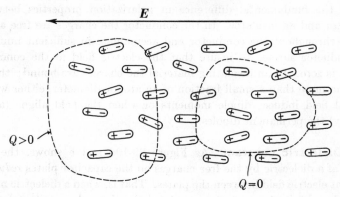

Figure 29-11. Polarization of nonpolar molecules by an external field. The net charge in a volume lying entirely within the dielectric is zero; but when the volume encloses one external surface of the dielectric, there is a nonzero net charge.

molecular dipoles are randomly oriented, as shown in Figure 29-12a. Now, when an external field E is applied, each dipole is subject to a torque $\tau = p \times E$ (Equation 26-12) which tends to align the dipole moments with the external field (Figure 29-12b). We say *tends* to align the dipoles because the polarizing influence of the external field competes with the depolarizing influence of thermal motion. (Recall that in a *uniform field*, each electric dipole, although subject to a resultant torque, is *not* subject to a resultant electric force.) Clearly, as the temperature falls, the degree of polarization of the dielectric increases for a given external field. In addition to aligning the permanent dipoles, the external field induces electric dipole moments in the molecules, just as in the case of nonpolar dielectrics. As before, the polarization of the dielectric produces net charges only at the surface of the material.

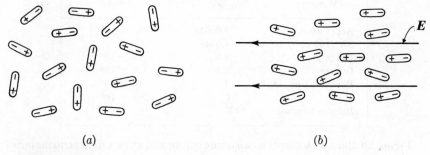

(a)   (b)

Figure 29-12. (a) Polar molecules in the absence of an external field. (b) Polar molecules in the presence of an external field.

Note the fundamental difference in polarization properties between a conductor and an insulator. In the conductor the charges are free and can wander throughout the conductor and accumulate in sufficient number at the conductor surface to insure that the electric field in the conductor's interior is zero. In an insulating material the charges are bound; they can travel no more than a small fraction of an atomic diameter, either when an external field induces dipole moments or when the field aligns (at least partially) the permanent dipoles.

29-5 Dielectric constant As Figure 29-10d and e shows, the polarization of a dielectric by the free charges on the capacitor plates *reduces* the resultant electric field between the plates. That is, when a dielectric material is introduced into the space between insulated charged capacitor plates, the potential difference between these plates, $V = Ed$, *decreases*. Since $C = Q/V$, the *capacitance increases*.

By definition, the *dielectric constant* κ of an insulating material is the capacitance C_d of a capacitor filled with dielectric divided by the corresponding capacitance C when the capacitor plates are immersed in a vacuum:

$$\kappa = C_d/C \qquad [29\text{-}11]$$

Clearly, κ is always greater than 1.00; the larger the κ, the larger the polarization of the dielectric by a given electric field. Table 29-1 lists dielectric constants and dielectric strengths (explained below) at room temperature of several common materials. Note that κ for air is very close to 1.00, which is, by definition, the dielectric constant for a vacuum.

Table 29-1

MATERIAL	DIELECTRIC CONSTANT κ	DIELECTRIC STRENGTH E_{max} AT ROOM TEMP. (v/m)
Air (1 atm)	1.00059	30×10^6
Air (100 atm)	1.0548	
Pyrex glass	5.6	15×10^6
Quartz	3.8	8×10^6
Paraffined paper	2	40×10^6
Mica	5	200×10^6
Barium titanate	1200	

Figure 29-13a and b shows a capacitor before and after a dielectric material has been placed between the capacitor plates; the *same free charge Q* is on the conducting plates in both instances. The electric field and potential difference are both reduced by the introduction of the dielectric, the dielectric constant being given by

$$\kappa = C_d/C = (Q/V_d)/(Q/V) = V/V_d = E/E_d$$

where E and E_d are the electric fields without and with the dielectric present.

In Figure 29-13c and d the situation is different. Here the capacitor remains attached to a battery, so that the potential difference between its plates cannot change. Then, when the dielectric is inserted, the free charge on the plates must increase, the dielectric constant now being given by

$$\kappa = Q_d/Q$$

where Q and Q_d are the charges on a capacitor plate before and after the dielectric is introduced.

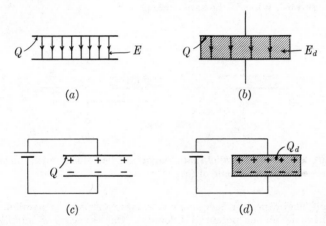

(a)   (b)

(c)   (d)

Figure 29-13. Insulated charged capacitor (a) before and (b) after dielectric is introduced. Charged capacitor maintained at constant potential difference (c) before and (d) after dielectric is introduced.

The *electrical permittivity of an insulating material,* designated by ϵ, is related to κ and ϵ_0 by the equation

$$\epsilon = \kappa\epsilon_0 \qquad\qquad [29\text{-}12]$$

When $\kappa = 1$, $\epsilon = \epsilon_0$; that is, ϵ_0 is the permittivity of the vacuum in this case.

It is an easy matter to generalize the formulas giving the capacitances for various configurations, whatever the dielectric material between the plates: one merely replaces ϵ_0, wherever it appears, by $\kappa\epsilon_0 = \epsilon$. Thus, the capacitance of a dielectric-filled parallel-plate capacitor is, from Equation 29-6,

$$C = \kappa\epsilon_0 A/d = \epsilon A/d \qquad\qquad [29\text{-}13]$$

Dielectric materials serve useful functions in actual capacitors: they insulate the plates from one another, and they enhance the capacitance by a factor κ. Thus, an ordinary "paper condenser" is formed by sandwiching thin paper between two metallic foils and rolling an essentially parallel-plate capacitor into cylindrical shape. Such a capacitor cannot maintain its insulating properties for any applied potential difference. When the electric field reaches the dielectric strength of the insulating material, electric discharge, or arcing, occurs through the dielectric. Therefore, a dielectric material is specified by the maximum electric field E_{max} (for example, 200 kv/mm for mica and 40 kv/mm for paraffined paper) as well as by its dielectric constant (see Table 29-1).

Example 3   A parallel-plate capacitor is half filled with a dielectric, as shown in Figure 29-14a. What is the capacitance?

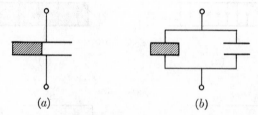

(a)   (b)

Figure 29-14. (a) Parallel-plate capacitor half filled with dielectric; (b) the equivalent circuit of (a).

The half-filled capacitor is equivalent to two capacitors in parallel, inasmuch as they have a common potential difference. One capacitor is completely filled with dielectric and has a capacitance C_d; the other is empty and has a capacitance C_e, shown in Figure 29-14b. The two capacitances are, from Equation 29-13,

$$C_d = \kappa\epsilon_0 A/2d \qquad \text{and} \qquad C_e = \epsilon_0 A/2d$$

where A represents the plate area of the whole capacitor. Then, from Equation 29-10,

$$C = C_d + C_e = \frac{\epsilon_0 A}{2d}(1 + \kappa)$$

29-6 Energy of a charged capacitor   Work is required to charge a capacitor because, after the first small charge is placed on either plate, this charge repels other charges of like sign that are subsequently added to the plate. We wish to find the total work U_e required to charge the capacitor to a final potential difference V_f with a final charge of magnitude Q on each plate. The potential difference between plates changes as the capacitor is being charged; therefore, we must integrate from the initial zero charge to the final charge Q:

$$U_e = \int_0^Q V \, dq = \int_0^Q \frac{q}{C} \, dq = \frac{Q^2}{2C}$$

We may write U_e, which represents the electric potential energy of the charges on the capacitor plates, in equivalent forms by using $C = Q/V_f$:

$$U_e = \frac{Q^2}{2C} = \tfrac{1}{2}CV_f^2 = \tfrac{1}{2}QV_f \qquad\qquad [29\text{-}14]$$

Example 4   The two oppositely charged plates of a charged capacitor attract one another. What is this force in a parallel-plate capacitor?

The force F can be computed by recognizing that in increasing the separation distance between the plates by dx one does work $F \, dx$. This corresponds to a change in the electric potential energy of the capacitor. From Equations 29-13 and 29-14 we have

$$U_e = \frac{Q^2}{2C} = \frac{Q^2 x}{2\epsilon A}$$

Therefore, $dU_e = (Q^2/2\epsilon A) \, dx = F \, dx$

$$F = Q^2/2\epsilon A \qquad\qquad [29\text{-}15]$$

The force given by Equation 29-15 is constant, of course, only if the change in plate separation leaves the capacitor with a uniform electric field confined entirely within the region between the plates. Equation 29-15 provides a method of measuring the charge Q on a capacitor as well as the potential difference $V = Q/C$ between its plates: one simply measures the force between charged capacitor plates. Thus, an electrometer, a device which measures potential difference, may consist simply of an ordinary balance so arranged that the known weight on one side is balanced against the electric force between the plates of a capacitor.

29-7   Energy density of the electric field   A charged capacitor has electric potential energy because work is required to assemble the charges at the plates. We may say the same thing differently: a charged capacitor has energy because an electric field has been established in the region between the plates. [That is, instead of attributing the potential energy to the relative positions of positive and negative charges, we may alternatively and equivalently ascribe the energy to the electric field itself.] Using Equations 29-13 and 29-14, for a parallel-plate capacitor, we have

$$U_e = \tfrac{1}{2}CV_f^2 = \frac{1}{2}\left(\frac{\epsilon A}{d}\right)(Ed)^2 = \tfrac{1}{2}\epsilon E^2(Ad)$$

Neglecting fringing, the uniform field is confined to the volume Ad between the plates. Therefore, the electric energy per unit volume, or the *electric* *energy density u_e is*

$$\ast \quad \boxed{u_e = U_e/Ad = \tfrac{1}{2}\epsilon E^2} \qquad\qquad [29\text{-}16]$$

The energy density is proportional to the *square* of the electric field. Although derived for the special case of a parallel-plate capacitor, Equation 29-16 is altogether general. It gives the electric energy density for *any* electric field.

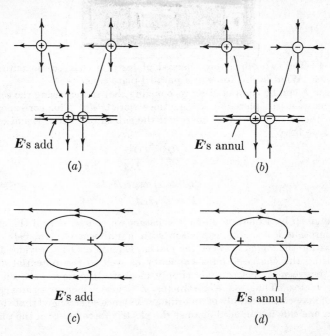

Figure 29-15. (a) Electric fields from two *like* point charges when separated and when close together; (b) electric fields from two *unlike* point charges separated and together. (c) Electric fields of external uniform field and electric dipole with dipole anti-aligned with the external field; (d) Electric fields for dipole aligned with field.

That one may properly associate energy with the electric field itself is justified by the fact that fields, existing in space *without* being attached to electric charges, are found for electromagnetic waves.

A dropped object falls toward the Earth because a downward gravitational force acts on it. One may equally well say that the dropped object approaches the Earth because, in so doing, the gravitational potential energy of the object-Earth system is reduced. In similar fashion one may use the concept of the energy of an electric field in space as an alternative way of describing electric interactions. For example, consider the simple case of the two oppositely charged plates of a parallel-plate capacitor. If there were no insulator holding the plates apart, the attractive force between them would cause them to approach one another. We can say equivalently that the plate separation distance decreases because the electric field energy between the plates is thereby reduced.

Whenever there are two charged objects in the same region of space we may, by the superposition principle for electric forces, regard each object as producing its own electric field. The energy of the resultant electric field, however, varies with the *square* of the resultant E. Thus, when the fields from two charge distributions add, the total electric energy of the system is high, but when the separate fields cancel, or partially cancel, the system's total energy is lessened. To see how this works, we may consider Figure 29-15a. We see that the total energy of the electric field for two *like* charges brought closer together corresponds to a greater E and therefore a greater E^2. On the other hand, when two *unlike* charges are brought together, as in Figure 29-15b, the fields annul and reduce E^2. We may say that like charges repel because the total energy of the electric field is reduced when like charges are separated and that unlike charges attract because the total energy of the electric field decreases when their separation distance is reduced. By the same token, as Figure 29-15c and d shows, an electric dipole is aligned with, rather than against, an external field, because alignment with the field corresponds to a lower electric-field energy.

Example 5   What is the total electric potential energy of a charged spherical conductor of radius R?

There are (at least) two ways of finding this energy: (a) by finding the total energy associated with the electric field surrounding the charged conductor, or (b) by finding the electric potential energy of the charges on a spherical capacitor.

(a) We know that the electric field of a charged conducting sphere of radius R and carrying charge Q is the same (for $r \geq R$) as that of a point-charge Q at the center of the sphere:

[27-8] $$E = kQ/r^2$$

The electric energy density u_e for any distance r from the sphere's center is

$$u_e = \tfrac{1}{2}\epsilon_0 E^2 = \tfrac{1}{2}\epsilon_0 k^2 Q^2/r^4$$

Within a spherical shell of radius r, thickness dr, and volume $4\pi r^2\, dr$ the energy is

$$dU_e = u_e(4\pi r^2\, dr)$$

and the total energy from $r = R$ outward is

$$U_e = \int_R^\infty (\tfrac{1}{2}\epsilon_0 k^2 Q^2/r^4)(4\pi r^2\, dr) = 2\pi\epsilon_0 k^2 Q^2 \frac{1}{R} = \frac{Q^2}{8\pi\epsilon_0 R} \qquad [29\text{-}17]$$

(b) The capacitance of a single spherical shell is, from Equations 29-1 and 29-2,

$$C = R/k$$

From Equation 29-14, the energy of a charged capacitor is

[29-17] $$U_e = \tfrac{1}{2}Q^2/C = \tfrac{1}{2}Q^2/(R/k) = Q^2/8\pi\epsilon_0 R$$

29-8 Summary The capacitance C of a capacitor is given by

[29-2] $$C = Q/V$$

where Q is the charge magnitude of either of two oppositely charged conductors and V is the potential difference between them. The unit of capacitance is the farad.

The capacitance of a parallel-plate capacitor of plate area A and plate separation distance d is

[29-13] $$C = \epsilon A/d$$

Capacitors in series all have the same charge; the single equivalent capacitance C is given by $1/C = \Sigma \, 1/C_i$. Capacitors in parallel have a common potential difference; the equivalent capacitance is $C = \Sigma \, C_i$.

The dielectric constant κ of a dielectric material is defined as

[29-11] $$\kappa = C_d/C$$

where C_d and C are the respective capacitances of a capacitor filled with, and empty of, the dielectric material.

The energy of a charged capacitor is

[29-14] $$U_e = Q^2/2C = \tfrac{1}{2}CV^2 = \tfrac{1}{2}QV$$

The energy density of an electric field is

[29-16] $$u_e = \tfrac{1}{2}\epsilon E^2$$

PROBLEMS

29-1 A coaxial cable has inner and outer conductors of 1.0 mm and 2.0 mm radius, respectively, and is filled with a dielectric having the dielectric constant 20. What is the capacitance per meter of such a cable?

29-2 What is the capacitance of the Earth (radius, 6.4×10^6 m) regarded as a single spherical capacitor?

29-3 An air capacitor of variable capacitance, of the sort used to tune radios, is shown in Figure 29-16. It consists of n parallel plates each of area A connecting alternately to opposite poles, adjacent plates being separated by the distance d. Show that the maximum capacitance of such a capacitor is given by $(n - 1)\epsilon_0 A/d$.

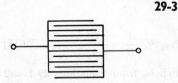

Figure 29-16

29-4 Derive the relation giving the capacitance of two concentric spherical conductors of radii r_1 and r_2.

29-5 A capacitor consisting of two concentric spherical conductors of nearly the same radius can be regarded as approximating a parallel-plate capacitor over any small portion of the sphere. Derive the relation giving the capacitance of a parallel-plate capacitor from that for a spherical capacitor on this basis. See Problem 29-4.

29-6 ★ A parallel-plate capacitor with a 1.0 cm plate separation and with 100 m² area on each plate is placed in an external field of 2000 v/m and at the same time is connected to a battery of 100 v, as shown in Figure 29-17. What is the charge on each of the four plate surfaces a, b, c, and d?

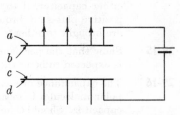

Figure 29-17

29-7 Five identical capacitors are so connected that their minimum equivalent capacitance is 20 $\mu\mu$f. What is the maximum equivalent capacitance that can be achieved with these five capacitors?

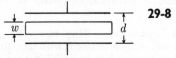

Figure 29-18

29-8 A solid conductor with flat sides is introduced into the region between the plates of a parallel-plate capacitor, as shown in Figure 29-18. What is the equivalent capacitance of this capacitor?

29-9 An unlimited number of 10 μf capacitors are each rated for breakdown whenever the applied potential difference exceeds 500 v. A capacitor of 10 μf operating across a potential difference of 2000 v is required. What arrangement with the minimum number of available capacitors can be used?

29-10 A capacitor C_1 whose capacitance is known is initially charged so that its potential difference is V_1. Then this charged capacitor is connected across a capacitor of unknown capacitance which is initially uncharged. The final potential difference across either capacitor is found to be V_2. Show that the capacitance of the unknown capacitor is given by $C_1(V_1 - V_2)/V_2$.

29-11 An unlimited number of capacitors are available, each of 10 μf. How does one construct a capacitor of (a) 35 μf, (b) 1.0 μf, and (c) 2.0 μf, using the minimum number of capacitors in each case?

29-12 The circuit shown in Figure 29-19 is comprised of identical capacitors each of capacitance C. What is the equivalent capacitance of this circuit? (*Hint:* From symmetry, what is the charge on the capacitor at the center?)

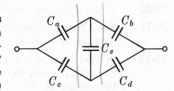

Figure 29-19

29-13 ★ (a) What is the equivalent capacitance of the circuit shown in Figure 29-19, with $C_a = C_d = 2\ \mu f$, $C_b = C_c = 1\ \mu f$, and $C_e = 3\ \mu f$. (b) If one of the 2 μf capacitors breaks down and becomes a conductor, what will the equivalent capacitance become?

29-14 Two capacitors, one of 1.0 μf and the other of 2.0 μf, are each charged initially by being connected to a 10 v battery. Then the two capacitors are connected together. What is the final potential difference across either capacitor, if the capacitors are connected such that (a) both positive plates are brought together and (b) plates of opposite charge are brought together?

29-15 Show that the permanent electric dipole moment of a polar molecule is expected to be of the order of 10^{-29} coul-m.

29-16 The capacitance of a capacitor filled with a dielectric material having polar molecules is measured as a function of the temperature of the capacitor. Should C increase or decrease as the temperature increases?

29-17 A paper capacitor is made by placing metallic foils, each of 50 cm² area, on the two sides of a piece of paper having a thickness of 0.020 mm. The dielectric constant of the paper is 4.0, and its dielectric strength is 12 kv/mm. What is the rating of the capacitor? That is, give its (a) capacitance, and (b) the maximum potential difference which can be applied across it.

29-18 The earliest capacitors were called Leyden jars. They consisted of glass containers coated on the inside and outside surfaces with metallic foils. Find the capacitance of a Leyden jar consisting of a coated cylinder 20 cm tall, 20 cm in diameter, and coated ends, all made of glass 3.0 mm thick. The dielectric constant of glass is 5.0.

29-19 A dielectric slab of dielectric constant κ is introduced into a parallel-plate capacitor so that it occupies only one half of the volume between the plates, as shown in Figure 29-20. What is the equivalent capacitance of the capacitor?

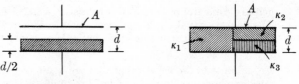

Figure 29-20   **Figure 29-21**

29-20 What is the capacitance of the capacitor shown in Figure 29-21?

29-21 Show that the force between two point-charges immersed in a dielectric medium of dielectric constant κ is given by $kq_1q_2/\kappa r^2$.

29-22 A dielectric is introduced between the plates of a capacitor. (a) Show that when the capacitor holds a constant charge on its plates, the energy of the capacitor *decreases* by a factor κ. (b) Show that when the capacitor maintains a constant potential difference between its plates, the energy of the capacitor *increases* by a factor κ. Is the dielectric material attracted toward the center of the capacitor in both cases? (*Hint:* Consider the electric forces acting on the leading edge of the dielectric as it is inserted between the capacitor plates.)

29-23 How many times can a 6.0 v battery, rated as having a chemical potential energy of 1.8×10^4 joules (5.0 amp-hours) be used to charge a 10 μf capacitor?

29-24 A 5.0 μf capacitor and a 10.0 μf capacitor are connected in turn across a 100 v battery. (a) If these two charged capacitor terminals are connected plus-to-plus and minus-to-minus, what is the total electric energy stored? (b) If they are connected plus-to-minus, what energy will be stored? (c) Account for the missing energy.

29-25 A parallel-plate capacitor is comprised of two conducting plates, each of area 0.50 m², separated from one another by a sheet of mica ($\kappa = 5$) 0.30 cm thick. The capacitor is charged to a potential difference of 1000 v, and then disconnected. Find the work necessary to pull the mica sheet out from between the plates.

29-26 ⋆ A 5.0 μf parallel-plate capacitor has a plate separation distance of 1.0 mm and a potential difference of 50 v across the plates. The capacitor is air-filled, and the dielectric strength of air is 30×10^6 v/m. Find the ratio of the electric force on a charge within a molecule of air (oxygen or nitrogen) due to the external field of the charged capacitor to that due to the internal fields from the other charges in the molecule.

29-27 Show that the electric stress (the force per unit area) on each of two plates in a parallel-plate capacitor is given by $\sigma^2/2\epsilon_0$, where σ is the surface charge density on either plate.

29-28 A flat metallic sheet having an area of 20 cm² and a weight of 2.0×10^{-3} nt is to be made to float under a second fixed conducting sheet oriented in a horizontal plane, by placing opposite charges on the two sheets when they are separated by 1.0 mm. What potential difference must be established between the two sheets?

29-29 What is the electric energy density at the surface of a spherical conductor of 1.0 m diameter maintained at a potential of 10 million volts?

29-30 ⋆ Two parallel-plate conductors, each of area 0.25 m², are separated by a distance of 2.0 cm and charged to a potential difference of 500 v. One of the plates is then released while the other plate is held fixed. Assume that the collision of the moving plate (mass, 50 gm) with the fixed plate is perfectly elastic (neglecting gravity). (a) Plot the position of the moving plate with respect to the fixed plate as a function of time. (b) Find the speed of the moving plate at the instant of collision. (c) Calculate the total time at which the moving plate will have returned to the original separation.

T H I R T Y

ELECTRIC CURRENT AND RESISTANCE

This chapter is concerned with the electric currents arising from electric charges in motion. We define electric current and current density, and relate these quantities to the properties of electric charge carriers. Then we consider how the fundamental laws of electric charge conservation and energy conservation apply to electric currents. From these considerations we arrive at, respectively, the equation of continuity for electric currents and the general relation giving the electric power delivered by an energy source to a load. We define the resistance for conductors in general, and consider the implications of Ohm's law as it relates to both the macroscopic and microscopic properties of conductors. We treat very briefly and qualitatively the characteristics which determine the resistivity of any material. Finally, we derive the time constant characterizing the exponential decay of an RC circuit.

30-1 Electric current Electric charges in motion constitute an *electric current*. By definition, the current i through a chosen surface is the total net charge dQ passing through that surface divided by the elapsed time dt:

$$\boxed{i = dQ/dt}$$ [30-1]

The direction of the so-called conventional current is taken to be that in which *positive charges move*. Thus, protons traveling to the right make a current to the right, while electrons traveling to the right make a current to the left. To obtain the total current i we must always count the *net* charge passing through the chosen surface per unit time. For example, if positive ions move to the right through a surface and at the same time negative ions move to the left through the same surface, as in the case of currents in liquids, *both* types of ions contribute to an electric current to the *right;* see Figure 30-1.

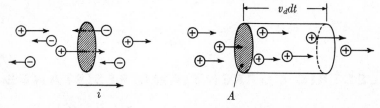

Figure 30-1. Both the positive charges to the right and the negative charges to the left contribute to a conventional current i to the right.

Figure 30-2. Charges drifting at speed v_d through a cylinder of cross-sectional area A in the time dt.

In the mksa system the unit of current is the *ampere* (abbreviated amp or a) named after André M. Ampère (1775–1836), who made significant contributions to the relation between an electric current and its associated magnetic field. Recall that one ampere corresponds to a net charge of one coulomb passing through a chosen surface in the time of one second. Whereas the coulomb is an uncommonly large amount of charge by laboratory standards, laboratory currents of a few amperes are typical. Related units are the milliampere (1 mamp = 1 ma = 10^{-3} amp) and the microampere (1 μamp = 10^{-6} amp).

A direct current (d-c) implies that net positive charges move in one direction only but *not* necessarily at a constant rate. As long as the current exists in one direction only, it is a direct current. For an alternating current (a-c), on the other hand, the current changes direction periodically.

How is the current i related to the properties of the charge carriers? Suppose that a current consists of n charge carriers per unit volume drifting at the speed v_d along a single direction, each carrier having a charge q (see Figure 30-2). Then, in the time dt each charge carrier advances a distance

$v_d \, dt$, and all of the charge carriers within a cylindrical volume of length $v_d \, dt$ and cross-sectional area A will have passed through one end of the cylinder. By the same token, an equal number of charge carriers will have entered the cylindrical column through the other end. The total charge dQ passing through the area A in time dt is the charge per unit volume qn multiplied by the cylinder's volume $Av_d \, dt$:

$$dQ = Aqnv_d \, dt$$

Consequently, the current i contributed by these charge carriers is

$$i = dQ/dt = Aqnv_d \quad \text{✳} \qquad \qquad [30\text{-}2]$$

If several species of charge carriers, differing in q, n, or v_d, contribute to the current, we may generalize this relation by writing

$$i = \Sigma \, A_i q_i n_i v_{di} \qquad \qquad [30\text{-}3]$$

We must emphasize that it need *not* be assumed that each charge carrier moves at a constant velocity. The charged particles may, in fact, have a very complicated motion, as do the free electrons in ordinary conductors. The drift speed v_d is the average displacement per unit time along the direction of the current.

The most commonly used current-measuring devices, called ammeters, depend in their operation upon the torque produced by a magnet on a current-carrying coil of wire (Section 32-7). A still simpler, but usually not very practical, type of ammeter is based on the *electrolysis* phenoménon: one simply measures the current by measuring the mass plated on an electrode in a conducting liquid (an electrolyte). When a current exists in the liquid between two electrodes, positive and negative ions migrate toward the negatively and positively charged electrodes, respectively. For example, silver ions, Ag^+, in an electrolyte migrate toward the negative anode and upon reaching it are neutralized and plated on this electrode. Since the atomic weight of silver is 108, we know that when 108 gm, or 1 mole, of silver has been plated, the total number of singly charged silver atoms neutralized at the anode is Avogadro's number, $N_0 = 6.025 \times 10^{23}$ atoms/mole. Furthermore, since each silver ion carries a charge of magnitude $e = 1.6 \times 10^{-19}$ coul, the total charge neutralized is eN_0. This quantity of charge, the charge carried by one mole of singly charged ions, is called the *Faraday* $F = eN_0$; its numerical value is $F = (1.60 \times 10^{-19} \text{ coul})(6.025 \times 10^{23} \text{ atoms/mole}) = 9.65 \times 10^4$ coul/mole. The electric current i through the electrolytic cell is directly proportional to the charge Q and, therefore, also proportional to the total mass m deposited on the electrode. By measuring the mass m deposited in a known time interval t, one measures the current through the cell. This effect, first elucidated in the experiments of Michael Faraday, is summarized in the relation

$$m = \frac{w}{eN_0 v} it \qquad [30\text{-}4]$$

where w is the atomic weight and v is the number of elementary charges per ion, or the valence, of the deposited material. Experiments with different types of ions show that v is always an *integer*. The electrolysis experiments were the first direct evidence of the quantization of the electric charge.

Example 1 A current of 1.0 amp exists in a copper conducting wire whose cross-sectional area is 1.0 mm². What is the average drift speed of the conduction electrons under these conditions?

In copper, as in other typical metallic conductors, there is approximately one free, or conduction, electron per atom. We can then find the density n of charge carriers by computing the number of atoms per unit volume from Avogadro's number N_0 (the number of atoms per mole), the atomic weight w (the number of grams per mole), and the mass density ρ_m (the number of grams per unit volume). Clearly,

$$n = \frac{\rho_m N_0}{w} = \frac{(9.0 \text{ gm/cm}^3)(6.0 \times 10^{23} \text{ atoms/mole})(1 \text{ free electron/atom})}{(64 \text{ gm/mole})}$$

$$= 8.4 \times 10^{22} \text{ free electrons/cm}^3 = 8.4 \times 10^{28} \text{ m}^{-3}$$

From Equation 30-2,

$$v_d = \frac{i}{Aqn} = \frac{(1.0 \text{ amp})}{(1.0 \times 10^{-6} \text{ m}^2)(1.6 \times 10^{-19} \text{ coul})(8.4 \times 10^{28} \text{ m}^{-3})}$$

$$= 7.4 \times 10^{-5} \text{ m/sec} = 0.074 \text{ mm/sec}$$

The free electrons drift through the conductor with an average speed which is actually less than 0.1 mm/sec, a remarkably low speed. It should *not* be inferred, however, that when such a current is established at one end of a copper conducting wire it takes almost 10 sec for the signal to travel a mere 1 mm. The speed at which the electric field driving the free electrons is established is close to the speed of light. One must distinguish here between the speed with which the charged particles drift and the speed at which the signal is propagated, just as one must distinguish between the speed (possibly very low) at which a liquid drifts through a pipe and the much higher speed at which a change in pressure is propagated along the pipe. The *drift* speed of conduction electrons is much less than the *random* thermal speeds of electrons at any finite temperature. We shall explore this point further in Section 30-6.

An important assumption was made in computing the drift speed above, namely, that the density of charge carriers n, or the density of free electrons, is the same at all points in the conductor. That n is, in fact, a constant is supported by the observation that no *net* charge accumulates at any point in the conductor.

Example 2 Electrons are released from rest at a constant rate at a negatively charged electrode (cathode), accelerated through a vacuum by an electric potential difference V, and strike a positively charged electrode (anode); see

Figure 30-3a. How do (a) the electric current, (b) the drift velocity, and (c) the charge density vary in space from the cathode to the anode?

We assume for simplicity that the only electric force acting on each electron arises from the external electric field produced by the electrodes. We thereby ignore any interaction between the electrons themselves (such interaction is called "space-charge," which may not always be negligible in electron emission). At the cathode the electrons move relatively slowly and have a high density; consequently, the mutually repulsive force acting between electrons in the cloud of charges near the cathode may be comparable to, or exceed, that arising from the external field. In the absence of space-charge effects, each electron is subject to a constant force and travels toward the positively charged electrode with constant acceleration.

(a) The electric current i, having a direction opposite to that of the electrons' velocities, is the *same* through any transverse surface chosen between the two electrodes. This follows simply from the fact that all electrons released at the cathode reach the anode and, therefore, the number of electrons passing any transverse area per unit time is constant, as shown in Figure 30-3b.

(b) Since the electrons have a constant acceleration, their velocity increases linearly with time ($v = at$). By the same token, the velocity varies with the distance x from the cathode according to $v^2 = 2ax$; that is, $v \propto \sqrt{x}$, as shown in Figure 30-3c.

(c) We find the variation in the number n of electrons per unit volume by using Equation 30-2, $i = Aqnv_d$. Since i, A, and q are constant and $v_d \propto x^{1/2}$, it follows that $n \propto x^{-1/2}$, as shown in Figure 30-3d. Thus, the electrons are crowded together near the cathode, where their speeds are small, but spread near the anode, where their speeds are high.

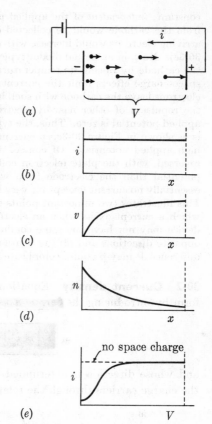

Figure 30-3. (a) Electrons accelerated from rest by a potential difference V through a vacuum. (b) Electron current as a function of distance x from the cathode (excluding space-charge effects). (c) Electron drift speed as a function of x. (d) Electron density as a function of x. (e) Current-potential difference curve when space charge is not negligible.

It is interesting to consider how the current in this diode varies with the potential difference V applied across the cathode and anode. If space-charge effects were entirely negligible under all conditions, the current i would be constant, *independent* of the applied potential difference: all electrons released from the cathode would be collected at the anode, although the speeds of the arriving electrons would increase with increasing V (see the dotted line in Figure 30-3e). Now, in an actual diode (typically one in which electrons are emitted at the cathode by raising its temperature and thereby "boiling" off electrons) the space-charge effects limit the current at low values of V. Furthermore, some electrons leave the cathode with such large speeds that they manage to overcome the repulsion of other near-by electrons and reach the anode even when the applied potential is zero. Thus, the typical current-voltage (i-V) plot for a diode is as shown in Figure 30-3e: a current rising to a constant value at sufficiently high applied potentials. Of course, if the polarity of the applied potential is reversed, with the plate (electron collector) at a lower, rather than a higher, potential than the electrode from which the electrons are emitted, there is essentially no current (except for very large applied potentials: "cold" emission). This illustrates two important points concerning the properties of any device in which a current exists when an electric potential difference is applied: (a) the device may not have the same conduction properties for electrons traveling in opposite directions and (2) the relation between the current i and the potential difference V may be quite complicated.

30-2 Current density Equation 30-3 can be written in a more useful form by introducing the *current-density vector j*, whose magnitude is

$$j = i/A = \Sigma\, q_i n_i v_{di} \qquad [30\text{-}5]$$

and whose direction is determined by the directions of velocity vectors of the charge carriers through the relation

$$\boldsymbol{j} = \Sigma\, q_i n_i \boldsymbol{v}_{di} \qquad [30\text{-}6]$$

Thus, if there is a single type of charge carrier and all such (positive) charge carriers move in a single direction, that direction (or its opposite for negative carriers) is the direction of the $\boldsymbol{j}$ vector.

To see the utility of the current-density vector, consider the situation shown in Figure 30-4. The vector $d\boldsymbol{S}$ represents a small element of a surface through which charges flow. We find the electric charge flux, or electric current di through dS, by multiplying the component of $\boldsymbol{j}$ along the normal to the surface by the area dS; that is,

$$di = \boldsymbol{j} \cdot d\boldsymbol{S}$$

The total current i through the surface S is

$$i = \int_S \boldsymbol{j} \cdot d\boldsymbol{S} \qquad [30\text{-}7]$$

related to

$$\phi = \int_s \vec{E} \cdot d\vec{S}$$

Of course, when j and dS are parallel and the surface is flat, Equation 30-7 reduces to $j = i/A$. The current i may be positive or negative, depending upon whether the angle between the j and dS vectors is less than or greater than 90°. Thus, when the surface element dS is outward from some enclosed volume and the vector j also points outward, the current i is positive out of the surface. It is in this sense that we may speak of the "direction" of an electric current; actually, of course, only the current-density vector j has direction.

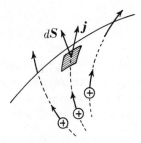

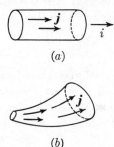

(a)

(b)

Figure   30-4. Current-density vector **j** and an element of surface dS.

Figure 30-5. Current-density vectors for two geometries: (a) the charge carriers move in a single direction along the axis of a cylinder, and all **j** vectors are parallel to the axis: (b) the charge carriers move in various directions, and the **j** vector differs from point to point within the conductor.

The vector j gives the direction and magnitude of the current density at each point in a region where electric charges are in motion. If the charges drift through a conducting solid of cylindrical shape, the j vectors are all along the cylinder axis, as shown in Figure 30-5a. If the conducting shape is not simple and the velocity of the charge carriers changes from point to point, the j vectors differ in magnitude and direction at various points in the conductor, as shown in Figure 30-5b.

30-3 Current and electric charge conservation According to the law of electric charge conservation, when the net charge within any closed volume changes, electric charges must pass through the surface. That is, if the net charge within changes, a net electric current must exist through the surface enclosing the volume. Let us express this formally.

First, we denote the charge per unit volume at any interior point by ρ_q, the charge density; ρ_q is in general a function of position within the closed volume as well as a function of time. The net charge Q within the volume is then

$$Q = \oint \rho_q \, dv$$

where the small circle on the integral sign reminds us that the integration must be carried over the entire interior volume. We denote the change in interior charge with time by

$$\frac{\partial Q}{\partial t} = \frac{\partial}{\partial t} \oint \rho_q \, dv$$

where partial derivatives are used, since ρ_q may also vary with position.

We wish to relate the change in interior charge to the electric current density j at the surface bounding the enclosure. The charge per unit time passing through an *outwardly* directed surface element dS is given by

[30-7] $$di = j \cdot dS$$

To evaluate the net current, or the net charge emerging per unit time, we extend the integration over the entire surface. It follows, then, that

$$\oint j \cdot dS = -\frac{\partial}{\partial t} \oint \rho_q \, dv \qquad [30\text{-}8]$$

The left side gives the net charge leaving the surface per unit time; the right side gives the corresponding *decrease* in the charge within (hence the minus sign in Equation 30-8). Equation 30-8, which is simply a formal statement of the law of electric charge conservation, is called the *equation of continuity for electric charge*. This relation is similar to the equation of continuity of mass (Equation 18-6), which we encountered in hydrodynamics and which expressed formally the law of mass conservation.

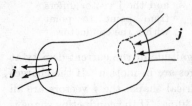

Figure 30-6. Currents into and out of a closed surface.

Consider Figure 30-6. The current into the surface is the same as the current out. Therefore, no net charges accumulate or become depleted within the surface's interior.

The equation of continuity is also illustrated in Figure 30-7. In part (a) of the figure there are two current leads to the closed volume (containing a capacitor in the process of being charged), and equal currents go into and come out of the surface. Thus, the left side of Equation 30-8 is zero and the net charge within is unchanged. Note that it *cannot* be inferred thereby that the charge carriers emerge from the enclosed volume at the same *speed* as those which enter, but simply that the two currents are of equal magnitude. In part (b) of the figure the volume encloses one plate only of a capacitor

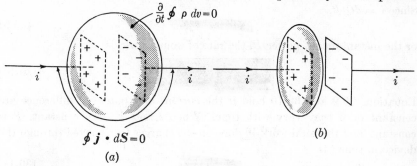

$$\frac{\partial}{\partial t} \oint \rho \, dv = 0$$

$$\oint \mathbf{j} \cdot d\mathbf{S} = 0$$

(a)

(b)

Figure 30-7. (a) The surface encloses a capacitor being charged; since the currents in and out are equal, no *net* charge accumulates on the interior. (b) Now the surface encloses one capacitor plate only; the current entering is matched by the charge accumulation within.

which is being charged. Positive charges *enter* the volume to produce a current *into* the volume; the left side of Equation 30-8 is, therefore, negative. The charges accumulating on the single plate are accounted for by the right side of Equation 30-8.

30-4　Current and energy conservation Here we set down a fundamental relation concerning the transfer of electric energy to a device through which charges flow and in which an electric current exists. Our arrangement is altogether general: we have some energy source, such as a battery or an electric generator, which maintains a potential difference $V_{ab} = V_a - V_b$ between the terminals of a device, or load, through which a current i passes. The source supplies electric energy to the load; see Figure 30-8. The load need not be specified in detail (except that it can contain no energy sources). It might,

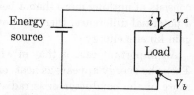

Figure 30-8. An energy source delivering energy to a load.

for example, be a single conductor, or an electric motor, or a vacuum tube. All that matters is that a current i exists within the device and that a potential difference V_{ab} be somehow produced across its terminals. We imagine V_a to exceed V_b, so that the conventional current is "in" at a and "out" at b (electrons then go "uphill" in potential from b to a).

If a positive charge dQ moves through the device and therefore across a potential difference V_{ab}, the work dW done on this charge by the electric forces associated with the potential difference is

$$dW = dQ V_{ab}$$

Since $i = dQ/dt$,

$$dW = i V_{ab} \, dt \qquad [30\text{-}9]$$

or the instantaneous power P, the rate of doing work, is

$$\boxed{P = dW/dt = i V_{ab}} \qquad [30\text{-}10]$$

Equations 30-9 and 30-10 hold if the current and potential difference are constant or if they vary with time. When i and V_{ab} are constant, P is constant, and the total work W done on the charges transported through the device in time t is

$$W = i V_{ab} t \qquad [30\text{-}11]$$

Otherwise, it is

$$W = \int P \, dt = \int iV \, dt$$

The instantaneous power to the load is simply the product of current and potential difference.

If the current i is in amperes and the potential difference V is in volts, the power P has the units of watts: (amp)(v) = (coul/sec)(joule/coul) = joule/sec = watt.

Let us be clear on the meaning of Equation 30-10. The delivered power P is simply the rate of energy transfer from the energy source to the load, whatever the details of the source or load. If the source establishes a potential difference across a motor and charges pass through this motor, the power to the motor appears (mostly) as work done on an external system. If the load consists of nothing more than a beam of charged particles accelerated across a potential difference, then the power P is the rate at which these particles gain kinetic energy.

An important case is that in which the load is a conductor or a resistor. Then the energy appears as heat, or thermal energy, which raises the temperature of the conductor or is radiated or conducted away. The power does *not* depend upon the way in which V and i are related. Their relation may, in fact, be quite complicated, as in the case of the vacuum-tube diode shown in Figure 30-3e, or the V-i relation may be simple, as in the case of a homogeneous solid conductor (taken up in the next section).

30-5 Resistance and Ohm's law An electrical *resistance* may be assigned to any current-carrying device in which the electric energy is dissipated and appears as thermal energy. *By definition*, the resistance R of a dissipative device across which there is a potential difference V and a current i is†

$$R \equiv V/i \qquad\qquad [30\text{-}12]$$

The resistance of a dissipative circuit element is *not* in general a constant. For example, in the diode of Figure 30-3e we see that, for sufficiently large applied potential differences, the current i is *independent* of V. In this case the resistance R increases with increasing V. When a potential difference is maintained between two electrodes immersed in a gas, the relation between i and V is also nonlinear, the resistance R again depending on the applied potential difference, as shown in Figure 30-9a. In semiconducting devices, such as transistors, the resistance R, defined as the ratio of V to i, is once more a complicated function of i (or of V), as shown in Figure 30-9b.

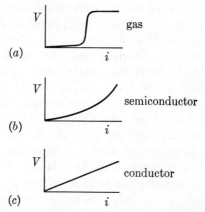

There is one important situation in which the resistance of a dissipative circuit element is simple, that of a homogeneous solid electrical conductor (including many poor conductors, or insulators). When a potential difference V is applied between any two points of a conductor of any shape and a current i exists in the conductor, it is found that

Figure 30-9. Voltage-current characteristics for (a) a gas, (b) a semiconducting device, and (c) a conductor obeying Ohm's law.

the V-to-i ratio, the resistance R, is a *constant* independent of V or of i; see Figure 30-9c. This relation, found by Georg S. Ohm (1787–1854) to hold for a large variety of materials and for an enormous range of currents and potential differences, is known as *Ohm's law.*

Ohm's law: $\qquad$ $$R = V/i = \text{a constant} \qquad\qquad [30\text{-}13]$$

Resistance is *defined* as the voltage-current ratio for any dissipative circuit element; Ohm's law is the experimental finding that this ratio is a *constant* for certain materials.

The mksa unit for resistance is the *ohm* (often abbreviated by the Greek omega, Ω). A resistor has a resistance of 1 ohm when a current of 1 amp exists with an applied potential difference of 1 v. Related units are the megohm (1

† The equivalent resistance of some electron vacuum tubes is, however, defined as $\Delta V/\Delta i$; that is, R is the slope of the V-i plot *at the operating conditions,* not the slope, V/i, of a line passing through the origin of the V-i plot.

Mohm = 10^6 ohms) or the micro ohm (1 μohm = 10^{-6} ohms). In circuit diagrams a resistor is depicted by the symbol -⋀⋀⋀-, and a variable resistor, or rheostat, is represented by -⋀⋀⋀-, or -⋀⋀⋀-. A dissipative circuit element whose resistance is *not* independent of V (or, therefore, of i) is known as a nonohmic, or nonlinear, resistor (its V-i plot is not a straight line through the origin).

It is remarkable that Ohm's law holds precisely over an enormous range of currents and potential differences (over a range of 10^{10} for many materials); it is even more remarkable, at least at first sight, that it holds at all. Recall that for an electrical conductor in electrostatic equilibrium the electric potential is the *same* at all points on the conductor's surface and in its interior. Furthermore, the electric field within the conductor is exactly *zero*. Now, if a potential difference is maintained between two points on a conductor, a nonzero electric field must exist within the conductor. It is this applied field, superimposed on the fluctuating local electric fields of the charged particles within the conductor, which drives the charge carriers through the conductor and so maintains the electric current. If the applied potential difference is constant, so too is the applied electric field at each point in the conductor. Then a net electric force acts on the free electrons comprising the current. But if an electron is acted on by a constant force, it moves with constant *acceleration*, not constant velocity. Such is the motion of an electron under the influence of an electric field in a vacuum tube. We have seen, however, that the conduction electrons in a conductor have a *constant* drift speed. Actually, there is no contradiction here, when we recognize that the conduction electrons undergo frequent collisions with the atoms of the conductor. In these collisions the kinetic energy acquired by the electrons from the external field is lost to the conductor lattice. The power *delivered to the conductor is dissipated* as thermal energy. We shall have more to say about Ohm's law from a microscopical point of view in Section 30-6.

In general, the power delivered to any circuit element is $P = iV$ (Equation 30-10). When a circuit element obeys Ohm's law and $V = iR$, then the power delivered to and dissipated in a resistor can be written

$$P = iV = i^2R = V^2/R \qquad [30\text{-}14]$$

That the thermal energy appearing in a resistor (the so-called i^2R loss) is, in fact, exactly equal to the electric energy delivered to it was first established by the historic experiments of James Joule. The effect is sometimes referred to as Joule heating. The thermal energy (in joules) is given by $W = i^2Rt = (V^2/R)t = iVt$, where t is the elapsed time. Joule's experiments show that the free electrons in a conductor do indeed travel at a *constant* drift speed, transferring electric energy into thermal kinetic energy in the resistor.

Ohm's law holds for a conductor of any shape and with the leads attached to any two points. For example, suppose that a potential difference is established between the ends of a cylindrical conductor of length L and cross-sectional area A, as in Figure 30-10. For a given material, experiment shows that the resistance for this simple geometrical configuration is directly proportional to the length and inversely proportional to the cross-sectional area. We may write the resistance as

$$R = \rho\, \frac{L}{A} \qquad \text{[30-15]}$$

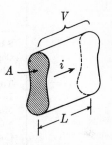

where ρ, called the *resistivity*, is a property of the material of which the conductor is made but does not depend on the conductor's physical shape. Resistivity carries the units ohm-meters (ohm-m) or ohm-centimeters (ohm-cm). Table 30-1 lists the resistivities of a number of common materials, both good and poor as conductors. Note the great range in resistivities: the best conductors are better than the worst conductor by a factor of about 10^{24}! From Equation 30-15 it is seen that the resistance

Figure 30-10. A potential difference V is maintained across the ends of a cylindrical conductor of length L and cross-sectional area A through which a current i passes.

of a cube, which is one meter along an edge and whose opposite faces are maintained at different potentials, is equal numerically to the material's resistivity in ohm-meters.

The reciprocal of the resistivity ρ is called the conductivity σ:

$$\sigma = 1/\rho \qquad \text{[30-16]}$$

Similarly, the reciprocal of the resistance (in ohms) is the conductance (in mhos).

Written as $V = iR$, Ohm's law is a macroscopical relation. We wish to express Ohm's law in microscopical form, that is, in terms of the external electric field E and the current density j for any point within any conductor.

Using Equations 30-13 and 30-15 we may write

$$V = iR = \frac{i}{A}\,\rho L \qquad \text{[30-17]}$$

The applied electric field E within a cylindrical conductor of Figure 30-10 is uniform along the axis of the cylinder and has the magnitude

[28-14] $E = V/L$

where V is the potential difference across the length L. The current density j has the magnitude

[30-5] $$j = i/A$$

Table 30-1

MATERIAL	RESISTIVITY AT ROOM TEMP. (ohm-m)
Silver	1.47×10^{-8}
Copper	1.72×10^{-8}
Aluminum	2.83×10^{-8}
Tungsten	5.51×10^{-8}
Iron	10×10^{-8}
Manganin (Cu 84%, Mn 12%, Ni 4%)	44×10^{-8}
Constantan (Cu 60%, Ni 40%)	44.1×10^{-8}
Nichrome	100×10^{-8}
Graphite	8.0×10^{-6}
Carbon	3.5×10^{-5}
Germanium	0.43
Silicon	2.6×10^{3}
Rock (granite)	$10^{5}-10^{7}$
Wood (maple)	4×10^{11}
Mica	9×10^{13}
Quartz (fused)	5×10^{16}

Substituting for i and V in Equation 30-17, we have

$$E = \rho j$$ [30-18]

or, in terms of the electrical conductivity σ,

$$j = \sigma E$$ [30-19]

We have written the last two equations in vector form, since we know that (positive) charge carriers will have drift velocities in the same direction as the applied field. Equations 30-18 and 30-19 are microscopical formulations of Ohm's law; they hold, not only for a cylindrical conductor, but also for any point within a conductor of any shape. In the next section we shall discuss how these relations are understood on an atomic basis, and we shall relate the resistivity ρ (and conductivity σ) to atomic properties of the conductor.

Example 3   A resistor consists of a cylindrical shell of length L with inner and outer radii r_1 and r_2, respectively; see Figure 30-11. When the inner and outer cylindrical surfaces are maintained at constant but different electric potentials, the current density and the electric field are radial. What is the resistance of this resistor in terms of L, r_1, r_2, and the conductor's resistivity ρ?

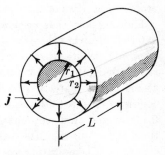

Equation 30-15, $R = \rho L/A$, which applies only when the current density $\boldsymbol{j}$ is constant in both direction and magnitude, may be applied here to a thin cylindrical conducting shell of thickness dr. We may imagine a thin flat conducting sheet to be bent into a cylindrical shell with a potential difference dV between its faces. Then

$$R = \rho \frac{L}{A} = \rho \frac{dr}{2\pi r L} = -\frac{dV}{i}$$

Figure 30-11. A cylindrical shell as a conductor.

The minus sign implies that the potential drops as r increases; that is, the inner radius is at a higher potential than the outer radius. Rearranging, we have

$$dV = -\frac{i\rho}{2\pi L} \cdot \frac{dr}{r}$$

We can also arrive at this relation by using the current density j and the microscopic form of Ohm's law:

[30-5] $i = jA = j(2\pi r L)$

[30-19] $j = \sigma E = -\sigma \frac{dV}{dr} = -\frac{1}{\rho} \cdot \frac{dV}{dr}$

Eliminating j from these two equations yields, as before,

$$dV = -\frac{i\rho}{2\pi L} \cdot \frac{dr}{r}$$

The total potential difference between the inner (r_1) and outer (r_2) cylindrical surfaces is $V_1 - V_2$. Therefore, upon integrating the equation above, we have

$$V_1 - V_2 = -\frac{i\rho}{2\pi L} \int_{r_1}^{r_2} \frac{dr}{r} = \frac{i\rho}{2\pi L} \ln \frac{r_1}{r_2}$$

Then, by definition, the resistor's resistance R is

$$R = \frac{V_1 - V_2}{i} = \frac{\rho}{2\pi L} \ln \frac{r_1}{r_2}$$

30-6 Ohm's law from a microscopic point of view   Expressed in microscopic form, Ohm's law is

[30-19] $\boldsymbol{j} = \sigma \boldsymbol{E}$

The current density at each point within a conductor is proportional to the external electric field at that point. We wish to show from an atomic point of view how it is that the conductivity is a constant and to relate it to the atomic properties of the conductor.

First suppose that *no* potential difference is applied to, and therefore *no* external electric field exists within, a conductor. The free, or conduction, electrons (typically one per atom) are in thermal motion; they travel randomly in all directions through the conductor, making collisions with the atoms of the material (the lattice) and with one another. Of course, the collisions are due to the scattering of the conduction electrons by the electric fields arising from the charged particles within the lattice. At the same time, the atoms oscillate with thermal vibrations. One may regard the free electrons as constituting a sort of "electron gas" within the conductor. At thermal equilibrium any one electron is just as likely to gain kinetic energy in a collision as to lose it. With what average speed do the electrons move? At 300° K, room temperature, the electrons in a typical metal have an average speed of about 10^6 m/sec. (The average kinetic energy $\bar{K}$ per electron is of the order of a few electron volts. The relation $\bar{K} = \frac{3}{2}kT$, with $\bar{K} = \frac{1}{25}$ ev for $T = 300°$ K, which applies for the molecules of a gas, does *not* apply for electrons within a conductor, for reasons relating to the quantum properties of electrons.)

What is the current through an arbitrarily chosen area within a conductor when no external electric field is applied? It is zero or, at least, zero on the average. Since the electrons are in random chaotic motion, over a long time interval, just as many electrons pass through an interior area in one direction as pass through in the opposite direction. The *average* velocity of the free electrons is zero. Actually, of course, because of statistical fluctuations in the motions of the free electrons, the current is zero only on a time average; the number of electrons through the area in opposite directions may not match exactly over a small time interval. Then there exists a randomly fluctuating current within the conductor which gives rise to the so-called Johnson noise, a small randomly fluctuating a-c voltage existing at the terminals of any resistor (Johnson noise is the electrical counterpart of Brownian motion in gas molecules).

Now suppose that a potential difference is applied, thereby creating an external electric field within the conductor. We have seen (Example 1 in this chapter) that in a typical conductor the *drift* speed of free electrons may be of the order of 10^{-4} m/sec; this is smaller than the average free-electron speed, 10^6 m/sec, by the very large factor of 10^{10}. What happens, then, on the atomic scale is this: an electron is accelerated by the external field, work is done on it, and it acquires a velocity opposite in direction to that of the field E. This velocity is in addition to the electron's thermal speed. Although the external field so accelerates the electrons that they acquire an additional speed of the order 10^{-4} m/sec in the direction of the field, this speed when added to the thermal speed of about 10^6 m/sec, leaves the thermal speed essentially unchanged. Great hordes of electrons advance, falteringly, at a very slow drift speed while still making very frequent collisions with the lattice. In these collisions the electrons lose the additional energy they have acquired from the driving electric field, thereby increasing the thermal-energy content of the conductor.

The essential point is that the average time between collisions is *not* changed when the free electrons drift under the influence of the electric field, because the magnitude of their drift velocity is so very small compared with the average free-electron speed. Although the average drift speed depends on the magnitude of the externally applied field, the time between collisions does not. This is precisely Ohm's law, as we shall now show analytically.

From equation 30-5 we have, for the current density,

$$j = \Sigma \, env_d = en \, \Sigma \, v_d$$

where e is the electronic charge, n is the density of free electrons, and v_d is the drift speed. Since for constant acceleration the velocity v acquired in the time t for an electron starting from rest is proportional to t (that is, $v = at$), we may write for the average drift velocity

$$v_d = at = \frac{eE}{m} \tau$$

where τ is a characteristic time constant giving a measure of the time between collisions. More properly, τ is the time required for an electron to be randomized after starting from rest and acquiring a drift velocity.

Combining the last two relations gives

$$j = \left(\frac{e^2 n \tau}{m}\right) E$$

Substituting this equation into Equation 30-19 we have

$$\sigma = (e^2 n/m)\tau \qquad [30\text{-}20]$$

The electrical conductivity *is* a constant, independent of E, because the time constant τ is independent of E.

The parameter which controls the magnitude of σ is τ. The density n of charge carriers is approximately the same for all solids (see Section 32-9). A typical conductivity for a metal (copper) at room temperatures is $\sigma = 1/\rho = 6 \times 10^7$ (ohm-m)$^{-1}$. Using $n = 8.4 \times 10^{28}$ electrons/m³ (see Example 1, this chapter), we have, from Equation 30-20, that $\tau = 2.5 \times 10^{-14}$ sec.

The average thermal speed of free electrons at room temperature is 10^6 m/sec, and the time between collisions is of the order of 10^{-14} sec. Thus, the average distance traveled between collisions, or the mean free path, is $(10^6$ m/sec$)(10^{-14}$ sec$) \simeq 10^{-8}$ m $= 100$ Å. We see that before making a collision a typical conduction electron in a conductor at room temperature travels, not merely one or a couple of atomic diameters, as we would expect, but about *fifty* atomic diameters on the average. This result is not only surprising in classical terms; it is, in fact, inexplicable. Only through the quantum theory, in which the free electrons in conductors are regarded as propagating as waves through the crystalline lattice, can such an extraordinarily large mean free path be understood.

30-7 Variation of resistivity   The electrical conductivity of a material is controlled basically by the time constant τ in Equation 30-20. When τ is large and the conduction electrons travel relatively large average distances before making a collision, the conductivity σ is large and its reciprocal, the resistivity ρ, is small. One may thereby see, at least qualitatively, how the resistivity varies when impurities are added to a conducting material, when crystalline defects are present, and when the temperature changes. The density of conduction electrons is essentially independent of temperature (Section 32-9).

A chemically pure material has a lower resistivity than the same material with impurity atoms present. Thus, an alloy has a higher resistivity than any one constituent element. An impurity atom disrupts the geometrical symmetry of the crystalline structure. As a consequence, conduction electrons have a smaller mean free path, τ is shorter, and ρ is larger.

The effect of a physical impurity is like that of a chemical impurity. If the atoms are not all arranged in a perfect geometrical array, and some are displaced from their proper positions in the crystalline lattice (lattice defects), the transits of the free electrons through the conductor are again interrupted, and the resistivity increases. For example, a well-annealed metal has a lower resistivity than an unannealed metal.

Since a crystal of oscillating atoms cannot, at each instant, have its atoms arranged in perfect geometrical symmetry, the resistivity of all metals at room temperature is produced in the main by thermal vibrations. Clearly, then, the resistivity of metals ought to decrease as the temperature is lowered, and this is what is observed; see Figure 30-12a. The effect of impurities or lattice defects on the resistivity is less important at room temperature than that of the thermal vibrations of the atoms in the crystalline lattice. The resistivity of a chemically and physically pure metal may closely approach zero at the absolute zero of temperature.

As Figure 30-12a shows, the resistivity varies linearly with temperature

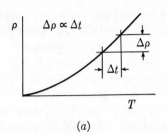
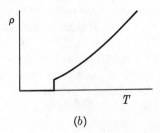

Figure 30-12. Temperature variation of resistivity for (a) an ordinary conductor and (b) a superconductor.

over a sufficiently small temperature range. That is, the fractional change in resistivity $\Delta\rho/\rho$ is directly proportional to the temperature change Δt. We may then write

$$\Delta\rho/\rho = \alpha\,\Delta t \qquad\qquad [30\text{-}21]$$

where α, the temperature coefficient of resistivity, is a constant (over a small temperature range) characteristic of the material. The temperature coefficient α represents the fractional increase in resistivity per unit temperature rise; see Table 30-2. For example, a copper conductor, which has an α of 0.0039 $(C°)^{-1}$ at room temperature, increases its resistance by 0.39 per cent for each Celsius degree temperature rise. Because resistivity changes with temperature, one may construct resistance thermometers which register temperatures through the change in their resistance. Platinum is commonly used in a resistance thermometer, because this material is relatively impervious chemically and because its resistivity is sensitive to temperature

Table 30-2

Material	Temp. (°C)	Temp. coefficient of resistivity $\alpha(C°)^{-1}$
Iron	20	0.0050
	500	0.0147
Copper	20	0.00393
Silver	20	0.0038
Platinum	20	0.003
Mercury	20	0.00089
Nichrome	20	0.0004
Constantin	25	0.000002
Manganin	12	0.000006
	25	0.000000
	100	−0.000042
	475	0.000000
	500	+0.00011

changes over a wide range. Note that the alloy manganin has a zero temperature coefficient at room temperature; that is, its resistivity does not change with temperature at 25° C. At 100° C, on the other hand, manganin's coefficient is negative: the resistivity decreases with a temperature rise.

Although the resistivity of metallic conductors increases with temperature rise, other materials, particularly semiconducting materials such as carbon, show the reverse behavior, a resistivity which falls as the temperature rises (that is, a negative temperature coefficient). Such materials have smaller resistivities than metallic conductors, principally because they have far fewer conduction electrons. When the temperature rises, the number of free electrons increases and the conductivity thereby increases to such a degree that it overcomes the decrease in conductivity resulting from increased thermal vibration.

Certain elements show a remarkable variation in electrical resistivity with temperature: below a certain critical temperature, the resistivity falls to zero—not merely a very small resistivity, but exactly zero (see Figure 30-12b)! Such materials are appropriately called *superconductors*. For example, the element lead exhibits superconductivity below 7.175° K. One expects that, since a superconductor offers no resistance to the flow of electric charge and dissipates no energy, an electric current once established in a superconducting loop would persist indefinitely. In so far as experiment will disclose, this is precisely what happens. Currents of several hundred amperes induced in a superconducting lead ring have been observed to persist with no measureable diminution for several years! Although bizarre, the phenomenon of superconductivity is now understood in terms of the quantum theory. In a certain sense, the conduction electrons of a superconductor never collide with the lattice.

30-8   RC circuits

We are now able to analyze a simple two-component electric circuit comprised of a resistance and a charged capacitor in series, as shown in Figure 30-13. A capacitor C, having an initial charge of magnitude Q_0 on each plate and a potential difference $V_0 = Q_0/C$ between the plates, is discharged across a resistor R. It is easy to describe qualitatively what happens after the instant the switch is closed. Electrons leave the negatively charged plate, pass through the resistor, and reach the positive plate. This continues until the capacitor is finally electrically neutral. A current, initially of magnitude $i_0 = V_0/R$, exists in the circuit, this current falling to zero as the charge Q and potential V of the capacitor also reach zero. At the same time, the electric potential energy associated with the

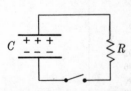

Figure 30-13. A circuit consisting of a charged capacitor and a resistor.

opposite charges initially residing on the capacitor plates (or, if you will, associated with the electric field between the capacitor plates) is dissipated as thermal energy while the charges move through the resistor.

Let us see how the charge Q and current i vary with time. We know that the net change in potential around a closed path is zero. That is, going clockwise around the circuit of Figure 30-13, the potential drop iR across the resistor plus the potential drop Q/C across the capacitor must equal zero at each instant of time:

$$iR + Q/C = 0$$

We substitute $i = dQ/dt$; then this relation is written

$$R \, dQ/dt = -Q/C$$

This equation holds at any instant of time. Rearranging terms and recalling that R and C are independent of time, we have

$$\int_{Q_0}^{Q} \frac{dQ}{Q} = -\frac{1}{RC} \int_0^t dt$$

$$\ln \frac{Q}{Q_0} = -\frac{t}{RC}$$

$$Q = Q_0 \, e^{-t/RC} \qquad\qquad [30\text{-}22]$$

The charge Q on each capacitor plate decreases exponentially in time, as shown in Figure 30-14a. The decay rate is controlled by the quantity RC,

the *time constant* of the RC circuit. As Equation 30-22 shows, when $t = RC$, then $Q = Q_0/e$; thus, the constant RC is the time elapsing until the capacitor's charge (and potential) is $(1/e)$th, or 37 per cent, of its initial charge. For example, in a circuit containing a 1.0 Mohm resistor and a 1.0 μf capacitor, the time constant is $RC = (1.0 \times 10^6 \text{ v/amp})(1.0 \times 10^{-6} \text{ coul/v}) = 1.0$ sec.

How does the current i vary with time? Taking the time derivative of Equation 30-22 we have

$$i = dQ/dt = -(Q_0/RC) \, e^{-t/RC}$$

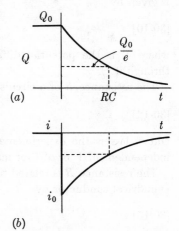

(a)

(b)

Since $Q_0/RC = V_0/R = i_0$, we may write this relation as

$$i = -i_0 \, e^{-t/RC} \qquad [30\text{-}23]$$

Figure 30-14. Variation with time of (a) the capacitor charge and (b) the current for an RC circuit.

The current, which is zero before the switch is first closed, rises abruptly to i_0 at $t = 0$ and then decays exponentially in time with the characteristic decay time RC, as shown in Figure 30-14b. (Note that since the rate of energy dissipation in the resistor i^2R is proportional to the *square* of i, the capacitor's energy decays more rapidly than the current and charge; the time constant for *energy* decay is $\frac{1}{2}RC$.)

30-9 Summary The electric current i through any surface is given by

[30-1] $i = dQ/dt$

where dQ is the total net charge passing through the surface in time dt. By convention, the direction of current is that direction in which positive charges move. Current is measured in amperes.

The current density j is related to the charge q_i of charge carriers, their density n_i, and their drift speed v_{di}, through the relation

[30-5] $j = i/A = \Sigma\, q_i n_i v_{di}$

In general, the current i through the surface element dS is given by

[30-7] $i = \int j \cdot dS$

The rate at which an energy source delivers electrical energy to a load is given by

[30-10] $P = iV$

where V is the potential difference across the load and i is the current through it.

The resistance R of a circuit element is defined by

[30-12] $R = V/i$

Ohm's law is the experimental finding that the resistance, so defined, is independent of V or of i for many conducting materials.

The resistance R is related to the length L and cross-sectional area A of a cylindrical conductor by

[30-15] $R = \rho(L/A)$

where the resistivity ρ is a constant, characteristic of the conducting material.

Ohm's law, expressed in microscopic form, is

[30-18] $E = \rho j$

where E is the applied electric field driving the charge carriers. Alternatively, one may write

[30-19] $$j = \sigma E$$

where $\sigma = 1/\rho$, the material's conductivity.

From an atomic point of view, Ohm's law holds because the drift speed acquired by conduction electrons under the influence of an applied electric field is so small compared with their thermal speeds that the time between collisions is essentially unchanged. The resistivity depends on the chemical and physical purity of a material and on its temperature.

When a charged capacitor C discharges through a resistor R, the charge on the capacitor decreases exponentially with time, the characteristic time constant of the decay being RC.

PROBLEMS

30-1   A 10.0 ev proton beam consisting of 4.0×10^6 protons/cm^3 travels to the left, while a 10.0 ev electron beam consisting of 4.0×10^6 electrons/cm^3 travels to the right. The area of each beam is 2.0 mm^2. What are the direction and magnitude of the resultant current?

30-2   What is the current density in a copper bus bar carrying 100 amp if the cross-sectional area is 20 mm^2?

30-3   A current of 10 amp exists along a cylindrical conductor having a circular cross section of radius 1.0 cm. What is the component of the current density normal to an area cutting the cylinder axis at 45°?

30-4   Two electrolytic cells, one in which silver ions, Ag$^+$ (atomic weight, 108), are deposited and another in which copper ions, Cu^{++} (atomic weight, 64), are deposited, have the same current passing through them. If 0.45 gm of silver are plated on one electrode, how much copper is plated on the other electrode in the same time?

30-5   A resistor is rated at 20 ohms, 10 watts. What is the maximum current allowed through the resistor?

30-6   An electric heater raises the temperature of 1.0 kg of water 20 C° when turned on for 30 min. If the current in the resistor is 10 amp, what is its resistance?

30-7   A cyclotron produces a beam of 5.0 Mev protons with a current of 10 μamp. What is the power output of the beam?

30-8   Consumers of electric energy pay by the kilowatt-hour. What is the cost of operating a 10-ohm resistor across a potential difference of 50 v for 20 hr at the rate of 3¢/kw-hr?

30-9   A certain 12 v battery carries an initial charge of 120 amp-hr. Assuming for simplicity that the potential difference across its terminals remains at 12 v until the battery is fully discharged, for how many hours can such a battery deliver 100 w?

30-10 A coil of wire dissipates energy at the rate of 5.0 w when a potential difference of 200 v is applied to it. A second coil made of the same wire dissipates 10.0 w when the same potential difference is applied to it. What is the ratio of the length of wire in the second coil to that in the first coil?

30-11 Electrons are emitted from the filament of a vacuum tube at the rate of 5.0×10^{18} electrons/sec. All the emitted electrons are collected at a plate, whose potential is 100 v above that of the filament. What are (a) the current at the plate and (b) the power dissipated at the plate? If the plate potential is now raised to 200 v, what are (c) the plate current and (d) the power now dissipated at the plate?

30-12 For small currents in a diode the current is proportional to $V^{3/2}$, where V is the potential difference between the anode and cathode. By what factor is the power delivered to the tube changed when the current is doubled?

30-13 What length of No. 30 copper wire (diameter, 0.01003 inch) must be wound on a spool to produce a resistor of 2.0 ohms?

30-14 What is the drop in electric potential along a 10 m length of copper wire having a diameter of 0.50 mm when a current of 10 amp exists in the wire?

30-15 A thin silver wire of 0.010 inch diameter carries a current of 2.0 amp. (a) What is the current density in the wire? (b) What is the drop in potential along a 1.0 m length of the wire? (c) What is the drift speed of electrons in the conductor?

30-16 A solid rectangular parallelepiped has edges of lengths a, b, and c, where $a < b < c$. Across which pair of opposite faces (ab, ac, or bc) will a constant potential difference give the maximum current?

30-17 What potential difference must be applied across opposite faces of a cube of maple wood 1 cm in edge length to produce a current of 1.0 μamp?

30-18 Two resistors are made of the same material and have identical resistances. Resistor A has a small cross section, resistor B a larger cross section. If both resistors are placed across identical batteries, which resistor is expected to show the smaller temperature rise?

30-19 ★ A resistor consists of a thick spherical shell of inner and outer radii r_1 and r_2 and has a conductivity σ. The current is radial between the inner and outer spherical surfaces, each of which is maintained at a constant electric potential. What is this resistor's resistance in terms of σ, r_1, and r_2? (*Hint:* First find how the electric potential, or the electric field, varies with r and then apply Equation 30-13 to a thin spherical shell.)

30-20 ★ A resistor is in the shape of a truncated right circular cone. The radii of its two ends are r_1 and r_2 and its length is L. Constant potentials are maintained at its two end surfaces. What is the resistance? (*Hint:* Apply the relation $R = \rho L/A$ to a thin slab and integrate.)

30-21   Show that Ohm's law can be written in the form $dQ/dt = \sigma A\, dV/dx$, where dV/dx is the electric potential gradient. This form of the fundamental law of electric-charge conduction is reminiscent of the fundamental law of thermal-energy conduction (Equation 23-6), $dQ/dt = kA\, dT/dx$, where dQ/dt is now the heat rate, k is the thermal conductivity, and dT/dx is the temperature gradient. That the two conductivity relations are similar and that they both apply to metals is hardly surprising: it is the free electrons of a conductor which are responsible for the transfer of both electric charge and thermal energy.

30-22   Manganin is an alloy having the very small temperature coefficient of resistivity of 1×10^{-5} $(C°)^{-1}$ at $20°$ C. Assuming the coefficient of resistivity remains constant, by how much must the temperature change for an increase in resistance of 1 per cent?

30-23   The potential difference between the plates of a slightly leaky capacitor of 0.10 μf is found to drop to half its initial value in 1.5 sec. What is the equivalent resistance between the capacitor plates?

30-24 ★ Show that the time constant for a leaky parallel-plate capacitor (one filled with a slightly conducting dielectric) is independent of both the area of the plates and their separation distance.

30-25 ★ Show that, when a charged capacitor is discharged across a resistor, the total energy initially stored in the capacitor, $Q^2/2C$, is equal to the total energy dissipated in the resistor, $\displaystyle\int_0^{\infty} I^2 R\, dt$.

30-26   A circuit such as that shown in Figure 30-15a may be used as a "differentiating circuit," the output voltage V_0 being proportional to

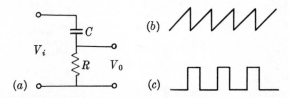

Figure 30-15. (a) A differentiating circuit. (b) A saw-tooth wave. (c) A square wave.

the time derivative dV_i/dt of the input voltage. The input voltage V_i is at any instant given by

$$V_i = iR + Q/C$$

Taking the time derivative we have

$$dV_i/dt = R\, di/dt + (1/C)i = (1/C)(RC\, di/dt + i)$$

If the time constant RC is very short, we may neglect the term involving it. Then

$$dV_i/dt = i/C = Ri/RC = V_0/RC$$
$$dV_i/dt \propto V_0$$

How does the output signal vary with time if the input signal is (a) a saw-tooth wave and (b) a square wave, as shown in Figure 30-15b and c?

THIRTY-ONE

20 pp

D-C CIRCUITS

This chapter concerns circuits in which the elements are batteries and resistors. First the emf of a battery, or of an energy source in general, is defined in terms of the nonconservative electric field around a circuit loop. The rules for handling resistors in series or in parallel are developed next. Then Kirchhoff's rules, the principles of energy conservation and charge conservation as applied to circuits, for dealing with multiloop circuits in general, are treated. Finally some d-c circuit instruments are discussed: the ammeter, voltmeter, Wheatstone's bridge, and the potentiometer.

31-1 The emf of a battery In all that follows we shall always speak of so-called conventional electric currents, in which the direction of the current is taken to be that in which positive charges move. Thus, to traverse a resistor in the direction of the current is to go from high to lower electric potential. Similarly, when the battery is discharging, positive charges are taken to be leaving the positive terminal of a battery and entering the negative terminal. We realize, of course, that in ordinary conductors it is the free, or conduction, electrons which actually move. Since these particles are negatively charged they travel "uphill" in potential, from a lower to a higher potential, and leave the negative terminal of a battery.

Consider the simple d-c circuit of Figure 31-1. Here we have a resistor R connected across the terminals of a battery. We label the positive battery terminal a and the negative terminal b. The potential V_a is higher than V_b. The battery maintains the potential difference $V_a - V_b = V_{ab}$ across its terminals at all times, whether the switch is open or closed.

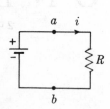

When the switch is open, there is, of course, no potential difference across the resistor R. When it is closed we find almost immediately the same potential difference appearing across the resistor with the concomitant current $i = V_{ab}/R$. Positive charges enter the resistor at a, go downhill in potential, and leave at b. The connecting wires between the battery and resistor terminals are imagined to have so small a resistance that the potential drop across them is negligible compared with that across R (at short circuit, $R = 0$).

Figure 31-1. A simple d-c circuit.

The electric power P_{ab} delivered to the load resistor R by the battery is given by

[30-10] $$P_{ab} = iV_{ab}$$

Since a resistor continuously dissipates the electric energy delivered to it as thermal energy, as long as a potential difference exists across it, the circuit must contain an energy source (here, the battery) which continuously maintains the electrostatic potential difference V_{ab} across its terminals. But how can one speak of a constant electric potential difference, which we have heretofore associated with a *static* distribution of charges, when the charges are always in motion? It is justified as follows. Every time a positive charge leaves any one point in the circuit it is immediately replaced by another positive charge. Consequently, there is no net change in charge at any point in the circuit, and there is a constant electrostatic potential at each point in the circuit.

Suppose that we follow a positive charge from a, through the resistor to b, and then through the battery back to a. From a to b the charge is acted upon by an electric field within the conductor. It thereby gains energy but, because of frequent collisions with lattice atoms, it disposes of this electric energy in the conductor and emerges at point b with exactly the *same* energy it had at a. The charge now enters the negative battery terminal and is transported through the battery back to the positive battery terminal; that is, the positive charge must move from a point at the potential V_b to the *higher* potential V_a. Clearly, this is *not* possible if the only force acting on the charge, as it passes through the interior of the battery, is the electric force derived from the potential difference (the force associated with the positive and negative charges residing at the battery terminals). There must exist, in addition to this electric force, a force *not* derived from the electrostatic charge distribution, which somehow drives the positive charge *uphill* in potential from V_b to V_a. In the case of an electrochemical cell, or battery, the nonconservative force which drives the charges *against* the opposing electrostatic force is called the *chemical force*.

When any two *dissimilar* metals are immersed in a conducting medium it is found that a potential difference exists between them; this is the most rudimentary form of an electrochemical cell. The chemical reactions which are the origin of this potential difference and the details of what goes on within a battery lie in the area of electrochemistry and will not be dealt with here. Suffice it to say, however, that the potential difference has its origin in the differences in the binding energy of electrons to atoms of different types. In this sense the nonelectrical, or chemical, forces are ultimately electrical in origin.

We may characterize any energy source that is capable of driving charges around a circuit against opposing potential differences as an *emf*. This is the abbreviation for *electromotive force*, a term so misleading (the emf is *not* a force) that we shall hereinafter refer to it simply as the emf or, symbolically, as $\mathscr{E}$. By the $\mathscr{E}$ of a battery is meant the energy per unit positive charge gained (or the work per unit charge done by the chemical forces within a battery) in the transfer of a charge *within* the battery from the negative to the positive terminal:

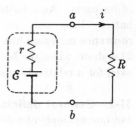

Figure 31-2. The dotted lines show what is within the battery: an emf and an internal resistance.

$$\mathscr{E} = \text{work per unit positive charge done}$$
$$\text{by the } \textit{nonconservative forces} \quad [31\text{-}1]$$

Since energy per unit charge, or joules per coulomb, is equivalent to volts, an emf, like a potential difference, is expressed in volts.

There is always some energy dissipation *within* an actual battery. One can account for this energy loss by ascribing an *internal resistance r* to the battery, where the rate of internal energy loss is $i^2 r$. Thus, a battery with emf $\mathscr{E}$ and internal resistance r, connected across a load resistor R, is represented by the circuit diagram shown in Figure 31-2. Let us apply energy conservation to this circuit. Since the emf is by definition the energy per unit charge gained from the battery, the rate at which nonelectric chemical potential energy is transformed into electric energy, or the power associated with the emf, is $\mathscr{E}i$. Some of this electric energy is dissipated into thermal energy within the battery at the rate i^2r; the remaining energy is delivered to the load resistance at the rate $iV_{ab} = i^2R$. Therefore,

$$\mathcal{E}i = i^2r + i^2R = i(ir + iR)$$
$$\mathcal{E} = ir + iR \qquad [31\text{-}2]$$

The current i in every element of the circuit is then

$$i = \frac{\mathcal{E}}{r + R} \qquad [31\text{-}3]$$

Since iR represents the potential difference V_{ab} across the load resistor and also across the battery terminals, Equation 31-2 can be written as

$$V_{ab} = \mathcal{E} - ir \qquad [31\text{-}4]$$

Thus, the potential difference across the battery terminals is the battery's emf less the potential drop across its internal resistance. The potential difference V_{ab} across the battery terminals will equal the emf $\mathcal{E}$ if the current i is zero but, as we see from Equation 31-2, this occurs only when the load resistor R is infinite. Said differently, the potential difference appearing across the battery terminals on open circuit ($R = \infty$) is the battery's emf.

The emf of a particular type of cell depends only on the chemical identity of its parts. As a battery ages or loses its "charge" (strictly, of course, a battery loses only its internal chemical potential energy), the internal resistance increases but the emf remains unchanged. As Equations 31-3 and 31-4 show, when the battery is "discharged," V_{ab} goes to zero as r increases, even for a relatively small load resistance R.

31-2 General definition of emf An electrochemical cell, or battery, is but one example of a device characterized by an emf, that is, a device which can convert nonelectric energy into electric energy. There are other arrangements in which an emf exists: (a) A thermocouple consists of two dissimilar conducting wires connected together in a circuit, the two junctions maintained at different temperatures; an electric current exists in such a circuit, driven by a *thermoelectric* emf. (b) In a photovoltaic cell, exemplified by a photographic exposure meter, visible light, or radiant energy, strikes a sensitive material and generates an electric current. (c) In an electric generator, mechanical energy is transformed into electric energy. (d) In an electric generator, an emf is produced by a changing magnetic flux (we shall have much to say about this in Chapter 34).

In every instance a *nonconservative force* is responsible for transporting charges against an opposing electric potential difference. It is appropriate to speak of a battery as the "seat" of an emf: obviously, the current stops when the battery is removed from the circuit, and we know that the origin of the emf is the chemical reactions taking place within. In other cases, however, one cannot necessarily identify one particular spot, or device, as the "seat" of the emf. It is useful, therefore, to define the emf more generally, in a way that is applicable for any energy source.

We denote the *total* electric field at any point in a circuit by E_t, where

$$E_t = E + E_s$$

E_t comprises two parts: the electric field E, having its origin in electric charges and derivable from an electric potential difference, and E_s, the *nonconservative* electric field associated with the energy source. We wish to find the total work W/Q done on a unit positive charge carried through all the elements in a closed loop:

$$W/Q = \oint E_t \cdot dr = \oint (E + E_s) \cdot dr$$
$$= \oint E \cdot dr + \oint E_s \cdot dr \qquad [31\text{-}5]$$

For definiteness we have supposed that we traverse the circuit loop in that sense in which the displacement dr is always parallel to the total electric force, $F_t = QE_t$. Then the work W is positive. This direction is also that of the electric current. For the first term on the right-hand side of Equation 31-5 we have

[28-11] $$\oint E \cdot dr = 0$$ [31-6]

The electric field E, derived from electrostatic charge distributions, is a *conservative* field; that is, the Coulomb force $F = QE$ is a conservative force, its line integral around any closed loop being zero.

Since E_s is nonconservative, its line integral around a closed loop is *not* zero, and Equation 31-5 reduces to

$$W/Q = \oint E_s \cdot dr$$

Now, the work done per unit positive charge in one round trip by the nonconservative forces is, by definition, the *emf of the circuit*. Therefore, the last equation can be written

$$\mathscr{E} = \oint E_s \cdot dr \qquad [31\text{-}7]$$

This is the most general definition of an emf. Note that it does not require that the emf be localized at some particular "seat," as in the case of a battery.

31-3 Single-loop d-c circuits We wish to find the general relation between the emf's in a circuit and the potential differences. Consider the circuit of Figure 31-3, which contains two batteries with emf's $\mathscr{E}_1$ and $\mathscr{E}_2$ and three resistors, r_1, r_2, and R, connected in series (r_1 and r_2 are the internal resistances of $\mathscr{E}_1$ and $\mathscr{E}_2$, respectively). We evaluate the line integral of the electric field around a clockwise closed path going through the several circuit elements. The arrows associated with the two batteries, pointing from the negative to the positive terminal in both cases, indicate the directions of

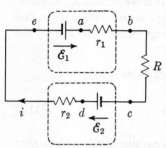

the electric field associated with the nonconservative electric forces; they give, so to speak, the "directions" of the emf. The "direction" of the current i is also clockwise. We can assert that the current i is, in fact, precisely the same at each point in the circuit loop according to the law of electric-charge conservation. It implies that electric charge does not pile up or become depleted at any one point in the circuit.

From Equation 31-7 we have

Figure 31-3

$$\oint E_s \cdot dr = \mathscr{E}_1 + \mathscr{E}_2 = \Sigma \mathscr{E}$$

Here we assume that our route has been taken in the clockwise sense, that is, with the electric field E_s always parallel to dr. Now, if we consider the *conservative* electric fields only, in going around the same circuit we have

$$\oint E \cdot dr = \int_a^b E \cdot dr + \int_b^c E \cdot dr + \int_c^d E \cdot dr + \int_d^e E \cdot dr + \int_e^a E \cdot dr \quad [31\text{-}8]$$

Each term on the right side of this equation can be given a simple interpretation. We use the relation between the line integral of a conservative electric field, between two points, and the corresponding potential difference between these points:

$$[28\text{-}11] \qquad \int_i^f E \cdot dr = -(V_f - V_i) = V_i - V_f = V_{if}$$

Note that $V_i - V_f = V_{if}$ is the potential *drop* from point i to point f. Equation 31-8 can then be written as

$$0 = V_{ab} + V_{bc} + V_{cd} + V_{de} + V_{ea} \qquad [31\text{-}9]$$

This relation says that the *total* potential drop around the circuit is *zero*. Of course, the potential drops V_{cd} and V_{ea} across the two batteries are *negative*; that is, the potential *rises* in going from the negative to the positive battery terminals. Equation 31-9 implies, then, that every potential rise is matched by a potential drop of equal magnitude as a closed loop around the circuit is completed.

Now consider how the conservation of energy principle applies to Figure 31-3. We simply match the total energy delivered *by* the energy sources with the total energy delivered *to* the circuit elements (here, resistors). The power delivered *by* the batteries is

$$\mathscr{E}_1 i + \mathscr{E}_2 i = i \sum \mathscr{E} \qquad [31\text{-}10]$$

Both terms on the left side are taken as positive, since the "directions" of $\mathscr{E}$ and i are the same for both batteries. The total power delivered *to* the circuit elements is

$$i V_{ab} + i V_{bc} + i V_{de} = i \sum V \qquad [31\text{-}11]$$

Note especially that we have included in $\sum V$ only the potential differences across circuit elements, *not* the potential differences of the batteries.

Equating Equations 31-10 and 31-11 we have

$$\sum \mathscr{E} = \sum V \qquad [31\text{-}12]$$

This is the fundamental relation for solving single-loop d-c circuits. One must be careful about signs in applying this relation. It must be emphasized that $\sum \mathscr{E}$ is the *algebraic* sum of the emf's in the circuit; that is, each emf is taken as positive if the battery is traversed from the negative to the positive terminal; on the other hand, the emf must be taken as negative if it is traversed in the other direction, see Figure 31-4a and b. Similarly, $\sum V$ is the *algebraic* sum of potential *drops* across circuit elements. Each V is taken

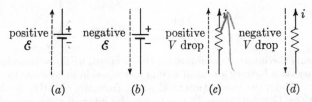

$$(a) \qquad (b) \qquad (c) \qquad (d)$$

Figure 31-4. Sign conventions for emf's and potential drops. The dotted arrows indicate the direction in which the circuit element is traversed. (a) The emf is taken as *positive* if the battery is traversed from the *negative to the positive terminal*. (b) The emf is *negative* if traversed from the *positive to the negative terminal*. (c) The potential *drop* is *positive* if the resistor is traversed in the *same* direction as the current. (d) The potential *drop* is negative if the resistor is traversed in the direction *opposite* to that of the current.

as positive if we traverse the circuit element from one potential to a lower potential *in* the direction of the conventional current; each V is taken as negative, if we traverse the circuit element in the direction opposite to that of the current; see Figure 31-4c and d. We *exclude* potential differences across battery terminals.

Example 1   Two batteries are connected in opposition, as shown in Figure 31-5; the emf's and internal resistances are 18.0 v and 2.0 ohms, 6.0 v and 1.0 ohms, respectively. (a) What is the current in the circuit? (b) What is the potential difference across the battery terminals? (c) At what rate does the discharging battery charge the charging battery? (d) At what rate is energy dissipated as heat in the 6.0 v battery?

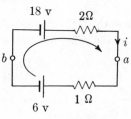

18 v   2Ω

b   a

6 v   1 Ω

Figure 31-5

(a) We decide to traverse the circuit of Figure 31-5 in the *clockwise* sense. Moreover, we take this clockwise sense as the direction of the current i, knowing that the current will, in fact, be clockwise, since its direction will be controlled by the emf of the larger, 18.0 v, battery. But it is *not* necessary to do so. We may choose the current direction arbitrarily and then, if it is not correct, the current will appear as *negative* in the solution; that is, the current will be shown actually to exist in the sense opposite to that chosen.

When the circuit traversal and current directions are taken as shown in Figure 31-5, we have

[31-12] $\Sigma \mathscr{E} = \Sigma V$

$$18 \text{ v} - 6 \text{ v} = 2i + 1i$$

Note that the emf of the 6 v battery must be assigned a minus sign, inasmuch as we pass through this battery from the positive to the negative terminal (see Figure 31-4). The potential drops across the two resistors, $2i$ and $1i$, are both positive, inasmuch we traverse each resistor in the same direction as the current. Solving for the current i in the relation above gives

$$i = \frac{12.0 \text{ v}}{3.0 \text{ ohms}} = 4.0 \text{ amp}$$

(b) Ignoring the internal resistance for the moment, we know that the potential difference across a battery's seat of emf is just equal in magnitude to the emf of the battery. Thus, the *rise* in potential going from the negative to the positive terminal of the 18 v battery is 18 v. Across the internal resistance of 2 ohms is a potential drop

$$V = iR = (4.0 \text{ amp})(2.0 \text{ ohms}) = 8.0 \text{ v}.$$

This 8 v potential difference occurs internally within the 18 v battery. Therefore, across the 18 v battery terminals is the potential difference 18.0 v − 8.0 v = 10.0 v. We can arrive at this result also by applying Equation 31-4:

[31-4] $V_{ab} = \mathscr{E} - ir = 18.0 \text{ v} - (4.0 \text{ amp})(2.0 \text{ ohms}) = 10.0 \text{ v}$

If a 10.0 v potential difference exists across the 18 v battery terminals, this same potential difference appears as well across the 6.0 v battery terminals. Let us confirm this result by using Equation 31-4:

$$V_{ab} = \mathscr{E} - ir = -6.0 \text{ v} - (4.0 \text{ amp})(1.0 \text{ ohms}) = -10.0 \text{ v}$$

Note that the emf was assigned a minus sign.

(c) The rate at which any source of emf delivers energy is given by $\mathscr{E}i$. If $\mathscr{E}i$ is positive—that is, if the emf and current are both in the same direction—chemical energy from the battery is delivered *to* other circuit elements. On the other hand, if $\mathscr{E}$ and i are of opposite sign, as is the case with the 6 v battery here, energy is delivered by other sources *to* it. Thus, the 18 v battery delivers energy (that is, loses chemical potential energy) at the rate

$$\mathscr{E}i = (18.0 \text{ v})(4.0 \text{ amp}) = 72 \text{ w}$$

The 6 v battery has energy delivered to it (that is, gains chemical potential energy) at the rate $\mathscr{E}i = (6.0 \text{ v})(4.0 \text{ amp}) = 24 \text{ w}$. The battery with the larger emf is being discharged at the rate of 72 w, while the smaller battery is being charged at the rate of 24 w. What happens to the difference, $72 \text{ w} - 24 \text{ w} = 48 \text{ w}$? It is dissipated in the two resistors.

(d) The rate at which energy is dissipated within the 6 v battery is

[30-14] $P = i^2R = (4.0 \text{ amp})^2(1.0 \text{ ohms}) = 16 \text{ w}$

and the rate at which thermal energy is developed within the 12 v battery is $P = i^2R = (4.0 \text{ amp})^2(2.0 \text{ ohms}) = 32 \text{ w}$. The total power dissipated in resistors, $16 \text{ w} + 32 \text{ w} = 48 \text{ w}$, is just the difference between the power delivered by the discharging battery (72 w) and the power delivered to the charging battery (24 w).

Example 2   An energy source, or generator, of emf $\mathscr{E}$ and having an internal or generator resistance R_G is connected to a load of resistance R_L. How are R_L and R_G related when the generator delivers maximum power to the load?

The circuit is that shown in Figure 31-2 with $r = R_G$ and $R = R_L$. The current in the circuit is

$$i = \mathscr{E}/(R_G + R_L)$$

Therefore, the power P_L delivered to the load is

$$P_L = i^2R_L = \frac{\mathscr{E}^2}{(R_G + R_L)^2} R_L$$

The generator delivers a maximum power to the load when

$$dP_L/dR_L = 0$$

$$\frac{dP_L}{dR_L} = \mathscr{E}^2\left[\frac{R_G - R_L}{(R_G + R_L)^3}\right] = 0$$

$$R_L = R_G$$

Thus, the generator delivers maximum power to the load when the generator and load resistances are the same. This is sometimes described by saying that the load is "matched" to the generator. Note that for maximum power transfer, the efficiency is only 50 per cent; half of the energy from the source is dissipated within the generator.

31-4   Resistors in series and in parallel   What is the equivalent resistance of resistors in series? By the equivalent resistance of a number of resistors in series, such as those shown in Figure 31-6, is meant the resistance of that single resistor which, when replacing the separate resistors, does *not* change the current drawn from the energy source.

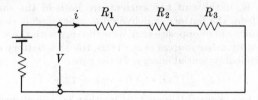

Figure 31-6. Resistors in series.

Clearly, the same current i passes through each resistor. Applying Equation 31-12 to the circuit we have

$$V = V_1 + V_2 + V_3$$
$$V = iR_1 + iR_2 + iR_3 = i(R_1 + R_2 + R_3) \qquad [31\text{-}13]$$

where V_1, V_2, and V_3 are the potential drops across resistors R_1, R_2, and R_3, respectively, and V is the potential drop across the battery terminals. The same current i will exist in the circuit when the single equivalent R replaces the group in series:

$$V = iR \qquad [31\text{-}14]$$

Comparing Equation 31-13 and 31-14 we have

$$\boxed{R = R_1 + R_2 + R_3}$$

The equivalent resistance is the sum of the separate resistances in series. The *same current* exists in each series resistor; the potential drop across the entire group is the same as that across the single equivalent resistance.

What is the equivalent resistance of resistors connected in parallel, as shown in Figure 31-7? We designate the potential drops across the resistors

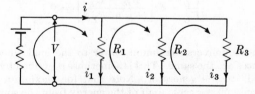

Figure 31-7. Resistors in parallel.

R_1, R_2, and R_3 as V_1, V_2, and V_3, respectively. The current through the battery is i, and the currents through the resistors are i_1, i_2, and i_3. Because we have more than one circuit loop in Figure 31-7, we do *not* have the same current in all circuit elements. In fact, the current i from the battery is divided into three currents through the resistors:

$$i = i_1 + i_2 + i_3$$
$$dQ/dt = dQ_1/dt + dQ_2/dt + dQ_3/dt \qquad \text{[31-15]}$$

This merely expresses the law of electric charge conservation; it implies that, since no charge accumulates at any point in the circuit, the charge dQ from the battery in time dt must appear as charges dQ_1, dQ_2, and dQ_3 through the resistors in the same time.

Now suppose that we apply Equation 31-12 in traversing the left-hand circuit loop of Figure 31-7:

[31-12] $$\Sigma \mathscr{E} = \Sigma V$$
$$V = V_1 = i_1 R_1$$

Applying the same relation to the second loop of Figure 31-7, we have

$$0 = -V_1 + V_2, \qquad \text{or} \quad V_1 = V_2$$

Note that we use a negative sign for the potential "drop" V_1, since we traverse this resistor in the opposite direction to that of the current i_1. In similar fashion we find that $V_2 = V_3$. In summary,

$$V = V_1 = V_2 = V_3 \qquad \text{[31-16]}$$

The potential difference is the *same* across each of the elements connected in parallel, and we designate this single potential drop by V.

From Ohm's law, we know that

$$V = i_1 R_1 = i_2 R_2 = i_3 R_3 \qquad \text{[31-17]}$$

Substituting Equations 31-17 in Equation 31-15 gives

$$i = \frac{V}{R_1} + \frac{V}{R_2} + \frac{V}{R_3} = V\left[\frac{1}{R_1} + \frac{1}{R_2} + \frac{1}{R_3}\right]$$

A single resistor R replacing the parallel resistors obeys the relation

$$i = \frac{V}{R}$$

Comparing the last two equations gives, finally,

$$\boxed{\frac{1}{R} = \frac{1}{R_1} + \frac{1}{R_2} + \frac{1}{R_3}}$$

The reciprocal of the equivalent resistance is equal to the sum of the reciprocals of the separate parallel resistances. The equivalent resistance is always less than the smallest of the parallel resistances. The essential feature of parallel connections is this: all elements have the *same potential difference*. Note also that, for any two resistors in parallel, the ratio of the currents is in the inverse ratio of the respective resistances, as Equation 31-17 shows. Thus, with 1.0-ohm and 3.0-ohm resistors in parallel, the 1.0-ohm resistor always has three times the current of the 3.0-ohm resistor, to insure that the potential difference across both is always the same.

Example 3 Consider the circuit of Figure 31-8. Find (a) the current in the battery, (b) the current in the 3.0-ohm resistor, (c) the potential difference across

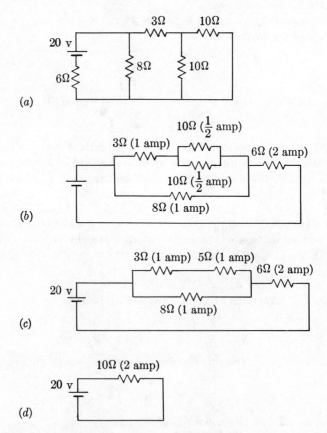

Figure 31-8. A circuit (a) and its evolution into progressively simpler equivalent forms: (b), (c), and (d). The currents in the various resistors (shown in parentheses) are found by starting with part (d) and working backward to (a).

the 6.0-ohm resistor, and (d) the rate at which thermal energy is dissipated in the 8.0-ohm resistor. Note that in Figure 31-8, the currents in parentheses are not given, but are calculated.

We first recognize that *any* of the questions that can be asked concerning a circuit like that in Figure 31-8a (potential differences, power dissipation, and the like) require that we first find the current through each resistor. Other quantities then can be easily computed. To find the current through each resistor we must first reduce the complex of resistors, through the rules for combining resistors in series and in parallel, until we are left with a single equivalent resistor connected across the battery.

Figure 31-8b, c, and d shows the evolution of the circuit, Figure 31-8a, into progressively simpler forms. (The numerical values of the resistances have been so chosen here that the computations can, without difficulty, be carried out in one's head.) We see that the current through the single equivalent resistor is 2 amp. Now we work backward, through Figure 31-8c, b, and a, in turn, to find the current in each resistor. Here we use the facts that the current through all series resistors is the same and that the potential difference across all parallel resistors is the same. Of course, as soon as we find the current through a given resistor, we can immediately compute the potential drop iR across it and the power $i^2R = iV$ dissipated in it. In this way we have, finally:

(a) current through battery = 2 amp,

(b) current through 3-ohm resistor = 1 amp,

(c) potential difference across 6-ohm resistor = 12 v,

(d) power dissipated in the 8-ohm resistor = 8 w.

31-5   Multiloop circuits

Some circuits involving more than one current loop, such as the one shown in Figure 31-8, can be solved simply by applying the rules for combining resistances in series and in parallel. In general, however, this is *not* possible. As an example, consider the relatively simple circuit shown in Figure 31-9. Here we have a circuit with *three* loops: a left inside loop, a right inside loop, and an outside loop going all the way around the circuit. There is no way to reduce this multiloop circuit into one involving a single battery and resistor.

A general method for solving multiloop circuit problems is to apply *Kirchhoff's rules*. These two rules are simply statements, in the language of electric circuits, of the fundamental *conservation laws of* (1) *electric charge*, and (2) *energy*.

(1) Consider a *junction*, a point in the circuit at which three or more conducting wires are joined together, as shown in Figure 31-10. The currents in the several wires are labelled i_1, i_2, i_3, and i_4, current i_1 being into the junction and the other currents being out of the junction. Now, according to the law of conservation of electric charge, no net charge can accumulate or be depleted at any point in the circuit, and certainly not at a junction. Therefore, the net charge flow per unit time into any junction must equal the net charge flow per unit time out of the junction. That is,

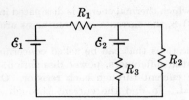

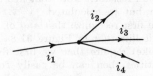

Figure 31-9. A simple multiloop circuit.

Figure 31-10. A circuit junction. The total current *into* the junction is zero.

the net current into the junction equals the net current out of the junction. For the situation shown in Figure 31-10 this implies that

$$i_1 = i_2 + i_3 + i_4, \quad \text{or} \quad i_1 - i_2 - i_3 - i_4 = 0$$

We may interpret the negative terms appearing in the second relation above as representing *negative* currents *into* the junction, which are, of course, equivalent to positive currents *out* of the junction. A general formulation of the junction requirement for currents is, then,

$$\boxed{\Sigma\, i = 0} \tag{31-18}$$

where it is understood that currents into and out of a junction are identified, respectively, as positive and negative currents. Equation 31-18 is the *junction theorem*, the first Kirchhoff rule.

    (2) Recall the general relation which we derived earlier for a single-loop circuit:

[31-12] $$\boxed{\Sigma\, \mathscr{E} = \Sigma\, V}$$ [31-19]

The algebraic sum of the emf's around a loop $\Sigma\, \mathscr{E}$ equals the algebraic sum of the potential drops $\Sigma\, V$ (*including* the potential drops across battery internal resistors) around the loop (we *exclude*, however, the potential differences appearing across a seat of emf). Equation 31-19 is merely an expression of the conservation of energy law: the left-hand side represents the energy per unit charge supplied by energy sources in the circuit loop, and the right-hand side represents the energy per unit charge delivered to circuit elements around the loop. Kirchhoff applied Equation 31-19 to any closed electric circuit loop; thus, this equation is known as the *loop equation*, or *Kirchhoff's second rule*. When we multiply the two sides of Equation 31-19 by the current we can interpret the left-side terms as representing the power delivered by energy sources in the circuit loop and the right-hand terms as representing the power delivered to circuit elements.

We remind the reader of certain conventions that must be adhered to faithfully in applying Equations 31-18 and 31-19. (a) Having decided, quite arbitrarily, on the sense in which a particular loop will be traversed (clockwise or counterclockwise), we must never reverse this sense through any circuit element around the loop. (b) We choose any unknown current direction arbitrarily, but we must observe the sign convention denoting currents into or out of a junction in using Equation 31-18. (c) As Figure 31-4 shows, we take the emf of a battery as *positive* when it is traversed from the *negative to the positive* terminal (and conversely), and we take a potential *drop* $V = iR$ across a resistor as *positive* when the resistor is traversed in the *same* direction *as* that of *current* flow (and conversely).

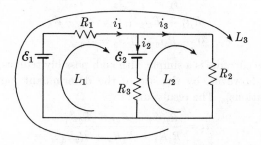

Figure 31-11. Three circuit loops (L_1, L_2, and L_3) for applying Kirchhoff's rules.

Let us see how these rules apply to the circuit of Figure 31-9, which is shown again in Figure 31-11. The currents in the three *branches*, i_1, i_2, and i_3, are assigned directions quite arbitrarily. These currents must be regarded as the unknowns to be solved for. From Equation 31-18 we have

$$i_1 - i_2 - i_3 = 0 \qquad [31\text{-}20]$$

Applying Equation 31-19 to the left loop, L_1, which we decide is to be traversed in the clockwise sense, we obtain

$$-\mathcal{E}_2 + \mathcal{E}_1 = i_2 R_3 + i_1 R_1 \qquad [31\text{-}21]$$

(when this loop is traversed in the counterclockwise sense, we find the signs reversed for all terms in the equation above).

Applied to the loop L_2, Equation 31-19 yields

$$\mathcal{E}_2 = i_3 R_2 - i_2 R_3 \qquad [31\text{-}22]$$

The reader should check the last two equations very carefully to see that he agrees with the signs given to the several terms.

Thus far we have three equations, Equations 31-20, 31-21, and 31-22, and three unknowns, the three currents. The problem is solved in principle, but we have not used the third loop, L_3, which yields

$$\mathscr{E}_1 = i_3 R_2 + i_1 R_1 \qquad [31\text{-}23]$$

We can see that Equation 31-23 is not actually necessary (given the three other equations) by adding Equations 31-21 and 31-22. Their sum is, in fact, just Equation 31-23. Redundancies of this sort may appear in applying Kirchhoff's rules.

It is useful in solving linear equations to organize the several terms as follows:

[31-20] $$i_1 - i_2 - i_3 = 0$$
[31-21] $$R_1 i_1 + R_3 i_2 + 0 = \mathscr{E}_1 - \mathscr{E}_2$$
[31-22] $$0 - R_3 i_2 + R_2 i_3 = \mathscr{E}_2$$

Solving for the currents is a simple, although possibly tedious, matter (which is facilitated, however, by the use of the determinant method for linear algebraic equations). The results are:

$$i_1 = \frac{R_2(\mathscr{E}_1 - \mathscr{E}_2) + R_3 \mathscr{E}_1}{R_1 R_2 + R_1 R_3 + R_2 R_3} \qquad [31\text{-}24a]$$

$$i_2 = \frac{R_2(\mathscr{E}_1 - \mathscr{E}_2) - R_1 \mathscr{E}_2}{R_1 R_2 + R_1 R_3 + R_2 R_3} \qquad [31\text{-}24b]$$

$$i_3 = \frac{R_3(\mathscr{E}_1 - \mathscr{E}_2) + (R_1 + R_3)\mathscr{E}_2}{R_1 R_2 + R_1 R_3 + R_2 R_3} \qquad [31\text{-}24c]$$

Equation 31-24a shows that the current i_1 *is* in the direction shown in Figure 31-11, that is, $i_1 > 0$, provided that $\mathscr{E}_1 > \mathscr{E}_2$; if $\mathscr{E}_1 < \mathscr{E}_2$, then $i_1 < 0$, and the actual direction of current i_1 is opposite to that chosen in the figure.

Solving any multiloop circuit, however complicated, is simply a matter of applying Kirchhoff's rules and solving a number of simultaneous linear equations. One can work this in reverse, using electric circuits to solve linear equations. One arranges the emf's and resistances in a circuit to correspond to the parameters of the linear equations; solving for the unknowns consists merely of measuring the currents in the various branches of the circuit. This is one simple example of an *analog computer* in which one studies the physical behavior of a system obeying a well-known mathematical relationship, to solve for mathematical unknowns.

31-6 D-c circuit instruments Here we consider the essential features of four commonly used instruments in d-c circuits: the ammeter, used for measuring electric current, the voltmeter, used for measuring electric potential difference, the Wheatstone bridge, used for comparing resistances, and the potentiometer, used for comparing emf's.

AMMETER AND VOLTMETER Before speaking of any construction details of an ammeter or voltmeter it is important that we be clear on how these instruments are used to measure current and potential difference. Figure 31-12a shows a simple circuit of a battery and resistor with a current i. When an ammeter (symbolized by $-\text{(A)}-$) is introduced in series with the resistor, to measure the current, as in Figure 31-12b, it changes the circuit so that the measured current i' is less than i, the original current. If the resistance R_a of the ammeter is much less than R, then $i' \simeq i$. In Figure 31-12c a voltmeter (symbolized by $-\text{(V)}-$) is connected in parallel across the resistor. Again the circuit is changed. The current i'' through the battery is now greater than i. Only if the voltmeter resistance is large compared with R will $i'' \simeq i$.

Ideally, no current or potential differences are altered by the addition of ammeters or voltmeters in a circuit; an ammeter has such a low resistance that the potential difference across it usually is negligible, and a voltmeter has such a high

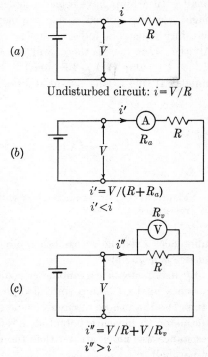

Undisturbed circuit: $i = V/R$

$i' = V/(R + R_a)$
$i' < i$

$i'' = V/R + V/R_v$
$i'' > i$

Figure 31-12. A circuit (a) undisturbed, (b) with an ammeter in series with the resistor, and (c) with a voltmeter in parallel with the resistor.

resistance that the current through it usually is negligible. Actually, any measuring instrument, electrical or otherwise, interferes with the quantity to be measured to some degree. In designing ammeters and voltmeters one wishes to minimize these perturbing effects, or at least to be aware of the amount of the disturbances caused by the instruments.

Both ammeters and voltmeters of the common variety employ a needle whose angular position registers the current or potential difference. The needle is attached to a coil through which current passes, and this coil is immersed in the magnetic field of a permanent magnet. Such a device is known as a *galvanometer*; it is an instrument whose details we shall discuss in Section 32-7. Suffice it to say here that a galvanometer (symbolized by –Ⓖ–) is capable of registering extremely small currents. For example, a galvanometer showing full-scale deflection for a current of 1.0×10^{-6} amp = 1.0 μamp and having a resistance of 1000 ohms might be typical (very much more sensitive galavanometers, giving full-scale deflection for currents as small as 10^{-12} amp, have been constructed). Now, such a galvanometer, which might also be termed a microammeter, when placed into a circuit will certainly register a full-scale deflection when 1.0 μamp passes through it. At the same time, there will exist a potential difference $V = iR = (1.0 \times 10^{-6}$ amp$)(1.0 \times 10^3$ ohms$) = 1.0 \times 10^{-3}$ v = 1.0 mv across its terminals. If this 1.0 mv potential difference is small compared with potential

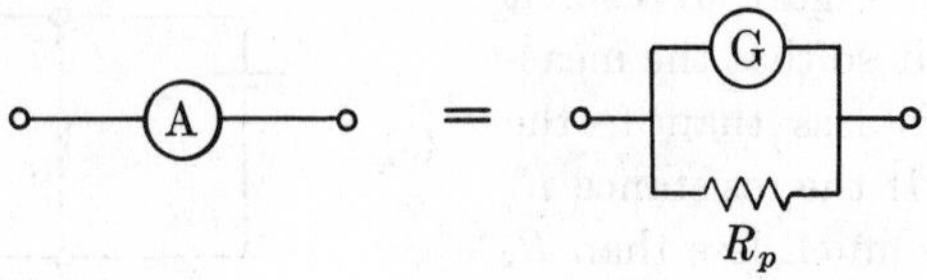

Figure 31-13. An ammeter is a galvanometer in parallel with a small resistance.

differences existing across other circuit elements, the galvanometer's influence is negligible.

By itself, such a galvanometer could be used as an ammeter to measure currents up to 1 μamp (provided that the galvanometer's resistance was much less than those of circuit elements with which it was in series), or as a voltmeter to measure potential differences up to 1 mv (provided that its resistance was much greater than those of circuit elements with which it was in parallel).

Suppose, however, that one wishes to construct an ammeter which registers 1.0 amp full-scale, using this galvanometer. Then one places a very small resistance R_p in parallel with the galvanometer, as shown in Figure 31-13; said differently, one "shunts" the galvanometer with a small resistance R_p. What is the required shunt resistance? We can asume that essentially all of the current, 1.0 amp, through the ammeter will pass through the shunt resistance R_p, since only 1.0 μamp is permitted through the galvanometer itself. Moreover, the potential differences across the galvanometer and its shunt must both be 1.0 mv at full-scale deflection. It follows that $R_p = V/i = (1.0 \times 10^{-3}$ v$)/(1.0$ amp$) = 1.0 \times 10^{-3}$ ohm.

The galvanometer, with $R = 1000$ ohms and full-scale deflection for 1.0 μamp, or for 1.0 mv across its terminals, is, in effect, a voltmeter registering 1.0 mv full scale. Suppose, now, that we wish to use this same galvanometer to construct a voltmeter registering 10 v full scale. We construct a voltmeter from a galvanometer by placing a high resistance R_s in series with it, as shown in Figure 31-14. Since the galvanometer alone can have a potential difference of only 1.0×10^{-3} v across its terminals, the potential difference V across the resistor R_s must be essentially 10 v, while the current i through it is 1.0×10^{-6} amp. Therefore, $R_s = V/i =$ (10 v)/(1.0 × 10^{-6} amp) = 1.0×10^7 ohms = 10 Mohms. Such a voltmeter has so large an internal resistance that it produces little perturbation of a circuit unless used across circuit elements whose resistance becomes comparable to 10 Mohms.

It is easy to construct multirange ammeters (or voltmeters) by having several shunt (series) resistors in the meter. Problems 31-17 and 31-19 illustrate multirange meters.

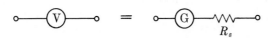

Figure 31-14. A voltmeter is a galvanometer in series with a large resistance.

A simple way of measuring resistance is shown in Figure 31-15a: one measures the current i through the device with an ammeter and the potential difference V across it with a voltmeter, and then applies Ohm's law, $R = V/i$. Strictly, however, the current measurement is not altogether correct, inasmuch as the ammeter of Figure 31-15a registers the current through both the resistor *and* the voltmeter. One might correct this by placing the ammeter inside the connections to the voltmeter, as in Figure 31-15b. Then the ammeter reads the current through R alone, but now the voltmeter reads the potential difference, not across R alone, but across the resistance *and* ammeter.

WHEATSTONE'S BRIDGE   These difficulties are eliminated when one measures a resistance or, more properly, compares a resistance with a known standard resistance R_s, using the bridge circuit devised by C. Wheatstone (1802–1875); see Figure 31-16. The bridge, in its simplest form, consists of four resistors, a battery, and a sensitive galvanometer. R_1, R_2, and R_s are all known; R_x is the unknown resistance. Like the ordinary beam balance, which indicates equal masses on its two pans when the needle shows no deflection from the vertical, the Wheatstone bridge is a *null instrument*. With a given unknown resistance R_x, the resistors R_1, R_2, and R_s are so adjusted that the galvanometer registers no current. Then points b and c are at the same potential. The current i_1 through resistor R_1 is the same as the current through R_2; likewise, R_x and R_s carry the current i_2. The

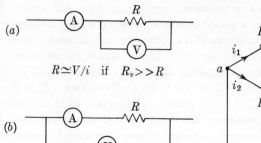

$$R \simeq V/i \quad \text{if} \quad R_v >> R$$

$$R \simeq V/i \quad \text{if} \quad R_a << R$$

Figure 31-15. Two arrangements for measuring the resistance R with an ammeter and voltmeter: (a) voltmeter across R; (b) ammeter in series with R.

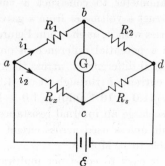

Figure 31-16. A Wheatstone bridge circuit.

potential differences V_{ab} and V_{ac} are alike, as are V_{bd} and V_{cd}. It follows that

$$V_{ab} = i_1 R_1 = V_{ac} = i_2 R_x$$
$$V_{bd} = i_1 R_2 = V_{cd} = i_2 R_s$$

Eliminating i_1 and i_2 from these relations yields

$$R_x/R_s = R_1/R_2 \qquad \text{[31-25]}$$

When the bridge has been balanced, one finds the unknown resistance R_x in terms of the standard resistance R_s and the ratio R_1/R_2, using Equation 31-25.

POTENTIOMETER   Suppose one is to measure the emf of a battery. The *approximate* emf is registered by a voltmeter placed across the battery terminals. Such a voltmeter reading V is always somewhat less than the true emf, since the potential difference appearing across a battery's terminals is the emf $\mathcal{E}$ *less* the potential drop ir across the battery's internal resistance r:

$$[31\text{-}4] \qquad V = \mathcal{E} - ir$$

Since all batteries have some internal resistance, the emf $\mathcal{E}$ and potential difference V are the same only if *no* current passes through the battery.

The potentiometer circuit permits the emf of a battery to be measured under the condition in which the battery current is actually zero. Strictly, the potentiometer permits an unknown emf $\mathcal{E}_x$ to be compared with the precisely known emf $\mathcal{E}_s$ of a *standard cell* by a *null* method. The circuit is shown in Figure 31-17. A so-called "*working battery*" with emf $\mathcal{E}_w$, which need *not* be known, maintains a *constant* current i through the resistor. The adjustable tap at the resistor is set so that the current through the sensitive galvanometer is zero. Then the potential drop across the galvanometer is zero, as is also the potential drop across the internal resistance of the unknown battery. Thus, the total potential drop across the branch in the circuit containing the unknown battery is equal to the battery's emf $\mathscr{E}_x$. But this is also the potential drop iR_x across the resistor from the tap to the right end. Therefore, $\mathscr{E}_x = iR_x$.

Now, if the unknown battery is replaced by the standard cell and the resistor tap is again adjusted for balance (zero galvanometer current), we

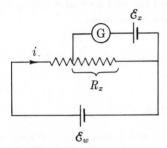

Figure 31-17. A potentiometer circuit for comparing emf's.

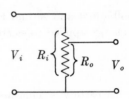

Figure 31-18. A "potentiometer" used as a voltage divider.,

have $\mathscr{E}_s = iR_s$, where R_s is the corresponding resistance from the tap to the end of the resistor. Eliminating i from these relations yields

$$\mathscr{E}_x/\mathscr{E}_s = R_x/R_s \qquad [31\text{-}26]$$

From Equation 31-26 we see that comparing emf's with a potentiometer circuit consists of comparing resistances (or, if the adjustable resistor is a wire of uniform cross section, of comparing lengths).

The term *potentiometer* is used in another sense in electric circuits; that of a *voltage divider*; see Figure 31-18. An input voltage V_i is applied across a variable resistor of total resistance R_i with a center tap. The output voltage is V_o, and R_o represents the resistance between the tap and the lower end of the resistor. Clearly, $V_o/V_i = R_o/R_i$.

31-7 Summary The emf $\mathscr{E}$ of an energy source is defined as the work done per unit positive charge by the nonconservative forces in the circuit. In formal terms:

[31-7] $$\mathscr{E} = \oint \mathbf{E}_s \cdot d\mathbf{r}$$

where E_s is the nonconservative electric force associated with the energy source, and the line integral is taken around the circuit loop.

The equivalent resistance R of resistors connected in series is given by $R = \Sigma\, R_i$. The equivalent resistance for resistors connected in parallel is $1/R = \Sigma\, 1/R_i$. All series resistors have the same current; all parallel resistors have the same potential difference.

One solves for the current in any branch of a multiloop circuit by applying Kirchhoff's rules. (1) The junction theorem: the total current into any junction is zero:

[31-18] $$\Sigma\, i = 0$$

(2) The loop theorem: the algebraic sum of the emf's around a loop equals the algebraic sum of the potential drops across resistors:

[31-19] $$\Sigma\, \mathscr{E} = \Sigma\, V$$

Kirchhoff's first and second rules are the conservation principles of charge and of energy applied to electric circuits.

PROBLEMS

31-1   A battery is connected to a resistor, and a current of 0.60 amp exists in the circuit. When an additional 4.0-ohm resistor is added to the circuit in series, the current drops to 0.50 amp. What is the emf of the battery?

31-2   When two identical 6.0 v batteries are connected together in series with one another and also with an external load of 4.0 ohms, the current is either 2.0 amp or 0 amp, depending upon whether the emf's of the batteries are in the same or in opposite directions. Find the internal resistance of one battery.

31-3   Two batteries of different emf's and internal resistances are connected in series with one another and with an external load resistor. The current is 3.0 amp. Then the polarity of one battery is reversed. The current is then 1.0 amp. What is the ratio of the emf's of the two batteries?

31-4   A 12 v battery has a potential difference of 10 v across its terminals when it is connected to a resistor of 4.0 ohms. (a) What resistance should be placed across the battery to run down the battery in the shortest possible time? (Assume, for simplicity, that the battery's internal resistance is unchanged, although, of course, the discharge of any battery is characterized by the fact that its internal resistance becomes infinite.) (b) What external resistance will give the maximum external power?

31-5   An electric generator dissipates energy internally at the rate of 20 w when the difference in potential across its output terminals is 120 v and it has a current of 2.0 amp through it. What is the generator's emf?

31-6 A changing magnetic field in the region of a single conducting loop of wire produces an emf in the wire. The current induced is 3.0 mamp. It is found that energy is dissipated into thermal energy in the wire at the rate of 30 mw. What is the magnitude of the emf induced by the changing magnetic field?

31-7 See Figure 31-19. (a) What is the potential difference across the 4.0-ohm resistor? (b) What is the current in the 8.0-ohm resistor?

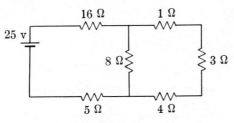

Figure 31-19

(c) At what rate is energy dissipated in the 16.0-ohm resistor? (Try to do this problem in your head.)

31-8 What single resistor placed between points a and b in Figure 31-20 will draw the same current as this combination?

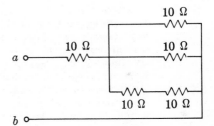

Figure 31-20

31-9 Twelve 1-ohm resistors are aligned along the edges of a cube and connected together at the corners. What is the equivalent resistance measured between two diagonally opposite corners of the cube? (*Hint:* Use the symmetry of the arrangement to find how the current divides at the junctions.)

31-10 Six 1-ohm resistors are aligned along the edges of a tetrahedron and connected together at the corners. What is the equivalent resistance measured between any two corners?

31-11 An unlimited number of 10-ohm resistors rated 1 w are available. How would one construct an equivalent resistance of 10 ohms with a power rating of at least 5 w from such resistors, using the smallest number?

31-12 Given an unlimited number of resistors rated 100 ohms and 10 w, how does one construct an equivalent resistor of 200 ohms and a power rating of at least 40 w, using the minimum number of resistors?

31-13

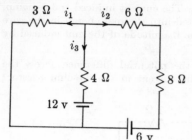

Find the currents i_1, i_2, and i_3 for the circuit of Figure 31-21.

Figure 31-21

31-14   Using Equations 31-24, (a) show that the current through the resistor R_2 in Figure 31-11 is always positive, (b) find under what conditions the current i_2 will be zero, (c) find under what conditions the current i_1 will be $-i_2$ when $\mathscr{E}_1 = 2\mathscr{E}_2$.

31-15   Use the determinant method to solve for the currents in Equations 31-20, 31-21, and 31-22, and show that they are given by Equations 31-24.

31-16   An alternative method to Kirchhoff's rules for solving for the currents in a multiloop network is the *principle of superposition*. One imagines all batteries save one to be shorted out; then one computes the current in each resistor. One does the same again with all batteries shorted save another one; again one finds the current in each resistor under these conditions. Continuing this process until the currents contributed by all batteries has been found, one then simply superposes, or adds, the currents in each resistor, with proper regard for relative direction, to find the actual current with all batteries in the circuit.

     Solve for the current in resistors R_1, R_2, and R_3 in the circuit of Figure 31-9 by the principle of superposition and compare your results with those found by the use of Kirchhoff's rules (Equations 31-24a, b, c).

31-17   On its most sensitive scale a multirange ammeter has full-scale deflection of 0.10 amp and an internal resistance of 2.0 ohms. What is the required shunt resistance when the ammeter is set to read (a) 1.0 amp full scale and (b) 10.0 amp full scale?

31-18   Sensitive galvanometers can measure currents of the order 10^{-12} amp. (a) How many electrons per second does this represent? (b) If this current passes through a wire of 0.050 mm diameter, how many electrons per second pass through an atom (radius, 1.0 Å) within the wire?

31-19   The internal wiring of a multirange voltmeter is shown in Figure 31-22. The galvanometer alone gives full-scale deflection when a current of 1.0 mamp exists in it. The galvanometer's resistance is 1000 ohms. Find the values of the resistors (a) R_a, (b) R_b, and (c) R_c.

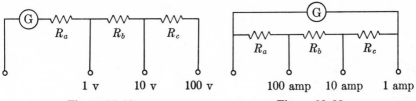

Figure 31-22   Figure 31-23

31-20 The internal wiring of a multirange ammeter is shown in Figure 31-23. When each of the three terminals is used, the full-scale reading of the ammeter is 1.0 amp, 10 amp, or 100 amp. The galvanometer gives full-scale deflection when a current of 1.0 mamp exists in it; its resistance is 1000 ohms. Find the values of the resistors (a) R_a, (b) R_b, and (c) R_c.

31-21 ★ (a) Find the current through the galvanometer (resistance R_G) in a Wheatstone bridge circuit (Figure 31-16) when the galvanometer current is *not* zero. (b) Show that the galvanometer achieves maximum sensitivity (the galvanometer current shows the greatest change in current) with the resistors so adjusted initially that $R_1 \approx R_2$ and $R_s \simeq R_x$.

31-22 An ammeter having a resistance of 0.10 ohm and a voltmeter having an internal resistance of 10,000 ohms are to be used in combination to measure an unknown resistance R. For what values of R will the resistance be given as V/i to within 1 per cent, irrespective of the order of connection of the ammeter and voltmeter to the resistance R (Figure 31-15)?

31-23 ★ An ammeter has a resistance of 0.20 ohm and reads 10 amp at full scale. A voltmeter has a resistance of 10,000 ohms and reads 500 v at full scale. These two instruments are used to measure the current and voltage of a 50-ohm resistor in series with a steady 250 v battery. To within two significant figures, calculate (a) the reading of the ammeter when it is inserted into the circuit in series with the resistor, (b) the reading of the voltmeter when inserted in series with the resistor, (c) the reading of the ammeter when inserted in parallel with the resistor, and (d) the reading of the voltmeter when inserted in parallel with the resistor. (e) Which instrument would be damaged when improperly connected?

31-24 ★ The circuit for the potentiometer (Figure 31-17) is basically the same as the multiloop circuit of Figure 31-11. Derive Equation 31-26 for the potentiometer from Equation 31-24.

THIRTY - TWO

27 pp

THE MAGNETIC FORCE

The most obvious statement one might make concerning magnetism, that it has to do primarily with the behavior of magnets and of magnetic materials, is, from the point of view of fundamental physics, actually misleading. To be sure, magnets are one important aspect of magnetism, but the *fundamental* magnetic effect is this: an electric charge in motion may produce a force on a second moving electric charge in addition to the Coulomb (electric) force. This velocity-dependent force between charges is the *magnetic force*.

Just as the electric force between charged particles may be thought to act via the electric field—charge q_a creates the electric field E at the site of charge q_b, and q_b, finding itself in this field, is acted upon by an electric force—so too the magnetic interaction between charged particles may be described as taking place via a magnetic field. In this view, moving charge q_a creates a *magnetic field* B at the site of moving charge q_b, and q_b, finding itself in this field, is acted upon by the so-called magnetic force. The magnetic force is more complicated than the electric force in that it depends on the velocities of the two interacting charges as well as the amount of the charges and separation distance. For this reason it is useful to discuss the magnetic interaction in two parts, (a) the creation of the magnetic field by one moving charge and (b) the effect of the magnetic field on a second moving charge. This chapter will deal with the second part.

We first consider the motion of a charged particle in a magnetic field and find the characteristics of the magnetic force. We are thereby led to the definition of the magnetic field. Then we treat the motion in general of a charged particle in a uniform magnetic field and find the cyclotron frequency. We consider as well the motion of a charge in an additional electric field. It is then an easy matter for us to devise arrangements of electric and magnetic fields for measuring the speed, mass, momentum, and kinetic energy of a charged particle. We discuss the principles of cyclotron operation. We find the expressions for the magnetic force on a current-carrying conductor and the magnetic torque on a current loop. The magnetic dipole moment is defined. Finally, we treat briefly the Hall effect.

32-I   Magnetic induction field defined   The term magnetic field immediately conjures up in the imagination pictures of one magnet attracting or repelling a second magnet or causing the alignment of iron filings or compasses. Now, this conception of the magnetic field, although familiar and indeed correct, is not fundamental. To define properly the magnetic field one must first investigate the motion of charged particles in the field, established, for example, by permanent magnets or, as we shall see, by electric currents. How the magnetic field is produced is not our concern here; this will be discussed in Chapter 33. We shall merely assume that a constant magnetic field can be maintained in a region where we place a beam of moving charged particles, the test object for exploring the nature of the magnetic force. We further assume that no electric force acts on the particles; the gravitational force is, of course, negligible.

We may explore the properties of the magnetic force and therefore, also, the magnetic field, by directing a beam of charged particles into a region where a magnetic field exists. One might, for example, use a small oscilloscope, in which a beam of electrons falls on a phosphorescent screen and produces a bright spot at its center (one might also have available a beam of positively charged particles). We assume that the speed of the particles is known and can be varied. We deduce the magnetic force acting on the charged particles by investigating their paths.

The experimental facts are these:

(a) Whenever the magnetic force F_m acts, it is always perpendicular to the particle's velocity v:

$$F_m \perp v$$

(b) The magnetic force is proportional to the particle's charge q, both in magnitude and sign:

$$F_m \propto q$$

If one replaces negative charges by positive charges moving in the same direction, the direction of F_m is reversed.

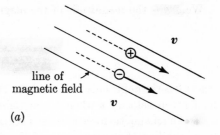

line of magnetic field

(a)

(c) The magnitude of the force is proportional to the magnitude of the particle's velocity

$$F_m \propto v$$

Here we assume that the speed is varied while the direction of v is unchanged.

(d) There exists one particular orientation of the velocity v for which the force F_m is zero; see Figure 32-1a. That is, there is a particular line in space along which charged particles can move without experiencing a magnetic force. The line of the magnetic field is, *by definition*, this line.† There remains the matter of assigning a *direction* to the magnetic field B.

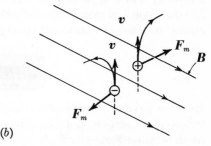

(b)

Figure 32-1. (a) When a charged particle moves through a magnetic field and is *not* subject to a magnetic force, the line of its velocity is, by definition, the line of the magnetic field. (b) When a charged particle moves at right angles to a magnetic field, it is deflected by a magnetic force at right angles to both v and B.

$$F_m = 0, \quad \text{when} \quad v \parallel B$$

(e) The magnitude of F_m is directly proportional, for all directions of the velocity v, to the component $v_\perp = v \sin \theta$ of the velocity at right angles to the line of the magnetic field:

$$F_m \propto v_\perp = v \sin \theta \qquad \text{[32-1]}$$

Thus, the force is zero when $\theta = 0$, the vectors v and B then being parallel (or antiparallel). When $\theta = 90°$ and the particles move at right angles to the magnetic field, the magnetic force is a maximum. In all other orientations it is only the perpendicular *component* of v relative to the line corresponding to zero magnetic force which determines the magnitude of F_m. See Figure 32-1b.

† It should be no secret that the direction of a magnetic field so defined is, in fact, also the line along which a small compass, or permanent magnet, will align itself.

We *define* the magnitude of the magnetic field **B** through the relation

$$B = \frac{F_m}{qv_\perp} = \frac{F_m}{qv \sin \theta} \qquad [32\text{-}2]$$

where θ is the angle between **v** and **B**. Thus, the magnetic force is a maximum for a given velocity **v** when **v** is at right angles to **B**.

(f) The magnetic force is always at right angles to the plane containing two lines, the line of the velocity and the line of the magnetic field (that is, the line along which a particle travels when no magnetic force is acting on it). The direction and magnitude of F_m observed in experiment are then correctly related to those of **v** and of **B** through the vector relation

$$\boxed{F_m = qv \times B} \qquad [32\text{-}3]$$

Here we have arbitrarily *chosen* a direction for the magnetic field through this vector relation and the convention of the *right*-hand rule for cross products; see Figure 32-2.

The electric force and the electric field *differ greatly* from the magnetic force and the magnetic field: The electric force acts whatever the state of motion of the charged particle, and the direction of the electric force on a positive charge is the *same* as the direction of the electric field. The magnetic force, on the other hand, depends on the charge's motion, and the magnetic field produces *no* magnetic force on a charge traveling along the line of the magnetic field in either sense.

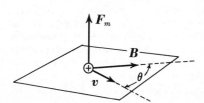

Figure 32-2. The magnetic force F_m is perpendicular to the plane of **v** and **B**.

Equation 32-3 implies that the magnetic field **B** is a vector. Certainly, **B** has magnitude, and we have now established a convention for its direction. But a true vector is not merely a quantity to which we can assign direction as well as magnitude; a vector is, by definition, a directed quantity which obeys the rules of vector addition found to hold for displacement vectors (Section 3-2). It is enough to say here that the magnetic field is indeed a vector in the following sense: two or more magnetic fields acting simultaneously on a charged particle produce a magnetic force, given by Equation 32-3, if by **B** is meant the *vector sum* of the separate fields. This is a result of experiment. (See, however, Section 43-4 on pseudovectors, of which the magnetic field is one example.)

We see from Equation 32-2 that appropriate units for the magnetic induction field are newtons per ampere-meter (nt/amp-m), as follows:

$$\text{nt/coul-(m/sec)} = \text{nt/(coul/sec)-m} = \text{nt/amp-m}$$

Thus, a charge of one coulomb moving at one meter per second at right angles to a magnetic field of one newton per ampere-meter is subject to a magnetic force of one newton.

In the mksa system of units the magnetic field is also assigned units of webers per square meter where, by definition,

$$1 \text{ weber/m}^2 = 1 \text{ nt/amp-m}$$

A magnetic field of one weber per square meter is, by laboratory standards, a field of relatively large magnitude. It is therefore often useful to specify magnetic fields in units of the *gauss*, where

$$1 \text{ weber/m}^2 = 10^4 \text{ gauss}$$

The gauss is, in fact, the unit for magnetic field in the cgs Gaussian system of units; see Appendix III. The magnetic field of the Earth is about 0.5 gauss. A typical small permanent magnet might produce a field of 100 gauss. Large electromagnets can produce magnetic fields up to 20,000 gauss, or 2 weber/m². Still larger magnetic fields are produced only by rather special procedures.

The quantity we have been calling simply the magnetic field is more properly referred to as the *magnetic induction field*, or the *magnetic induction*. It is also termed, for reasons soon to be evident, the *magnetic flux density*. All three terms denote the field vector here designated *B*. They must be distinguished from the so-called *magnetic field intensity*, a field vector symbolized by *H*, having a different physical significance from *B* and different units from *B* but, nevertheless, sometimes referred to also as the "magnetic field" (see Section 36-2). When we speak of "the magnetic field" we shall mean the vector *B*, not *H*, unless noted specifically otherwise. We thereby avoid a more cumbersome nomenclature.

32-2 Magnetic flux Just as one may represent an electric field by electric lines of force whose direction and density give the direction and magnitude of the electric field, so too one may represent the direction and magnitude of a magnetic field *B* by magnetic field lines. One should speak of magnetic *field* lines rather than magnetic lines *of force*, since it is only for charged-particle velocities along (or against) such lines that there is *no* magnetic force. The magnetic field is strong where the magnetic lines are crowded and weak where they are far apart. A constant, or uniform, magnetic field is represented by uniformly spaced parallel straight lines.

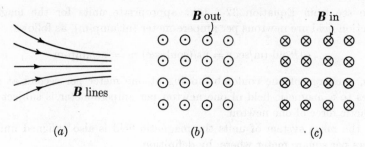

(a) (b) (c)

Figure 32-3. (a) Magnetic field lines. Field lines (b) out of the paper and (c) into the paper.

We shall have occasion to portray magnetic field lines going into or out of the plane of the paper. In such cases we use the symbol ⊙ to show a magnetic field *out* of the paper and the symbol ⊗ to show a magnetic field *into* the paper; see Figure 32-3. These symbols remind us, respectively, of an arrow point emerging from the paper, and the feathers on the tail of an arrow going into the paper.

The electric flux $d\phi_E$ over the surface element dS was defined as

[27-1] $d\phi_E = E \cdot dS$

Similarly, we define the *magnetic flux* $d\phi_B$ through the surface element dS, where the magnetic field has the value B, as

$$d\phi_B = B \cdot dS = (B \cos \theta)\, dS$$

That is, we take the component $B \cos \theta$ of the magnetic field lying along the normal to the surface in computing the flux through this surface element; see Figure 32-4.

The total magnetic flux ϕ_B through a finite surface area is then given by

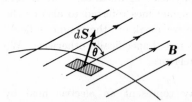

$$\phi_B = \int B \cdot dS \qquad [32\text{-}4]$$

Figure 32-4. Magnetic flux through a surface element dS.

where the integration is carried out over the surface area through which we wish to find the total magnetic flux.

For the special case in which a magnetic field B is uniform over a flat area A oriented at right angles to the magnetic field lines, Equation 32-4 becomes

$$\phi_B = BA \qquad [32\text{-}5]$$

$$B = \phi_B/A$$

The magnetic field B is, from Equation 32-5, the magnetic flux density, that is, the magnetic flux divided by the transverse area through which it penetrates. Thus, B can be thought of as the number of magnetic lines per unit transverse area. We may imagine the number of magnetic field lines per unit transverse area as corresponding to the numerical value of B. In the mksa system the unit for magnetic flux, which is a measure of the *total* number of the magnetic lines crossing a chosen transverse area, is the *weber*. Clearly, then, the corresponding unit for magnetic field B (magnetic flux density) is the weber/m².

Example 1   The cosmic radiation consists of highly energetic, positively charged particles (mostly protons) which rain upon the Earth in all directions from outer space. How does the magnetic field of the Earth affect protons approaching it (a) toward the North or South Poles and (b) at the Equator?

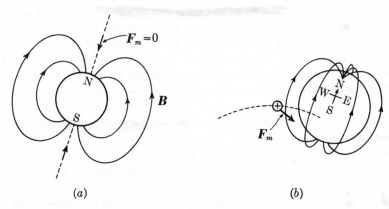

(a)   (b)

Figure 32-5. (a) Magnetic field of the Earth; charged particles approaching along the axis are undeflected. (b) Positively charged particles approaching the Earth at the Equator are deflected toward the east.

The Earth's magnetic field lines are shown in Figure 32-5. Protons approaching the Earth at the poles travel along magnetic field lines and are, consequently, undeflected (Figure 32-5a). On the other hand, protons approaching the Earth at the Equator cross magnetic field lines going from geographic South to North at right angles. Using Equation 32-3, we see that the particles are acted upon by a magnetic force which deflects them toward the east (Figure 32-5b).

The incoming cosmic-ray particles have a large range of energies. Some are highly energetic (energies up to 10^{13} Mev), and the Earth's magnetic field is feeble (of the order of 0.5 gauss near the surface). Yet, because the Earth's magnetic field extends far out into space, it is able to influence the motion of these particles. For low-energy particles arriving at the Equator, the Earth's magnetic field deflects them so strongly that they even miss hitting the Earth's atmosphere. As a consequence, the intensity of the cosmic radiation is found to be greater at the North and South Poles than near the Equator (the so-called *latitude effect*). This shows that the incoming particles are electrically *charged*. Moreover, experiment shows that those particles arriving at the Equator come preferentially from the west (the so-called *East-West effect*). This shows that the primary particles carry a *positive* charge.

32-3 Motion of charged particles in a uniform magnetic field The basis of all our considerations here is the fundamental relation for the magnetic force on a moving charge:

[32-3] $$F_m = q\boldsymbol{v} \times \boldsymbol{B}$$

The magnetic force is unlike any of the other fundamental forces we have encountered heretofore, such as the gravitational force or the electric force. For one thing, the magnetic force is *velocity-dependent*. This means that it is not possible to associate a scalar potential energy with the magnetic inter-action. Furthermore, the magnetic force can do *no work*. A charged particle does *not* have its kinetic energy changed as it moves through a constant magnetic field. This is easy to prove. The displacement dr of a moving charge over any small time interval dt is $d\boldsymbol{r} = \boldsymbol{v}\,dt$. Since the force $\boldsymbol{F}_m$ always acts at right angles to the particle's velocity $\boldsymbol{v}$, there is no component of the force along the direction of the particle's displacement $\boldsymbol{v}\,dt$ and, hence, no work done by $\boldsymbol{F}_m$. Thus, a particle subject to a magnetic force will have its velocity changed but not its speed; it will be deflected, but it will not gain or lose energy.

What is the most general path of a charged particle in a uniform magnetic field? First consider two special cases, (1) $\boldsymbol{v}$ parallel (or antiparallel) to $\boldsymbol{B}$ and (2) $\boldsymbol{v}$ perpendicular to $\boldsymbol{B}$.

(1) As Equation 32-3 shows—and as our definition of the direction of the magnetic field requires—a charged particle moving initially in (or opposite to) the direction of a magnetic field coasts in this direction with unchanged speed; see Figure 32-6a.

(2) When the particle's *velocity* is at *right angles* to the *magnetic field*, we have the condition for *uniform circular motion*. The magnetic force points at each instant toward the center of the circular path in which the charged particle moves with the constant speed v. The charged particle encircles the magnetic field lines in a plane at right angles to $\boldsymbol{B}$; see Figure 32-6b.

Taking the charge's speed to be $v_\perp$ when the velocity is perpendicular to $\boldsymbol{B}$, we may write Newton's second law as

$$F_r = ma_r$$

where the resultant radial force F_r is the magnetic force $F_m = qv_\perp B$, and the radial (or centripetal) acceleration is $a_r = v_\perp{}^2/r = \omega^2 r$. Therefore,

$$qv_\perp B = mv_\perp{}^2/r = m\omega^2 r \qquad \text{[32-6]}$$

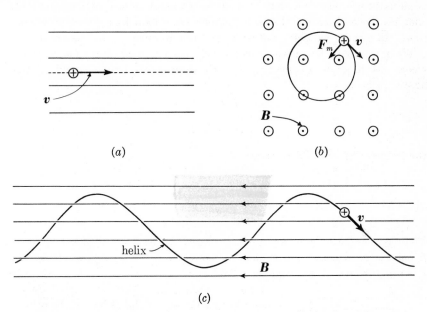

Figure 32-6. A charged particle moving in a uniform field: (a) with v parallel to B, the path is a straight line; (b) with v perpendicular to B, the path is a circle; (c) for other angles between v and B, the path is a helix.

In this equation r is the radius of the circle and ω is the angular velocity of the orbiting charged particle.

What is the path of a charged particle whose velocity v is *not* at right angles to B? There is, then, a velocity component $v_{\parallel} = v \cos \theta$ along B, this component being unchanged in direction and magnitude, and there is a component $v_{\perp} = v \sin \theta$ perpendicular to B, this component being constant in magnitude but continuously changing direction. The resulting motion is the superposition of drift at constant speed along a straight line and uniform circular motion in a plane perpendicular to that of the straight line. That is, the charged particle moves in a *helix* whose axis of symmetry is the direction of the magnetic field; see Figure 32-6c.

Thus, whenever a charged particle is fired into a uniform magnetic field, it travels at constant speed in a helix wrapped around the magnetic field lines. Suppose, now, that we have a number of charged particles of one type, such as electrons, differing in initial velocity and energy and all injected into the same constant magnetic field. Each particle moves in a helical path (or, in special cases, a circle and a straight line). The electrons differ in speed from one another, but each one maintains a constant speed. Now, it is an extraordinary fact that *all* such electrons, despite differences in their energies, speeds, and paths, will complete one loop in precisely the *same time!* All cycling particles will have the same frequency. Let us prove it.

We may write the perpendicular velocity component $v_\perp$ as $v_\perp = \omega r$, where ω is the angular velocity and r is the radius of the helix. Then Equation 32-6 may be written

$$q\omega r B = m\omega^2 r$$

$$\omega = \frac{q}{m} B$$

the frequency $f = \omega/2\pi$ is, then,

$$\boxed{f = \left(\frac{q}{2\pi m}\right) B} \qquad \text{[32-7]}$$

The characteristic frequency given in Equation 32-7 is called the *cyclotron frequency* (for reasons to be evident in Section 32-5). The cyclotron frequency f is proportional to the magnetic field and to the charge-to-mass ratio q/m of the particles, but f does *not* depend on the particle speed v nor on the radius of the orbit r.

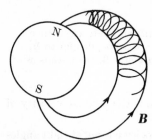

When a charged particle moves in a nonuniform magnetic field, its path is, in general, quite complicated. Nevertheless, one can still recognize the essentially helical path if the magnetic field does not depart too greatly from a constant field. For example, charged particles are trapped in the Van Allen belts surrounding the Earth, as shown in Figure 32-7. The particles

Figure 32-7. Charged particles trapped in the Earth's Van Allen belt.

spiral the magnetic field lines and are actually "reflected" at regions where the magnetic field becomes strong near the Earth's North and South Poles. This is one illustration of the curious possibilities of an inhomogeneous magnetic field trapping charged particles in what can appropriately be called a "magnetic bottle."†

Example 2 What is the cyclotron frequency for electrons in a magnetic field of 3000 gauss = 0.30 weber/m²?

From Equation 32-7 we have

$$f = qB/2\pi m = (1.6 \times 10^{-19} \text{ coul})(0.30 \text{ nt/amp-m})/(2\pi)(9.1 \times 10^{-31} \text{ kg})$$
$$= 8.4 \times 10^9 \text{ cycle/sec}$$

† See "Plasma Physics," by S. C. Brown, in *The Physics Teacher*, **2**, 103 (1964), on magnetic reflection of charged particles, and "The Van Allen Radiation Zone," by W. G. V. Rosser, in *Contemporary Physics*, **5**, 198 (1963) and **6**, 255 (1964).

The cyclotron frequency is 8.4 kilomegacycles per second, a frequency lying in the microwave region of the electromagnetic spectrum. When the free electrons in materials immersed in an external magnetic field of 3000 gauss are irradiated with microwaves of this frequency (with wavelengths of a few centimeters), the electrons absorb energy in an effect known as *cyclotron resonance*.

32-4   Charged particles in uniform B and E fields   Neglecting the altogether trivial gravitational force, the resultant force *F* on a charged particle is merely the vector sum of the electric force F_e and the magnetic force F_m:

$$F = F_e + F_m = qE + qv \times B = q(E + v \times B)$$ [32-8]

Equation 32-8 is often referred to as the *Lorentz force* relation, after H. A. Lorentz (1853–1928), who made many important contributions to the theory of electromagnetism. If one knows *E* and *B* at each point in space and the

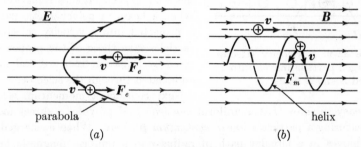

parabola   helix
(a)   (b)

Figure 32-8. (a) In a uniform electric field the path of a charged particle is a parabola. (b) In a uniform magnetic field the path of a charged particle is a helix.

particle's charge and initial velocity, one may use the Lorentz formula to predict in complete detail the future motion of a charged particle.

Here we consider only the special cases in which both *E* and *B* are constant. We know that a charged particle moving in a uniform *E* field alone follows a parabolic path whose symmetry axis lies along the direction of *E*. When *v* is initially parallel or antiparallel to *E*, the parabola reduces into a straight line; see Figure 32-8a. As we have seen, when a charged particle moves in a constant *B* field alone, it follows a helical path whose symmetry axis lies along the direction of *B* (Figure 32-8b). When *v* is initially parallel or antiparallel to *B*, the helix reduces into a straight line.

Suppose that we so arrange a uniform *E* field and a uniform *B* field that the resultant force on a charged particle is always zero. This can be accomplished by having the particle move at right angles to both *E* and to *B*, which are mutually perpendicular, as shown in Figure 32-9. The electric force F_e

and magnetic forces F_m are then both at right angles to the particle's velocity and opposite to one another. F_e and F_m are of equal magnitude when

$$F_e = F_m$$
$$qE = qvB$$
$$v = E/B \qquad [32\text{-}9]$$

If we so adjust the relative magnitudes of E and B that one charged particle will pass undeflected through the region of the two crossed fields, we see from Equation 32-9 that *any other charged particle with the same initial velocity* will also pass through undeflected, quite apart from differences in the magnitude or sign of the charge, or of the particle's mass. Such a device is known as a *velocity selector*, since it will pass only those particles whose speed satisfies Equation 32-9. When a beam of polyenergetic particles is projected into a velocity selector, all particles save those of the proper speed given by Equation 32-9, will fail to pass undeviated through the selector.

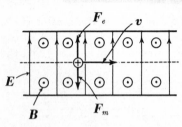

Figure 32-9. A velocity selector: a charged particle moves through crossed E and B fields.

Next consider a momentum selector. It is easy to show that a uniform *magnetic field* provides a direct method of measuring a particle's *linear momentum* $p = mv$. When a charged particle moves in a circular path of radius r in a uniform magnetic field B we have

$$F_r = ma_r$$
$$qvB = mv^2/r$$

$$\boxed{p = mv = qrB} \qquad [32\text{-}10]$$

The linear momentum is directly proportional to the path radius and to the magnitude of the magnetic field. If B is known and r is measured, the momentum p can be computed. Thus, one can easily measure the momentum of a charged particle whose wake of small bubbles is photographed in a bubble chamber by measuring r and B (the product rB is sometimes referred to as the "magnetic rigidity"); see Figure 32-10.

A uniform electric field provides a direct method of measuring a particle's kinetic energy $K = \frac{1}{2}mv^2 = p^2/2m$. Consider the simple arrangement shown in Figure 32-11a, where a uniform field E is established by a potential difference V across two parallel oppositely charged conducting plates separated by the distance d. From Equation 28-14 we have $E = V/d$, so that measuring

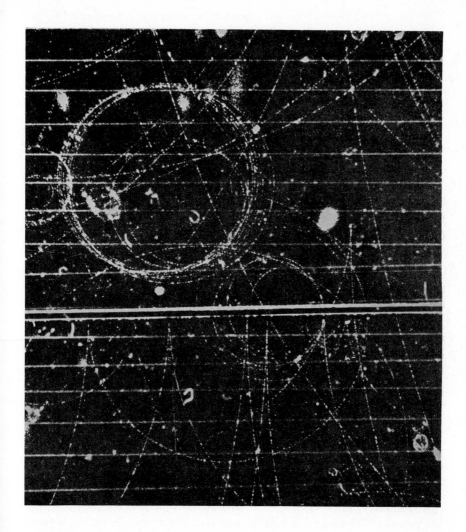

Figure 32-10. Cloud-chamber photograph showing the creation of electron-positron pairs (Section 25-4). The oppositely charged particles are deflected into paths of opposite curvature by an external magnetic field. (From *Cloud Chamber Photographs of the Cosmic Radiation*, C. D. Rochester and J. G. Wilson, Pergamon Press, Ltd., 1952. Courtesy of Pergamon Press, Ltd.)

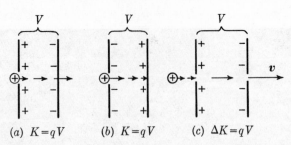

(a) $K = qV$ (b) $K = qV$ (c) $\Delta K = qV$

Figure 32-11. A charged particle moving across (a) an accelerating electric potential from rest, (b) a retarding potential to rest, (c) a potential which changes the kinetic energy.

the potential difference, which is easily done, immediately gives the magnitude of the uniform field. A particle accelerated from rest by a potential difference V acquires a kinetic energy, where

$$K = qV = qEd \qquad [32\text{-}11]$$

Similarly, a charged particle with initial kinetic energy K traveling in the opposite direction and parallel to the electric field lines is brought to rest just in front of the second conducting plate (and therefore fails to register an electric current there) when $K = qV$, where V is now the retarding potential; see Figure 32-11b. For example, electrons with an initial kinetic energy of 50 ev are brought to rest by a retarding potential of 50 v. Even more generally, whenever a charged particle moves through a potential difference V, as in Figure 32-11c, its kinetic energy changes by

$$\Delta K = qV$$

The potential difference V may either increase or decrease the particle's kinetic energy, depending on whether the electric field is an accelerating or retarding field.

In summary, knowing B we find the momentum $p = mv$, and knowing the potential difference V (or E) we may find the kinetic energy $K = \frac{1}{2}mv^2$. We have already seen that crossed electric and magnetic fields provide a means of measuring the charged particle's speed v (Equation 32-9). It is clear, then, that there are a variety of ways in which one might measure the mass of a charged particle:

(a) Measure v and $p = mv$; that is, use a velocity selector and a magnetic field, as shown in Figure 32-12a.

(b) Measure $K = \frac{1}{2}mv^2$ and $p = mv$; that is, use an accelerating electric field to fix the kinetic energy, followed by a magnetic field to find to the momentum, as shown in Figure 32-12b.

(c) Measure v and $K = \frac{1}{2}mv^2$; that is, use a velocity selector to produce an undeflected beam, then turn off the magnetic field, leaving the electric field to determine the kinetic energy (see Example 4, Chapter 26), as shown in Figure 32-12c.

Still other combinations can, of course, be devised. The arrangement shown in Figure 32-12c was used by J. J. Thomson in 1897, to measure the mass of the electron. Strictly, any of these procedures will yield only the

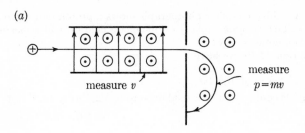

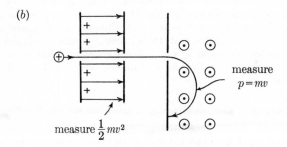

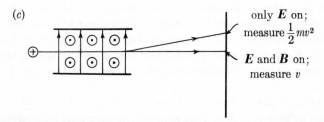

Figure 32-12. Arrangements for measuring the mass of a charged particle: (a) a velocity selector followed by a momentum selector, (b) an accelerating electric field followed by a momentum selector, and (c) a velocity selector followed by a deflecting electric field (the Thomson arrangement for measuring the electron q/m ratio).

charge-to-mass ratio q/m, not the mass alone. Therefore, one must have an independent measurement of a particle's charge, as through the Millikan oil-drop experiment, to permit the mass to be computed. Although Thomson's experiment gave q/m for an electron, the electron mass was known only after $q = e$ was measured in the Millikan experiment (Section 26-5). The experimental arrangements described above are used in mass spectrometers for measuring atomic masses with high precision. It is a relatively easy matter to distinguish among the isotopes of an element; indeed, one can measure atomic masses to a few parts in 10^5.

Example 3 A bubble chamber photograph shows a proton moving in a circular arc 20 cm in radius at right angles to a magnetic field of 0.30 weber/m². What is the proton's kinetic energy?

Using Equation 32-10, we have

$$K = \tfrac{1}{2}mv^2 = p^2/2m = (qrB)^2/2m$$
$$= (1.6 \times 10^{-19} \text{ coul} \times 0.20 \text{ m} \times 0.30 \text{ nt/amp-m})^2/2(1.67 \times 10^{-27} \text{ kg})$$
$$= 1.0 \times 10^{-12} \text{ joule} = 17 \text{ Mev}$$

Although the classical relations for the kinetic energy and linear momentum are applicable to proton kinetic energies of several million electron volts, for much higher energies one must use relativistic relations for K and p. The formulas of classical mechanics apply only when the particle speed is much less than the speed of light, 3×10^8 m/sec (see Chapter 2, Weidner and Sells, *Elementary Modern Physics*, Allyn and Bacon, 1960). In the case of electrons, the relativistic relations are required at much lower energies; that is, the classical relations are seriously in error for electron kinetic energies much above a few tens of kiloelectron volts.

32-5 The cyclotron The cyclotron is a machine for accelerating charged particles to relatively high kinetic energies. Its operation is based on the fact that a charged particle cycles magnetic field lines at a rate, the cyclotron frequency, which is independent of the radius of the particle's orbit and of the particle's speed (Equation 32-7). Therefore one may give *multiple* accelerations to the particle traveling in circular arcs in a constant magnetic field by applying an electric field each half-cycle. The cyclotron was invented in 1932 by E. O. Lawerence (1901–1958) and M. S. Livingston (1905–   ); it is the simplest of a whole class of cyclic accelerators based on the cyclotron principle.

The essential parts of the cyclotron are shown in Figure 32-13. Positive ions (such as protons), deuterons (heavy hydrogen nuclei), or alpha particles (helium nuclei) are injected into the central region (point C in Figure 32-13a) between two flat D-shaped hollow metal conductors called "dees." An alternating high-frequency electric potential difference is applied to the dees, thereby producing an alternating electric field in the region between them.

During the time that the left dee is positive and the right dee is negative, the injected positive ions are accelerated to the right by the electric field between the dees. Upon entering the interior of the right dee, these ions are electrically shielded from any electric field, and they move in a semicircle at a constant speed under the influence of the constant magnetic field alone. When the ions emerge from the right dee they will be further accelerated across the gap, if the left dee is now negative. This requires that the frequency of the alternating voltage applied to the dees be equal to the orbital frequency

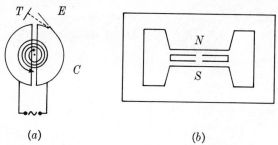

(a)   (b)

Figure 32-13. (a) Top view of cyclotron dees. (b) Side view of cyclotron dees in magnetic field.

of the ions. That is, the alternating voltage must be at the cyclotron frequency f of the particles, where

[32-7] $$f = (q/2\pi m)B$$

During each acceleration the ions gain energy, move at a higher speed, and travel in semicircles of larger radii. For example, if the applied potential difference is 100,000 v, protons increase their kinetic energy by 100 kev each time they pass the gap between the dees, or 200 kev for each round trip. As the ions spiral outward in the dees, they remain synchronized with, and in resonance with, the alternating accelerating voltage, inasmuch as the time for an ion to move through 180° is independent of the ion's speed or radius (provided, of course, that the ion's mass m remains constant). When the accelerated particles reach the circumference of the dees, perhaps after 100 loops, they are deflected by the electric field of an ejector plate E to strike a target there. The accelerated particles may then have energies of several million electron volts, so that upon encountering nuclei in the target they are able to approach these nuclei closely despite the repulsive Coulomb force.

The final kinetic energy K of a particle emerging from a cyclotron is

$$K = \tfrac{1}{2}mv_{\max}^2 = p_{\max}^2/2m$$

Figure 32-14. A synchrocyclotron for accelerating protons to 720 Mev. (Courtesy of the University of California Lawerence Radiation Laboratory.)

Using Equation 32-10, we may write the energy K as

$$K = \frac{(qBr_{max})^2}{2m} \qquad [32\text{-}12]$$

Equation 32-12 shows that the final kinetic energy of the particle depends on the square of r_{max}, the radius of the cyclotron's dees, and on the square of B. To achieve the highest possible energies, B and r_{max} are made as large as possible. When the maximum B attainable with electromagnets (~ 2 weber/m²) is used, the cyclotron frequency is in the region of several megacycles per second (radio frequencies) for positive ions. The diameter of the dees, which is also the diameter of the electromagnet pole faces, may be as large as 8 feet. A typical alternating electric potential difference is 200 kv.

Ions may be accelerated with a cyclotron to energies of about 25 Mev. For still higher energies the classical relations of mechanics are inapplicable and relativistic relations must be used. The most important relativistic modification is that the particle's mass m increases with speed, so that the cyclotron frequency, which is inversely proportional to m, according to Equation 32-7, changes as the particle increases its speed until it becomes comparable to the speed of light. Therefore, as the particles spiral outward, they fall progressively behind the applied frequency, finally arriving at the gap between the dees so late that they are no longer accelerated by the electric field. This difficulty is overcome in the *synchrocyclotron*, in which the frequency of the applied voltage is reduced, to remain in synchronism with the particle's orbital motion as the particles spiral outward. A large synchrocyclotron is shown in Figure 32-14.

Because relativistic effects occur at much lower energies in the case of electrons, the cyclotron is *not* a suitable accelerator for them. When an electron acquires a kinetic energy of only several hundred kiloelecton volts, its speed becomes comparable to the speed of light, its mass is appreciably higher than its mass at low speeds, and it cannot remain in synchronism with the alternating potential difference of a cyclotron. An appropriate accelerator for electrons, one operating on a somewhat different principle from that of the cyclotron, is the betatron (to be discussed in Section 34-6). Linear accelerators, such as the Van de Graaff generator, may also be used to accelerate electrons.

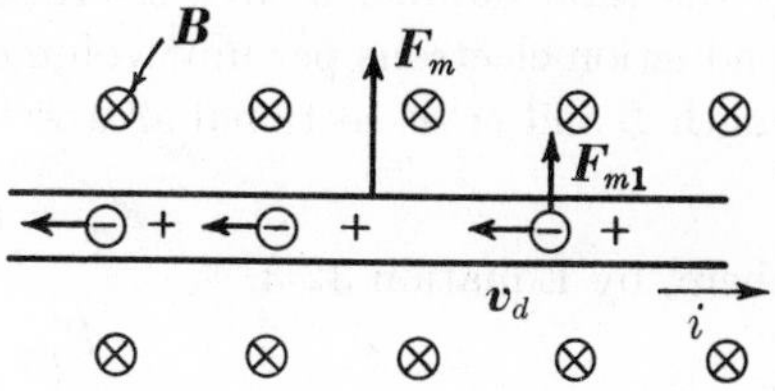

Figure 32-15. Magnetic force on a conduction electron in a current-carrying conductor.

32-6 Magnetic force on a current-carrying conductor

Since a magnetic field exerts a force on a moving charge, it must also exert a force on the moving charges in a current-carrying conductor. Consider Figure 32-15, where we see electrons moving to the left at the drift speed v_d through a conductor of small cross-sectional area A. The conventional current i is then to the right. The conductor is immersed in a constant magnetic field **B**, whose direction is into the paper. Applying Equation 32-3, we find that each free electron is subject to a magnetic force F_m which is upward. Now, although the electrons are free to move within the conductor, they are constrained to remain within it. Rather than moving in a circular arc about the magnetic field, the electrons continue their motion to the left at speed v_d. The magnetic force on the conduction electrons is transmitted to the lattice of the conductor, and the conductor as a whole is subject to an upward magnetic force F_m whose direction is perpendicular to both the magnetic field lines and the direction of the current.

Note that with a current-carrying conductor we need *not* be concerned with a possible electric force on the conducting wire from an external electric field in addition to the magnetic force. Any section of the conductor is electrically neutral. One might then say that the magnetic force on a current-carrying conductor represents a pure magnetic effect, since there is no possible complicating additional electric force. Moreover, we find the same magnetic force acting on the conductor when we view the conductor from *any* reference frame. For example, if we view the conductor from a reference frame moving to the left with the electron drift speed v_d, the electrons are at rest (now neglecting their random thermal motions), while we see the positive charges in the conductor moving to the right at the speed v_d. Once again, we have the current i to the right. Since the net current in a conductor is independent of the reference frame, the magnetic force is also independent of the reference frame.

Let us compute the magnitude of the magnetic force F_m acting on a current-carrying conductor of length L, oriented at right angles to an external magnetic field B, when a current i exists in it. The total force F_m acting over the length L is simply the magnetic force F_{m1} on *one* electron multiplied by the total number of free electrons within this length. If the number of conduction electrons per unit volume is n, then the total number within the length L and cross-sectional area A is nAL. We have, then,

$$F_m = (nAL)F_{m1}$$

where, by Equation 32-3,

$$F_{m1} = qv_d B$$

Therefore,

$$F_m = nALqv_d B = (qv_d n)ALB$$

Now, the current density $j = i/A$ is given by

[30-5] $$j = i/A = qv_d n$$

Substituting this relation in the equation for F_m above, we have

$$F_m = iLB \qquad \text{[32-13]}$$

Thus, the magnetic force on a conductor one meter long, carrying a current of one ampere, and immersed in a tranverse field of one weber per square meter, is one newton. One may, in fact, use this relation to measure a magnetic field: one measures the magnetic force on a conductor of known length carrying a known current.

It is easy to generalize Equation 32-13 by noting that, if the current-carrying conductor makes an angle θ with respect to the magnetic field, the force F_{m1} on one electron becomes $qv_d L \sin\theta$, and Equation 32-13 contains an additional factor, $\sin\theta$. Then we may write Equation 32-13 in vector form as follows:

$$\boldsymbol{F}_m = i\boldsymbol{L} \times \boldsymbol{B} \qquad \text{[32-14]}$$

The vector **L** represents, in magnitude, the length of the conductor; its direction is chosen to correspond to the direction of positive charge flow, or the direction of conventional current.

Equation 32-14 holds only for a *straight* conductor. We can, of course, never have an infinitely long straight conductor, inasmuch as there must always be a return loop of some sort to complete the electric circuit. Therefore, it is useful to have a relation giving the magnetic force dF_m on only a short segment of conductor of length dL. From Equation 32-14 we have

$$dF_m = i\, dL \times B \qquad\qquad [32\text{-}15]$$

Once again the direction of dL is taken to be the direction of the current; see Figure 32-16. One may find the resultant force on a conductor of

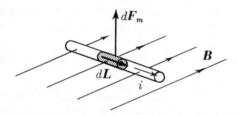

Figure 32-16. Magnetic force dF_m on an element of length dL of a current-carrying conductor.

arbitrary shape by integrating the magnetic force on the length elements that comprise it, taking into account, as well, that the magnetic field **B** may not have the same magnitude and direction at all points in the current loop. Such an integration is, in general, quite complicated, although it may be simple in certain special cases, as the following example illustrates.

Example 4   A conductor of arbitrary shape carrying current i runs from point A to point B, as shown in Figure 32-17a. A constant magnetic field of magnitude B acts into the plane of the paper. What is the resultant force on this segment of conductor?

We may approximate the continuously varying conductor shape by a series of straight-line segments lying, respectively, parallel and perpendicular to the straight line L_{AB} from point A to B. The magnetic forces on these segments are, from Equation 32-15, in the directions shown in Figure 32-17b. We see that the total force component parallel to the line L_{AB} is zero, each force to the right being matched by an equal force to the left. This leaves only the magnetic forces perpendicular to L_{AB}. The resultant force perpendicular to the line L_{AB} is exactly the same as the magnetic force on a straight conductor running from A to B. Therefore, the net magnetic force has a magnitude $F_m = iL_{AB}B$, and its direction is perpendicular to the line joining the end points. The arbitrarily

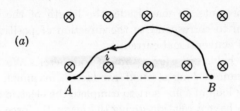

(a)

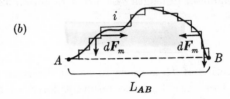

(b)

Figure 32-17. (a) A current-carrying conductor of arbitrary shape in an external magnetic field. (b) Equivalent conductor comprised of segments parallel and perpendicular to the line joining the end points.

shaped conductor is equivalent to a straight wire between its end points carrying the same current.

Now suppose that we form a current loop by imagining points A and B to be brought together. From the arguments above, the resultant magnetic force on the loop must be *zero*. A little thought will show that this conclusion applies, whatever the shape of the loop and whether the loop lies entirely in a plane or not, and that it also is independent of the loop's orientation relative to the magnetic field lines. *The magnetic field must, however, be uniform.* Although a closed current loop is subject to no resultant magnetic force in a uniform magnetic field, it may be subject to a resultant torque, as we shall see in the next section.

32-7 Magnetic torque on a current loop Consider the situation shown in Figure 32-18a: a rectangular loop, with sides W and L and carrying a current i, is placed in a uniform magnetic field. The angle between the magnetic field lines and the normal to the plane of the loop is θ. We wish to find the magnetic forces on the four sides of the loop. (One cannot, of course, have a current loop of this sort unconnected to a source of current. There must be two lead wires, one to bring the current into the loop and another to take the current out of it. If these two lead wires are placed next to each other, as by wrapping or twisting them together, then the resultant magnetic force on the lead wires is zero, since one has equal currents in opposite directions.)

We see that there are two pair of equal but opposite magnetic forces acting on the four sides of the current loop. The resultant *force* is *zero*. Although the forces on the sides of length W are along the same line, the two forces on the sides of length L are not. Therefore, these equal and opposite forces apply a torque to the loop, tending to align its normal with the direction of the magnetic field. Let us find the torque.

Equation 32-13 gives the magnitude of each force on the sides of length L:

$$F_m = iLB$$

We choose as axis for computing the torques the lower of the two sides of length L, see Figure 32-18b. Then, in magnitude, we have

$$\tau = r_\perp F = (W \sin \theta)(iLB)$$

We may write this in simpler form by recognizing LW as the area A of the current loop:

$$\tau = iAB \sin \theta \qquad\qquad [32\text{-}16]$$

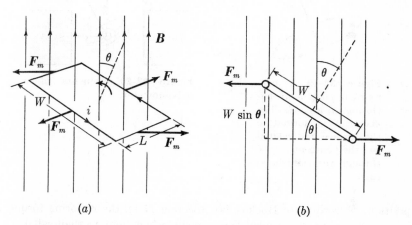

(a) (b)

Figure 32-18. (a) Magnetic forces on a rectangular current-carrying conducting loop in a magnetic field. (b) A side view of part (a).

The direction of the torque is out of the paper; that is, the magnetic torque on the loop turns it in the counterclockwise sense. We may write Equation 32-16 in vector form as follows:

$$\boxed{\tau = i\mathbf{S} \times \mathbf{B}} \qquad\qquad [32\text{-}17]$$

Here the magnitude of the vector $\mathbf{S}$ represents the loop's area. The direction of $\mathbf{S}$ is perpendicular to the plane of the loop and is so chosen that we may use the right-hand rule to relate the sense of the current to the direction of the normal. See Figure 32-19.

Although we have derived Equation 32-17 under the assumption of a rectangular current loop, this relation gives the magnetic torque on a plane current loop of *any* shape. To see this, we imagine the conducting wire to be approximated by small straight segments at right angles to one another. Of course, if a loop consists of N turns (in the *same* sense) rather than a single turn, the torque of Equation 32-17 is increased by the factor N.

The magnetic torque on a current-carrying conducting loop forms the basis of the galvanometer. The current to be measured passes through a coil of many turns placed in the magnetic field of a permanent magnet; see Figure 32-20. The coil is attached to an elastic helical spring which applies a restoring torque to the coil whenever the coil is turned from its equilibrium

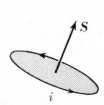

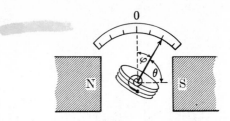

Figure 32-19. A current-carrying loop enclosing an area S. The vector S is normal to the surface and related to the current sense through the right-hand rule.

Figure 32-20. Elements of a galvanometer.

position. According to Hooke's law (Section 17-1), the restoring torque τ_r is proportional to the angular displacement, which here we shall call φ,

[17-2] $$\tau_r = \kappa\varphi$$

where κ, the torque constant of the spring, is typically very small so that the galvanometer coil is extremely sensitive to angular displacements. When a current exists in a coil of N turns, the magnitude of the magnetic torque acting on it is, by Equation 32-16,

$$\tau_m = NiAB \sin \theta$$

Now, the angle θ is set equal to 90° when the coil is in the equilibrium position; that is, $\varphi = 0$ when $\theta = 90°$. Since $\theta + \varphi = 90°$, we have

$$\tau_m = NiAB \cos \varphi$$

Equating the two torques gives

$$\kappa\varphi \ NiAB \cos \varphi$$

If the deflection angle φ is not too large, $\cos \varphi \simeq 1$, and

$$i \propto \varphi \qquad \text{[32-18]}$$

The angular deflection is proportional to the current.

In a sense, an electric motor is nothing more than a big galvanometer. It is another example of the magnetic torque acting on a current loop. The moving coil is called an armature, and provisions are made for reversing the current through the armature (by a commutator) so that the armature rotates continuously.

32-8 Magnetic dipole moment The relation for the magnetic torque on a current loop, Equation 32-17, is of exactly the same form as the relation derived earlier (Section 26-6) giving the torque on an electric dipole moment p placed in a uniform electric field E:

[26-12] $\qquad\qquad \boldsymbol{\tau} = \boldsymbol{p} \times \boldsymbol{E}$

This suggests that we attribute a *magnetic dipole moment*, symbolized by the vector $\boldsymbol{\mu}$, to a current loop where, by definition,

$$\boxed{\boldsymbol{\mu} = i\boldsymbol{S}} \qquad \text{[32-19]}$$

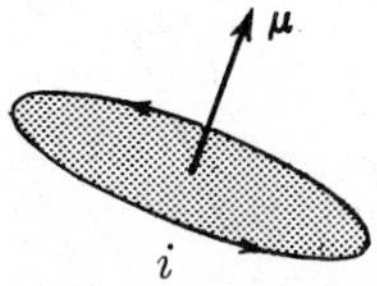

Figure 32-21. Magnetic dipole moment $\boldsymbol{\mu}$ associated with a current loop.

See Figure 32-21. Note that the direction of $\boldsymbol{\mu}$ is related to the sense of the conventional current in the loop by the right-hand rule. Then Equation 32-17 can be written in the form

$$\boxed{\boldsymbol{\tau} = \boldsymbol{\mu} \times \boldsymbol{B}} \qquad \text{[32-20]}$$

An electric dipole in a *uniform* electric field is subject to *no* resultant force; similarly, a magnetic dipole in a uniform magnetic field is subject to no resultant force. But both electric and magnetic dipoles *are* subject to resultant forces in nonuniform, or inhomogeneous, electric and magnetic fields, respectively. The dipoles are attracted into the region where the field is strongest.

We found earlier that the electric potential energy of an electric dipole in a uniform electric field was given by

[26-14] $\qquad\qquad U_E = -\boldsymbol{p} \cdot \boldsymbol{E}$

the zero for potential energy corresponding to the angle $\theta = 90°$ between $\boldsymbol{p}$ and $\boldsymbol{E}$. In similar fashion we can immediately write the potential energy of a magnetic dipole in a magnetic field as

$$\boxed{U_B = -\boldsymbol{\mu} \cdot \boldsymbol{B}} \qquad \text{[32-21]}$$

The potential energy U_B is a maximum $(+\mu B)$ when the dipole is aligned against the magnetic field ($\theta = 180°$), and it is a minimum $(-\mu B)$ when the dipole is aligned with the magnetic field lines ($\theta = 0°$). The zero for U_B again corresponds to $\theta = 90°$.

All this reminds us of the behavior of a permanent magnet, such as a compass needle, in the presence of a magnetic field. The magnet is subject to a magnetic torque when it is out of alignment with the magnetic field, and one must do work to turn the magnet from alignment with the field. Indeed, one can attribute a magnetic dipole to any object, a current-carrying loop, or a magnet that follows Equations 32-20 and 32-21 for the torque and potential energy; see Figures 32-21 and 32-22.

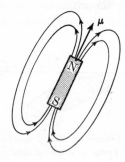

Figure 32-22. Magnetic dipole moment **μ** associated with a permanent magnet.

The magnetic effects of a permanent magnet seem to be concentrated at the two ends of a long thin magnet, the points where the magnetic field of the magnet is greatest. One might even be inclined to think of the magnet as having two distinct magnetic poles (a dipole) at its ends. Certainly, with an electric dipole moment $p = qd$, one can always associate the dipole moment with two distinct and separated charges of opposite sign. Can one do the same for a magnet; that is, can one properly speak of a single magnetic pole just as one speaks on a single electric point charge? The answer is *no*. In so far as the most subtle experiments can show, single magnetic poles, or *magnetic monopoles*, do *not* exist in nature. In every case in which a magnetic dipole moment exists, one can invariably attribute the magnetic effects to electric charges in motion; for example, the magnetism of an ordinary bar magnet has its origin in the spinning of electrons and of their electric charge. Therefore, the familiar north and south poles of a common magnet are merely a useful fiction.

32-9 The Hall effect The magnetic force on the charge carriers in a current-carrying conductor causes a *transverse* electric potential difference to be set up across the conductor. This is the Hall effect, developed by E. H. Hall in 1879. By measuring the sign and the magnitude of this potential difference one can infer the sign of the charge carriers and their density within the conductor.

Consider the broad flat conducting plate in Figure 32-23a, which is immersed in a uniform magnetic field directed into the paper and which carries a conventional current i to the right. The negatively charged carriers, the electrons, travel at the drift speed v_d to the left and are subject to an upward magnetic force F_m, as shown earlier in Figure 32-15. The electrons cannot escape the conductor. They drift to the left but, because the magnetic force on them is upward, they are also pushed to the upper edge of the conductor. Thus, an excess of electrons is found at the upper edge of the conductor and a deficiency of electrons at the lower edge. That is, the upper conductor edge acquires a net negative charge and the lower edge a net positive charge. An electric potential difference V_H, the *Hall potential difference*, exists across the conductor, the lower edge being at the higher potential.

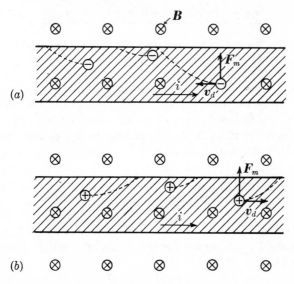

(a)

(b)

Figure 32-23. The Hall effect: (a) negative charge carriers are deflected upward by a magnetic force; (b) positive charge carriers for the *same* current as in part (a) are deflected upward by the magnetic force.

It is easy to show the sign of the Hall potential difference is reversed if the charge carriers are positive rather than negative, that is, if positive charge carriers drift to the right to produce a current in this direction. In Figure 32-23b we have the same magnetic field and current as in Figure 32-23a, but now we suppose that *positive* charge carriers drift to the right to produce the same conventional current to the right. As before, the magnetic force is upward, driving the charge carriers to accumulate at the upper edge. Again a Hall potential difference exists between the upper and lower edges of the conductor, but now the positively charged upper edge is at the higher electric potential. Experiments with ordinary metallic conductors show that the Hall potential difference has the sense shown in Figure 32-23a, thereby confirming that the charge carriers are, in fact, negatively charged electrons.†

We wish to relate the Hall potential difference V_H to measurable quantities. First we note that the conduction electrons of Figure 32-23a are not subject only to an upward magnetic force F_m as they move through

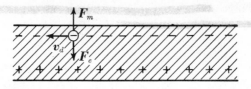

Figure 32-24. A conduction electron drifts at the speed v_d while subject to equal and opposite electric and magnetic forces.

the conductor. Since any electron moving toward the conductor's upper edge is repelled by electrons already there, a downward transverse electric force F_e also acts on conduction electrons; see Figure 32-24. In fact, a conduction electron will be in equilibrium (neglecting thermal motion) as it moves to the left at constant speed when

$$F_e = F_m$$

Introducing the transverse Hall electric field E_H, we have

$$eE_H = ev_dB$$

This uniform field exists across the conductor of width d; therefore, from Equation 28-14,

$$eV_H/d = ev_dB$$
$$V_H = dv_dB \qquad [32\text{-}22]$$

The electron drift speed is related to the current density j and density of charge carriers, n by

$$[30\text{-}5] \qquad j = i/A = nev_d \qquad [32\text{-}23]$$

---

† The situation with semiconductors, such as silicon and germanium, is somewhat more complicated. Conduction takes place by the motion of conduction electrons but, in addition, there may exist electron "holes" within the semiconductor which move under an applied electric field as if they were positively charged particles. Thus, if an electron moves to the left to fill the space "occupied" by a hole, the hole moves to the right. One may then think of the hole, or electron vacancy, as moving in the fashion of an actual particle, but always in the direction opposite to that of an electron which fills the holes; the hole moves like an apparently positively charged particle. Since the conduction of electric current in a semiconductor may be due to both electrons and holes, the sign of the Hall potential difference then shows which type of charge carrier predominates.

Eliminating v_d from Equations 32-22 and 32-23, we have

$$V_H = diB/Ane \qquad\qquad [32\text{-}24]$$

All quantitatives appearing in Equation 32-24 are measurable or known, except for the density of charge carriers, n, which can then be determined from a measurement of the Hall potential difference. For monovalent metallic conductors one finds the density of conduction electrons to be very nearly the same as the density of atoms; that is, there is essentially one conduction electron per atom. Moreover, the density of charge carriers is found to be nearly independent of temperature.

Example 5 A copper conducting strip 1.0 cm wide and 0.50 mm thick carries a current of 100 amp. What is the Hall potential difference across it, when a transverse magnetic field of 1.8 weber/m² is applied to the conductor? Assume the density of conduction electrons to be 8.4 × 10^{28}/m³, which is the density of copper atoms (see Example 1, Chapter 30).

Taking the thickness of the conducting strip to be t, the cross-sectional area A is td. Then Equation 32-24 can be written

$$V_H = iB/tne$$

Note that the width d of the strip does not enter. Substituting the quantities given above, we have

$$V_H = \frac{(100 \text{ amp})(1.8 \text{ nt/amp-m})}{(0.50 \times 10^{-3} \text{ m})(8.4 \times 10^{28} \text{ m}^{-3})(1.6 \times 10^{-19} \text{ coul})}$$
$$= 2.7 \times 10^{-5} \text{ v} = 27 \text{ } \mu\text{v}$$

The actually measured potential difference for copper would be found to be somewhat higher (by 30 per cent) than the rather small 27 μv computed above. Consequently, the number of conduction electrons per copper atom is 1.3.

32-10 Summary The fundamental magnetic effect is that a moving electric charge creates, in addition to the electric force between charges, a magnetic field which acts to produce a magnetic force on a second moving charge.

The magnetic force on a particle of charge q and velocity v, moving in magnetic induction field B, is

[32-3] $$F_m = qv \times B$$

In the mksa system of units the magnetic induction field is measured in newtons per ampere-meter, or webers per square meter (nt/amp-m = weber/m²). The magnetic flux ϕ_B is defined as

[32-4] $$\phi_B = \int B \cdot dS$$

The magnetic force, always acting at right angles to the moving charge's velocity, does *no* work. A particle of charge q and mass m travels in a helix in a uniform magnetic field at the cyclotron frequency

[32-7] $$f = (q/2\pi m)B$$

The cyclotron is an accelerating machine which utilizes the fact that the frequency of an orbiting charged particle in a magnetic field is independent of the charge's speed and the radius of its orbit.

The linear momentum p of a charged particle traveling in a circle of radius r at right angles to the field lines of the magnetic field B is given by

[32-10] $$p = qrB$$

The magnetic force $d\boldsymbol{F}_m$ on an element of length $d\boldsymbol{L}$ in which a current i flows (along the direction of $d\boldsymbol{L}$) immersed in a magnetic field $\boldsymbol{B}$ is

[32-15] $$d\boldsymbol{F}_m = i\,d\boldsymbol{L} \times \boldsymbol{B}$$

The magnitude of the magnetic torque on a conducting loop of area A, carrying current i and immersed in a magnetic field B, is

[32-16] $$\tau = iAB \sin \theta$$

where θ is the angle between the normal to the plane of the loop and the magnetic field.

The magnetic torque on a magnetic dipole moment $\boldsymbol{\mu}$ in a magnetic field $\boldsymbol{B}$ is

[32-20] $$\boldsymbol{\tau} = \boldsymbol{\mu} \times \boldsymbol{B}$$

and the potential energy of the magnetic dipole is

[32-21] $$U_B = -\boldsymbol{\mu} \cdot \boldsymbol{B}$$

A current loop has a magnetic dipole moment

[32-19] $$\boldsymbol{\mu} = i\boldsymbol{S}$$

where $\boldsymbol{S}$ is the vector representing the magnitude of the loop's area and the direction of the normal to the plane of the loop (using the right-hand rule) and i is the current.

The magnetic force on the charge carriers in a current-carrying conductor causes a transverse electric potential difference to be set up across the conductor; this is the Hall effect.

PROBLEMS

32-1   When a particle of charge q and mass m passes the coordinate origin, its velocity v is in the XY plane and makes an angle θ relative to the positive X-axis. A uniform magnetic field of magnitude B exists along the direction of the positive X-axis. What is the next time the particle passes through the X-axis?

32-2 A positively charged particle of charge q and mass m moves initially with speed v in the XY-plane, at an angle θ above the X-axis and starting at the origin. A constant magnetic field of magnitude B exists along the positive Z-axis. Write relations giving the X, Y, and Z coordinates of the particle as a function of the time t.

32-3 When protons traveling north enter a uniform magnetic field of 0.80 weber/m² in the downward direction, they are bent into horizontal circles of a 20 cm radius. What is the magnitude and direction of a uniform electric field, applied over the same region as the magnetic field, which will allow the protons to pass through undeflected?

32-4 Show that the kinetic energy of a particle of given mass and charge moving in a magnetic field of constant flux density is proportional to the square of the radius of curvature of its path when the particle is traveling at right angles to the magnetic field lines.

32-5 A charged particle having a charge-to-mass ratio equal to that of the electron is found to be moving in a circle 20 cm in radius in the clockwise sense, when a constant magnetic field of 5.0 gauss acts downward on the plane of path. (a) Is the particle an electron or a positron (a positively charged electron)? (b) What is its speed? (c) What is its kinetic energy?

32-6 At the Equator the Earth's magnetic field is horizontal, toward the north, and has the magnitude 0.70 gauss. (a) In what direction (east or west) should a proton be fired to encircle the Earth at constant speed? (b) What is the proton's speed? (c) What is the proton's kinetic energy? (d) Is the gravitational force significant here?

32-7 At some location in the northern hemisphere on Earth, the magnitude of the Earth's magnetic field is 0.25 gauss and the dip angle, the angle between the direction of the field lines and the horizontal (pointing north), is 70°. A compass points to geographic north at this location. What is the magnetic flux through an area of 1.0 m² in the horizontal plane?

32-8 ⋆ A charged particle moves in a circular orbit about a straight current-carrying conductor which also carries a uniform electric charge. The particle's orbit is in a plane at right angles to the conducting wire and centered on the wire. Experiment shows that the motion of the charged particle can be explained *completely* in terms of the *electric force only* between the charged wire and the moving charged particle. (a) Does this mean that there is no magnetic field associated with the current-carrying conductor? (b) How must the magnetic field lines be arranged, to be consistent with these observations?

32-9 Find the angle with respect to the direction of the uniform magnetic field B at which one must project a charged particle into this field, such that the distance it moves along the field line is just equal to the distance it moves along a circular arc perpendicular to the field.

32-10   A beam of electrons having a kinetic energy of 10 kev moves north to enter a downward magnetic field in which they are bent into circular paths 50 cm in radius. What are the magnitude and direction of a uniform electric field which, when applied over the same region as the magnetic field, will permit the electrons to pass through undeflected?

32-11   Charged particles of mass m and charge q are accelerated from rest through a potential difference V. Then these particles pass at right angles to a magnetic field of flux density B and move in circular arcs of radius r. Derive an expression for q/m in terms of the measured quantities V, B, and r.

32-12   Devise two arrangements of electric and magnetic fields, different from those listed in the text, for measuring the mass of a charged particle.

32-13   A beam of charged particles is directed along the field lines of a constant magnetic field. If the particle velocities coincide exactly with the field lines, the particles are, of course, undeflected. Now suppose that the particles are very slightly misaimed. Show that the magnetic field acts as a sort of lens, in the sense that the particles are returned to the desired direction.

32-14   A charged particle, initially at rest, is accelerated in a uniform electric field E through a distance d. It then enters a uniform magnetic field B perpendicular to its velocity, and the particle is turned through 180°. If it spends the same time traveling in the magnetic field that it does in the electric field, what is the ratio of the path distance in the magnetic field to that in the electric field?

32-15   A beam of singly ionized chlorine atoms, composed of a mixture of the two isotopes of masses 35 amu and 37 amu, enters perpendicularly a uniform magnetic field of 0.50 weber/m². All ions have the same speed, 2.0×10^5 m/sec. After bending through 180°, the ions strike a photographic plate. (a) What is the separation distance between the two regions on the film where the ions strike? (b) If one used, instead, two isotopes of oxygen having masses 16 amu and 18 amu with the same initial speed of 2.0×10^5 m/sec, what would be the separation on the film?

32-16   A cyclotron employing a magnetic field of flux density 2.0 weber/m² is to accelerate protons to 10 Mev. (a) What is the frequency of the alternating voltage applied to the dees? (b) What is the required radius of the dees? (c) If the alternating voltage applies a maximum potential difference of 100 kv to the dees, how many cycles do the protons complete before emerging from the cyclotron?

32-17   The cost of a cyclotron is approximately proportional to its volume, that is, to the volume of the electromagnet. The size of the electromagnet is determined, in turn, by the radius of the cyclotron dees. By approximately what factor does the cost of a cyclotron increase when the energy of the accelerated particles is doubled?

32-18   The current in a straight conductor lying in a horizontal plane has the direction 30° east of north. What is the direction of the magnetic force on the conductor when a constant external magnetic field exists along the conductor in the direction (a) north and in a horizontal plane, (b) vertically downward, and (c) west and in a horizontal plane?

32-19 A 20 cm straight section of conducting wire is oriented horizontally east-west. It is placed in a constant magnetic field of 1.0 weber/m² flux density to the north. (a) In what direction, east or west, must free electrons move through the conductor to reduce the apparent weight of the wire? (b) By what amount is the weight apparently reduced when the current is 4.0 amp?

32-20

A 1.0 m conductor having a weight of 0.80 nt is oriented along the horizontal. A current of 100 amp passes through the conductor to the east. What magnetic field would render the conductor weightless?

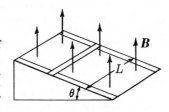

Figure 32-25

32-21 A conducting rod of length L and mass m slides without friction on two parallel fixed conducting bars separated by L and attached to an inclined plane of angle θ. A constant magnetic field acts upward. See Figure 32-25. What current must exist in the movable conductor to have it ascend the inclined plane at constant speed?

32-22 (a) Find the internal force between adjoining segments of a plane circular loop, 5.0 cm in radius and carrying a current of 100 amp, which is immersed in a uniform magnetic field of 2.0 weber/m² perpendicular to the plane of the loop. (b) Is the force tensile or compressive?

32-23 A coil 2.0 cm in diameter has 300 turns. What is the maximum torque on this coil when it carries a current of 10 mamp while immersed in a constant magnetic field of 500 gauss?

32-24 Suppose that one has a fixed length of wire from which one is to construct a coil, not necessarily circular, with one or more loops. The shape of the coil and the number of turns is to be so chosen that, for a given current through it, the torque on the coil, placed in a magnetic field, is a maximum. What is the shape of the coil and how many turns should be used?

32-25 A torque of 40 m-nt is required to hold a magnet at 30° from alignment with magnetic field lines of flux density 200 gauss. What is the magnet's magnetic dipole moment?

32-26 The maximum torque acting on a magnetic dipole in a field of 100 gauss is 50 m-nt. How much work is required to turn the dipole from initial alignment with the field lines to the position in which it is oriented against the magnetic field?

32-27 The vector representing the magnetic dipole of a permanent magnet is directed from the magnet's south to its north pole. The magnet's dipole moment is due to spinning electrons within the iron. If one "looks" through the magnet from the south to the north pole, in what sense, clockwise or counterclockwise, are the electrons spinning?

32-28 The electron of the hydrogen atom can be imagined to circle the proton in an orbit of 0.53 Å in radius at a frequency of 7×10^{15} cycles/sec. Compute the magnetic dipole moment of the electron's orbital motion.

32-29 A permanent magnet, having a moment of inertia I relative to a vertical axis about which it is pivoted and a magnetic dipole moment μ, is placed in a magnetic field of flux density B. (a) Show that when the dipole moment is brought slightly out of alignment with the magnetic field lines and is released, the dipole undergoes angular simple harmonic motion. (b) Show that the period of oscillations is given by $2\pi \sqrt{I/\mu B}$.

32-30 ★ (a) Show that the magnetic dipole moment of a particle of charge q and mass m, moving in an orbit, is proportional to the particle's angular momentum relative to an axis at the force center. (b) Show that the *magnetogyric ratio*—the ratio of the magnetic moment to the angular moment—is $(q/2m)$.

32-31 ★ Assume that an electron moves in a circular orbit with an angular frequency ω_0 under the influence of a centripetal force $m\omega_0^2 r$. A magnetic field B is applied at right angles to the plane of the orbit. (a) Show that, if the radius r remains the same, the new angular frequency is given by $\omega = \sqrt{\omega_0^2 + (eB/2m)^2} \pm (eB/2m)$. (b) In all cases of interest $(eB/2m) \ll \omega_0$. Using this approximation show that the final frequency is $f = f_0 + eB/4\pi m$, where $f_0 = \omega_0/2\pi$.

This is one example of the *Larmor theorem*, according to which the frequency of a motion under the influence of a magnetic field B is changed by $eB/4\pi m$. This effect is illustrated by the change in the frequency of light emitted by atoms placed in a magnetic field. The measured frequency shift, called the *Zeeman effect*, permitted the ratio q/m to be measured for the charged particles responsible for the light emission. Since this ratio agreed with the e/m ratio measured by Thomson for electrons in flight through a vacuum tube, it was shown that light emission has its origin in the motion of electrons within atoms.

THIRTY-THREE

THE SOURCES OF THE MAGNETIC FIELD

In the last chapter we dealt with one part of the magnetic interaction between charged particles in motion: the magnetic force on a charged particle moving in a magnetic field. Now we complete our discussion of the magnetic force by discussing how the magnetic induction field is created by moving electric charges, or electric currents.

We first consider the fundamental experiments of Oersted and Rowland, which established that a magnetic field has its origin in an electric current, or moving electric charges. Then we turn to the law of Biot and Savart, by which one may compute the magnetic field produced by a moving charge or by an element of electric current. Through this relation we find the magnetic field distribution for current-carrying conductors of several simple geometries. The force between two current-carrying conductors, the fundamental magnetic effect, leads to the definition of the ampere. We then consider Gauss's law for magnetism, the formal mathematical statement that magnetic field lines form closed loops and that isolated magnetic poles do not exist. Ampere's law permits us to find the current threading any loop by an examination of the magnetic field along the loop. Finally, we consider the solenoid as a current-carrying device of considerable practical importance.

33-1   The Oersted and Rowland experiments   How does one know whether a magnetic induction field **B** exists at any point in space? As we saw in Chapter 32, one may observe whether a charged particle fired into the region is acted upon by a magnetic force; this force is given by

[32-3] $$F_m = qv \times B$$

Unless the magnetic field is uniform, the path of the deflected charged particle may be complicated. Another procedure for exploring a magnetic

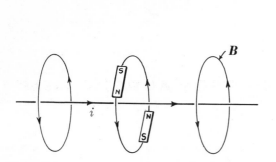

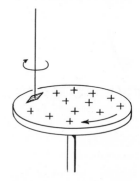

Figure 33-1. The Oersted effect: a current-carrying conductor generates magnetic field loops.

Figure 33-2. Schematic representation of the Rowland experiment: a charged rotating dielectric disc generates a magnetic field which acts on a magnet.

field is to observe the magnetic torque on an object such as a compass or a current-carrying conducting loop, with a magnetic dipole moment μ:

[32-20] $$\tau = \mu \times B$$

Freely turning magnetic dipoles line up with the magnetic field. Thus, one may explore a region in space, to find the magnetic field there, by using small permanent magnets or even small iron filings which, under the influence of a magnetic field, acquire a magnetic dipole moment and align themselves with the field.

Electric charges in motion create a magnetic field. This was first demonstrated in the fundamental experiments of H. C. Oersted (1777–1851) in 1820. Oersted showed that a current-carrying conductor could produce torques on magnetic dipoles surrounding it; see Figure 33-1. The magnetic field lines consist of circular loops surrounding the conductor and lying in planes perpendicular to that of the conductor. It is found that the sense of the magnetic field is related to the sense of the electric current through a right-hand rule: if the thumb of the right hand points in the direction of i, the right-hand fingers give the sense of the B lines. Reversing the current then reverses the direction of the magnetic field at each point. By observing the frequency at which a magnetic dipole oscillates when displaced from alignment with the magnetic field (high frequency for high B, low frequency for low B), one finds that the magnitude of the magnetic field drops off as one goes away from the conductor. One also finds that the magnitude of B at each point in space is directly proportional to the current i.

Now, an electric current within a conductor *implies* the motion of charged particles, and one may therefore infer from the Oersted effect that the magnetic field has its origin in the motion of charged particles through the conductor. But it is more satisfying to see this demonstrated directly, that is, to show that an electrically charged object in motion produces a magnetic torque on a compass. Such an experiment was performed by H. A. Rowland (1848–1901) in 1878. The essentials of the experimental arrangement are shown in Figure 33-2. A flat insulated dielectric disc, highly charged, is rotated at a high speed. The magnetic field produced by this charge in motion is detected by the torque on a permanent magnetic dipole suspended from a torsion fiber. The effect is actually very subtle, the magnetic field in Rowland's experiment being less than 0.001 gauss. (The reason is that in a current-carrying conductor there are many more charges in motion, albeit at relatively low speeds, then there are in the moving charged dielectric disc. Consequently, the magnitude of the current in the conductor is greater by far. Because the electric force is so very strong, it is difficult to keep very large charges on the rotating disc.)

Example 1   A magnetic dipole oscillates when displaced from alignment with an external magnetic field B. How is the period of oscillation T related to the magnitude of the field?

The magnitude of the magnetic torque on the dipole is given by

[32-20] $$\tau = \mu B \sin \theta$$

where μ is the magnetic dipole moment and θ is the angle between the magnetic field lines and the dipole axis. If θ is small, then $\sin \theta \simeq \theta$ and the above relation becomes

$$\tau = \mu B \theta = \kappa \theta$$

Here we write μB as the torque constant κ. This relation is merely Hooke's law for angular displacements: the restoring torque is proportional to the angular displacement from equilibrium. Therefore, the period of angular oscillation is given by

[17-16] $$T = 2\pi \sqrt{I/\kappa} = 2\pi \sqrt{I/\mu B}$$

The quantity I is the dipole's moment of inertia relative to the oscillation axis.

33-2   The Biot-Savart law   Here we set down the fundamental relation giving the magnetic field produced by a moving electric charge or, equivalently, by a small element of a current-carrying conductor. It is called the *Biot-Savart law*. Since the magnetic field from a single moving charge, or from a short element of current, is very feeble, one tests the correctness of the Biot-Savart law indirectly by noting that all predictions of the magnetic field made from it are in accord with observation.

Consider Figure 33-3, where we see a positive point-charge q in motion with the velocity v. We wish to find the magnetic field at some point in space, say P. The radius vector from the moving charge to the point P is r, and the angle between the vectors v and r is ϕ. The direction of the magnetic induction field B at point P, perpendicular to the plane containing the vectors v and r, is given by a right-hand rule: if the vector v (for a positive charge) is imagined to be turned through the smaller angle into alignment with r by the right-hand fingers, then the right-hand thumb gives the direction of B.

The magnitude of B at point P is given by

$$B = \left(\frac{\mu_0}{4\pi}\right)\frac{qv \sin \phi}{r^2} \qquad \text{[33-1]}$$

The induction field is proportional to the charge and its speed and inversely proportional to the square of the distance. Since B also varies as $\sin \phi$, the field is zero along the line containing the velocity vector.

The quantity μ_0, called the *permeability of free space*, is a constant and, in the rationalized mksa system of units, is *assigned* the numerical value

$$\mu_0 = 4\pi \times 10^{-7} \text{ weber/amp-m} \qquad \text{[33-2]}$$

The reader should verify that, when μ_0 is given the units webers per ampere-meters, the magnetic field B in Equation 33-1 has the units webers per square meter or their equivalent, newtons per ampere-meter. The factor 4π appears in the Biot-Savart relation *so that* it will not appear later in the mathematical formulation of Ampere's law (Equation 33-23). (This parallels the situation for the electric force: in the rationalized unit system, 4π appears in Coulomb's law but then does not appear in Gauss's law.)

From Equation 33-1 we see that the magnetic induction field at a perpendicular distance of one meter from a one-coulomb charge moving at one meter per second is $B = 10^{-7}$ weber/m², or 10^{-3} gauss.

We can incorporate the relative directions of v, r, and B in Biot-Savart's law by writing Equation 33-1 in vector form with the cross product:

$$B = \left(\frac{\mu_0}{4\pi}\right)\frac{qv \times r}{r^3} \qquad \text{[33-3]}$$

Note that the distance r now appears to the third power in the denominator, to compensate for the additional factor r in the numerator.

It is easy to see that the magnetic field lines associated with a moving charge consist of circular loops centered about the moving charge and lying in planes perpendicular to the particle's velocity, as shown in Figure 33-4. Imagine all quantities on the right side of Equation 33-3, except the direction of r, to be fixed. Then turn the vector r about the vector v, while keeping the angle ϕ between them fixed. The vector B, unchanged in magnitude, then turns through a circle in a transverse plane.

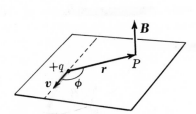

Figure 33-3. A moving charged particle and the magnetic field B at point P.

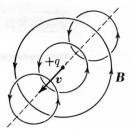

Figure 33-4. Magnetic field loops from a moving charged particle.

Although the Biot-Savart relation must be expressed fundamentally in terms of the magnetic field produced by a moving charge, we shall deal primarily with current-carrying conductors in applying this relation. Therefore, we wish to have an expression for the magnetic field dB produced by an infinitesimal current element dl carrying the current i. The direction of the length element dl is chosen to correspond to the direction of conventional current through it; that is, dl corresponds to the direction of moving positive charges. We found earlier that

[32-3], [32-15] $$qv = i\,dl$$

Using this identity in Equation 33-3, we have the Biot-Savart law for a current element:

$$dB = \left(\frac{\mu_0}{4\pi}\right)\frac{i\,dl \times r}{r^3} \qquad \text{[33-4]}$$

The field dB is now written in differential form. This is necessary, since we can never have a single infinitesimal current element contributing the magnetic field at a given point. All current elements of the loop contribute their respective differential fields at a given point. The resultant field B is the vector sum of the infinitesimal fields; see Figure 33-5.

Now that we know the magnetic field created by one electric charge in motion and also the magnetic force it exerts on a second moving charge, we are prepared to write down the entire magnetic interaction. Here we take charge q_a as creating the magnetic field B_a, which then acts on moving charge q_b. From Equations 33-3 and 32-3 we have the following.

Magnetic interaction between charges:

$$B_a = \left(\frac{\mu_0}{4\pi}\right)\frac{q_a v_a \times r}{r^3} \quad \text{and} \quad F_b = q_b v_b \times B_a \qquad [33\text{-}5]$$

The radius vector r extends from q_a to q_b.

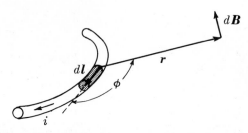

Figure 33-5. Magnetic field from an element dL of a current-carrying conductor.

The corresponding relations for the electric force between the two charges are the following.

Electric interaction between charges[6]

$$E_a = \left(\frac{1}{4\pi\epsilon_0}\right)\frac{q_a r}{r^3} \quad \text{and} \quad F_b = q_b E_a \qquad [33\text{-}6]$$

Combining the two separate relations in Equation 33-6 into a single one we have

Electric force:

$$F_e = \left(\frac{1}{4\pi\epsilon_0}\right)\frac{q_a q_b r}{r^3}$$

This is, of course, just Coulomb's law in vector form.

When we combine the two relations in Equation 33-5 we get

Magnetic force:

$$F_m = \left(\frac{\mu_0}{4\pi}\right)\frac{q_a q_b v_b \times (v_a \times r)}{r^3}$$

This, the fundamental relation for the magnetic interaction, is mathematically complicated by the appearance of a double cross product. Altogether, it is quite cumbersome. It is far simpler to deal with the magnetic force in two steps—through the intermediary of the magnetic field, as given in Equation 33-5—and this has been just our procedure.

We now know the part of the force between charged particles that does not depend on their speeds (the electric force) and we also know the velocity-dependent part of the interaction between charged particles (the magnetic force). We might be inclined to think that, in so far as basic electromagnetism is concerned, this is the whole story. It is not! Not only can electric and magnetic fields be created by electric charges at rest or in motion, but an electric field can be created by a changing magnetic field (Chapter 34) and a magnetic field can be created by a changing electric field (Section 38-1). Furthermore, we shall see (Chapter 41) that electric and magnetic fields can become detached from accelerated electric charges and so exist independently as electromagnetic waves.

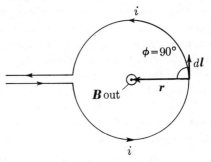

Figure 33-6. Magnetic field at the center of a circular conducting loop.

33-3 The magnetic field for some simple geometries

The law of Biot-Savart, Equation 33-4, gives the magnetic field produced by an *infinitesimal* current element. No such isolated current element can exist by itself, however. There is always a complete loop of current in any circuit. Therefore, to find the magnetic field arising from a current-carrying conductor at any point, we must sum up, or integrate, the contributions from all significant current elements.

CENTER OF CIRCULAR LOOP   First consider the magnetic induction field at the center of a plane circular loop of radius r carrying current i; see Figure 33-6. We must, of course, have current leads to and from the loop but, if these two conducting wires are placed together, their magnetic effects cancel exactly because there are equal currents in opposite directions. The direction of the magnetic field dB produced by the element dl along the circumference is perpendicular to the plane of the paper and is out of the paper. Indeed, all elements of the loop contribute to the field at the center in the same direction, so that we may sum these contributions algebraically. The angle ϕ between r and dl is 90°; therefore, Equation 33-4 gives for the magnitude of dB

$$\int dB = \left(\frac{\mu_0}{4\pi}\right) i \cdot \frac{\int dl}{r^2} = \left(\frac{\mu_0}{4\pi}\right) \frac{i2\pi r}{r^2}$$

The radius vector r here is equal in magnitude to the radius of the loop. In summing the length element around the circle above we get simply the circumference $2\pi r$, so that the field B at the center of the loop is

$$B = \frac{\mu_0 i}{2r} \qquad [33\text{-}7]$$

Figure 33-7 shows the magnetic field lines in a plane transverse to the plane of the loop through the axis. Near the conducting wires the field lines are almost circular, since at such locations the more distant current elements are unimportant. The field lines are symmetrical about the loop's axis of symmetry. We may, of course, find the direction of the magnetic field at the loop's center by applying the right-hand rule to an element of the loop, taking the right-hand thumb to give the current direction and the right-hand fingers to give the magnetic field loops. But we can also relate the current and field directions as follows. Let the fingers of the right hand give the sense of the *current* around the loop; then the right-hand thumb points in the direction of the magnetic *field* at the loop's center.

To get an idea of the magnitude of the field from a circular loop, suppose that a current of 10 amp flows through a loop having a radius of 2π cm. Then, from Equation 33-7, the field at the center is

$$B = \frac{(4\pi \times 10^{-7} \text{ weber/amp-m})(10 \text{ amp})}{2(2\pi \times 10^{-2} \text{ m})} = 10^{-4} \text{ weber/m}^2 = 1 \text{ gauss}$$

The field in this situation is just slightly greater than the Earth's magnetic field. Of course, if there were N nearly coincident circular loops, the field at all points would be enhanced by the factor N.

LONG STRAIGHT CONDUCTOR Now we find the magnetic field produced by a current i through an infinitely long straight conducting wire. Of course, no such conductor can be constructed, since there must always be return leads; therefore, the results we shall find will apply whenever the distance from a straight wire is small compared with the distance out to where the straight wire bends.

We first concentrate on the field dB at the point P produced by a straight current element dx, Figure 33-8. For the upward current direction shown, the field at P is into the paper and is a perpendicular distance R from the conductor. The angle between the current element and the radius vector r is φ. From Equation 33-4 we have

$$dB = \left(\frac{\mu_0}{4\pi}\right)\frac{i\,dx\,\sin\phi}{r^2} \qquad [33\text{-}8]$$

Now, every current element of the conductor produces a field into the paper at P, so that we merely integrate this equation over the entire length of the conductor, to find the total field. The quantities x, r, and ϕ are not

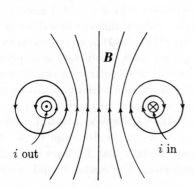

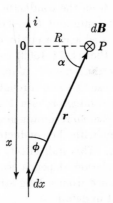

Figure 33-7. Magnetic field lines in a plane transverse to a circular conducting loop.

Figure 33-8. Magnetic field from a long straight current-carrying conductor.

independent; in fact, we can write Equation 33-8 in terms of a single variable. The integration is most easily carried out if we choose the angle α, the complement of ϕ, as the variable. From the geometry of Figure 33-8 we see that

$$x = R \tan \alpha$$

Hence,
$$dx = R \sec^2 \alpha\, d\alpha$$

Also,
$$r = R \sec \alpha$$

and
$$\sin \phi = \cos \alpha$$

Making these substitutions in Equation 33-8, we have

$$dB = \left(\frac{\mu_0}{4\pi}\right)\frac{i(R \sec^2 \alpha\, d\alpha)(\cos \alpha)}{(R \sec \alpha)^2} = \left(\frac{\mu_0}{4\pi}\right)\frac{i}{R}\cos \alpha\, d\alpha$$

To account for the entire infinite length of the conductor, we integrate from $\alpha = -90°$ to $90°$. Therefore,

$$\int dB = \frac{\mu_0 i}{4\pi R} \int_{-\pi/2}^{\pi/2} \cos \alpha \, d\alpha$$

$$B = \frac{\mu_0 i}{2\pi R} \qquad [33\text{-}9]$$

The magnetic field consists of circular loops circling the conductor in planes transverse to the wire, the magnitude of the field falling off inversely as the distance from the conductor. (It is easy to show from Equation 33-9 that, for $i = 10$ amp and $R = 2$ cm, the induction field B is just 1 gauss.) This can be tested accurately by experiment. Indeed, this was first done in 1820 by J. B. Biot (1774–1862) and F. Savart (1791–1841) in an ingenious experimental arrangement. A magnet is placed on a freely rotatable platform along whose axis and through which runs perpendicularly a straight current-carrying conductor; see Figure 33-9. When the current is turned on in either sense, *no* resultant magnetic torque acts on the magnet about an axis coincident with the conductor. Hence, the platform on which it rests does not turn. This null effect, which is one direct confirmation of the Biot-Savart relation, depends crucially upon the fact that B varies inversely as the distance from a long straight conductor. The reader should carry out the proof in detail.

It is interesting to compare Equation 33-9, which gives the magnetic field from a long straight current-carrying conductor, with Equation 26-6, which gives the electric field of a uniformly charged infinite wire: $E = (1/2\pi\epsilon_0)(\lambda/r)$. Both are of similar form, and this is hardly surprising. The electric and magnetic fields both fall off inversely as r, a consequence of the fact that the electric and magnetic interactions between *point*-charges are both inverse-*square*. The current i is a measure of the source of the magnetic field, and the linear charge density λ is a measure of the source of the electric field. The quantities ϵ_0 and μ_0 are proportionality constants for the electric and magnetic interactions, respectively.

FIELD FAR FROM A CURRENT LOOP   Now let us find the magnetic field at a great distance r along the axis of the circular current loop of radius R carrying current i; see Figure 33-10. We first concentrate on the magnetic field $d\mathbf{B}$ produced by a current element at the top of the loop. From Equation 33-4, the direction of $d\mathbf{B}$ is perpendicular to both $d\mathbf{l}$ and $\mathbf{d}$. Its magnitude is

$$dB = \left(\frac{\mu_0}{4\pi}\right)\frac{i\,dl}{d^2} \simeq \left(\frac{\mu_0}{4\pi}\right)\frac{i\,dl}{r^2} \qquad [33\text{-}10]$$

Here we have taken the distance d, from point P to the upper portion of the loop, to be the same as the distance r to the loop's center, since we assume that $R \ll r$. When we consider the field contribution from a diametrically opposite element of the loop, we see that its field cancels the component $d\mathbf{B}_\perp$ of $d\mathbf{B}$, which is perpendicular to the axis of the loop. In fact, this cancellation of perpendicular components occurs for all pairs of length elements around the loop, so that we need consider only the component along

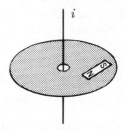

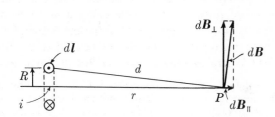

Figure 33-9. Experimental arrangement of Biot and Savart for showing that the magnitude of the magnetic field from a long straight current-carrying conductor varies inversely as the distance from the conductor.

Figure 33-10. Magnetic field at a large distance from a circular conducting loop.

the loop axis. From the geometry of Figure 33-10, the parallel component $d\mathbf{B}_{\parallel}$ of $d\mathbf{B}$ is seen to have the magnitude.

$$dB_{\parallel} = (R/d)\, dB \simeq (R/r)\, dB$$

Using Equation 33-11, we then have

$$dB_{\parallel} = \left(\frac{\mu_0}{4\pi}\right)\frac{Ri\, dl}{r^3}$$

Every current element $d\mathbf{l}$ contributes the same magnitude and direction to the field at point P; thus, the total field at P from the entire loop is

$$B = \int dB_{\parallel} = \left(\frac{\mu_0}{4\pi}\right)\frac{Ri}{r^3}\oint dl$$

The integration is trivial with $\oint dl = 2\pi R$, and we have

$$B = \left(\frac{\mu_0}{2\pi}\right)\frac{(\pi R^2 i)}{r^3} \qquad\qquad [33\text{-}11]$$

From Equation 32-19 we recognize the quantity $(\pi R^2 i)$, the product of the loop's area and current, to be the magnetic dipole moment μ of the current loop. Therefore, Equation 33-11 can be written as

$$B = \left(\frac{\mu_0}{2\pi}\right)\frac{\mu}{r^3} \qquad [33\text{-}12]$$

It can be shown that Equation 33-12 holds for any magnetic dipole loop, circular or otherwise, as long as the distance r is large compared with the dimensions of the loop. Thus, the magnetic field along the axis of a dipole is proportional to the dipole moment and falls off inversely as the *cube* of the distance. Indeed, this variation is found for any direction from the magnetic dipole. It is altogether similar to the variation in the electric field at large distances from an electric dipole (see Example 2, Chapter 26).

Example 2 Find the magnetic field at the center of a square conducting loop having sides of length L and carrying current i.

If we take the current to be in the clockwise sense, Figure 33-11, we see that all four sides of the loop will produce a magnetic field into the paper at the center of the loop. Therefore, the total field B at the center is just four times the contribution from any one side. We can find the field arising from a straight conductor of *finite* length by using appropriate limits on the integral preceding Equation 33-9, which was used to find the field from an infinite straight conductor. The angle α is now to be integrated from $-45°$ to $45°$, and the distance R is now $\frac{1}{2}L$.

Thus, the total field is given by

$$B = 4B_{\text{one side}} = 4\left(\frac{\mu_0}{4\pi}\right)\frac{i}{\frac{1}{2}L}\int_{-\pi/4}^{\pi/4}\cos\alpha\,d\alpha$$

$$= \frac{2\sqrt{2}\,\mu_0 i}{\pi L}$$

The reader should confirm that this result falls between the field at the center of a circular loop of radius $L/2$ and the field at the center of a circular loop of radius $\sqrt{2}L/2$, as it must.

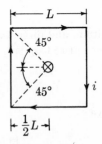

Figure 33-11

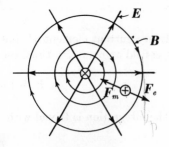

Figure 33-12

Example 3 A straight conducting wire with current i into the paper carries a uniform positive charge of linear charge density λ. At what speed can a charged particle be fired parallel to the straight conductor and in the direction of the current so as to maintain its constant speed in a straight line?

The radial electric field and the circular concentric magnetic field loops are shown in Figure 33-12. A positively charged particle traveling at speed v into the paper is subject to an electric force $F_e = qE$ radially outward and a magnetic force $F_m = qvB$ radially inward. (A *negatively* charged particle also traveling *into* the paper is subject to electric and magnetic forces in the reverse directions. On the other hand, for a charged particle of either sign traveling *out* of the paper, both the electric and magnetic forces are in the *same* direction.)

The charged particle is undeflected when

$$F_e = F_m, \quad \text{or} \quad qE = qvB$$
$$v = E/B$$

Note that the relation is the same as for the velocity selector, Equations 32-9. Now the magnetic and electric fields are given by

[33-9] $$B = \mu_0 i/2\pi R$$
[26-6] $$E = \lambda/2\pi\epsilon_0 R$$

Therefore, substituting for E and B above, we have

$$v = \lambda/i(\epsilon_0\mu_0)$$

Note that the charged particle's distance R from the wire cancels out.

It is easy to show that the magnetic force is typically much less than the electric force by assuming that a charged particle moves at 1.0 m/sec parallel to a wire with a current of 1.0 amp. Then the relation for v, given above, shows that the required linear charge density is a mere 10^{-17} coul/m $= 10^{-5}$ $\mu\mu$coul/m.

33-4 Some special properties of the magnetic interaction We first look at the situation shown in Figure 33-13a, in which two positively charged particles a and b are moving at right angles to one another. An electric repulsive force acts on each of the two particles, and these two equal and opposite Coulomb forces act along the line connecting the particles. Now consider the magnetic interaction. From Equation 33-3 we see that a produces *no* magnetic field at charge b, while there *is* a magnetic field at a arising from the motion of b. Consequently, a magnetic force F_m acts on a, as shown in the figure, but *no* magnetic force acts on b! As far as the magnetic forces are concerned, there is a violation, or an apparent violation, of Newton's third law of motion. Another way of saying the same thing is this: the system consisting of the two interacting particles *violates* the fundamental law of linear momentum conservation and, inasmuch as the resultant force on one particle is *not* equal and opposite to the resultant force on the other, the two particles gain linear momentum at *different* rates.

The paradox is resolved when we define "the system" to include not only the interacting particles but also the electric and magnetic fields surrounding them. As we shall see in Section 41-3, one may attribute linear momentum

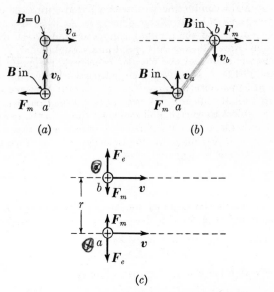

Figure 33-13. (a) A magnetic force acts on only *one* of two interacting charged particles. (b) The magnetic forces between the two moving charged particles do *not* lie along the line joining the charges. (c) Electric and magnetic forces between charged particles moving together in parallel lines.

to an electromagnetic field; that is, an electromagnetic field in itself is capable of exerting a force. The linear momentum carried by the electromagnetic field is, as detailed analysis shows, just sufficient to insure that the total linear momentum of the entire system of interacting charges and fields is indeed constant.

Now consider the situation shown in Figure 33-13b, where two charges *a* and *b* are moving in opposite directions. Here again the electric forces are equal and opposite, and act along the line joining the particles. Furthermore, the magnetic forces are equal in magnitude and opposite in direction, but they do *not* act along the line joining the charges. The magnetic force is *not*, in general, a *central force*. Including in the system only the angular momenta of the two charges, we find a *violation* of the conservation law of angular momentum, and again it is the electromagnetic field of the charges which saves the conservation law. As we shall see in Section 47-6, an electromagnetic field in itself can carry angular momentum; that is, an electromagnetic field is capable of exerting a torque. Including the angular momentum of both the particles and the field, we find no violation of the conservation law.

Now let us find the relative magnitudes of the magnetic force and the electric force between two interacting charges. A simple arrangement is shown in Figure 33-13c, where two positive charges, a and b, both of magnitude q, are initially traveling side by side in the same direction and with the same initial velocity v. The electric force between them is repulsive; its magnitude on either charge is

$$F_e = \left(\frac{1}{4\pi\epsilon_0}\right)\frac{q^2}{r^2} \qquad [33\text{-}13]$$

where r is the charge separation distance.

The magnetic field at charge a arising from charge b is into the paper, and that at b arising from a is out of the paper. The magnetic forces, now along the line joining the particles, are attractive. Thus, for the situation shown in Figure 33-13c, the charges repel by the Coulomb force and attract by the magnetic force.

The magnitude of the magnetic force F_m on either charge (the angle between v and B being 90°) is

[32-3] $\qquad\qquad\qquad F_m = qvB \qquad\qquad\qquad [33\text{-}14]$

The magnetic field B at the site of one charge arising from the second has the magnitude

[33-1] $$B = \left(\frac{\mu_0}{4\pi}\right)\frac{qv}{r^2} \qquad [33\text{-}15]$$

Again the angle between the radius r and the velocity v is 90°. Combining Equations 33-14 and 33-15, we have

$$F_m = \left(\frac{\mu_0}{4\pi}\right)\frac{q^2v^2}{r^2}$$

and taking the ratio of the magnetic to the electric force (Equation 33-13), we have

$$F_m/F_e = (\epsilon_0\mu_0)v^2 \qquad [33\text{-}16]$$

The charge magnitudes cancel out (they could have been *unequal*), as does the separation distance r.

The force ratio depends only on the particles' speed v and the quantity $\epsilon_0\mu_0$, involving the fundamental constants of the electric and magnetic fields. We shall later see (Section 41-1) that, both in magnitude and dimensions,

[41-9] $$\epsilon_0\mu_0 = \frac{1}{(3.0 \times 10^8 \text{ m/sec})^2} = \frac{1}{c^2}$$

where c is 3.0×10^8 m/sec, the speed of light. Therefore, we can write Equation 33-16 still more simply as

$$F_m/F_e = (v/c)^2 \qquad [33\text{-}17]$$

The magnetic force is smaller than the electric force by a factor $(v/c)^2$, a number which is very small indeed unless the particle speed is comparable to the speed of light. Thus, the magnetic force is ordinarily very much weaker than the electric force.

How is it, then, that one can so readily observe the magnetic force? It is simply that commonly one deals, not with two interacting point-charges, as in Figure 33-13, but with magnetic fields from *electrically neutral* current-carrying conductors. The feeble magnetic force can manifest itself because the much stronger electric force is masked by the presence of equal amounts of positive and negative charge.

Having just seen that the magnetic force is typically very small compared with the electric force, let us now see how one can make the magnetic force between the interacting charges exactly *zero*. We shall use a simple stratagem. We observe the two particles of Figure 33-13c from a different frame of reference, one moving with the speed v to the right, in which the two particles are then seen to be (momentarily) *at rest*. In this reference frame, the electric force is still present, but the magnetic force has, so to speak, been turned off. This is an extraordinary result. One can turn the magnetic force on or off and vary the magnitude of the magnetic interaction, simply by the arbitrary choice of a reference frame!

It would seem that the magnetic field and the magnetic interaction are not effects independent of the electric interaction, but rather are intimately related to it and to reference frames. This is precisely the case. The theory of special relativity shows that, in a sense, magnetic effects are really just manifestations of, and can be derived from, electric effects. Electromagnetic theory is inextricably involved in the theory of relativity.†

33-5 The magnetic force between current-carrying conductors
Let us take another look at the magnetic force on a single straight conducting wire with current i in a uniform magnetic field, as shown in Figure 33-14a. The current is out of the paper; the uniform field B is to the right. Applying the relation

[32-14] $$F_m = iL \times B$$ [33-18]

we find the direction of the magnetic force to be upward as shown. Since the conductor and field lines are at right angles, the magnitude of F_m is simply iLB.

Now, the combined magnetic field in the vicinity of the conductor consists of the applied field B together with the magnetic field produced by the current in the conductor. The circular field lines from the straight conductor are

† For a development of electromagnetic theory from the point of view of relativity, at a moderately sophisticated level, see E. M. Purcell, *Berkeley Physics Course*, Vol. II, McGraw-Hill, 1965.

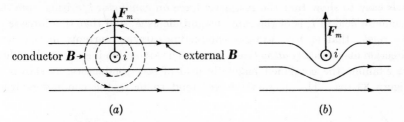

Figure 33-14. The magnetic force on a current-carrying conductor in an external magnetic field. (a) The external magnetic field and the field of the conductor (dotted) shown separately. (b) The combined magnetic field of external field and conductor.

shown dotted in Figure 33-14a. The resultant field, found by adding the separate magnetic fields vectorially, is shown in Figure 33-14b. We see that this field is intense below the conductor and weak above it. We have already determined that the magnetic force on the conductor is upward. Therefore, when we consider the total magnetic field, the magnetic force on a conductor is in that direction which will take it from a region of strong field toward a region of weak field. This is simply an alternative, and often useful, procedure for finding the direction of the magnetic force. Note, however, that in computing the magnetic force we include only the external field on the conductor, not the field which the conductor itself generates.

Now let us find the magnetic force between two long straight parallel wires separated by a distance d. Let the currents be i_a and i_b, and first suppose that the currents are in the same direction; see Figure 33-15. We see the magnetic field loops from current i_a producing a magnetic field whose magnitude B_a at the site of wire b is, by Equation 33-9,

$$B_a = \left(\frac{\mu_0}{2\pi}\right)\frac{i_a}{d} \qquad [33\text{-}19]$$

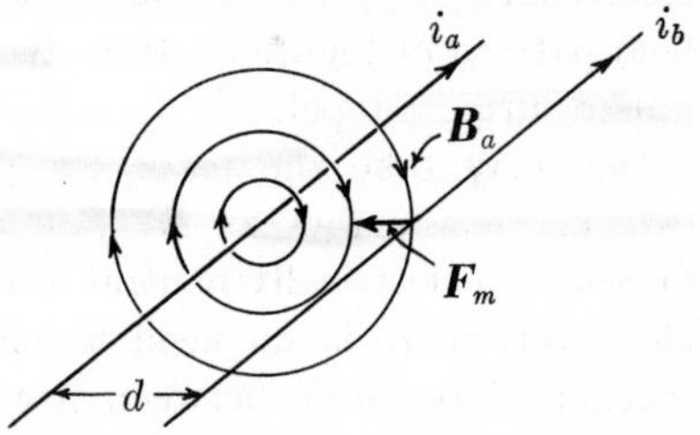

Figure 33-15. The magnetic force of conductor a on the parallel conductor b.

The magnetic force F_b on current i_b in the magnetic field B_a is, from Equation 33-18, to the left and of magnitude

$$F_b = i_b L B_a \qquad [33\text{-}20]$$

where L is the length of both interacting conductors. Substituting Equation 33-19 in Equation 33-20 we have then

$$F_b = \left(\frac{\mu_0}{2\pi}\right)\frac{i_a i_b L}{d} \qquad [33\text{-}21]$$

It is easy to show that the magnetic force on conductor i_a arising from the magnetic field of i_b is of the same magnitude as F_b and that this force is to the *right*; that is, two straight conductors carrying currents in the *same* direction magnetically *attract* each other. The attraction is evident also when we examine the combined magnetic field of *both* conductors, as shown in Figure 33-16a. The magnetic forces tend to move the conductors from

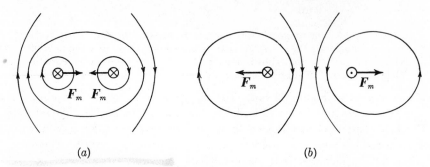

(a)   (b)

Figure 33-16. Magnetic fields and magnetic forces for two parallel conductors with currents in (a) the same direction and (b) in opposite directions.

regions of strong to weak magnetic field. On the other hand, if the currents are in *opposite* directions, the two conductors *repel* one another, as can be confirmed by applying Equation 33-18 and also by examining the magnetic field pattern in Figure 33-16b. Roughly speaking, like currents attract and unlike currents repel.

One may take the magnetic attraction between two parallel current-carrying conductors as *the fundamental magnetic effect*. Since the conductors are electrically neutral, there can be no complicating electric forces. Moreover, there is no need to employ magnetic materials as such. The magnetic interaction between straight conductors was first studied in 1822 by A. M. Ampère (1775–1836), who found that the force varied inversely as the separation distance, in agreement with Equation 33-21.

Let us find the magnitude of the magnetic force from Equation 33-21, assuming two conductors each carrying a current of exactly 1 amp and separated by exactly 1 m. The magnetic force per unit length, F/L, on either conductor is

$$F/L = \left(\frac{\mu_0}{2\pi}\right)\frac{i_a i_b}{d} = \frac{(4\pi \times 10^{-7} \text{ weber/amp-m})(1 \text{ amp})^2}{2\pi(1 \text{ m})}$$

$$= 2 \times 10^{-7} \text{ nt/m}$$

Note that 1 weber = 1 nt-m/amp. The force per meter is *exactly* 2×10^{-7} newton.

Recall that the permeability constant μ_0 is *assigned* the value $4\pi \times 10^{-7}$ weber/amp-m. Actually, the relation giving the magnetic force between two parallel straight conductors serves to *define the ampere* as the unit of electric current in the mksa system of units. At long last we have the *definition* of the ampere (and therefore also of the coulomb, which is one ampere-second): the equal currents in two parallel straight conductors separated by one meter in a vacuum are each, *by definition*, exactly one ampere when the magnetic force per unit length between them is exactly 2×10^{-7} nt/m. The quantities can be measured with precision: the magnetic force can be compared through a balance with a standard weight, and the lengths can be calibrated against the standard meter. In practice, the so-called current balance used in measuring the magnetic force employs two parallel concentric plane circular *loops* of current, rather than two straight conductors, because complications arising from noninfinite straight conductors are thereby avoided.

33-6 Gauss's law for magnetism   First recall Gauss's law for electricity:

[27-3] $$\phi_E = \oint \boldsymbol{E} \cdot d\boldsymbol{S} = q/\epsilon_0$$

The total electric flux ϕ_E through any closed surface is proportional to q, the net charge enclosed by the surface. Gauss's law implies that the Coulomb force between point-charges is inverse-square, that electric field lines terminate on electric charges, and that electric fields may be superposed as vectors. Furthermore, Gauss's law justifies representing the direction and magnitude of an electric field at any point by the direction and density of electric field lines through a transverse area at that point.

A similar law can be written for the magnetic flux ϕ_B

[32-4] $$\phi_B = \int \boldsymbol{B} \cdot d\boldsymbol{S}$$

Since the magnetic force between moving point-charges is also an inverse-square force, one may properly represent the flux density $\boldsymbol{B}$ of a magnetic induction field by magnetic field lines. Such lines indicate the direction of the field at any point in space by their tangent, and their "density" through a transverse area is proportional to the magnitude of the field $\boldsymbol{B}$.

We find the total magnetic flux $\oint \boldsymbol{B} \cdot d\boldsymbol{S}$ through any closed surface by adding the contributions $\boldsymbol{B} \cdot d\boldsymbol{S}$ from all small surface elements. By convention, the vector $d\boldsymbol{S}$ is taken as positive when it points toward the outside of a closed surface; see Figure 33-17. Then, the magnetic flux is positive when the magnetic lines pass outward through a surface and is negative when the lines pass inward. If the total magnetic flux over a closed surface

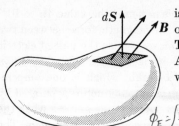

Figure 33-17. Magnetic flux through the outward surface element dS.

is zero, it is implied that an equal number of magnetic lines enter and leave the surface. This is precisely what is found in every case. All experimental observations are consistent with the statement:

$$\phi_E = \int \vec{E} \cdot d\vec{S} = \frac{q}{\varepsilon_0} \qquad \phi_B = \oint \boldsymbol{B} \cdot d\boldsymbol{S} = 0 \qquad [33\text{-}22]$$

This is *Gauss's law for magnetism*. What it says, in effect, is this: one can never find a magnetic field line terminating on anything but its own tail end; or, magnetic field lines always form closed loops. If this were not the case, one would find situations in which the magnetic flux out of some closed surface would not match exactly the magnetic flux into the same surface. That is, if the magnetic flux were not always zero through a closed surface, the magnetic field lines would terminate on magnetic "charges," or single magnetic poles, in the same way that electric field lines terminate on electric charges.

What about permanent magnets, then, with which one clearly sees (in magnetized iron filings) field lines emanating from what appear to be magnetic poles at the ends of the magnet, as in Figure 33-18? The magnetic field lines do not originate in a single magnetic pole at the "north" end of a magnet and then terminate on another single magnetic pole at the "south" end. The field lines *pass through* the interior of the magnet, again forming closing loops.

Gauss's law for magnetism asserts that no isolated magnetic poles, or magnetic monopoles, exist in nature. The most subtle experiments confirm this.

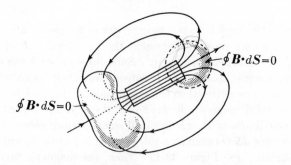

Figure 33-18. Gauss's law for magnetism: the net magnetic flux through any closed surface is zero.

33-7   Ampère's law   Ampère's law is an alternative to the Biot-Savart relation for electric currents and the magnetic field they generate. In some ways it is analogous to Gauss's law for electricity, which is an alternative formulation of Coulomb's law. Ampère's law is particularly useful for finding the magnetic field in situations of high geometrical symmetry.

First consider again the relation for the magnetic field produced by an infinitely long straight conductor:

[33-9] $$B = \frac{\mu_0 i}{2\pi R}$$

Rearranging, we have

$$B(2\pi R) = \mu_0 i$$

We recognize the left-hand side of this equation as the field B, at all points a distance R from the conductor, multiplied by $2\pi R$, the circumference of a circular loop at this distance; see Figure 33-19. We may write this as

$$\oint \boldsymbol{B} \cdot d\boldsymbol{l} = \mu_0 i \qquad \text{[33-23]}$$

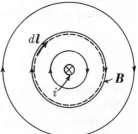

Figure 33-19. Magnetic-field for a straight conductor.

where the line integral on the left-hand side of the equation implies that we take the component of $\boldsymbol{B}$ along the path element $d\boldsymbol{l}$ around a closed loop. Of course, with a circular loop about a straight conductor, the direction of $\boldsymbol{B}$ always coincides with the direction of $d\boldsymbol{l}$, provided that we traverse the loop in the same direction as the magnetic field line. The current i is the current enclosed by the loop about the conductor.

Now, the remarkable thing about Equation 33-23, which is the formal statement of *Ampère's law*, is this: it holds for *any* closed path about *any* configuration of electric conductors when the current i is taken to be the net current enclosed by the loop. Let us prove it.

We first restrict ourselves to the field from a single infinitely long straight conductor and to path loops in a plane perpendicular to the conductor. Consider the loop of Figure 33-20a. Here we have a path consisting of circular arcs coinciding with the field lines, and of radial lines at right angles to the field lines. The field has magnitude B_1 for radius r_1 and B_2 for radius r_2. From Equation 33-9, $B_1 r_1 = B_2 r_2$; that is, the field falls off inversely as the distance from the conductor. Along the radial lines there is no contribution to the line integral, since $\boldsymbol{B} \perp d\boldsymbol{l}$ along these segments. Moreover, if the path is traversed in the same sense as the magnetic field lines, we see

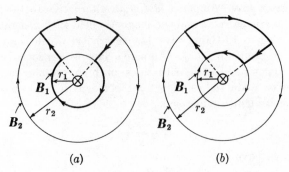

(a)   (b)

Figure 33-20. (a) When the loop encloses the current, the line integral $\oint B \cdot dl$ is $\mu_0 i$; (b) when it does not, the line integral is zero.

that the decrease from B_1 to B_2 in going from r_1 to r_2 is exactly matched by the change in the arc lengths. For this loop, then, we again have

[33-23] $$\oint B \cdot dl = \mu_0 i$$

Now suppose the path loop does *not* enclose the conductor, as in Figure 33-20b. Again there is no contribution to the line integral along the radial lines. Once more $B_1 r_1 = B_2 r_2$, so that the contributions along the two circular arcs are of the same magnitude. The signs, however, are now different. If the path is traversed in the same direction as the field along the arc of radius r_1, it is traversed in the opposite sense for r_2, and conversely.

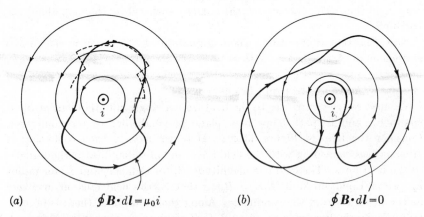

(a) $\oint B \cdot dl = \mu_0 i$ (b) $\oint B \cdot dl = 0$

Figure 33-21. Ampère's law applied to a general loop shape (a) enclosing the conductor and (b) not enclosing the conductor.

Consequently, the *total* line integral is now zero:

$$\oint B \cdot dl = 0$$

This corresponds to zero current threading the chosen path loop.

It is easy to deal with more complicated paths. One may regard a path of arbitrary shape as replaced by a number of circular arcs and radial segments; see Figure 33-21. In every case, then, the line integral of the magnetic induction field around a closed path is equal to the current threading the loop multiplied by μ_0. Notice, further, that if we reverse the sense in which the path is traversed, a factor -1 appears on the left side of Equation 33-23. This corresponds to the fact that when the current direction is reversed, the sense of the magnetic field lines is also reversed. A path that does *not* lie in a plane transverse to the conductor introduces no complications, since the magnetic field from a long straight conductor is confined entirely to transverse planes; traversing a path element parallel to the conductor will not contribute to the line integral.

Now suppose that we have two or more infinitely long conductors, not necessarily parallel to one another nor carrying the same current. This introduces nothing new. Magnetic fields are added by using the rules of vector addition; therefore, if Ampère's law applies to any one conductor, it also applies to a collection of conductors. We must, however, take the current i to be the *net* current enclosed by the chosen path loop, using *different* signs for currents into and out of one side of the path loop. To show that Ampère's law holds for conductors of any shape, not merely long straight conductors, one proves that *any* current distribution and its associated magnetic field can be replaced by equivalent straight conductors (the proof is complicated and will be omitted here).

In summary, if we know the line integral of the magnetic field around a closed loop, we know at once the net current threading the loop. If the line integral is zero, there can be no net current within. Currents *outside* the loop make no contribution. Although Ampère's law is altogether general, it is easy to apply in practice only when the magnetic field has a geometry that can be deduced in advance on the basis of symmetry. Then we know what sort of path to choose. (This is reminiscent of Gauss's law for electricity: if the geometry of the electric field is known in advance on the basis of symmetry, we know how best to choose the Guassian surface.)

One final remark concerning Ampère's law must be made at this point: as written in Equation 33-23, it is *not* complete. In Section 38-1 we shall see that a changing electric flux, as well as an enclosed current, can contribute to the line integral of the magnetic field.

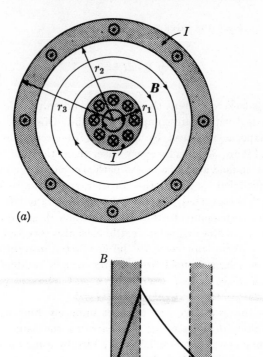

Figure 33-22. (a) A pair of coaxial conductors carrying equal but opposite currents. (b) Magnitude of B as a function of r for part (a).

Example 4   A coaxial conductor consists of a solid inner cylinder, of radius r_1 and carrying a current I, and a concentric outer conductor, of inner and outer radii r_2 and r_3 and carrying a current I in the opposite direction; see Figure 33-22a. What is the magnetic induction field at all points (a) between the two conductors, (b) outside the outer conductor, (c) within the inner conductor, and (d) within the outer conductor?

(a) On the basis of symmetry alone one can assert that the magnetic field, wherever it is not zero, must consist of circular loops concentric with the conductors. For the region between the two conductors, we choose a circular path of radius r, to apply Ampère's law. Only the current I *within this loop* contributes to the field; the current in the outer conductor, whatever its magnitude or direction, has *no* effect on the region inside. From Ampère's law we have, then,

$$\oint \boldsymbol{B} \cdot d\boldsymbol{l} = \mu_0 i$$

$$B(2\pi r) = \mu_0 I$$

$$B = \frac{\mu_0 I}{2\pi r} \qquad \text{for} \quad r_1 < r < r_2$$

(b) For a circular path around the *outside* of both conductors, the *net* enclosed current $(I - I)$ is zero. Consequently, the field is zero at all exterior points:

$$B = 0, \quad \text{for} \quad r > r_3$$

(c) We assume the current I to be uniformly distributed over the cross section of the inner conductor. For a circular path of radius r inside the inner conductor, the fraction of the current within the path loop is just in the ratio of the circular areas, $\pi r^2 / \pi r_1^2$; that is, within radius r the current is $(r/r_1)^2 I$. Then Ampère's law gives

$$B(2\pi r) = \mu_0 (r/r_1)^2 I$$

$$B = \frac{\mu_0 r}{2\pi r_1^2} I, \quad \text{for} \quad 0 < r < r_1$$

(d) We again assume that the current is uniformly distributed over the cross section of the outer conductor. Then for a circular path lying within the outer conductor we enclose the entire current I of the inner conductor, together with that fraction of current $(-I)$ in the outer conductor which lies within r (we take the outer current to be negative to correspond to its opposite direction). Ampère's law yields, in this case,

$$B(2\pi r) = \mu_0 \left[I - I \left(\frac{r^2 - r_2^2}{r_3^2 - r_2^2} \right) \right]$$

$$B = \frac{\mu_0 I}{2\pi r} \left(\frac{r_3^2 - r^2}{r_3^2 - r_2^2} \right), \quad \text{for} \quad r_2 < r < r_3$$

The variation of B with r is shown in Figure 33-22b.

33-8 The solenoid

A solenoid consists of a tightly wound helix of conducting wire. It is, in effect, a series of circular conducting loops arranged into a cylindrical shell. The magnetic field within a long solenoid is essentially uniform near its center, as shown in Figure 33-23. Altogether, the external magnetic field configuration for a long solenoid is quite similar to that of a long permanent magnet.

Let us find the magnitude of the magnetic field at the center of an infinitely long solenoid. Strictly of course, this implies a solenoid whose

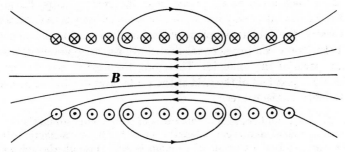

Figure 33-23. Magnetic field lines for a long solenoid.

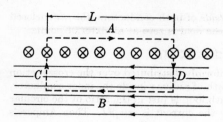

Figure 33-24. Ampère's law applied to a solenoid.

length is much greater than its diameter. Each loop carries a current i_1 and the *number of turns per unit length* is designated n. Consider, then, the closed path shown in Figure 33-24, to which we apply Ampère's law. The magnetic field just outside the solenoid at A must be essentially zero; if it were not, the solenoid could not be regarded as of infinite length. The field inside at point B must be parallel to the solenoid axis; again, if it were not, this would imply a noninfinite solenoid length. Consequently, the field is perpendicular to the path along the transverse portions C and D, and these parts of the closed path do not contribute to the line integral of B. The only contribution comes from the inside segment of length L. Within the length L the *total* current enclosed is nLi_1. Therefore, Ampère's law gives

$$\oint B \cdot dl = \mu_0 i$$

$$BL = \mu_0 nLi_1$$

$$B = \mu_0 ni_1 \qquad\qquad [33\text{-}24]$$

The magnetic field at any point near the center of a long solenoid is uniform, independent of the transverse distance from the axis, and dependent only on the number of turns per unit length and the current i_1 through each.

The magnetic flux at the center of the solenoid is BA, where B is given by Equation 33-24 and A is the circular cross-sectional area. It is easy to show that the flux at either end of a very long solenoid is exactly *half* that at the center. That is, exactly half of the field lines existing at the center leak out through the solenoid turns between the center and one end. First consider a single very long solenoid, in which the magnetic field is, then, of the same magnitude at all points near the center. Now imagine this solenoid to be cut into two parts while the same current is maintained in all turns. Clearly, the field at the plane of the imaginary cut is unchanged. But the field there now comprises equal contributions (by symmetry) from each of the *two* parts of the solenoid. Therefore, the field at one end of a very long solenoid is just half of the field at the center and the flux at one end just half of the flux at the center.

Example 5 A solenoid consists of 200 turns of wire wound around a cylindrical shell 2.0 cm in radius and 50 cm in length. (a) What is the magnetic field at the solenoid's center when a current of 4.0 amp is sent through the solenoid? (b) What is the average magnetic field at one end?

(a) The number of turns per unit length is $n = 200/50$ cm $= 4.0/$cm $= 4.0 \times 10^2/$m. Since the radius is small compared with the length, the solenoid is relatively long, and we may apply Equation 33-24:

$$B = \mu_0 n i_1$$

$$B_{center} = (4\pi \times 10^{-7} \text{ weber/amp-m})(4.0 \times 10^2/\text{m})(4.0 \text{ amp})$$
$$= 2.0 \times 10^{-3} \text{ weber/m}^2 = 20 \text{ gauss}$$

Since the magnetic flux at one end is half that at the center, the *average* magnetic field at either end has the approximate magnitude

$$\bar{B}_{end} = 1.0 \times 10^{-3} \text{ weber/m}^2 = 10 \text{ gauss}$$

33-9 Summary The magnetic field B generated by a charge q moving at velocity v is

[33-3] $$B = \left(\frac{\mu_0}{4\pi}\right)\frac{qv \times r}{r^3}$$

where r is the radius vector from the charge to the point at which B is measured. The magnetic, or velocity-dependent, force between two moving point-charges varies inversely as the square of the distance between them. The permeability of the vacuum, μ_0, is assigned the magnitude $4\pi \times 10^{-7}$ weber/amp-m.

Another form of the Biot-Savart law, applicable for the field dB produced by a current element dl, is

[33-4] $$dB = \left(\frac{\mu_0}{4\pi}\right)\frac{i\,dl \times r}{r^3}$$

Applying the Biot-Savart relation to an infinitely long straight conductor, one finds that the magnetic field falls off inversely as the perpendicular distance from the conductor. Likewise, the magnetic force between two parallel current-carrying conductors is inversely proportional to their separation distance. The ampere is defined in terms of the magnetic force in such an arrangement.

The net magnetic flux through any closed surface is always zero. Equivalently, single magnetic monopoles do *not* exist, according to Gauss's law for magnetism:

[33-22] $$\oint B \cdot dS = 0$$

According to Ampère's law, the line integral of the magnetic induction field around any closed path is proportional to the net current enclosed by the path:

[33-23] $$\oint B \cdot dl = \mu_0 i$$

PROBLEMS

33-1   The beam of a particle accelerator consists of 10 Mev protons with a current of 1.0 μamp. What is the magnitude of the magnetic field at a distance of 1.0 mm from the beam, assumed to be of infinitesimal cross section?

33-2   A 10 Mev proton passes at a distance of 1.0 Å from a certain point. What is the maximum magnetic field at this point?

33-3 ★ A point-charge q moves a constant speed v along the X-axis. The magnetic field generated by the moving charge is observed at the point $x = 0$, $y = d$. Show that the magnetic field is given as a function of time by $B = \mu_0 qvd/4\pi(d^2 + v^2t^2)^{3/2}$, if the particle passes the origin at time $t = 0$.

33-4   Two electrons travel in the same direction at the speed of 2.0×10^6 m/sec while being separated by 10 Å. (a) What is the electric force between the electrons? (b) What is the magnetic force between the electrons?

33-5   A straight conductor carrying 5.0 amp is separated by 10 cm from a second parallel conductor carrying 10.0 amp in the same direction. At what distance from the first conductor and along the line connecting the two conductors is the magnetic field zero?

33-6   A horizontal uniform magnetic field of flux density 0.080 weber/m² is in the direction north. A horizontal straight conducting wire carries a current of 10 amp east. At what points near the wire is the resultant magnetic field zero?

33-7   The Earth's magnetic field at a certain location has a magnitude of 0.70 gauss. This field is to be annulled by the magnetic field at the center of a circular conducting loop 5.0 cm in radius. What is the required current?

33-8   The electron in the hydrogen atom can, according to a simple atomic model, be regarded as moving in a circle 0.53 Å in radius about the proton at a speed of 2.2×10^6 m/sec. What is the magnitude of the magnetic field, at the site of the proton, arising from the circling electron?

33-9   A small loop of current produces a field of 0.030 gauss at a point along the axis of the loop and 4.0 m from it. What is the maximum torque on this loop when it is placed in a magnetic field of 100 gauss?

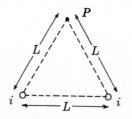

33-10   Two long straight wires separated by L each carry a current i. Find the magnitude of the magnetic field at point P in Figure 33-25, when the currents are (a) in the same direction and (b) in opposite directions.

Figure 33-25

33-11 ★ Find the magnetic field at the point P in Figure 33-26. (*Hint:* Use the superposition principle for magnetic fields, according to which the resultant field from a number of conducting elements is the vector sum of the separate fields; see also Example 2, this chapter.)

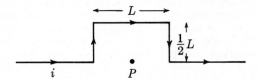

Figure 33-26

33-12 ★ A conductor consists of a circular arc of 60° and two lead wires to this arc, which are radial from the center of the arc and effectively infinite in length; see Figure 33-27. Find the magnetic field at the center of the arc. (*Hint:* Consider separately the fields from the straight wires; what fraction of a whole loop is a 60° arc?)

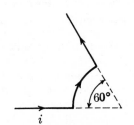

Figure 33-27

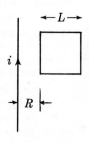

Figure 33-28

33-13 A square loop L on a side is placed a distance R from an infinitely long straight wire carrying a current i. The plane of the loop contains the conducting wire, and two sides of the square are parallel to this wire. See Figure 33-28. Compute the total flux through the square.

33-14 A large number N of long straight conducting wires are placed on the curved surface of a right circular cylinder of radius R, the wires being parallel to the cylinder axis. Each conductor carries the same current i. Find the magnetic field at the center of the cylinder.

33-15 ★ A rectangular loop carrying a current I is placed near a fixed long straight wire carrying a current i as shown in Figure 33-29. (a) Describe the motion of the loop after it has been released. (b) Suppose, now, that the straight conductor passes *through* the center of the rectangular loop; what is the loop's motion?

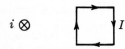

Figure 33-29

33-16 Show that the magnitude of the magnetic field, from a circular loop of radius R carrying a current i at a point along the axis of the loop a distance x from the plane of the loop, is given by $\frac{1}{2}\mu_0 iR^2/(R^2 + x^2)^{3/2}$. Confirm this relation by applying the limits $x = 0$ and $x \gg R$.

33-17 ★ Two circular loops each of radius R and carrying a current i have a common axis with their planes separated by a distance R. Show that the magnetic field at the central position between the two coils is highly uniform by showing that the magnetic field is unchanged for small displacements along the axis of the loops. Such coils, often used in the laboratory to produce a highly uniform magnetic field, are known as *Helmholtz coils*. (See Problem 33-16 for the relation giving B for a point along the axis of a coil.)

33-18 Two parallel straight conductors 50 cm long carry currents each of 10 amp in opposite directions. At what separation distance is the repulsive force between them 10 dynes?

33-19 A conducting wire of radius 1.00 mm carries a current of 100 amp. What is the magnetic field (a) at the surface of the wire, (b) at a point 0.50 mm from the center of the wire, and (c) 2.00 mm from the center of the wire?

33-20 What is the magnetic field at a distance of 4.0 m from a long straight coaxial conductor, the inner conductor carrying a current of 4.0 amp and the outer one a current of 10.0 amp in the opposite direction?

33-21 A solid conducting cylinder of radius R carries a current i. How must the current density vary with distance r from the center of the conductor, if the magnitude of the magnetic field within the conductor is to have the same value at all points?

33-22 A "conducting sheet" is produced by laying together on a flat surface many long straight wires, each carrying current i in the same direction. Find the magnetic field at any point near the conducting sheet.

33-23 Show that the magnetic field at the center of a long solenoid, Equation 33-24, applies even when there are several layers of windings.

33-24 Suppose that a solenoid has a diameter which is *not* small in comparison with its length. Is the flux through one end greater or less than the flux through the center of the solenoid? A detailed computation is *not* required.

33-25 A toroid is a solenoid bent into the form of a doughnut. Show that the magnetic field at any point within the current loops varies inversely with the distance from the center of the toroid and that the field is zero at all other points.

33-26 ★ A small circular loop of wire, of mass 50 gm and radius r cm, has a current of 2.0 amp. The coil is placed inside a long solenoid which has 6 turns per centimeter, is 1.0 m long, and carries a current of 10 amp. If the axis of the coil is displaced through a small angle with respect to the magnetic field of the solenoid and then released, at what frequency will the coil oscillate about the solenoid field?

33-27 ★ Derive the relation for the magnetic field at the center of a long solenoid by integrating the contributions of thin circular loops.

THIRTY-FOUR

ELECTROMAGNETIC INDUCTION

Up to this point, whenever we considered an electric field, this field had its origin directly in electric charges. In this chapter we shall deal with electric fields not originating from electric charges directly, but having their origin in a changing magnetic flux. The phenomenon is known as electromagnetic induction, and its quantitative statement is, after its originator, Faraday's law.

We begin by considering one simple example, the emf produced in a conducting loop moved through a magnetic field. We next find the relationship between the induced emf and the magnetic flux change. Then we consider other examples of electromagnetic induction and arrive at the general form of Faraday's law, which relates the rate of magnetic flux change to the nonconservative electric field that it generates. Finally, we consider, as applications, eddy currents, the betatron, and the ballistic galvanometer.

34-1 Motional emf When an electric current passes through a conductor immersed in a magnetic field, a magnetic force acts on the conductor to

move it. Does the reverse happen? That is, if one applies a force to a
conductor to move it through a magnetic field, is an electric current generated
in the conductor? The answer is Yes, as we shall see. Figure 34-1 shows a
conductor of length l in a uniform magnetic flux density B directed into the
paper. Suppose that the conductor is moved to the right with the velocity v,
this velocity being at right angles to both the conductor and the magnetic
field lines. As the conductor is pulled to the right, so are the free electrons
within it. Now, if a negatively charged particle moves to the right through a
magnetic field into the paper, it is subject to a magnetic force F_m acting
downward, as shown in Figure 34-2.

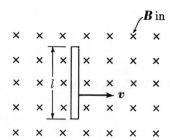

Figure 34-1. A conductor
moved through a magnetic
field.

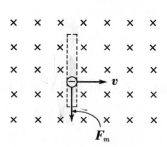

Figure 34-2. Magnetic force
F_m on a free electron within
a moving conductor.

Thus, moving the conductor to the right causes free electrons within it to be
forced toward the lower end of the conductor and to leave the upper end.
(Of course, magnetic forces also act on the positive charges and on bound
electrons, but these charges are locked to the conductor lattice and do not
move up or down.) The lower end of the conductor acquires a net negative
charge while the upper end acquires a positive charge of the same magnitude.
Electrons will not, however, continue to move toward the lower end indefinitely. The first electrons arriving at the lower end repel those arriving
later. Thus, an electric field is created within the rod by the charge separation. As more charge accumulates at the ends, the electric field increases,
until the electric force on a free electron within the rod balances the magnetic
force on the electron and no further charge separation takes place.

The electric field within the rod gives rise to a potential difference across
its ends. This potential difference exists, however, only as long as the
conductor is in motion through the magnetic field. When the conductor is
brought to rest, there is no charge separation and the potential difference
drops to zero. When the conductor is moved toward the left, the potential
difference is reversed in polarity.

Suppose, now, that our conductor is made one end of a rectangular conducting loop, as shown in Figure 34-3. We imagine (unrealistically) that the magnetic field drops abruptly to zero at left and right boundaries and that the left end of the conducting rectangle lies outside the magnetic field initially. Then, as the loop is moved to the right, there is no charge separation in the left conductor end, but there is one in the right end. Moreover, no magnetic force acts on electrons within the two horizontal segments of the loop.† As the loop is moved to the right, the electrons can leave the lower end of the conductor, travel clockwise around the loop, and enter again at the upper end. That is, as we move the conductor through the magnetic field (the left end, however, remaining outside the magnetic field), we generate a counterclockwise current i in the conducting loop. The current is driven, of course, by the charge separation maintained across the ends of the right-hand conductor, and this charge separation has its origin in the magnetic force on the electrons within the conductor.

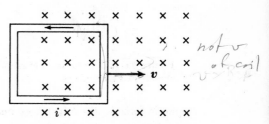

Figure 34-3. A conducting loop one end of which moves through a transverse magnetic field.

The induced current exists as long as the right end passes through the magnetic field. It ceases when the conductor is at rest, and the current circulates about the loop in the opposite sense when the direction of motion is reversed.

When the entire conducting loop is traveling within the region of the constant magnetic field, a charge separation occurs at *both* the right and left conducting ends. Then there is no induced current. Moreover, if we continue moving the conductor until the right end emerges from the magnetic field while the left end is still within the field, the charge separation occurs in the left conducting end only, and the direction of the induced current is now reversed; see Figure 34-4. We may summarize these effects by saying that an *induced current is generated* in the loop *when the magnetic flux through* the loop *changes*, and that this changing magnetic flux produces a so-called *motional emf* in the loop. This is but one example of the general phenomenon of *electromagnetic induction*.

Let us now analyze the situation of Figure 34-3 in more detail, to find how the induced emf is related to the changing magnetic flux; see Figure 34-5. We must first recognize that a constant external force F must be applied to the conductor, to move it through the magnetic field at the constant velocity v. An external agent must apply the force F to balance the

† Strictly, a magnetic force acts to produce a Hall potential difference (Section 32-9) across the wire diameter.

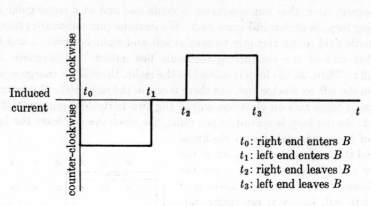

t_0: right end enters B
t_1: left end enters B
t_2: right end leaves B
t_3: left end leaves B

Figure 34-4. The induced current as a function of time for the situation shown in Figure 34-3.

magnetic force to the left, whose magnitude is

[32-13] $$F = Bil$$ [34-1]

Since the conductor is displaced a distance $\Delta x = v\,\Delta t$ in the time Δt, the work ΔW done by the external agent in this time is, from Equation 34-1,

$$\Delta W = F\,\Delta x = (Bil)(v\,\Delta t)$$ [34-2]

The current i is $\Delta q/\Delta t$, where Δq is the net charge transferred in the time interval Δt. Therefore, with $\Delta q = i\,\Delta t$, Equation 34-2 can be written

$$\Delta W = Blv\,\Delta q$$ [34-3]

Now the work ΔW done by the external agent can be interpreted also as work done by an emf in circulating charges around the conducting loop.

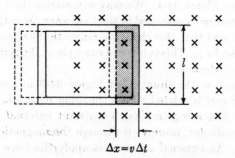

$$\Delta x = v\,\Delta t$$

Figure 34-5. The loop area through which the magnetic-field lines pass increases with time.

Since the emf $\mathscr{E}$ is, in general, the work done per unit charge by an energy source in a circuit,

[31-1] $\mathscr{E} = \Delta W / \Delta q$

With this relation we may write Equation 34-3 in the form

$$\mathscr{E} = Blv \qquad [34\text{-}4]$$

The emf $\mathscr{E}$ exists as long as the conductor is in motion and *one* of its ends is moving through the magnetic field. Equation 34-4 applies, however, only when v, B, and the direction of the conducting wire are at right angles. If a 1 m conductor is moved at 1 m/sec through a constant field of 1 weber/m², the induced emf is 1 v.

Now we wish to relate the emf to the change in the magnetic flux enclosed by the conducting loop. We recall that the magnetic flux ϕ_B is given, in general, by

[32-4] $$\phi_B = \int B \cdot dS$$

As Figure 34-5 shows, when the loop advances a distance Δx, the loop area through the magnetic field lines increases by $\Delta A = l \, \Delta x$. Thus, the change in magnetic flux through the loop in time Δt, is

$$\Delta \phi_M = B \, \Delta A = Bl \, \Delta x$$

We may write Equation 34-4 as

$$\mathscr{E} = Bl(\Delta x / \Delta t) = B(l \, \Delta x)/\Delta t$$

$$\boxed{\mathscr{E} = -\frac{\Delta \phi_B}{\Delta t} = -\frac{d\phi_B}{dt}} \qquad [34\text{-}5]$$

The emf induced in the conducting loop equals the rate at which the magnetic flux through the loop changes. (The meaning and purpose of the minus sign in Equation 34-5 will be discussed in Section 34-4; it relates to the direction of the emf.) Note that, when the entire conducting loop is immersed in the magnetic field and the flux through the loop is unchanged, Equation 34-5 predicts a zero emf, in accord with our earlier arguments.

Although we have arrived at Equation 34-5, the basic relation for electromagnetic induction, by considering a rather special situation, this relation is altogether general. It gives the emf induced by a changing magnetic flux for all possible situations.

An external agent does work on the conducting loop at a constant rate as it is moved through the magnetic field, yet the speed of the conducting loop is constant. Where does the energy go? It is easy to show that the power into the loop generated by the external agent is exactly equal to the power dissipated in the loop by the induced current.

The power P_a delivered to the loop by the *agent* is

[11-21] $P_a = Fv$

From Equation 34-1,

$$P_a = (Bil)v \qquad [34\text{-}6]$$

Now the current i in terms of the emf $\mathscr{E}$ and the resistance R of the loop is given by

$$i = \mathscr{E}/R = Blv/R \qquad [34\text{-}7]$$

from Equation 34-4. Therefore, Equation 34-6 can be written

$$P_a = (Blv)^2/R \qquad [34\text{-}8]$$

What is the power P_d dissipated as thermal energy in the conduction loop? Since the power delivered by any energy source of emf $\mathscr{E}$ is given by

[31-10] $P = i\mathscr{E}$

we have, using Equations 34-4 and 34-7,

$$P_d = (Blv/R)(Blv) = (Blv)^2/R$$

which is in agreement with Equation 34-8.

34-2 Electromagnetic induction and reference frames Before examining other types of electromagnetic induction, it is worth considering to what extent the induction effect we have just discussed is a *new* and distinctive electromagnetic effect. Actually, in analyzing the current induced in the moving conductor we seem to have invoked *no new fundamental principles*. We accounted for the existence of the induced current and found the magnitude of the emf quite directly, by applying relations already well known. Does this mean, then, that electromagnetic induction involves nothing new? Not at all! To see this we merely take another look at the conductor moving through the magnetic field, but now from the point of view of an observer in *another reference frame*.

Rather than view the conductor moving to the right at velocity v relative to the reference frame in which the magnetic field is at rest, we observe the conductor as if we were traveling with the loop. We are now in a reference frame in which the conductor is *at rest*. The conduction electrons in the conductor are no longer pulled through the magnetic field to the right; they are at rest. Consequently, the magnetic force of Figure 34-2 does not so act upon the electrons as to circulate them about the loop. It would appear that merely by viewing the conductor from a different reference frame we have, so to speak, turned off the induced current and the induced emf, which is its origin.

What does experiment show? Is there actually induced current in one reference frame only—that is, the one in which the source of the magnetic field is at rest—and not in others? Do charges circulate in the loop only when we see it in motion, and not when we are at rest relative to the loop and when the source of the magnetic field is in motion? The answer of experiment is *no*. An induced current and induced emf are found to exist for *any* reference frame. What matters is the *relative* motion of the loop and source of the magnetic field, *not* the absolute motion of the loop. See Figure 34-6. We do indeed have a distinct and new physical phenomenon, not explainable simply in terms of magnetic forces on moving charges.

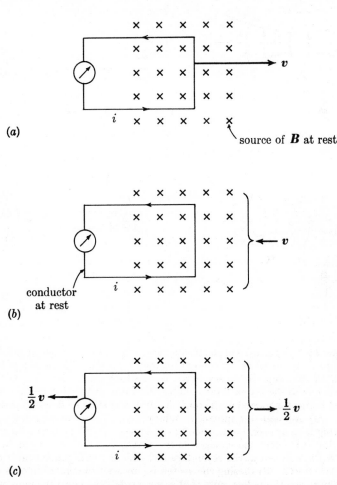

Figure 34-6. The induced current in the conducting loop does *not* depend on the reference frame. The current is the same whether (a) the loop moves while the field source is at rest, (b) the field source moves while the loop is at rest, or (c) both field source and loop move.

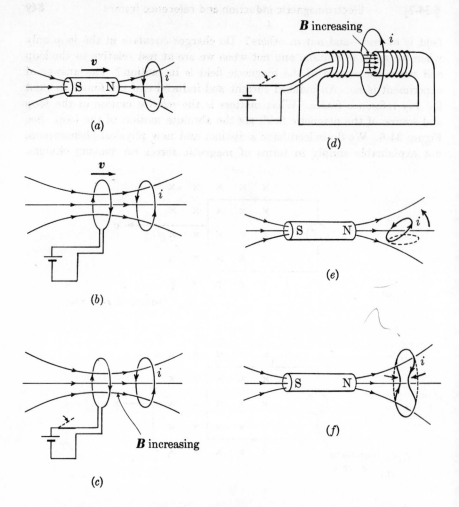

Figure 34-7. Examples of electromagnetic induction. In each an induced current is produced in the conducting loop by a changing magnetic flux through the loop. In every example in which one object moves and another is at rest, one finds exactly the same induced current if the second object is moved in the opposite direction and the first object is at rest. (a) A magnet approaches a loop. (b) A current-carrying conducting loop approaches a second loop at rest. (c) The current through the first (primary) coil changes as the switch is closed, and an induced current is induced in the secondary coil (this is the fundamental transformer effect). (d) Closing the switch on an electromagnet changes the field between the poles; note that a current is induced in the loop even though the magnetic field *at the loop* is essentially *zero*. (e) A loop is turned in the region of a magnetic field. (f) A loop is deformed; here the magnetic flux changes because the area through which it passes is reduced.

Only when we admit that an emf is created whenever the magnetic flux through the loop changes can we account for induced currents in any reference frame. Because electromagnetic induction is independent of the reference frame it must be taken as a fundamental electromagnetic effect.

Let us recall that we expect *all* laws in physics to be the same for all inertial reference frames (Section 10-6). Certainly the laws of Newtonian mechanics hold equally well in all inertial frames. We would be surprised, not to say astonished, to find that electromagnetic effects were different in different inertial frames. If this were the case we would be confronted with an extraordinary situation: there would exist in Nature a single unique reference frame in which one set of phenomena was observed, with different phenomena in other reference frames. The special theory of relativity begins with the assertion that all the laws of physics are indeed the same for all inertial frames and, through relativistic arguments, it can be shown that the existence of induced emf's for all reference frames is, in a deep sense, simply a manifestation of the fact that electromagnetic phemomena are the same for all inertial frames (relativistically invariant). We shall not be able to pursue this further, except to assert that the relation between the emf and the rate of magnetic flux change holds for *any* reference frame and depends only upon the *relative* motion.

34-3 Examples of electromagnetic induction We have seen one simple example of electromagnetic induction. There are many others. Most were investigated and discovered by Michael Faraday starting in 1831 (and independently by Joseph Henry at the same time), and Equation 34-5 is referred to as *Faraday's law*.

We see a number of examples in Figure 34-7. In each example the induced emf arises because the magnetic flux through a conducting loop changes. The change in ϕ_B may have several origins: the motion of a magnet or, equivalently, the motion of a current-carrying conductor, the change in the current through a conductor and thus, also, a change in the magnetic field and flux which the current is generating. Whenever we move one object to produce an induced emf in a second circuit, we can also move the second circuit toward the object at rest and find the same effect. One of the most striking results is that a changing current in one circuit can create a (changing) current in a second circuit to which it is not physically connected—except, of course, through the magnetic flux which links the two circuits. In every case we can compute the induced emf through Faraday's law:

[34-5] $$\mathscr{E} = -d\phi_B/dt$$

Example 1 A 1.0 m conductor moves in a uniform magnetic field of 300 gauss at the speed of 4.0 m/sec. The conductor is at right angles to the magnetic field lines, but the velocity vector makes an angle of 30° with respect to the rod; see Figure 34-8. What is the potential difference appearing across the ends of the conductor?

Only the component of the conductor which is at right angles to the velocity contributes to the induced emf, or potential difference, across the conductor.

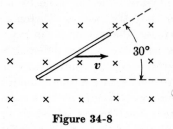

[34-4]

$$\mathcal{E} = Blv$$
$$\mathcal{E} = (0.030 \text{ weber/m}^2)(1.0 \text{ m})$$
$$(\sin 30°)(4.0 \text{ m/sec})$$
$$= 60 \text{ mv}$$

Figure 34-8

Example 2 A coil of N turns, each of area A, is rotated at constant angular speed ω in a uniform magnetic field of magnitude B. What is the emf induced in the coil?

The arrangement here is that of a simple electric generator. The magnetic flux through each turn of the coil is given by

$$\phi_B = AB \cos \theta$$

where θ is the angle between the normal to the plane of the coil and the direction of B; see Figure 34-9a. If the coil is rotated at the constant angular speed ω, then $\theta = \omega t$ and we may write

$$\phi_B = AB \cos \omega t$$

Now, the emf induced in *one* turn is given by

[34-5] $$\mathcal{E} = -d\phi_B/dt$$

Here we have N conductor turns connected in series, so that the total emf across the terminals of the coil is enhanced by a factor N over that produced by a single turn. Therefore,

$$\mathcal{E} = -Nd\phi_B/dt = \omega NAB \sin \omega t = \mathcal{E}_0 \sin \omega t$$

The output of the coil is a sinusoidally varying alternating emf, as shown in Figure 34-9b.

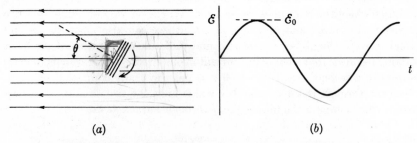

(a)   (b)

Figure 34-9. (a) A coil rotating at constant angular speed in a uniform magnetic field. (b) The resulting sinusoidally varying alternating emf across the leads to the rotating coil.

34-4 Lenz's law   There are always *two* possible directions for the electric current in any conducting loop, but when a current is induced by a changing magnetic flux, it goes, of course, in one direction only. Which is it? The basis for finding the direction of the induced current, or of the induced emf, is Lenz's law, named for H. F. E. Lenz (1804–1865).

Let us return to the situation shown in Figure 34-3. Here a current is induced in a conducting loop pulled by an agent through a magnetic field. We found, by analyzing the magnetic force on the electrons within the conductor, that the current was counterclockwise when the loop was moved to the right and with only the right end of the loop immersed in the field. As a consequence, the magnetic force on the right-end conductor segment was to the left; that is, an external agent had to apply a force to the right to over-come the retarding magnetic force. Then the work done by the agent appeared as thermal energy dissipated through the conducting loop's resistance.

Suppose it were otherwise; that is, suppose that the current were clock-wise in Figure 34-3. Then the magnetic force on the right-end conductor would be to the right, and an agent would not be required to pull the con-ductor in that direction. Once given a little push to the right, the conductor would be pushed further toward the right by a magnetic force, it would accelerate, the current would grow, and the conductor would go still faster, gaining kinetic energy, and all the while there would be increasing amounts of thermal energy dissipated in the conductor. Clearly, this is impossible, because it violates the principle of energy conservation. In this example, as in all other examples of induced currents, *the direction of the current is always such as to preclude a violation of energy conservation.* This is one way of stating Lenz's law.

There are others. We might say: the direction of *the induced current is always such as to oppose the change (in magnetic flux) that produces it.* Thus, in Figure 34-3, the magnetic force to the left tends to keep the conductor from being moved to the right; that is, the magnetic force "tries" to keep the magnetic flux through the loop from changing. If the conductor were moved to the left rather than to the right, the direction of the induced current and of the retarding magnetic force would be reversed; in both instances the magnetic force arising from the existence of the induced current is opposite to the external force causing the motion.

Let us see how Lenz's law operates in another situation, that shown in Figure 34-10a. Here one current-carrying loop is being moved toward a second fixed loop, in which a current is then induced. The magnetic flux through the fixed loop on the right increases with time to the *right*. Consequently, the situation in the fixed loop must be as follows: the magnetic field produced by the induced current must be in such a direction that it annuls (or tends

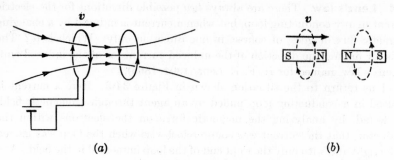

Figure 34-10. An example of Lenz's law. (a) The left-hand current-carrying conductor is moved to the right, inducing a current in the second coil in the opposite sense. (b) Magnets equivalent to the coils of part (a).

to annul) the magnetic field producing the increasing flux to the right through the fixed loop. That is, the induced current must produce a magnetic field to the *left*. Clearly then, from the right-hand rule relating the current to the magnetic field, the current in the fixed loop must be in the sense shown in Figure 34-10a.

There is another way of looking at this. We may imagine any current-carrying loop to be equivalent to a magnet, with magnetic field lines emanating from the north pole and converging into the south pole. Then, we see from Figure 34-10b that the magnets associated with the two loops *repel* each other and thereby tend to keep the two loops from coming closer together. Actually, of course, it is the magnetic force between the two current-carrying conducting loops which is responsible for the repulsion between them. We have already found that the two currents are in opposite senses. This is in accord with the general result that two parallel current-carrying conductors *repel* one another when the currents are in *opposite* directions (Section 33-5).

The reader should, for practice in applying Lenz's law, confirm that all of the directions of induced current shown in Figure 34-7 are correct.

The minus sign appearing in the mathematical statement of Faraday's law, $\mathcal{E} = -d\phi_B/dt$, is a symbolic representation of Lenz's law. We shall treat the relative "directions" of the induced emf and magnetic flux change in the next section.

34-5   Faraday's law and the electric field   We know that a changing magnetic flux produces an induced electric current in a conducting loop; that is, the changing magnetic flux creates an electric field which drives electric charges around the conducting loop. Does a changing magnetic flux create an electric field in space, even when there are present no electric charges to be set in motion? The answer is Yes. Indeed, the fundamental electromagnetic induction effect is this: *a changing magnetic flux generates an electric field*.

We recall that an emf $\mathscr{E}$ is, in general, defined in terms of the electric field E around a closed loop by the relation

[31-7] $$\mathscr{E} = \oint E \cdot dl$$

The emf around any closed path is the line integral of a *nonconservative* electric field around the chosen path. Therefore, since the induced emf around any path is given, through Faraday's law, as the time rate of the magnetic flux through the area enclosed by the chosen path, or

[34-5] $$\mathscr{E} = -d\phi_B/dt$$

we may write the law of electromagnetic induction in the following general form:

$$\oint E \cdot dl = -d\phi_B/dt$$ [34-9]

We must distinguish carefully between (1) an electric field arising from a changing magnetic flux and (2) an electric field originating from electric charges directly. Let us consider the second case first.

The electric field originating from electric charges is a *conservative* electric field. The line integral $\oint E \cdot dl$ is *zero*; that is, if one transports an electric charge around a closed loop in a *conservative* electric field, there is *no net work* done on the charge. Consequently, one can associate an electric potential with a conservative electric field and with the electric-charge distribution from which it originates. Then, the electric field lines originate from positive charges, terminate on negative charges, and are continuous in between.

The electric field originating from a changing magnetic flux is quite different. Of course, by definition, the electric field is still the electric force per unit positive point-charge, but the electric field is now *nonconservative*, and the line integral $\oint E \cdot dl$ is *not* zero. Rather, this line integral (the emf) depends upon the rate at which the magnetic flux ϕ_B changes through the closed path. One *cannot* associate a scalar electric potential with the nonconservative electric field; the work done on a unit positive charge taken around a closed path is *not* zero but is equal, in fact, to the emf around that loop. Moreover, since the electric field lines do *not* originate from and terminate upon electric charges, but must nevertheless be continuous, the *electric field lines* from a changing magnetic flux *form closed loops*.

To see what the electric field lines generated by a changing magnetic flux look like, consider the situation shown in Figure 34-11. Here a uniform magnetic field directed into the paper is confined to a cylindrical region of a space of radius R. The magnitude of the magnetic field is imagined to increase with time. By symmetry, we know that the closed electric field loops must consist of *circles* concentrically surrounding the magnetic field. To find the sense of the electric lines (their direction), we imagine a circular conducting loop around the changing magnetic field, and we determine the direction of the induced current (hence, the direction of E) by Lenz's law. A counterclockwise induced current will produce a magnetic field which is out of the paper in the center of the loop. Therefore, the induced electric field is also counterclockwise, as shown.

Now let us see how the magnitude of E depends upon the distance r from the center of the magnetic field. We first consider the region of space *outside* the magnetic field, with $r > R$. Evaluating the line integral of Equation 34-9 around a circular loop of radius r, we have

$$E(2\pi r) = -\left(\frac{d\phi_B}{dt}\right)_r = -\left(\frac{d\phi_B}{dt}\right)_R$$

or, for $r > R$,
$$E = -\left(\frac{1}{2\pi r}\right)\left(\frac{d\phi_B}{dt}\right)_R \qquad [34\text{-}10]$$

where $(d\phi_B/dt)_R$ represents the *total* rate of flux change inside the region of radius R (and also inside r, since $B = 0$ for $r > R$). We shall presently remark on the significance of the minus sign in Equation 34-10.

The electric field at any point *outside* the changing magnetic field falls off inversely as the distance r. Note a curious circumstance: we have a *nonzero* electric field in a region of space in which there is *no* magnetic field. In finding an induced emf around a loop, what matters is not whether the magnetic *field* is changing *at* the location of chosen path but whether the total magnetic *flux* is changing at any region *within* the loop. Put an electric charge in such an electric field and it is accelerated. In fact, electrons are accelerated in the betatron (Section 34-6) in exactly this way.

In finding the electric field for $r < R$ we must recognize that only a fraction of the *total* rate of flux change within R, $(d\phi_B/dt)_R$, penetrates through a transverse area of radius r. Indeed, that fraction is $(\pi r^2/\pi R^2)(d\phi_B/dt)_R =$ $(r/R)^2(d\phi_B/dt)_R$, assuming the magnetic field to be uniform. Evaluating the line integral of Equation 34-9, we then have

$$E(2\pi r) = -\left(\frac{r}{R}\right)^2\left(\frac{d\phi_B}{dt}\right)_R$$

or, for $r < R$,
$$E = -\left(\frac{r}{2\pi R^2}\right)\left(\frac{d\phi_B}{dt}\right)_R \qquad [34\text{-}11]$$

Inside R, we find that the electric field is directly proportional to r.

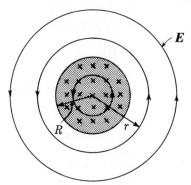

Figure 34-11. A uniform magnetic field is into the paper over a region of radius R. The field increases with time. The induced electric field lines consist of counterclockwise circular loops.

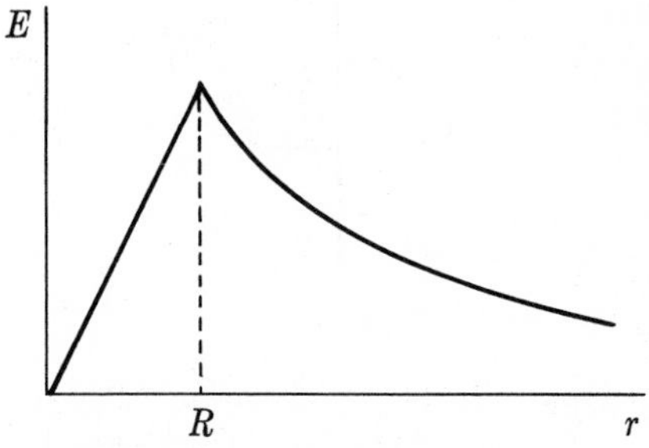

Figure 34-12. Electric field E as a function of the distance r for the situation shown in Figure 34-11.

The magnitude of the circumferential electric field is shown in Figure 34-12 as a function of r. In actuality, the electric field will not change abruptly, inasmuch as the magnetic field cannot change discontinuously to zero at $r = R$. (This plot is like that for the electric field from a uniformly charged sphere, Figure 27-10, but the situations are altogether different. Here the electric field is tangential; there it is radial. More importantly, here the electric field is nonconservative and originates from a changing magnetic flux; there the electric field is conservative and originates from charges at rest.)

It is instructive to consider other closed loops than circles to represent the situation shown in Figure 34-11. For the loop L_1 of Figure 34-13, consisting of two circular arcs and two radial segments, the line integral $\oint E \cdot dl$ obviously is zero, since E varies inversely with r. This does not mean that E is zero at all points around L_1. In more general terms, the emf around this loop is zero because the magnetic flux through it does not change. Similarly, there is no emf around the loop L_2. There *is*, however, an emf around

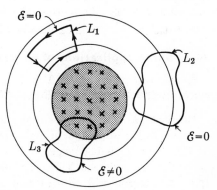

Figure 34-13. Some loops for computing the induced emf in a region where the magnetic flux is changing.

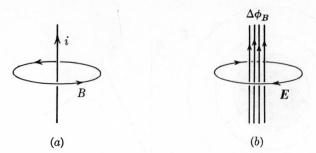

(a)   (b)

Figure 34-14. (a) Relation between the electric current and the surrounding magnetic field loops, following the right-hand rule. (b) Relation between the magnetic flux change and the surrounding electric field loops, following a left-hand rule.

the loop L_3 since $d\phi_B/dt$ changes through the area enclosed by this loop.

Given a knowledge of how the magnetic flux is changing, we can always find the direction of the induced electric field by means of Lenz's law. We can also use the minus sign appearing in Faraday's law (Equation 34-5) for this purpose. First recall that we use the right-hand rule for relating the directions of an electric current and the magnetic field loops that surround it; see Figure 34-14a. In mathematical terms, the relation between B and i is given by Ampère's law (Equation 33-23), $\oint B \cdot dl = \mu_0 i$. Note that *no* minus sign appears here. The relative "directions" of the electric field E and the magnetic flux change $\Delta\phi_B$ are shown in Figure 34-14b. The right-hand rule does *not* apply here; that is, if the right-hand thumb gives the direction in which the magnetic flux is *increasing*, the right-hand fingers are in a direction *opposite* to that of the induced electric field lines. This is indicated formally by the minus sign in Faraday's law.

34-6   Some applications of electromagnetic induction

In this section we apply Faraday's law of electromagnetic induction to eddy currents, the betatron, and the ballistic galvanometer.

EDDY CURRENTS   Suppose that a magnet approaches a conducting sheet, as shown in Figure 34-15a, or moves parallel to the sheet, as shown in Figure 34-15b. The changing magnetic flux through the sheet generates induced current loops, as shown. These currents dissipate energy as heat; at the same time, the currents will, through Lenz's law, produce a retarding force on the moving magnet. Such induced current loops in solid conductors or in conducting sheets, generated by any sort of changing magnetic flux, are known as *eddy currents* (they form eddies of electric charge somewhat like

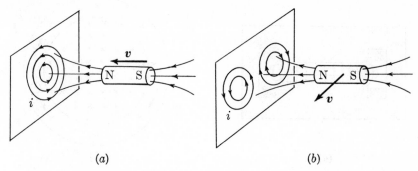

(a)   (b)

Figure 34-15. Two examples of eddy currents: a magnet is moved (a) toward a conducting sheet and (b) along a conducting sheet.

the eddies in liquids). Eddy currents are always accompanied by energy dissipation and, when a moving object is involved, the eddy currents produce a retarding magnetic force on the moving object.

Eddy-current losses are usually undesirable. They are minimized in such devices as transformers or motors by using laminated sheets of metal rather than solid conductors: the high resistance between layers reduces considerably the eddy currents. On the other hand, the braking effect of eddy currents may be used to advantage; for example, in a magnetically damped analytical balance, the oscillations of the beam are quickly damped out because a conducting sheet attached to the beam moves in the vicinity of a permanent magnet.

THE BETATRON   That a changing magnetic flux produces an electric field in space, which can, in turn, accelerate charged particles, is strikingly demonstrated in the operation of the *betatron*. The betatron is a machine for accelerating electrons to high kinetic energies, that is, to energies comparable to or exceeding the energies of beta particles (or electrons) emitted from radioactive nuclei. It was invented by D. W. Kerst (1911–   ) in 1941.

The fundamental principle is this: a changing magnetic field creates electric field loops (in the fashion shown in Figure 34-10), which accelerate the electrons; at the same time, the magnetic field produces the required radial force to hold the electrons in circular orbits of constant radius.

The essential parts of the betatron are shown in Figure 34-16a. A sinusoidally alternating current (usually 60 cycles/sec) through the electromagnet produces an alternating magnetic field. For a clockwise electron beam (looking downward), a pulse of electrons is injected into the doughnut-shaped evacuated tube during that part of the cycle in which the magnetic field is *increasing into the paper* (Figure 34-16b). Then the electrons are

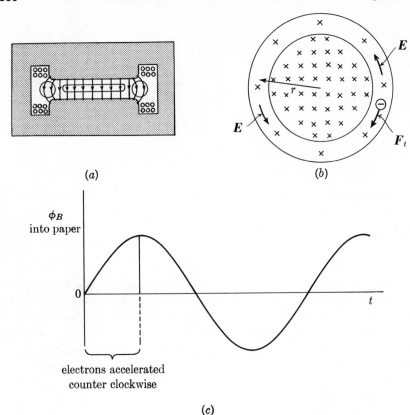

(a)   (b)

(c)

Figure 34-16. (a) Cross section of a betatron. (b) Top view of the beta-tron doughnut during the time when the magnetic field is increasing, the electric field is increasing and is counterclockwise, and the electric force on electrons is increasing and is clockwise. (c) Magnetic flux as a function of time.

subject to a tangential electric force F_t which increases their speed as they travel in the clockwise sense. Only *one quarter* of the full cycle is usable: during half of the cycle the magnetic field is *out* of the paper, and the electrons are then accelerated in the counterclockwise sense; during the other half-cycle, when the magnetic field is directed into the paper, the magnetic field is *increasing* only half the time; see Figure 34-16c.

When an electron of charge e moves in a circle of radius r, its momentum p at each instant is

[32-10] $$p = er B_r$$

where B_r is the magnetic field *at the radius r* at that same instant. Therefore,

$$F_t = dp/dt = er\, dB_r/dt \qquad [34\text{-}12]$$

We have identified the *tangential* force F_t as the rate of the particle's momentum, dp/dt.

Now we can relate, through Equation 34-10, the tangential force to the rate at which the magnetic flux changes:

$$F_t = eE = \left(\frac{e}{2\pi r}\right)\frac{d\phi_r}{dt} \qquad [34\text{-}13]$$

Here ϕ_r refers to the *entire* magnetic flux within the circle of radius r. We may write the total flux as

$$\phi_r = \pi r^2 \bar{B}$$

where $\bar{B}$ is the *average* magnetic field over this inner region. Then Equation 34-13 becomes

$$F_t = \left(\frac{e}{2\pi r}\right)(\pi r^2)\frac{d\bar{B}}{dt} = \tfrac{1}{2}er\,d\bar{B}/dt \qquad [34\text{-}14]$$

Combining Equations 34-12 and 34-14, we have

$$dB_r/dt = \tfrac{1}{2}d\bar{B}/dt$$

If the magnetic field changes at the same rate at all points, we may integrate this relation to find

$$B_r = \tfrac{1}{2}\bar{B} \qquad [34\text{-}15]$$

The magnetic field at the location of the electron beam must be just half of the average magnetic field over the region inside r; that is, the magnetic field must be relatively more intense in the center. When the condition of Equation 34-15 is achieved, we have the remarkable result that, although the magnetic field changes with time and the electrons gain energy from the induced electric field, nevertheless the electrons will remain in an orbit of constant radius.

The electrons are ejected from the betatron doughnut when the magnetic field has achieved its maximum magnitude (otherwise, the electrons would be decelerated, as the magnetic field decreases and the induced emf reverses direction). The electrons may be deflected from their stable orbit by sending a pulse of current through an auxiliary coil. The high-energy electron beam may consist of particles with energies of up to several hundred millions of electron volts. Since the emf for one turn is typically several hundred volts, the electrons may circle more than a million times and travel several hundred kilometers during the acceleration process.

As was pointed out in Section 32-5, electrons cannot be accelerated by a cyclotron because, even for relatively low kinetic energies (say, 100 kev), they move at speeds approaching that of light. Because of the relativistic change in the electron mass with speed, electrons would easily come out of synchronism at the cyclotron frequency. The derivation given above for

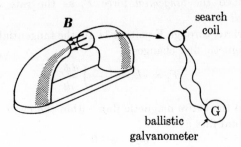

Figure 34-17. A search coil connected to a ballistic galvanometer is removed from a magnetic field.

betatron operation *is* applicable, even for relativistic speeds, because the relations $F_t = dp/dt$ and $p = qrB$ are relativistically correct (a fact that must be asserted here without proof).

THE BALLISTIC GALVANOMETER   Suppose that a coil of N turns, each of area A, with a total resistance R, is initially immersed in a magnetic field B normal to the plane of the coil. The coil is connected to a galvanometer; see Figure 34-17. Then the coil is quickly removed from the field; a current i is thereby induced through the coil and galvanometer. At each instant the current is

$$i = \frac{\mathscr{E}}{R} = -\frac{1}{R}\frac{d(N\phi_B)}{dt} = -\frac{NB}{R}\frac{dA}{dt}$$

The current varies with time, as shown in Figure 34-18, and the total charge Q that passes any point in the circuit is

$$Q = \int i \, dt = -\frac{NB}{R}\int\left(\frac{dA}{dt}\right) dt = -NBA/R \qquad [34\text{-}16]$$

That is, the total charge Q is the area under the i-t curve of Figure 34-18. As Equation 34-16 shows, the change in flux through the coil (sometimes called a *search coil* or *flip coil*) is proportional to the total charge Q produced by the induced current.

The charge arising from an impulsive electric current can be measured directly with a *ballistic galvanometer*. Consequently, through Equation 34-16, a ballistic galvanometer and search coil can be used to measure a magnetic flux. To see how a ballistic galvanometer measures electric *charge*, *not* current, and also to see why it is called

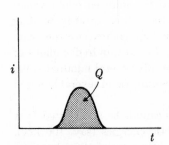

Figure 34-18. Current as a function of time through the ballistic galvanometer.

ballistic, we shall digress for a moment to consider how the ballistic pendulum (Example 9, Chapter 12) is used to measure the speed of a bullet shot into it.

The bullet (mass m) comes to rest within the pendulum (mass M) in a time that is short compared with the time for the pendulum to complete one oscillation; that is, the impulse $\int F\,dt = (m + M)V$ on the pendulum from the bullet allows the pendulum to acquire the linear momentum $(m + M)V$ before it has time to rise appreciably. Then the pendulum swings upward, losing kinetic energy and gaining gravitational potential energy. If we record the pendulum's highest point y, we find the speed V and therefore also the impulse $\int Ft$, through the law of energy conservation: $\frac{1}{2}(M + m)V^2 = (M + m)gy$.

The ballistic galvanometer works in the same way. The current pulse through the *galvanometer* coil imparts an impulsive torque, or angular impulse, to it. Since the galvanometer current i is proportional to the torque τ on the coil (Section 32-7),

$$Q = \int i\,dt \propto \int \tau\,dt = L \qquad [34\text{-}17]$$

Here L represents the angular momentum of the coil immediately after the charge Q has passed through it. The galvanometer is attached to a torsional spring (or suspension) which produces a restoring torque on the coil that is proportional to the coil's angular displacement from equilibrium. Now, if the period of the coil's oscillation is long compared with the time for the charge Q to pass through it, the coil will not have turned appreciably while acquiring the angular momentum L. As it turns, it loses rotational kinetic energy $L^2/2I_c$ (where I_c is the moment of inertia of the galvanometer coil), and the spring gains elastic potential energy $\frac{1}{2}\kappa\theta^2$ (where κ is the spring's torsion constant). If θ_{max} is the maximum angle through which the galvanometer coil swings,

$$L^2/2I_c = \kappa\theta_{max}^2/2, \quad \text{or} \quad \theta_{max} \propto L$$

Using Equation 34-17 we have, finally,

$$\theta_{max} \propto Q \qquad [34\text{-}18]$$

Thus, the maximum angular displacement of the galvanometer's coil is directly proportional to the charge and, from Equation 34-17, to the change in magnetic flux through the *search* coil.

34-7 Summary A changing magnetic flux induces an emf where, by Faraday's law,

$$[34\text{-}5] \qquad \mathscr{E} = -\frac{d\phi_B}{dt}$$

The current induced in a conductor is not dependent on the reference frame. In direction, the induced emf is, according to Lenz's law, always such as to preclude a violation of energy conservation; alternatively, the direction of the induced current is always such as to oppose the change which produces it.

The line integral of the *nonconservative* electric field *E* induced by a changing flux is given by

[34-9] $$\oint E \cdot dl = -d\phi_B/dt$$

The electric field lines induced by a changing magnetic flux form closed loops in space.

PROBLEMS

34-1   A circular loop of radius 10.0 cm is placed in a uniform magnetic field of 0.80 weber/m² and normal to the plane of the loop. The loop shrinks to a radius of 8.0 cm in 0.10 sec. What is the emf induced in the loop?

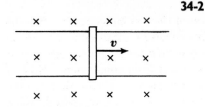

Figure 34-19

34-2   When a conducting rod 0.50 m long slides at right angles over two parallel straight conductors at a speed of 1.0 m/sec it is subject to a retarding force of 0.80 nt (see Figure 34-19) because of an induced current in the moving rod. What force must be applied to the rod to move it along the parallel conductors at a speed of 3.0 m/sec?

34-3   Confirm that the induced emf is given in units of volts when the magnetic flux is in units of webers.

34-4   Explain how one could tell, using only a coil of wire, a compass, and a galvanometer, whether he is in the northern or southern hemisphere.

34-5   A door has a metal frame for a square window 50 cm on a side. The door is initially aligned along a north-south line and hinged at the south side. A man facing west pulls the door open through 90° in 0.20 sec. What is the magnitude and sense of the average emf induced around the door window? The Earth's magnetic field is north, has a magnitude of 0.70 gauss, and is inclined downward toward the north at an angle of 70° with respect to the horizontal.

34-6   A coil lies on a horizontal plane at the Equator. It is turned over about an east-west axis at a constant angular speed. (a) What is the direction of the normal to the plane of the coil when the induced emf is a maximum? Suppose that the coil is turned over about a north-south axis. (b) What is now the orientation of the normal to plane when the emf is a maximum?

34-7   The north pole of a permanent magnet is moved downward toward a circular conducting loop lying in a horizontal plane. In what sense, clockwise or counterclockwise, does the induced current pass?

34-8   At the Equator the Earth's magnetic field is essentially horizontal and north and has a magnitude of approximately 0.80 gauss. A satellite circles the Earth (near the surface) at the Equator and has a 1.0 m antenna oriented perpendicular to the Earth's surface. What is the potential difference between the ends of the rod measured by (a) an observer on Earth and (b) an astronaut riding in the satellite?

34-9   A coil having 5 turns and a radius of 1.0 cm is made of flexible wire. The coil is initially oriented with its plane perpendicular to a magnetic field of 0.80 weber/m². Then the two leads to the coil are pulled apart in 0.50 sec, until the coil has become a straight wire. What is the magnitude of the average emf induced in the wire?

34-10 You are given a fixed length of wire to be used to form a coil in an electric generator. How should the wire be arranged to give the largest induced emf (assuming the magnetic field to be uniform over a region of unlimited size): in one large circular loop or in a large number of turns of smaller size?

34-11 ★ A solenoid consists of 500 turns wound uniformly on a cylindrical shell 50 cm in length and 1.0 cm in radius. Then a secondary coil of 10 turns is wound around the center of the solenoid. When the solenoid is connected to a battery the current through it initially changes at the rate 5.0 amp/sec. What is the induced emf across the terminals of the secondary coil at this time?

34-12 It requires a force of 50 nt to move a conducting loop through a nonuniform magnetic field at a constant speed of 2.0 m/sec. At what rate is thermal energy produced in the loop?

34-13 A coil of wire has a radius of 5.0 cm, 100 turns, and a total resistance of 50 ohms. At what rate must the transverse magnetic field through the coil change to produce joule heating in the coil at the rate of 1.0 mw?

34-14 An electric generator produces an alternating sinusoidal emf having an amplitude of 150 v and a frequency of 60 cycles/sec. The generator coil has an area of 3.0×10^{-3} m² and it rotates in a constant magnetic field of 10,000 gauss. How many turns are in the generator coil?

34-15 A magnetic field of 1.0 weber/m² acts vertically downward. A conducting rod 0.50 m in length rotates clockwise (looking down) in a horizontal plane about a vertical axis at one end and at angular speed of 2.0 turns/sec. (a) What is the potential difference between the two ends of the rod? (b) Which end of the rod, the fixed one or the moving one, carries a positive charge?

34-16 ★ A single-turn conducting loop of area A is a large distance R from a permanent magnet of magnetic dipole moment μ, as shown in Figure 34-20. The magnet

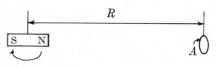

Figure 34-20

is turned around in the time t, reversing the north and south poles. What is the average emf induced in the loop?

34-17 ★ A conducting rod of length L and mass m slides down an inclined plane of angle θ while resting on two straight parallel conductors, as shown in Figure 34-21. A magnetic field of flux density B acts vertically downward. The circuit is completed by a resistor R. Assuming that the rod slides without friction, derive an expression giving the constant terminal speed of the rod down the incline.

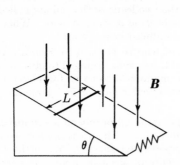

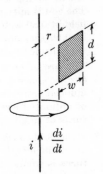

Figure 34-21 **Figure 34-22**

34-18 ★ A rectangular conducting loop lies in a plane containing an infinitely long conducting wire, as shown in Figure 34-22. The loop has dimensions of w and d, and at its closest point is a distance r from the long straight wire. The current through the long straight wire changes at the rate di/dt. What is the emf induced in the conducting loop?

34-19 A conducting bar of length L moves at a constant velocity v in a direction transverse to its length through a field-free region of space. The rod then enters a uniform magnetic field which is perpendicular to the velocity and length of the rod. While traveling through the uniform magnetic field, the rod is observed to move at only one-half its initial speed. Explain what velocity you might expect the rod to have upon emerging from the magnetic field, and discuss any energy transformations taking place.

34-20 ★ A conducting rod slides across the U-shaped fixed conductor of Figure 34-23 with an initial velocity v_0

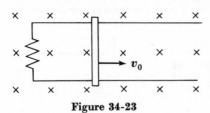

Figure 34-23

to the right. A constant magnetic field B exists normal to the paper. The resistance R in the U-shaped wire can be assumed to be constant, and the mass of the sliding rod is m. (a) Find the magnetic retarding force F_m on the rod in terms of B, L, R, and v. (b) Show that the velocity decreases as a function of time according to $v = v_0\, e^{-t/\tau}$, where $\tau = (mR/B^2L^2)$. (c) Show that the total distance traveled by the rod before coming to rest is τv_0. (d) Show that the total thermal energy dissipated is just equal to the original kinetic energy of the rod, $\frac{1}{2}mv_0{}^2$.

34-21 A magnetic field is uniform over a cylindrical region of space of radius 0.20 m, and it changes magnitude at the rate of 200 gauss/sec. What is the electric field in a plane perpendicular to the magnetic field lines and at a distance from the center of the magnetic field of (a) 0.10 m, (b) 0.25 m, and (c) 0.50 m?

34-22 When an electromagnet is turned on, a magnetic field of 15,000 gauss is established in 1.0 sec between the pole faces whose radii are 15 cm. What is the magnitude of the average induced electric field at a point 200 cm from the axis of the pole faces and in a plane perpendicular to the magnetic field lines?

34-23 The current through an electromagnet oscillates sinusoidally at a frequency of 1 cycle/sec. The maximum magnetic field is 10,000 gauss and this field is uniform over an area of $1.2 \times 10^{-2}\,m^2$. Write an expression giving the magnitude of the electric field as a function of time for a point 2.0 m from the axis of the electromagnet and in a plane perpendicular to the magnetic field lines.

34-24 ⋆ A magnetic field is confined to a cylindrical region of space of radius R. The field lines are parallel to the axis. The magnitude of the field varies with the distance r from the center. How must the magnitude of B vary with r if the electric field induced by a changing magnetic field magnitude is the same at each point r within the cylindrical region? Assume that B can be written as a product of a spatial part and a time part.

34-25 Show that, other things being equal, the rate at which energy is dissipated in eddy currents is proportional to the *square* of the relative speed of a conducting object through the magnetic field which it passes. (*Hint:* To what are the induced current and the induced emf proportional?)

34-26 An electron in a betatron is moving in an orbit of 100 cm in radius and gaining kinetic energy at the rate of 200 ev per orbit. At what rate is the magnetic flux inside the electron's orbit changing?

34-27 Electrons in a betatron accelerator travel at all times at a speed that is essentially the speed of light (3.0×10^8 m/sec). Suppose that electrons are accelerated to a kinetic energy of 5.0 Mev while traveling in an orbit whose radius is 1.0 m. The electrons gain an energy of 200 ev for each complete turn. (a) How many orbits do the electrons make before gaining their full energy? (b) What total distance do they travel? (c) What is the magnitude of the electric field accelerating the electrons (assuming it to be constant with time, for simplicity)? (d) At what rate is the magnetic flux changing inside the electron's orbit?

34-28   A coil of 200 circular turns of a 2.0 cm radius and having a total
resistance of 50 ohms is initially immersed in a magnetic field at right
angles to the plane of the coil. When the coil is removed quickly from
the magnetic field, the total charge passing through the coil is found
to be 4.0×10^{-3} coul. What was the flux density of the magnetic
field?

THIRTY - FIVE

$8\,pp$

INDUCTANCE

When the current through one conductor varies, an emf is induced in a near-by conductor, but in addition an emf is induced in the first conductor. This is the phenomenon of self-induction, and a conductor's inductance is a quantitative measure of the effect.

We first define the self-inductance and compute it for a simple geometry. Then we compute the characteristic time constant for the decay or growth of current in a circuit containing an inductor and resistor. Finally, we derive the energy of a current-carrying inductor and the energy density of the magnetic field.

35-1 Self-inductance defined Consider the simple circuit of Figure 35-1. A battery is connected to a conducting loop. The current increases from zero to the final value determined by the battery's emf and the circuit's resistance. At the same time, the magnetic flux through the conducting loop changes. Consequently, from Faraday's law, there must be an emf induced in the loop itself whose direction, from Lenz's law, is opposite to the direction of the emf generating the current in the circuit. Similarly, if the current has been established in the circuit and the switch is now opened, the current drops to zero. As the current changes, so does the magnetic flux through the circuit, and again there is an induced emf, whose direction now is such as to tend to maintain the magnetic flux through, and the current in, the loop.

In general, then, whenever the current and, therefore, the magnetic flux change in a circuit, an induced emf (or "back" emf) is generated in that circuit, its direction always being in the direction which opposes the magnetic flux change. This self-induction effect is of small consequence when a circuit consists simply of a single current loop. It becomes significant, however, when the magnetic flux is concentrated in a relatively small region

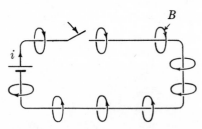

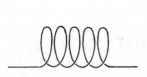

Figure 35-1. The buildup of current and the associated magnetic field upon the closing of a switch in a con-ducting loop connected to a battery.

Figure 35-2. An inductor.

of space, as is the case when a conducting wire is wound into the shape of a coil or a solenoid. For a coil of N turns, the magnetic flux through each loop is enhanced by a factor N over the flux for a single turn. Furthermore, the induced emf is enhanced by another factor N, inasmuch as the emf is induced in each of the N turns. Thus, winding a conductor into a coil with N turns increases the self-induction effects by a factor of N^2.

Any device, such as a coil, showing the effect of self-induction is called an *inductor*; see Figure 35-2. It is represented in a circuit diagram by the symbol $\underline{QQ}$. An inductor can be characterized by its self-inductance or, simply, *inductance*, which we now relate to the rate of current change.

According to Ampère's law the magnetic field produced by any current element at any point in space is directly proportional to the current i. Therefore, the magnetic flux over any given region is also proportional to i. For a coil of N turns we may write

$$N\phi_B = Li \qquad\qquad [35\text{-}1]$$

where the proportionality constant L, the coil's inductance, depends only on the dimensions of (and the material within) the conductor.

Now, from Faraday's law the induced emf $\mathscr{E}$ is given by

[34-5] $\mathscr{E} = -d(N\phi_B)/dt$ [35-2]

Substituting Equation 35-1 into Equation 35-2, we then have

$$\boxed{\mathscr{E} = -L\, di/dt}$$ [35-3]

$$L = -\frac{\mathscr{E}}{di/dt}$$ [35-4]

The inductance is defined either through Equation 35-1 or the equivalent Equation 35-4. We use Equation 35-1 for computing the inductance of a particular conductor arrangement, and we use Equation 35-4 to describe the behavior of an inductor in an electric circuit.

From Equation 35-4 we see that inductance has the units of volts per amperes per second, or v/(amp/sec) = v-sec/amp. A special name, the *henry* (in honor of J. Henry), is given to this combination of units:

$$1 \text{ h} = 1 \text{ v-sec/amp}$$

Thus, if the current through an inductor changes at the rate of 1 amp/sec and an induced emf of 1 v is thereby produced, the inductor's inductance is 1 h. Related units are the millihenry (1 mh = 10^{-3} h) and the microhenry (1 μh = 10^{-6} h). Air-filled laboratory coils of moderate size may have inductances on the order of several millihenries. With cores of magnetic materials (see Section 36-3) the inductance may rise to several henries.

To compute a conductor's inductance is, in general, quite complicated, because one must know the magnetic field at each point in space around the conductor. As in the case in computing a capacitor's capacitance, it is only with geometrically simple situations that the inductance is readily found. Of these, the simplest is that of a *toroid.* The magnetic field is confined entirely within the turns of a *finite* but long solenoid bent into a circle whose ends are joined together to form a doughnut shape, as shown in Figure 35-3. The magnetic field within the coils is uniform and independent of the toroid's radius if this radius is large compared with the radius of any one turn.

We found that the magnitude field B at any point near the center of a long solenoid (and therefore at any interior point for the toroid) is given by

[33-24] $B = \mu_0 n i$ [35-5]

Here i is the current and n is the number of turns per unit length; that is, $n = N/l$, where the length l is the circumference of the toroid.

From the definition of inductance,

[35-1] $$L = \frac{N\phi_B}{i} = \frac{NBA}{i}$$ [35-6]

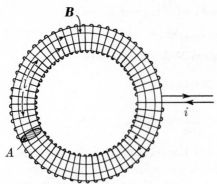

Figure 35-3. A toroid produces a magnetic field confined entirely within the turns of the toroid.

where A is the cross-sectional area of any one turn and B is the magnetic flux anywhere within the turns.

Substituting Equation 35-5 into Equation 35-6, we have

$$L = \mu_0 N n A$$
$$= \mu_0 (N/l) n (Al) = \mu_0 n^2 (Al)$$
$$\boxed{L = \mu_0 n^2 V} \qquad [35\text{-}7]$$

We have used V to represent the volume Al of a toroidal section of length l. Equation 35-7 gives not only the inductance of a toroid of small cross section but also the inductance *near the center* of a long straight solenoid.

Example 1 What is the inductance of a 2000-turn toroid with a mean radius of 10.0 cm and having a cross-sectional area of 2.0 cm²?

The total volume V over which the magnetic field exists in a toroid is the cross-sectional area A multiplied by the toroid's mean circumference $2\pi r$; that is, $V = 2\pi r A$. If N is the total number of turns, then $N = 2\pi r n$. Using Equation 35-7, we have

$$L = \mu_0 n^2 V = \mu_0 (N/2\pi r)^2 (2\pi r A) = \mu_0 N^2 A / 2\pi r$$
$$= (4\pi \times 10^{-7} \text{ weber/amp-m})(2000)^2(2.0 \times 10^{-4} \text{ m}^2)/2\pi(0.10 \text{ m}) = 1.6 \text{ mh}$$

We see that the inductance of this moderate-sized *air-filled* inductor is a mere 1.6 mh. By winding the toroid's turns about a strongly magnetic material, such as iron, the inductance can be increased more than a thousandfold.

35-2 LR circuits When a charged capacitor C is connected across a resistor R, the charge on either plate does not fall to zero instantaneously. Rather, the charge Q decays exponentially in time,

$$[30\text{-}22] \qquad\qquad Q = Q_0\, e^{-t/RC}$$

with a characteristic time constant RC, the time required for the charge to fall to $1/e$ of its initial value.

The same sort of behavior is found when a current-carrying inductor is connected across a resistor. The sluggishness, or inertia, of an inductor is a consequence of Lenz's law: when the current through an inductor changes, the inductor resists the change, and the induced emf is always such as to tend to offset the change in current and in magnetic flux.

Consider the circuit of Figure 35-4. We assume that the constant current $i = \mathscr{E}/R$ has been established by the battery. Now suppose that the switch in Figure 35-4a is suddenly changed from contact A to contact B. This

$v = iR + \dfrac{Q}{C}$

$\dfrac{dq}{dt} R - \dfrac{dt}{R}$

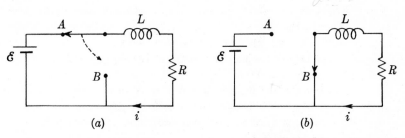

Figure 35-4. An LR circuit (a) in series with battery $\mathscr{E}$ with steady current $i = \mathscr{E}/R$, and (b) quickly disconnected from external battery $\mathscr{E}$.

removes the battery from the LR circuit, as shown in Figure 35-4b. The current in the closed circuit does not, however, drop to zero instantaneously. Although the battery's emf no longer drives charges around the circuit, the changing current through the inductor creates an emf which attempts to replace the battery's emf. That is, the inductor's emf is in the same sense as was formerly the battery's emf, inasmuch as the inductor attempts to sustain the current.

Applying the loop theorem (Kirchhoff's second rule, energy conservation) to the closed circuit of Figure 35-4b, we have

[31-12] $\Sigma \mathscr{E} = \Sigma V$

                                $-L \, di/dt = iR$ [35-8]

Note that in Equation 35-8 we have counted $-L(di/dt)$ as an emf, which it is, and *not* as a potential drop. Sometimes an inductor's emf is taken to be a potential drop; then the term $L(di/dt)$ is added to the right side of Equation 35-8 (and *not* counted as an emf). This yields:

$$0 = iR + L \, di/dt$$

which is, of course, the same as Equation 35-8.

To find how the current i varies with time t, we rearrange Equation 35-8 and integrate the current from its initial value i_0 at $t = 0$ to the value i at time $t = t$:

$$\int_{i_0}^{i} di/i = -1/(L/R) \int_{0}^{t} dt$$

$$\ln i/i_0 = -t/(L/R)$$

$$i = i_0 \, e^{-t/(L/R)} \qquad [35\text{-}9]$$

The current decays exponentially in time, as shown in Figure 35-5. The characteristic time constant for the LR circuit is

$$\boxed{\tau = L/R} \qquad [35\text{-}10]$$

As Equation 35-9 shows, after the time $t = \tau = L/R$ has elapsed, the current is $i = i_0/e$. That is, the time constant L/R is the time elapsing as the current falls to $1/e$, or 37 per cent, of its initial value. For example, if an LR circuit consists of an inductor of 1.0 h and a resistor of 1.0 ohm, the current drops to $1/e$ of its initial value in 1.0 sec.

Any actual inductor will have some finite resistance, simply because the conducting wire of which it is made has a nonzero resistance. Therefore, a pure inductance cannot exist isolated from resistance, and any inductor will have its own characteristic decay time.

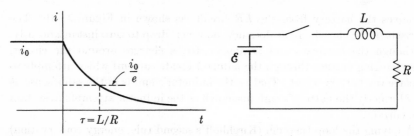

Figure 35-5. The exponential time decay of the current in the circuit of Figure 35-4b.

Figure 35-6

The current through a short-circuited current-carrying inductor decays exponentially in time. It is easy to show that the current through an inductor grows exponentially immediately after a constant emf has been applied to it. Consider the circuit of Figure 35-6. We wish to find how the current i varies in time from the moment the switch has been closed until the current reaches its final value $i = \mathscr{E}/R$. Clearly, as the current first passes through the inductor and the magnetic flux through the inductor changes, an emf is induced which, by Lenz's law, *opposes* the battery's emf. We apply the loop theorem as follows:

$$\Sigma \mathscr{E} = \sum V$$
$$\mathscr{E} - L\, di/dt = iR \qquad [35\text{-}11]$$

The term $L(di/dt)$ again appears on the left side as an emf. As before, we may move the term $L(di/dt)$ to the right side of the equation, and regard it as a potential drop; then Equation 35-11 can be written as

$$\mathscr{E} = L\, di/dt + iR \qquad [35\text{-}12]$$

Solving for i as a function of t for this differential equation is not difficult. We state the results, which may easily be verified by substituting i and

di/dt from Equation 35-13 into Equation
35-12:

$$i = (\mathscr{E}/R)[1 - e^{-t/(L/R)}] \quad [35\text{-}13]$$

A plot of this equation is shown in Figure
35-7.

The current grows exponentially in
time with the same characteristic time
constant $\tau = L/R$ as the circuit of Figure
35-4. After the time L/R has elapsed, the
current i differs from its final value $\mathscr{E}/R$
by $1/e$, or 37 per cent.

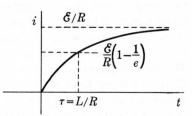

Figure 35-7. The exponential increase in current through the circuit of Figure 35-6 after closing the switch (plot of Equation 35-13).

Example 2 The inductance and internal resistance of a certain coil are unknown.
Experiment shows that the inductor's current decays to $1/e$ of its initial value
in 0.60 msec when a 4.0-ohm resistor is placed in series with the inductor. When
the additional series resistor is removed, the inductor's initial current falls to
$1/e$ of its initial value in 0.80 msec. What are the inductor's inductance L and
internal resistance R_i?

From Equation 35-10,

$$\tau = L/R_i = 0.80 \times 10^{-3} \text{ sec}$$

$$L/(R_i + 4.0 \text{ ohms}) = 0.60 \times 10^{-3} \text{ sec}$$

Solving the equations, we get

$$L = 9.6 \text{ mh}$$

$$R_i = 12 \text{ ohms}$$

35-3 Energy of an inductor If an inductor can sustain, at least for a
short while, an electric current in a circuit *after* an external source of emf,
such as a battery, has been disconnected from the circuit, clearly one must
associate energy with an inductor through which a current is passing. We
wish to find it.

Consider again the circuit of Figure 35-6, in which a battery is connected
to a circuit containing an inductor and a resistor. The loop theorem was
found to yield

[35-12] $$\mathscr{E} = L \, di/dt + iR$$

Multiplying this equation by the instantaneous current i, we have

$$\mathscr{E}i = Li \, di/dt + i^2 R \qquad [35\text{-}14]$$

It is easy to interpret the meaning of the terms in this equation. The left-
hand term, $\mathscr{E}i$, represents the rate at which the battery or, more generally,

$\mathcal{E}i = Li\frac{di}{dt} + i^2 R$

the energy source delivers electric energy to the circuit elements; it is the input power. The term i^2R on the right is, of course, the rate at which electric energy is being dissipated into thermal energy in the circuit's resistance: it is, so to speak, the output power. This leaves $Li(di/dt)$. This term is positive, since the current increases with time and $di/dt > 0$. Thus, the term $Li(di/dt)$ must represent electric power delivered to the circuit but not yet dissipated. It is the rate at which energy is supplied to and stored in the inductor. Labeling the instantaneous power into the inductor P_L and the energy associated with the inductor U_L, we may then write

$$P_L = Li\,di/dt$$

$$U_L = \int_0^t P_L\,dt = \int_0^t Li(di/dt)\,dt = \int_0^i Li\,di$$

Here we find the total energy U_L stored in the inductor by integrating the power from the initial time $t = 0$ to the time t, and the current from its initial zero value to the final value i.

$$\boxed{U_L = \tfrac{1}{2}Li^2}$$ [35-15]

The energy stored in an inductor carrying a current i is proportional to the inductance and to the square of the current. This relation is similar to that giving the electric energy stored in a charged capacitor of capacitance C and having a charge of magnitude Q on each plate:

[29-14] $$U_C = \tfrac{1}{2}Q^2/C$$

The magnetic energy stored in a 1h inductor carrying 1 amp is, from Equation 35-15, 0.5 joule. Such an inductor is, as inductors go, relatively large. On the other hand, a relatively large capacitor of 1 μf would have to be charged to a potential difference of 1 million volts to store the same amount of energy ($U_C = \tfrac{1}{2}CV^2$ from Equation 29-14) in its electric field.

35-4 Energy of the magnetic field A charged capacitor establishes an electric field between its plates, and we may speak of the capacitor's energy as residing in the electric field between the plates. Similarly, a current-carrying inductor stores energy in its magnetic field. We wish to compute the energy density u_B, or magnetic energy per unit volume, of a magnetic field of flux density B.

The energy U stored in the magnetic field of an inductor carrying current i is

[35-15] $$U = \tfrac{1}{2}Li^2$$

We imagine the inductor to be a toroid, because only in such case is the magnetic field confined entirely to the region within the windings. The inductance L can be found from Equation 35-7; the current i, from Equation 35-5. Then Equation 35-15 becomes

$$U_B = \tfrac{1}{2}(\mu_0 n^2 V)(B/\mu_0 n)^2 = \tfrac{1}{2}(B^2/\mu_0)V$$

Recall that V is the volume of the inductor. Therefore, since the magnetic energy density u_B is U_B/V,

$$\boxed{u_B = \tfrac{1}{2}B^2/\mu_0}$$ [35-16]

The energy density of the magnetic field is proportional to the *square* of the magnetic flux density.

Although derived for the special case of a toroid, Equation 35-16 can be shown to hold in general. The relation for the magnetic energy density is similar to that for the energy density u_E of an electric field:

[29-16] $$u_E = \tfrac{1}{2}\epsilon_0 E^2$$

Example 3 How does the magnetic energy density vary with distance from a magnetic dipole (at large distances)?

We found (Equation 33-12) that the flux density B varies inversely as the *cube* of the distance from a magnetic dipole for large distances. Therefore, since u_B is proportional to B^2, the energy density varies inversely as the sixth power of the distance. Halving the distance increases the magnetic energy density sixty-four-fold.

35-5 Summary Changing the current through a circuit loop induces an emf in the loop itself, by Faraday's law. By Lenz's law, this self-induced emf $\mathscr{E}$ is always in a direction opposing the current and magnetic flux change. The self-inductance L (in henries) is defined by

[35-1] $$L = N\phi_B/i$$

[35-3]   or $$\mathscr{E} = -L\,di/dt$$

The time constant for the exponential growth or decay of current through an inductor in an LR circuit is

[35-10] $$\tau = L/R$$

When current i passes through an inductor L, the energy stored in the magnetic field is

[35-15] $$U_B = \tfrac{1}{2}Li^2$$

The magnetic energy per unit volume, or the magnetic energy density, is

[35-16] $$u_B = B^2/2\mu_0$$

PROBLEMS

35-1 A circular loop of 10 cm radius carries a current of 10 amp. A second circular loop of 1.0 cm radius is concentric with, and lies in the plane of, the first loop. (a) What is the magnetic field through the inner loop? (b) What is the magnetic flux through the inner loop? If the current in the outer loop changes at the rate of 20 amp/sec, what is the emf induced in the inner loop?

35-2 Show that the unit, henry, is equivalent to kg-m²/coul².

35-3 When the current through a certain coil is 1.0 amp and the current is changing at the rate 0.50 amp/sec, the potential difference across the coil terminals is 6.0 v. When the current through the coil is again 1.0 amp but changing at the rate of 0.50 amp/sec in the opposite direction, the potential difference across the coil terminals is 4.0 v. What are (a) the inductance and (b) the internal resistance of the coil?

35-4 A single circular loop of conductor has an inductance L. What is the inductance of a coil of the same radius with N turns?

35-5 Show that the inductance per unit length of two concentric cylindrical conductors of radii r_1 and r_2 $(r_2 > r_1)$ having equal currents in opposite directions is $L = (\mu_0/2\pi) \ln (r_2/r_1)$. Assume that the inner conductor is so small in radius that we may properly assume that the magnetic field is entirely between the two conductors, a negligible field being found within the surface of the inner conductor.

35-6 Show that the equivalent self-inductance for inductors connected in series is given by $L = \Sigma L_i$ and for inductors in parallel by $1/L = \Sigma 1/L_i$. Assume that there is no magnetic coupling between separate inductors, that is, that the magnetic field from one inductor does not affect a second inductor. In formal terms, this amounts to saying that there is no *mutual inductance* between any two inductors.

35-7 Show that the time constant L/R for an LR circuit has the units of seconds.

35-8 An LR circuit is connected to a battery. Show that the rate at which the current initially changes with time is $i_0/(L/R)$, where i_0 is the final steady state current.

35-9 It is found that the time constant for the decay of current through a certain coil is halved when a 10-ohm resistor is added in series to the coil. Furthermore, when a pure inductance of 30 mh is added in series to the original coil and series resistor, the time constant is the same as that for the coil alone. What are the coil's (a) inductance and (b) internal resistance?

35-10 ★ The circuit shown in Figure 35-8 is one form of *integrating circuit*: the output voltage V_o is proportional to the integral $\int V_i \, dt$ of the input voltage V_i. (See Problem 30-26 for a differentiating circuit using a capacitor and resistor.) Applying the loop theorem to the left-hand loop we have

$$V_i = L \, di/dt + iR = L[di/dt + i/(L/R)]$$

Now, if the time constant L/R is long (compared with the period of the changing current), the second term in this equation can be ignored, and we have

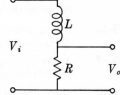

$$V_i = L \, di/dt, \quad \text{or} \quad \int V_i \, dt = \int L \, di = Li$$

Figure 35-8. An integrating circuit.

But the output voltage V_o is proportional to i (since $V_o = iR$); therefore, $V_o \propto \int V_i \, dt$. What would the output wave form look like if (a) a saw-tooth wave and (b) a square wave were applied to the input? See Figure 35-9.

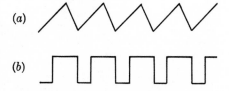

Figure 35-9. (a) A saw-tooth input wave applied across the left-hand terminals of Figure 35-8. (b) A square-wave input applied across the left-hand terminals of Figure 35-8.

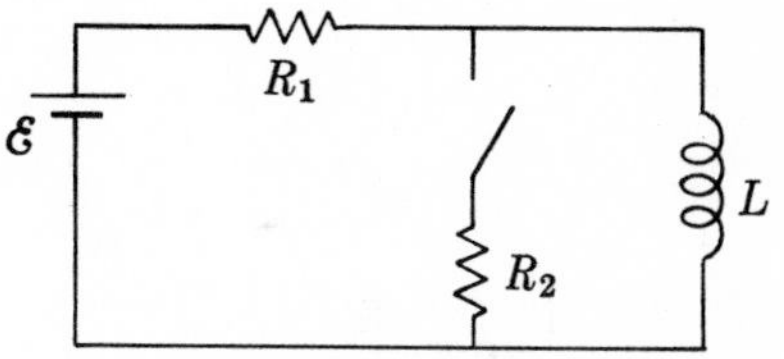

Figure 35-10

35-11 ★ Consider the circuit shown in Figure 35-10. Assume that the switch has been open for a long time. (a) What are the currents through R_1, R_2, and L? (b) If the switch is now closed at time $t = 0$, what are the expressions for the currents through R_1, R_2, and L as functions of time, from Kirchhoff's rules? Verify your answer by finding the values of the currents as t approaches infinity.

35-12 A current of 4.0 amp passes through an inductor of 30 mh. What is the total energy dissipated as thermal energy, when the inductor is connected across a resistance and disconnected from everything else?

35-13 The current through an inductor of 50 mh is 2.0 amp and changes at the rate 5.0 amp/sec. What are (a) the emf induced in the coil and (b) the energy stored in the coil?

35-14   The current through a coil of 50 mh decays to half its initial value in
1.2 msec. (a) What is the coil's internal resistance? (b) How long
does it take for the energy stored in the coil to fall to one-half its
initial value?

35-15   A coil having an inductance of 4.0 mh and a resistance of 10 ohms is
connected to a battery with an emf of 12 v and internal resistance of
2.0 ohms. How long must one wait after the switch is closed until (a)
the current is 90 per cent of its steady-state value and (b) the energy
stored in the inductor is 90 per cent of its steady-state value?

35-16   A long straight conductor carries a current i. What is the magnetic-
energy density of the magnetic field at a distance r from the conductor?

35-17   A flat circular coil of N turns, each of radius r, carries a current i.
What is the energy density of the magnetic field at the center of the coil?

35-18   Show, by considering the energy of the resultant magnetic field, that
a magnetic dipole free to align itself with an external magnetic field
will do so.

THIRTY - SIX

ELECTRIC AND MAGNETIC FIELD
VECTORS

This chapter is concerned with the electric and magnetic field vectors which are particularly useful in describing the electric and magnetic properties of materials. We first define the electric displacement and electric polarization vectors and relate these vectors to the electric field and the properties of a dielectric. Then we define the magnetic field intensity and the magnetization and relate these vectors to the magnetic flux density and the magnetic properties of materials. Finally, we consider briefly the properties of dia-, para-, and ferromagnetic materials.

36-1 Electric field vectors The polarization of a dielectric material by an electric field was treated qualitatively in Section 29-4. Here we return to the relatively simple situation (shown earlier in Figures 29-10d, e, and f) in which the region between the plates of a parallel-plate capacitor is filled by a dielectric material of dielectric constant κ.

The electric field E is uniform and confined entirely to the space between the plates, each plate being of area A and both being separated by a distance

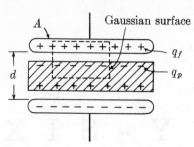

Figure 36-1. A parallel-plate capacitor filled with a dielectric. The free charge on conducting plates is q_f; the induced charge on the dielectric surface is q_p.

d; see Figure 36-1. The magnitude of the *free charge* on either of the capacitor plates is q_f; this charge is so designated because it is *free* to enter or leave the capacitor plate. The magnitude of the *polarization charge* is denoted by q_p. This induced charge is bound to the dielectric material and arises from the induced and permanent electric dipole moments within it. As was shown in Figure 29-11, a net polarization charge appears only on the two surfaces of the dielectric slab. The dotted line in Figure 36-1 shows the boundaries of a Gaussian surface to which we will shortly apply Gauss's law.

Now consider the dielectric slab itself, shown in Figure 36-2. Positive and negative charges, each of total magnitude q_p, are spread uniformly over opposite faces of the dielectric. If we denote the total charge per unit area on one charged surface by P, then

$$P = q_p/A$$

Multiplying the numerator and denominator of this relation by d, the distance separating the two opposite sheets of polarization charge, we have

$$P = q_p d/Ad \qquad [36\text{-}1]$$

Now from Equation 26-10 we recognize $q_p d$ to be the *total* electric dipole moment for all of the polarization charges within the volume Ad. Actually, there is a very large number of electric dipoles extending through the dielectric, from the negative to the positive surface, but the separation distance d between the two opposite polarization charges of equal magnitude is the same for all such dipoles (recall that there is no *net* polarization charge *within* the dielectric). The total volume of dielectric, Ad, appears on the right side of Equation 36-1. Therefore, we may interpret the quantity P in a new way. It is the *electric dipole moment per unit volume* of the polarized dielectric material, and we call the vector $\mathbf{P}$ the *electric polarization vector*.

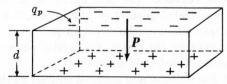

Figure 36-2. Dielectric slab with induced surface charge.

The direction of the polarization vector P is that of any of the electric dipole moments of the polarization charges; that is, P is perpendicular to the charged surfaces of the dielectric and goes from the negative to positive surface. Note, by comparing Figures 36-2 and 36-1, that the direction of the polarization vector P is the *same* as that of the electric field E within the dielectric (from positive to negative free charges on the *plates*). Said differently, the electric field produced through the dielectric by the polarization charges at the outside surfaces is *opposite* to the field E which induces this field.

Now let us apply Gauss's law to the Gaussian surface in Figure 36-1. In general, we may write

[27-3]
$$\epsilon_0 \oint E \cdot dS = (q_f + q_p) \qquad \text{[36-2]}$$

The total electric flux through any Gaussian surface (multiplied by ϵ_0) is the total charge enclosed by this surface. In Equation 36-2 we separate the total charge into two parts: the free charge q_f and the polarization charge q_p (we will take the difference in signs of q_f and q_p into account later). For the Gaussian surface of Figure 36-1, that of a cylinder one end of which lies within the conductor and the other within the dielectric and perpendicular to the electric field there, electric flux lines exist only through the cylinder end lying within the dielectric.

For the chosen Gaussian surface we may express the polarization charge q_p in terms of the electric polarization P within the dielectric by generalizing Equation 36-1:

$$-q_p = \oint P \cdot dS \qquad \text{[36-3]}$$

Here we recognize that the magnitude of P is the surface charge density of polarization charges. A minus sign appears in Equation 36-3, because the polarization charge within the Gaussian surface is negative but the value of the right-hand term is positive (the only contribution is across the cylinder end within the dielectric for Figure 36-1). When Equation 36-3 is substituted into Equation 36-2, we have

$$\epsilon_0 \oint E \cdot dS = q_f - \oint P \cdot dS$$

$$\oint (\epsilon_0 E + P) \cdot dS = q_f \qquad \text{[36-4]}$$

Now, it is convenient to define the *electric displacement vector* D as

$$D \equiv \epsilon_0 E + P \qquad \text{[36-5]}$$

Using this definition in Equation 36-4, we then have the simple relation

$$\oint D \cdot dS = q_f \qquad \text{[36-6]}$$

Equation 36-6 is *Gauss's law for a dielectric*. The vector $\epsilon_0 E$ of Equation 36-2 is replaced by the displacement vector D, and appearing on the right side is *not* the total charge but *only* the *free charge*. The electric displacement D is so named because it relates to the properties of the electric field in a material where charges are displaced. The motivation for introducing this new electric vector is to allow us to write Gauss's law in the simple form of Equation 36-6. Through the definition of D we can account for the induced, or polarization, charges and the change in the resultant electric field in the dielectric. Another reason for defining an electric displacement D in addition to the electric field E is that certain problems involving dielectric materials can be analyzed very easily, because the boundary conditions at the surface of a dielectric material are simple when expressed in terms of E and D.

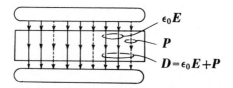

Figure 36-3. Field lines within a dielectric; P lines are dotted, $\epsilon_0 E$ lines are solid, and D lines are both.

Both the polarization P and electric displacement D carry units of charge per unit area, or coulombs per square meter. We may represent D and P by field lines; in fact, the field lines for these vectors help clarify their physical significance; see Figure 36-3. Here we see that the electric displacement does *not* change as we go from the air-filled region immediately adjoining the capacitor plate to the region within the dielectric. With no dielectric material, $P = 0$, and then $D = \epsilon_0 E$, from Equation 36-5. Within the dielectric we add P to $\epsilon_0 E$ there, to find the *same* displacement D. It must be emphasized that the resultant electric force per unit positive charge at any point is still given by the electric field E.

We can relate the electric vectors to the dielectric constant of the medium within the parallel-plate capacitor. As we found in Section 29-5, if the electric field between the capacitor plates is E_0 when no dielectric is present, then the electric field is $E = E_0/\kappa$ when the capacitor is filled with a dielectric of dielectric constant κ, provided that the *same* free charge q_f remains on the capacitor plates. Now, the vector D does *not* change when a dielectric is introduced into a capacitor and the same free charges remain on the plates, as Equation 36-6 requires. When $P = 0$ and $E = E_0$, then Equation 36-5 gives

$$D = \epsilon_0 E_0$$

With the dielectric present, we have

$$D = \epsilon_0 E + P = \epsilon_0 E_0/\kappa + P$$

Eliminating D from these two equations gives

$$P = \epsilon_0 E_0(1 - 1/\kappa) = \epsilon_0 \kappa E(1 - 1/\kappa)$$
$$P = \epsilon_0 E(\kappa - 1) \qquad [36\text{-}7]$$

We see from Equation 36-7 that if $\kappa = 1$ (that is, if the capacitor has no dielectric within), then $P = 0$, as we would expect. Finally, substituting Equation 36-7 into Equation 36-5, we have

$$D = \epsilon_0 E + \epsilon_0 E(\kappa - 1)$$
$$D = \kappa \epsilon_0 E \qquad [36\text{-}8]$$

The electric displacement D is then larger than $\epsilon_0 E$ by the factor κ or, if we use the electric permittivity $\epsilon = \kappa \epsilon_0$ (Equation 29-12), then Equation 36-8 can be written

$$D = \epsilon E \qquad [36\text{-}9]$$

The polarization properties of a dielectric material are also described by its *electric susceptibility* χ_e where, by definition,

$$\chi_e = P/\epsilon_0 E \qquad [36\text{-}10]$$

The quantity χ_e gives a quantitative measure of the degree to which a dielectric material is susceptible to polarization by the electric field E. If the polarization P is proportional to the field E, as is the case for electric fields of moderate magnitude, the susceptibility of any given material is a constant.

From Equations 36-10, 36-8, and 36-5 we see that the electric susceptibility is related to the dielectric constant as follows:

$$\kappa = 1 + \chi_e$$
$$\chi_e = \kappa - 1 \qquad [36\text{-}11]$$

The susceptibility shows to what degree the dielectric constant differs from 1.

36-2 Magnetic field vectors In discussing the electric field vectors we considered the characteristics of a dielectric material completely filling a parallel-plate capacitor. We used this configuration because the electric field is constant and confined entirely within the region between the plates, the region containing the dielectric material. We shall follow the same procedure in introducing the magnetic field vectors. That is, we choose a configuration in which the magnetic field is entirely within the material and constant in magnitude at each point in the material. The only arrangement satisfying these conditions is a toroidal solenoid, such as that shown in Figure 36-4. The toroid has n turns per unit length along the circumference with a current i in each turn. If the toroid's mean radius r is large compared

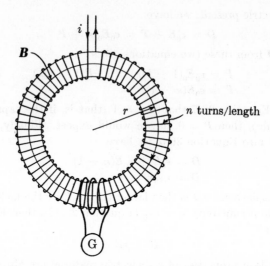

Figure 36-4. Toroid of mean radius r with confined magnetic field, which is approximately constant in magnitude throughout the windings.

with the radius of one turn, the magnetic flux density B at any interior point is directed perpendicular to the plane of the loop and has the magnitude

[33-24] $$B_0 = \mu_0 n i$$ [36-12]

when a *vacuum* exists within the toroid.

We can measure the flux density in the toroid by winding a secondary coil about it and connecting this coil to a ballistic galvanometer (Section 34-6). Then, when the current i is turned on or off, the momentary emf induced in the secondary coil produces a galvanometer deflection which is directly proportional to the flux change through the secondary coil. Now if one compares the flux density B, measured when a material is placed within the toroidal windings, with the flux density B_0 for the same (or an identical) toroid empty of material, one finds that B is *not* in general the same as B_0. Indeed, one can classify materials magnetically as follows:

Diamagnetic: $B/B_0 < 1$

Paramagnetic: $B/B_0 > 1$

Ferromagnetic: $B/B_0 \gg 1$

For a *diamagnetic* material (such as bismuth) the magnetic flux density is *reduced* (this corresponds to the electric case, in which any material introduced between the capacitor plates reduces the electric field). For a *paramagnetic* material (such as molecular oxygen) the magnetic flux density is *enhanced*,

and for a very strongly paramagnetic, or *ferromagnetic*, material (such as iron) the magnetic flux density is *increased by a large factor* (there is *no* electrical analog to paramagnetism or ferromagnetism). The physical reasons for the different behaviors of the three general types of materials are discussed in some detail in Section 36-3. For definiteness in what follows, we shall assume the material within the toroid to be paramagnetic or ferromagnetic, its effect being that of *increasing* the magnetic flux.

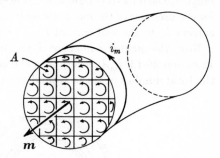

The magnetic flux density increases when a core (sometimes called a Rowland ring) is placed inside the toroidal windings. We could achieve the same enhancement of B with no material within by increasing the current i in the toroid, according to Equation 36-12. In fact, any additional current

Figure 36-5. Cross section of core material within toroid, showing induced current loops.

running around the outside of the toroid in the same sense as the current i would produce an enhancement of B. This is, in fact, precisely what happens with the core inside the windings. We may think of the magnetization of the core material as arising from the alignment of elementary magnets, or magnetic dipoles, within the material; when current passes through the toroid windings the magnetic dipoles are aligned, at least partially, along the direction of the field B. That is, the magnetic field of the dipoles in the material *adds* to the magnetic field produced by the current through the toroid windings.

In Figure 36-5 we see a large number of current loops at a cross section in the core material. We recall that we may always associate a current loop with a magnetic moment m following the relation

[32-19] $$m = iA$$ [36-13]

where i is now the current around the loop and A is the loop's area. (Here we symbolize the magnetic moment by m, rather than μ, because we shall later use μ for another magnetic quantity.) The direction of the magnetic moment m is the same as that of the magnetic field B produced at the center of the loop. The little current loops of Figure 36-5 represent the aligned magnetic moments in the core. Actually, all *interior* currents cancel, and we are left with only the current circling the magnetic core around the periphery. Thus, the entire effect of the aligned magnetic moments is equivalent to a single current loop. We effectively have one big current loop whose magnetic effects are equivalent to that of the magnetized material in the core. We call this *the magnetization current* i_m (which is also sometimes referred to as the *Amperian current*). It will be convenient to imagine the magnetization current to flow through helical windings, n turns per unit length, in the same fashion as that of the *real current* i_r (the equivalent magnetization current i_m is actually no less "real" than i_r, because every magnetic field has its origin in moving electric charges). Then we can account for the presence of the magnetic material merely by adding the *magnetization* current i_m to the *real* current i_r.

Now, the magnetic moment of one loop of magnetization current is, from Equation 36-13, $i_m A$, where A is the cross-sectional area of the core. Since the total number of turns around the toroid is $n(2\pi r)$, the magnitude of the

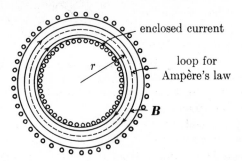

enclosed current

loop for
Ampère's law

B

Figure 36-6. Application of Ampère's law around a closed path within a magnetic material.

core's total magnetic moment is $i_m A n(2\pi r) = ni_m(2\pi r A)$. The total volume of the core is $2\pi r A$; therefore, the magnitude of the core's magnetic moment M per unit volume is

$$M = ni_m \qquad [36\text{-}14]$$

We call M, the magnetic moment per unit volume of the magnetic material, the *magnetization vector*. Its direction at any point within the core is perpendicular to the cross-sectional plane and in the same direction (for paramagnetic materials) as the magnetic flux B produced by the real currents.

It is useful to apply Ampère's law to the toroidal solenoid in Figure 36-6:

$$[33\text{-}23] \qquad \oint B \cdot dl = \mu_0 i$$

The line integral of the magnetic flux density around any closed path is the net current enclosed by the loop (multiplied by μ_0). When we include the magnetization current, Ampère's law becomes

$$\oint B \cdot dl = n(2\pi r)\mu_0(i_r + i_m) \qquad [36\text{-}15]$$

The factor $n(2\pi r)$ on the right-hand side represents the total number of loops with a current $i_r + i_m$ through each. Note that we take account of the magnetic material merely by adding the magnetization current to the real current.

When we apply Ampère's law to the closed path indicated by the dotted line in Figure 36-6, that is, a circle of radius r passing through the center of the toroid, Equation 36-11 becomes

$$B(2\pi r) = n(2\pi r)\mu_0 i_r + n(2\pi r)\mu_0 i_m \qquad [36\text{-}16]$$

Substituting Equation 36-14 into Equation 36-16 we have

$$B2\pi r = n(2\pi r)\mu_0 i_r + \mu_0 M 2\pi r$$

We may write the quantity $M(2\pi r)$ as $\oint M \cdot dl$ for the path we have chosen, since the vector M is along the path at each point. Therefore, the above equation can be written in more general form as

$$\oint B \cdot dl = n(2\pi r)\mu_0 i_r + \mu_0 \oint M \cdot dl$$

$$\oint \left(\frac{B - \mu_0 M}{\mu_0} \right) \cdot dl = I_r \qquad [36\text{-}17]$$

Here we have represented the *total* real current $n(2\pi r)i_r$ inside the closed path by I_r. We may write Equation 36-17 in still simpler form by defining a *magnetic field intensity*, or *magnetic field strength*, H as

$$H \equiv (B - \mu_0 M)/\mu_0$$
$$B = \mu_0 H + \mu_0 M \qquad [36\text{-}18]$$

Then Equation 36-17 is equivalent to

$$\oint H \cdot dl = I_r \qquad [36\text{-}19]$$

The line integral of the magnetic field intensity around any closed loop is equal to the total real current enclosed by the path. This is an alternative form of Ampère's law, in which one takes account of magnetic material (and of its equivalent magnetization current) by using the magnetic field intensity rather than the magnetic flux density; then one includes the contributions of the real *currents only* (in addition, the constant factor μ_0 is omitted).

From Equation 36-19 we see that the magnetic field intensity H has dimensions of total current per length, or amperes per meter (sometimes this is written as ampere *turns* per meter, because in finding the *total* real current enclosed by the Amperian loop we must count the total number of turns enclosed). We can see the physical significance of H from Equation 36-18. The magnetic flux density B, which is always the field vector determining the magnetic force on a moving charged particle, is composed of two parts, the field $\mu_0 H$, arising from the real currents, and $\mu_0 M$, the additional magnetic field arising from the magnetic moments induced in a magnetic material by the magnetizing field. Roughly speaking, for the toroidal configuration, H is the magnetic "cause," and B is the total magnetic "effect." (Of course, for a diamagnetic material, in which the induced magnetic moments *oppose* the magnetizing field and thereby reduce the resultant magnetic flux density, the magnetization M is negative.) From Equation 38-18, when $M = 0$, $B = \mu_0 H$.

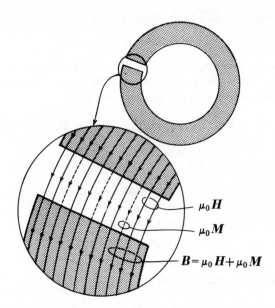

Figure 36-7. Field lines within a magnetic material; $\mu_0 M$ lines are dotted, $\mu_0 H$ lines are solid, and B lines are both.

We may draw field lines for H and M as well as for B. This is illustrated, for the toroidal configuration, in Figure 36-7. The core has a small gap; in this gap there is *no* magnetization M. In the absence of magnetic material within the toroid windings we have only the $\mu_0 H$ lines. With the core present there are additional $\mu_0 M$ lines which, when added to $\mu_0 H$, yield the resultant magnetic flux density B.

The H and M vectors are particularly useful when the geometry of the magnetic material is more complicated than that of the toroid. One can deal with such cases fairly readily, because the boundary conditions on B and H between different magnetic materials are simple. We shall not pursue this matter here.

When the magnetization M is zero, we have $B = \mu_0 H$. It is useful to write a relation of this form which holds even when M is not zero:

$$B = \mu H \qquad [36\text{-}20]$$

The quantity μ is the *permeability* of the material in which B and H are measured; it has the same units as μ_0, the so-called permeability of a vacuum. It is also useful to define a relative permeability κ_m, according to

$$\kappa_m = \mu/\mu_0 \qquad [36\text{-}21]$$

Then Equation 36-20 may be written in the form

$$B = \kappa_m \mu_0 H \qquad [36\text{-}22]$$

Finally, we may define a *magnetic susceptibility* χ_m through the relation

$$\chi_m = M/H \qquad [36\text{-}23]$$

The parameter χ_m gives a quantitative measure of the degree to which a material is susceptible to being magnetized in the field H. Comparing Equations 36-23, 36-22, and 36-18 shows that

$$\kappa_m = (1 + \chi_m) \qquad [36\text{-}24]$$

36-3   Diamagnetic, paramagnetic, and ferromagnetic materials   In this section we shall concentrate on the physical reasons for the different behaviors of dia-, para-, and ferromagnetic materials. Although diamagnetism is readily explained in terms of Lenz's law, the phenomena of paramagnetism and ferromagnetism can be understood on a fundamental basis only through the quantum theory.

DIAMAGNETISM   When a diamagnetic material, such as bismuth, is placed in an external magnetic field, the resultant magnetic flux density within the material is *reduced*. Magnetic moments within the material are aligned *against* the external field. A diamagnetic rod partially expels an external magnetic field, as shown in Figure 36-8a, and when a diamagnetic rod is placed in an inhomogeneous external magnetic field, it is repelled from the region of the strong field and aligns itself at right angles to the magnetic field lines, as shown in Figure 36-8b. A superconductor (Section 30-7) is the only example of a *perfect diamagnet*; it expels the magnetic field lines completely.

In terms of the magnetic parameters, a diamagnetic material is characterized by a magnetization M *opposite* to B, by a relative permeability *less* than 1 ($\kappa_m = \mu/\mu_0 < 1$), and by a constant *negative* magnetic susceptibility ($\chi_m < 0$). For a strictly diamagnetic material (one in which the effect is not masked by para- and ferromagnetic effects), the permeability μ is typically less than μ_0 by about 1 part in 10^6.

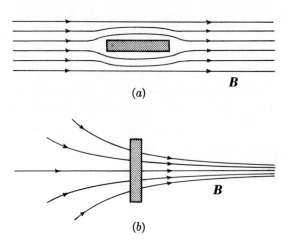

Figure 36-8. (a) Magnetic flux density **B** within a diamagnetic material is less than that in vacuum. (b) In an inhomogeneous magnetic field, the diamagnetic rod aligns itself perpendicular to the field.

We can easily see that diamagnetism is a consequence of Lenz's law. First consider the simple situation shown in Figure 36-9, in which a charged particle has been injected into a uniform magnetic field. The particle spirals around the magnetic-field lines in a helix (Section 32-3). Such a moving charged particle constitutes an electric current, and it generates a magnetic field of its own. As Figure 36-9 shows, the magnetic field produced by the cycling particle is *opposite* in direction to the external magnetic field; that is, the external field is partially annulled. We may regard this as the fundamental diamagnetic effect.

Excluding ferromagnetic materials for the moment, the magnetization of *all* materials in the absence of an external magnetic field is zero. That is, all materials, when not influenced by an external magnetic field, are, so to speak, magnetically neutral. On a simple atomic model, the electrons in a material can be thought of as orbiting about their parent nuclei; therefore, each orbiting electron constitutes a current loop and produces a magnetic moment. Now, if the total magnetization of a material is zero in the absence of an external field, then the electron orbits must be so paired off that the magnetic moments cancel. For every electron orbiting clockwise in one plane, there must be another electron orbiting counterclockwise in the same plane. This is shown in Figure 36-10a, where two electrons move with speed v_0 and angular speed ω_0 in similar circular orbits but in opposite senses. The orbital magnetic moments, each of magnitude m, are oppositely aligned. Now suppose that an external field **B** is turned on. For simplicity, we imagine the direction of **B** to be perpendicular to the planes of the electron

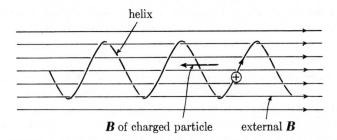

B of charged particle   external **B**

Figure 36-9. Spiralling charge in uniform magnetic field; the field produced by the moving charge is opposite to that of the external field.

orbits. The change in the magnetic field from zero to **B** has two effects, discussed below.

(1) The changing magnetic flux through the current loop (the electron orbit) induces an emf; the electric field from the emf is tangential to the electron's orbit, and the linear speed v and angular speed ω are changed.

(2) A magnetic force acts on the electron. This force is radial and acts in addition to the radial electrostatic force holding the electron in its circular path about its nucleus.

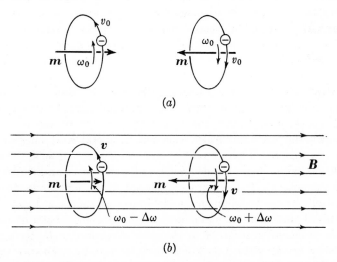

Figure 36-10. Magnetic moments of two electrons orbiting in opposite senses: (a) in a zero external field and (b) in a magnetic field **B**.

The effects are shown in Figure 36-10b. The electron speed for the left orbit is reduced, as is also the angular speed from ω_0 to $\omega_0 - \Delta\omega$. Consequently, the magnitude of its magnetic moment, still aligned with B, is reduced. For the electron orbit on the right, we have the reverse: the electron speed increases, as does the angular speed, from ω_0 to $\omega_0 + \Delta\omega$, and the magnitude of the magnetic moment, still aligned opposite to B, is increased. It is easy to confirm these results qualitatively in detail, and the reader should do so. We assert a curious result without proof: the additional magnetic force (radially outward for the left orbit and radially inward for the right orbit) is just of the right magnitude to compensate for the change in electron speed (decrease on left, increase on right), and both electrons continue to orbit circles of the *same radius*. It is for this reason, coupled with the fact of change in electron speed, that the magnitudes of the magnetic moments change.

Comparing Figure 36-10a with 36-10b we see that the net result of the external magnetic field is *diamagnetic*. With the field on, the magnetic moments of the two similar orbits no longer cancel. *Both* magnetic moments change, and the net induced magnetization is *opposite* to the applied field.

The argument used here can be extended to orbits whose plane is *not* perpendicular to the applied field. The results are the same. Although the electron orbits may change in some characteristics, the net effect of the external magnetic field is to induce a net *negative* magnetization. As a consequence, *all* materials show a diamagnetic effect, although this diamagnetism may be masked by a stronger para- or ferromagnetic effect. (It is interesting to note that the diamagnetic effect in materials is analogous to the polarization effects of electric fields on dielectric materials: for the electric case, the induced electric field is always *opposite* in direction to the external electric field.)

PARAMAGNETISM When a paramagnetic material, such as platinum, is placed in an external magnetic field, the resultant magnetic flux within the material is *enhanced*. Thus, the magnetic moments of the material are aligned *with* the external field. External magnetic field lines penetrate through a paramagnetic material aligned with an external field, as shown in Figure 36-11a, and when a paramagnetic rod is placed in an inhomogeneous external magnetic field, it is attracted toward the region of the strong field to align itself parallel to the magnetic field lines, as shown in Figure 36-11b.

In terms of the magnetic parameters, a paramagnetic material is characterized by a magnetization M in the *same* direction as B, by a relative permeability *greater* than 1 ($\kappa_m = \mu/\mu_0 > 1$), and by a *positive* magnetic susceptibility ($\chi_m > 0$). For a paramagnetic material at room temperature, the permeability μ may exceed μ_0 by 1 to 100 parts in 10^6.

Paramagnetism is completely inexplicable in terms of classical electromagnetism. If the magnetization of materials were attributed solely to orbiting electrons, one would, from Lenz's law, expect the effect of the external magnetic field to be diamagnetic in all cases. The origin of paramagnetism is (for the most part) the constant magnetic moment of electrons associated with *electron spin*. There is no complete classical analogue to electron spin, a strictly quantum mechanical effect, but we may visualize the effects of electron spin by imagining an electron as a sphere of negative

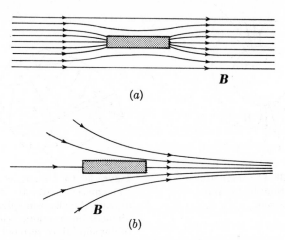

(a)

(b)

Figure 36-11. (a) Magnetic flux density **B** within a paramagnetic material is greater than that in vacuum. (b) In an inhomogeneous magnetic field the paramagnetic rod aligns itself parallel to the field.

charge spinning perpetually about an internal axis of rotation; see Figure 36-12. The circulating charge produces an electron-spin magnetic moment **μ** as shown. The special and, from the classical point of view, peculiar property of electron spin is this: the electron-spin magnetic moment is exactly of the *same* magnitude for *all* electrons [1.61×10^{-22} joule/(weber/m²)] and, if we visualize this effect as arising from spinning charge, the rate of spin is *always the same*. The magnitude of the spin magnetic moment is *not* affected by an external magnetic field, as is the magnetic moment arising from an electron's orbital motion. One might say that the magnetic effects of a spinning electron offer an example of a *perfect* permanent magnet. Thus, the magnetic moment from an electron spin can affect the magnetization of a material only by a change in its orientation, *not* by a change in the magnitude of the magnetic moment.

We have, in general, two principal contributions to the magnetism of any material: the magnetic moments from electron orbital motion, and the magnetic moments from electron spin. (The magnetism of atomic nuclei, or *nuclear magnetism*, arising from *nuclear spin*, is typically smaller than the electronic magnetism by a factor of 10^3.) For *nonparamagnetic* chemical compounds in a zero external magnetic field, the magnetic moments of pairs of orbiting electrons within the molecule are antialigned and yield no net orbital magnetization; furthermore, the electron spins are also paired off in

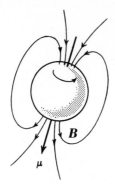

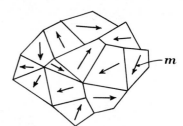

Figure 36-12. Magnetic field surrounding a spinning electron.

Figure 36-13. Unmagnetized ferromagnetic material. In each domain the electron spins are all aligned, but random orientation of domains gives zero net magnetization.

antialignment, to yield zero electron-spin magnetization. When an external magnetic field is turned on, the electrons remain paired together and the *electron-spin* magnetization remains *zero*. Now, in certain materials containing so-called paramagnetic ions, such as copper, manganese, and chromium, there are *unpaired* electron spins. In zero external field the magnetic moments of these unpaired spins do *not* produce a net magnetization, because the spin magnetic moments of the ions are oriented at random through the material. But when a magnetic field is turned on, more electron-spin magnetic moments align themselves with the field than against the field. There is then a net magnetization along the direction of the external field; that is, the material is *paramagnetic*. The alignment of electron-spin magnetic moments by the external field competes with the disorganizing effect of thermal motion within the paramagnetic material; the atomic vibrations tend to produce random spin orientations and no net magnetization. Therefore, the magnetization of a paramagnetic material typically increases as the temperature is lowered and the thermal vibrations diminish.

FERROMAGNETISM   The peculiar property of such ferromagnetic materials as iron, nickel, and cobalt (and certain alloys of these materials) is that the magnetic susceptibility, the magnetization, and the permeability are *not* constants but depend, for a particular material, on its past magnetic and thermal history. All ferromagnetic materials are strongly paramagnetic, however, in the sense that an applied external field can enhance the magnetic flux density by a very large factor. For example, the permeability μ may exceed μ_0 by a factor well over 10^3.

Ferromagnetic ions have unpaired electron spins. In a ferromagnetic material these electron spins are strongly coupled together by a quantum-mechanical force, for which there is no classical analogue, known as "exchange coupling." As a consequence, there are fairly large groups of atoms, or *magnetic domains*, in which the electron spins are all aligned together to form a fairly large magnetic moment, or magnetization vector, for the domain. A typical domain has a size of about 10^{-7} m (about 10^3 atomic diameters). In an unmagnetized ferromagnetic material there are a large number of domains whose various magnetization vectors are oriented at random so as to give no net magnetization for the material as a whole; see Figure 36-13.

Now suppose that an external magnetic field is turned on. The boundaries of the domains change, so that those domains whose magnetization is pointed along the direction of the external field grow in size at the expense of other domains whose magnetization direction is different. In addition, the orientation of M within any one domain may change direction toward an alignment with the external field. As a consequence, the net magnetization of the whole material grows. This magnetization is, in fact, considerably larger than that for a paramagnetic material because, within any one domain, *all* unpaired electron spins point in the same direction. Consequently, a very large fraction of the electron-spin magnetic moments may become aligned with the external field.

Figure 36-14 shows the magnetic flux density B plotted as a function of the magnetizing magnetic field intensity H for the experimental arrangement shown in Figure 36-4, that of a ring of material in a toroidal solenoid. The line is *not* straight; that is, the permeability μ and magnetic susceptibility χ_m are *not* constants. For sufficiently large H, the curve becomes nearly horizontal; that is, the magnetic material becomes saturated, with essentially all of the elementary magnetic dipoles aligned with the field. (Any further increase in B is then due to an increased current through the toroid, not to further alignment of dipoles.)

Now suppose that the magnetic field intensity H is reduced. The magnetic flux density B decreases, but *not* along the same path as for the rising H. Indeed, when the magnetizing field has reached zero, B is *not* zero;

there is still magnetization remaining in the ferromagnetic material. The material retains some magnetization. This value of B (for zero H) is called the *remanence*, or *retentivity*. In terms of domain behavior, the domain boundaries and the directions of the magnetization vectors within each domain change as H decreases, but not enough to restore the material to its initial magnetic condition. One must reverse the direction of the magnetizing field H to bring B to zero. This value of H (for zero B) is called the *coercive force*. As H is increased still further (toward negative H values), B

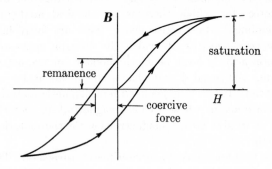

Figure 36-14. Magnetic hysteresis loop.

increases in magnitude in the opposite sense and again reaches saturation, the elementary magnets now being aligned completely in the opposite direction. One may complete the cycle by again reversing the change in H. The curve of Figure 36-14 is called a *hysteresis loop* (from the Greek word for "lag"). The magnetization of a ferromagnetic material lags behind the magnetizing field.†

A material having a large remanence has a sizable magnetic moment even in the absence of an external field; if, in addition, the coercive force is large, so that only a large external field can change this magnetic moment, we have a permanent magnet. A permanent magnet can be demagnetized, and thereby be made to lose its magnetization in zero external magnetic field, by carrying the material through a succession of hysteresis loops of progressively smaller amplitude, until finally both H and B are zero. A so-called "soft" ferromagnetic material has both a small remanence and a small coercive force.

---

† An effect similar to ferromagnetism is found in certain dielectric materials called ferroelectrics, such as barium titanate. Such materials show a *ferroelectric* effect in that they can be carried around an *electric* hysteresis loop (D against E) and may have a permanent electric dipole moment even in the absence of an external field.

36-4 Summary The table below summarizes the relations among the electric and magnetic field vectors.

Electric Vectors	*Magnetic Vectors*
Electric field E defined:	Magnetic flux density B defined:
[26-1] $\quad F_e = qE$	$F_m = qv \times B \qquad$ [32-3]
Polarization P of material: electric dipole moment per unit volume.	Magnetization M of material: magnetic dipole moment per unit volume.
Electric displacement D:	Magnetic field intensity H:
[36-5] $\quad D = \epsilon_0 E + P$	$B = \mu_0 H + \mu_0 M \qquad$ [36-18]
Gauss's law:	Ampère's law:
[27-3] $\quad \epsilon_0 \oint E \cdot dS = q$	$\oint B \cdot dl = \mu_0 i \qquad$ [33-23]
where q is entire enclosed charge, or	where i is entire enclosed current, or
[36-6] $\quad \oint D \cdot dS = q_f$	$\oint H \cdot dl = I_r \qquad$ [36-19]
where q_f is free charge only.	where I_r is real current only.
ϵ_0 = electric permittivity of vacuum	μ_0 = magnetic permeability of vacuum
ϵ = permittivity of material	μ = permeability of material
$\epsilon/\epsilon_0 = \kappa$ = relative electric permittivity, or dielectric constant	$\mu/\mu_0 = \kappa_m$ = relative permeability
χ_e = electric susceptibility	χ_m = magnetic susceptibility
[36-9] $\quad D = \epsilon E$	$B = \mu H \qquad$ [36-20]
[36-10] $\quad \chi_e = P/\epsilon_0 E$	$\chi_m = M/H \qquad$ [36-23]
[36-11] $\quad \kappa = 1 + \chi_e$	$\kappa_m = 1 + \chi_m \qquad$ [36-24]

Effect	*Magnetic susceptibility*	*Origin*
Diamagnetism	$\chi_m < 0$	Lenz's law
Paramagnetism	$\chi_m > 0$	Electron-spin magnetic moments
Ferromagnetism	χ_m dependent on H, but possibly very large	Magnetic domains

THIRTY-SEVEN

ELECTRIC OSCILLATIONS AND A-C CIRCUITS

In this chapter we deal with sinusoidally oscillating electric currents. We first discuss the simplest form of electric oscillator, an inductor connected across an initially charged capacitor. We derive the frequency of free oscillations and consider some analogies between electrical and mechanical oscillations.

Then we turn to alternating current, first treating the rotating-vector method for representing sinusoidally varying oscillations. We treat in turn the relations between the exciting emf and current for a pure resistor, inductor, and capacitor. We find that the current and voltage are not, in general, in phase. Then we consider a series RLC circuit, define the impedance, derive the relation giving the power delivered to the circuit elements, and consider the frequency response of the resonant circuit.

37-1 Electric free oscillations In this section we treat the free electric oscillations of a simple circuit consisting of an initially charged capacitor connected across an inductor. The more general case of an electric oscillator driven by a sinusoidally varying emf of arbitrary frequency is treated in Section 37-7.

Consider the circuit of Figure 37-1, where a capacitor C, initially carrying a charge of magnitude Q_m on each plate, is connected across an inductor L by the closing of a switch. For simplicity we assume (unrealistically) that the circuit contains no resistance. Of course, if the connecting wire across the capacitor plates had no self-inductance, the charges on the capacitor would immediately be neutralized. With the inductor present, however, any change from the initial zero current through the inductor, and therefore also any change in the magnetic flux through the coil, will give rise to a self-induced emf whose direction is always such as to tend to maintain a constant current.

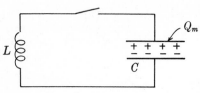

Figure 37-1. An electric oscillator.

After the switch is first closed and charges leave the capacitor plates, creating a current in the circuit, an opposing emf is set up by the inductor. When the charge q on either plate has reached zero, a current exists in the circuit, and this current continues to exist under the influence of the induced emf, which now opposes a decrease in this current. But as the current continues and charges again accumulate on the capacitor plates in the reverse sense, the current decreases in magnitude as the first charges arriving on the capacitor plates repel other charges arriving later. The current falls to zero, and now the capacitor is again fully charged, but with opposite polarity, again with charges of magnitude Q_m on each plate. At this point the electric oscillator has completed exactly one half of an oscillation cycle. After this the process is repeated: the capacitor again loses its charge, a current is created, now in the opposite direction, until the capacitor has again reached its initial charge state. Then one oscillation has been completed.

The oscillations in the electric charge and electric current continue. No energy is dissipated in resistance. Indeed, the electric oscillations consist of a continuous alternation of energy stored in the electric field of the charged capacitor and energy stored in the magnetic field of the current-carrying inductor. The two-circuit elements play different roles: (a) the capacitor C stores energy in its electric field when charged, but it tends to lose its charge and be restored to its equilibrium state of electric neutrality, and (b) the inductor L stores magnetic energy when carrying a current, and it displays an electrical inertia in that its self-induced emf tends to maintain the charges in motion. These results are all qualitative. Now let us consider the electric oscillator analytically.

Applying Kirchhoff's second rule (energy conservation) to the circuit loop of Figure 37-1, we have

$$\Sigma \mathscr{E} = \Sigma V$$

$$-L \, di/dt = q/C \tag{37-1}$$

Here the inductor's emf is $-L \, di/dt$ (Equation 35-4); and the electric potential difference across the capacitor is q/C (Equation 29-2), q being the charge on one capacitor plate at any instant. By definition, $i = dq/dt$; substituting this into Equation 37-1, we have

$$-L \, d^2q/dt^2 = q/C$$

$$d^2q/dt^2 = -(1/LC)q \tag{37-2}$$

Equation 37-2 is a linear second-order differential equation, whose solution is

$$q = Q_m \cos \omega t \tag{37-3}$$

as can easily be verified by substituting Equation 37-3 into Equation 37-2. Q_m is the maximum charge on the capacitor; it is also, in this problem, the initial charge, since $q = Q_m$ at $t = 0$.

The charge varies sinusoidally with time, as shown in Figure 37-2, and the angular frequency ω of the free oscillations is given by

$$\boxed{\omega = \frac{1}{\sqrt{LC}}} \tag{37-4}$$

The frequency $f = \omega/2\pi$ is, then,

$$f = \frac{1}{2\pi\sqrt{LC}} \tag{37-5}$$

The instantaneous current $i = dq/dt$ also oscillates sinusoidally, as we confirm by taking the time derivative of Equation 37-3,

$$i = -\omega Q_m \sin \omega t = -I_m \sin \omega t \tag{37-6}$$

where I_m is the maximum value of i.

Comparing Equations 37-6 and 37-3 (and Figures 37-2a and b), we see that the charge (here varying as the cosine) and the current (here varying as the sine) are 90° out of phase. That is, when the capacitor is fully charged and the energy resides entirely in the capacitor's electric field, the current through the inductor and magnetic field associated with it is zero, and conversely.

The circuit's total energy U remains constant; it consists of the capacitor's energy $U_C = q^2/2C$ and the inductor's energy $U_L = \frac{1}{2}Li^2$:

$$U = U_C + U_L = q^2/2C + \tfrac{1}{2}Li^2 = \tfrac{1}{2}(Q_m \cos \omega t)^2/C + \tfrac{1}{2}L(I_m \sin \omega t)^2 \tag{37-7}$$

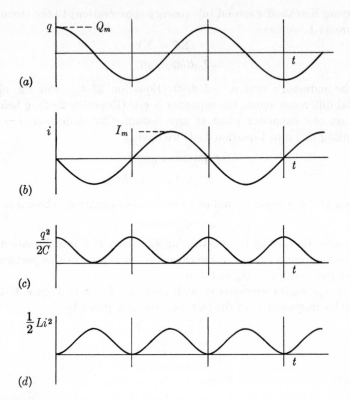

Figure 37-2. Time variation for an electric oscillator of (a) charge, (b) current, (c) capacitor's energy, and (d) inductor's energy.

From Equation 37-6, $I_m = \omega Q_m$, and from Equation 37-4, $\omega^2 = 1/LC$; therefore,

$$LI_m{}^2 = L\omega^2 Q_m{}^2 = Q_m{}^2/C$$

and Equation 37-7 becomes

$$U = (Q_m{}^2/2C)(\cos^2 \omega t + \sin^2 \omega t) = Q_m{}^2/2C \qquad [37\text{-}8]$$

Although the energies of the capacitor and inductor vary sinusoidally with time, as Figures 37-2c and d show, their sum is constant with time.

Any actual electric circuit has some resistance, even if only the resistance of the inductor's windings. When this effect is included, we have a damped harmonic electrical oscillator. The energy decreases with time exponentially (in the fashion of Figure 17-13 for a damped mechanical oscillator) because of the ever-present i^2R loss in the resistor (see Problem 37-5).

As Equation 37-5 shows, the frequency of free oscillations of an LC circuit depends on L and C. For example, with $C = 1.0\ \mu f$ and $L = 1.0$ mh, we find from Equation 37-5 that $f = 5.0 \times 10^3\ \text{sec}^{-1} = 5.0$ kcycles/sec. The frequency rises as the magnitudes of L and C decrease. Thus, if one is to construct an electric oscillator of very high frequency, the capacitor and inductor must be small, not only in the magnitudes of C and L, but also in the actual dimensions of these circuit elements.

Figure 37-3 shows the evolution of an ordinary LC circuit, with obvious capacitance and inductance elements, into two varieties of high-frequency

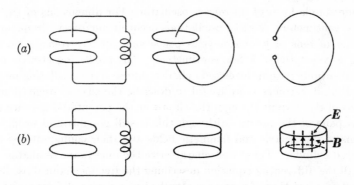

Figure 37-3. Evolution of an ordinary electric oscillator into (a) a high-frequency oscillator consisting of single conducting loop with a gap and (b) a microwave cavity oscillator consisting of a hollow right-circular cylindrical conductor.

oscillators, for which these circuit parameters are less easily recognized. In Figure 37-3a first the inductance is reduced considerably by replacing the coil with a single conducting wire; then the capacitance also is reduced considerably by reducing the area of the capacitor plates. There is left a single conducting loop broken by a gap at one point. This is indeed an electric oscillator, and if the loop's size is of the order of 1 m with a gap of perhaps 1 cm, it oscillates at a frequency of tens of megacycles per second, a frequency lying in the radiofrequency region of the electromagnetic spectrum.

Oscillators of just this type were, in fact, used in the historic experiments of Heinrich Hertz (1857–1894), who first demonstrated the existence of electromagnetic radiation in 1887. Hertz used two such oscillators, both resonant at the same frequency. The oscillations were observed through a spark at the gap. The electromagnetic radiation was detected by observing that, when the second oscillator was moved relatively far from the first oscillator, the sparks across its gap persisted, although this effect could *not* be attributed to the direct action of the electric and magnetic fields of the first oscillator on the second.

Figure 37-3b shows the evolution of a simple LC circuit into a different type of high-frequency oscillator. Here the inductance is reduced first by connecting the capacitor plates with a single straight conducting wire. Then the inductance is reduced still further by connecting additional wires in parallel with the first. Indeed, one constructs an entire cylindrical surface between the two capacitor plates, and so forms a hollow closed right-circular cylinder of conducting material. This certainly does not look, at least superficially, like an LC oscillator of the ordinary variety. It is, in fact, one simple form of *microwave* oscillator. For dimensions of the order of a few centimeters, the free oscillations occur at microwave frequencies of the order of tens of kilomegacycles per second (or electromagnetic waves having wavelengths of a few centimeters). The oscillating electric field is confined entirely within the closed cylinder, and so is the oscillating magnetic field. Here it becomes more useful to describe the electric oscillations, not in terms of the current through the circuit or the potential difference across various pairs of the points—although this is still possible and proper—but in terms of the electric and magnetic fields and their configurations within the closed cylinder. These best characterize the microwave oscillator.

Recall the differential equation describing the free mechanical oscillations of a system consisting of a mass m attached to a spring of force constant k:

$$[17\text{-}7] \qquad\qquad d^2x/dt^2 = -(k/m)x \qquad\qquad [37\text{-}9]$$

This equation is of exactly the same form as Equation 37-2 for the electric oscillations. Indeed, one may transform Equation 37-2 into Equation 37-9 by making the following replacements:

$$x \quad \text{for} \quad q$$
$$v = dx/dt \quad \text{for} \quad i = dq/dt$$
$$a = dv/dt = d^2x/dt^2 \quad \text{for} \quad di/dt = d^2q/dt^2$$
$$m \quad \text{for} \quad L$$
$$k \quad \text{for} \quad (1/C)$$

The correspondence is more than formal. Like the mass m, which shows an inertial tendency to maintain a particle at constant velocity v, the inductance shows such a tendency to maintain a constant current i. Likewise, the spring's restoring constant k corresponds to what might be called the capacitor's restoring constant $1/C = V/q$. (Although both an inductance coil and a helical spring are typically represented in a diagram by the same symbol, it must be emphasized that the capacitor goes with the elastic spring and the inductance coil with the mass.)

Furthermore, the electric potential difference q/C corresponds to the elastic restoring force kx, and the induced emf $L\,di/dt$ to the force $m\,dv/dt$. There is also a parallel to the mechanical dissipative force $F = rv$, proportional to the particle's velocity. It is the electrical resistance R, whose potential difference is Ri. Similarly, the potential energy $\frac{1}{2}kx^2$ of the stretched spring and the kinetic energy $\frac{1}{2}mv^2$ of the moving particle correspond, respectively, to the electric energy $q^2/2C$ of the charged capacitor and the magnetic energy $\frac{1}{2}Li^2$ of the inductor.

There is, then, a complete analogy, both in mathematical terms and in physical behavior, between mechanical and electrical "circuit" elements. Indeed, it is often useful to analyze a complicated mechanical system by constructing its electrical analogue with ordinary electric circuit elements. Then the measured charges, currents, and potential differences give the corresponding particle displacements, velocities, and forces. The entire analysis of an oscillating mechanical system, as given in Sections 17-5 and 17-6, can be carried over directly into the electrical equivalents.

37-2 Sinusoidally varying emf's   A coil of wire rotated at a constant angular speed ω in a uniform magnetic field will have a sinusoidally varying emf $\mathscr{E}$ induced across its terminals, whose frequency is the same as that of the rotating coil (Example 2, Chapter 34):

$$\mathscr{E} = \mathscr{E}_m \sin{(\omega t + \phi)} \qquad [37\text{-}10]$$

where the phase constant ϕ determines the value of the emf at the arbitrarily chosen zero of time:

$$\mathscr{E}(\text{at } t = 0) = \mathscr{E}_m \sin{\phi}$$

Figure 37-4 illustrates the variation in time of a d-c source of emf and an a-c source. It is customary to represent the d-c source by the symbol $\frac{\perp}{\top}$ and the a-c source by $\sim$.

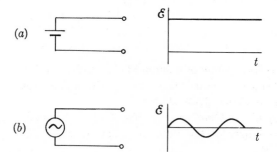

(a)

(b)

Figure 37-4. (a) A d-c source and emf as a function of time. (b) An a-c source and emf as a function of time.

If a voltmeter were capable of responding sufficiently rapidly to the variation in an alternating emf, it would read the instantaneous emf given by Equation 37-10. Common a-c power sources oscillate at 60 cycles/sec. Then a voltmeter would read the instantaneous voltage only if it were capable of responding to voltage changes over a time which is much smaller than the period of oscillation, $T = 2\pi/\omega$. The voltmeters commonly used to measure a-c voltage differences typically operate over much longer time intervals. Such instruments measure, therefore, an average value of a sinusoidally varying voltage. Thus, we must, as a preliminary to the study of a-c circuits, be clear about the average values of a sinusoidally varying function.

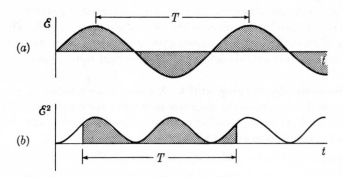

Figure 37-5. (a) The time average of a sinusoidally varying emf is zero. (b) The time average of the square of a sinusoidally varying emf is not zero, and is the same for any period T.

By definition, the average value f_{av} of any periodic function f over the period T is

$$f_{av} = \frac{\int_0^T f \, dt}{T} \qquad [37\text{-}11]$$

Clearly, the average value of a sinusoidally varying emf over any complete cycle is *zero*, since there are then equal positive and negative areas under the $\mathscr{E}$-t curve, as Figure 37-5a shows.

A more useful, and *nonzero*, average for a sinusoidal function is that involving the square of the function. The average value of $\mathscr{E}^2$ is, from Equation 37-10,

$$(\mathscr{E}^2)_{av} = (1/T) \int_0^T \mathscr{E}_m^2 \sin^2 (\omega t + \phi) \, dt$$

Figure 37-5b shows $\mathscr{E}^2$ as a function of time. Note that ϕ can have any value from 0 to 2π, depending on the arbitrarily chosen zero time. Inasmuch as the area under the $\mathscr{E}^2$-t curve is *independent* of the starting point along the t axis,

$$\int_0^T \sin^2(\omega t + \phi)\, dt = \int_0^T \sin^2 \omega t\, dt = \int_0^T \cos^2 \omega t\, dt$$

Using the trigonometric identity, $\sin^2 \theta + \cos^2 \theta = 1$, we have

$$(\mathscr{E}^2)_{av} = \frac{\mathscr{E}_m{}^2}{T}\left[\frac{\int_0^T \sin^2 \omega t\, dt + \int_0^T \cos^2 \omega t\, dt}{2}\right]$$

$$(\mathscr{E}^2)_{av} = \frac{\mathscr{E}_m{}^2}{T}\frac{\int_0^T dt}{2} = \tfrac{1}{2}\mathscr{E}_m{}^2 \qquad [37\text{-}12]$$

The average, or mean, of $\mathscr{E}^2$ is just half of $\mathscr{E}_m{}^2$. Taking the square root of $(\mathscr{E}^2)_{av}$, we have the *root-mean-square*, or rms, value of the sinusoidal function. It is the rms value of sinusoidally varying voltages and currents that plays a key role in the description of a-c circuitry:

$$\mathscr{E}_{rms} = \sqrt{(\mathscr{E}^2)_{av}} = \mathscr{E}_m/\sqrt{2} = 0.707\mathscr{E}_m \qquad [37\text{-}13]$$

A-c voltmeters and ammeters typically register rms values, although they may be so calibrated as to register peak-to-peak, or maximum, values. One must be careful.

Since we shall be concerned with instantaneous, rms, and maximum values of sinusoidal functions throughout the remainder of this chapter, we shall adopt the following conventions for designating these quantities:

instantaneous value:	small letter	v
rms value:	capital letter	V
maximum value:	capital letter with	V_m
	subscript m	

In this notation, Equation 37-10 becomes

$$\varepsilon = \mathscr{E}_m \sin(\omega t + \phi) = \sqrt{2}\mathscr{E} \sin(\omega t + \phi)$$

The instantaneous voltage from a 115 v (rms value, or $\mathscr{E}$) source therefore oscillates between $\mathscr{E}_m = \sqrt{2}\mathscr{E} = +163$ v and $-\mathscr{E}_m = -163$ v.

We shall find it extremely useful to represent sinusoidal functions by rotating vectors, as discussed earlier in Sections 5-4 and 17-3. Thus, the $\mathscr{E}$-t curve of Figure 37-5a can be represented by a vector of length $\mathscr{E}_m$ rotating at the constant angular speed ω and making an angle ϕ with the

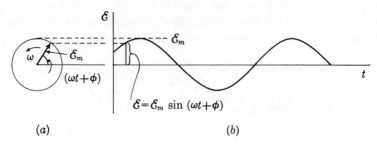

Figure 37-6. (a) A rotating vector. (b) The corresponding sinusoidal oscillation.

positive X-axis at $t = 0$. The Y-component of the vector $\mathcal{E}_m$ then gives Equation 37-10; see Figure 37-6. The special advantage of rotating vectors is apparent when we have two or more vectors, such as A and B in Figure 37-7a, rotating together at the *same* frequency ω in the counterclockwise sense. Then the angle between A and B, that is, the relative phase difference between the two oscillations, remains fixed with time. Vector B lags vector A in phase by the angle ϕ. If vector A lies along the X-axis at time $t = 0$, then the equation describing the Y-component of vector A is simply

$$y_A = A \sin \omega t$$

Similarly, the equation for the Y-component of B is

$$y_B = B \sin (\omega t - \phi)$$

Figure 37-7b shows both y_A and y_B plotted as a function of time. Note again that y_B lags behind y_A by the angle ϕ; that is, y_A reaches a peak at an earlier time than y_B. That this is so is shown by the fact that the curve

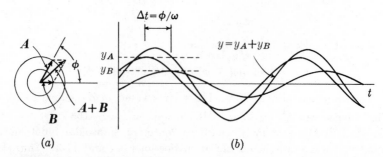

Figure 37-7. (a) Rotating vectors A and B, and their sum $A + B$. (b) The corresponding sinusoidal oscillations.

for y_B is shifted, relative to y_A, to the *right* (to *later* times) by Δt. The shift in time Δt between the two curves is easily related to the phase difference ϕ and the common period T of the oscillation by

$$\Delta t/T = \phi/2\pi$$
$$\Delta t = (\phi/2\pi)T = \phi/\omega \qquad [37\text{-}14]$$

Now suppose that one wishes to find the sum of two sinusoidal functions with the same frequency ω but differing in phase by the angle ϕ. The resultant y would be

$$y = y_A + y_B = A \sin \omega t + B \sin (\omega t - \phi)$$

There is a simpler way of finding this sum. We simply recognize that the projection of the vector sum of two vectors is equal to the sum of the projections of the two vectors. Thus, we can immediately find the resultant oscillation of A and B by adding these as vectors and then taking the component along the Y-axis of their vector sum. The resultant oscillation is at the same frequency as the component oscillations, but it differs from them both in amplitude and in relative phase, as one can see from Figure 37-7. The three vectors, A, B, and $A + B$ remain locked together as they all rotate at the same rate ω, and the amplitude of each oscillation is merely the length, A, B, or $|A + B|$, of the respective vector, A, B, or $A + B$. In general, the amplitude of the resultant oscillation is *not* the sum of the amplitudes of the component oscillations.

Example 1 Use the rotating-vector method to find the sum, or resultant, of the two sinusoidal oscillations $y_A = 2 \cos \omega t$ and $y_B = 3 \sin \omega t$.

The rotating-vector diagram associated with oscillations y_A and y_B is shown in Figure 37-8a. Vector A leads vector B by 90°; that is, A reaches a maximum one-quarter cycle before vector B. To find the resultant oscillation, we merely

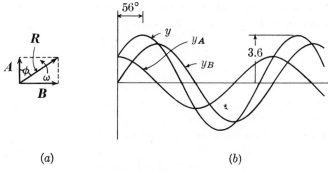

(a)   (b)

Figure 37-8

add the vectors A and B to obtain R, and then take the Y-component of this rotating resultant to obtain $y = y_A + y_B$. From Figure 37-8 we see that R lags vector A by

$$\tan \phi = \frac{B}{A} = \frac{3}{2} = 1.5$$

$$\phi = 56°$$

and the amplitude of R is

$$R = \sqrt{A^2 + B^2} = \sqrt{2^2 + 3^2} = \sqrt{13} = 3.6$$

Therefore, the equation for the resultant oscillation is given by

$$y = R \cos (\omega t - \phi) = 3.6 \cos (\omega t - 56°)$$

Figure 37-8b shows the curves for y_A, y_B, and y as functions of time.

37-3   A-C circuit with resistance only   A sinusoidally varying emf is applied across a pure resistor as shown in Figure 37-9a. What is the instantaneous current, and how is it related to the applied voltage? (Here, for brevity, we shall use the common term *voltage* to denote the emf or electric potential difference.)

Assuming that the instantaneous voltage v and current i are related through Ohm's law,

$$i = v/R$$

and that the voltage oscillates sinusoidally, following

$$v = V_m \sin \omega t$$

then we have

$$i = v/R = (V/R) \sin \omega t = I_m \sin \omega t$$

That is, i oscillates *in phase* with v, as shown in Figure 37-9b and c. The amplitudes of i and v are related by

$$I_m = V_m/R$$

It is convenient to express these results in terms of the rms values of i and of v, namely, in terms of I and of V, where $I = V/R$, as defined in Section 37-2:

$$v = \sqrt{2}V \sin \omega t$$
$$i = \sqrt{2}I \sin \omega t \qquad [37\text{-}15]$$

The average rate at which thermal energy is produced in the resistor can be found easily by first finding the instantaneous power delivered to the resistor and then averaging over many cycles. The instantaneous power is given by

[30-10] $p = vi = (V_m \sin \omega t)(I_m \sin \omega t) = V_m I_m \sin^2 \omega t$

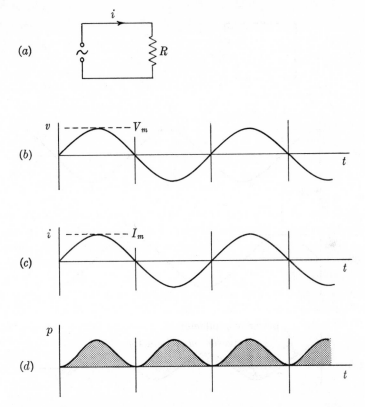

Figure 37-9. (a) A sinusoidal emf applied across a pure resistance. As a function of time: (b) the applied voltage, (c) the current, and (d) the power delivered to the resistor.

The instantaneous power p is plotted as a function of time in Figure 37-9d. Note that the power is always positive and that it oscillates at *twice* the frequency of v and i.

The average power p_{av} is then given by

$$p_{av} = (1/T)\int_0^T p\, dt = V_m I_m \frac{\displaystyle\int_0^T \sin^2 \omega t\, dt}{T} = \tfrac{1}{2}V_m I_m$$

$$p_{av} = P = VI \qquad\qquad [37\text{-}16]$$

Thus, the average rate at which thermal energy is dissipated in the resistor is the product of the rms voltage across it and the rms current through it.

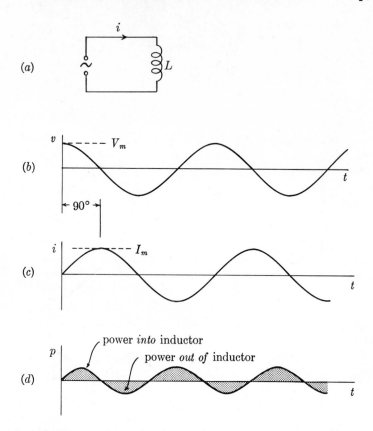

Figure 37-10. (a) A sinusoidal emf applied across a pure inductance. As a function of time: (b) the applied voltage, (c) the current, and (d) the power delivered to the inductor.

37-4 A-C circuit with inductance only Although all inductors have some resistance, we first consider an ideal inductor having zero resistance; see Figure 37-10a. When an alternating voltage of angular frequency ω and amplitude V_m is applied across a pure inductor of inductance L, a current i is generated through it; we wish to find this current. We know that the induced current is related to the applied voltage by

[35-3] $$v = L\, di/dt$$ [37-17]

If v oscillates sinusoidally, as shown in Figure 37-10b,

$$v = V_m \cos \omega t$$ [37-18]

Using Equation 37-18 in Equation 37-17, we have

$$V_m \cos \omega t = L \, di/dt$$

$$i = \int di = \int (V_m/L) \cos \omega t \, dt$$

Integrating, we have

$$i = (V_m/\omega L) \sin \omega t = I_m \sin \omega t \qquad [37\text{-}19]$$

The current through the inductor oscillates with the *same* frequency as the applied voltage, but the current i is *not* in phase with v. As Figure 37-10b and c shows, the *current lags the voltage* by 90° with respect to time; equivalently, the *voltage across the inductor leads the current* by 90°.

The relation between the current amplitude I_m and voltage amplitude V_m is, by Equation 37-19,

$$I_m = V_m/\omega L \qquad [37\text{-}20]$$

The quantity ωL behaves similarly to the resistance R in a pure resistance, and is called the *inductive reactance* X_L:

$$\boxed{X_L = \omega L} \qquad [37\text{-}21]$$

Equation 37-20 can then be written

$$I_m = V_m/X_L$$

or, in terms of the rms values,

$$I = V/X_L \qquad [37\text{-}22]$$

The unit for the inductive reactance X_L is the same as that for resistance, namely, the ohm. Whereas the resistance R is independent of the oscillating frequency ω, the inductive reactance varies directly as ω. Thus, increasing the oscillation frequency results in a smaller current i through an inductor for a given voltage V.

The fact that the voltage leads the current in a pure inductor by 90° results in an interesting property concerning the average power delivered. to the inductor. By Equations 37-18 and 37-19, we have

$$p = vi = (V_m \cos \omega t)(I_m \sin \omega t) \qquad [37\text{-}23]$$

In Figure 37-10d we show the instantaneous power p delivered to the pure inductor of Figure 37-10a as a function of time t. The average power is

$$P_{\mathrm{av}} = (1/T) \int_0^T p \, dt = V_m I_m (1/T) \int_0^T \cos \omega t \sin \omega t \, dt$$

Integrating over one period, we have

$$P_{\mathrm{av}} = (V_m I_m/2T\omega) \sin^2 \omega t \Big|_0^T$$

and recalling that $\omega T = 2\pi$

$$P_{\mathrm{av}} = (V_m I_m / 4\pi)(\sin^2 2\pi - \sin^2 0) = 0$$

The average power transferred from the external energy source to the inductor L is *zero*. During that part of the cycle (see Figure 37-10d) when v and i are both positive, the power is being transferred *to* the inductor. But when v and i are in opposite directions, the energy residing in the inductor coil is transferred back to the external circuit. Thus, a pure inductor alternately takes and gives equal amounts of energy to the rest of the circuit. As in the case of a resistance, the instantaneous power oscillates at *twice* the frequency at which v and i oscillate.

Example 2 A pure inductor having an inductance of 2.0 h is connected across the terminals of a 60-cycle/sec a-c voltage source, the rms voltage being 115 v. Find (a) the inductive reactance X_L, (b) the rms current, (c) the maximum power delivered to the inductor, and (d) the maximum energy stored in the inductor. (e) Show that the result of part (d) is consistent with Equation 35-15 giving the maximum energy in the magnetic field of the inductor as $\frac{1}{2}LI_m^2$.

(a) The inductive reactance is given by Equation 37-21:

$$X_L = \omega L = 2\pi f L = (2\pi)(60 \text{ cycles/sec})(2.0 \text{ h}) = 750 \text{ ohms}$$

(b) Equation 37-22 gives the rms current:

$$I = V/X_L = (115 \text{ v})/(750 \text{ ohms}) = 0.15 \text{ amp}$$

(c) One can obtain the maximum power by first finding those times at which the slope of the p-t curve of Figure 37-10d, or Equation 37-23, equals zero. Differentiating Equation 37-23 and equating it to zero yields

$$dp/dt = V_m I_m \omega(-\sin \omega t \sin \omega t + \cos \omega t \cos \omega t) = 0$$
$$\sin^2 \omega t = \cos^2 \omega t$$
$$\tan \omega t = \pm 1$$

The power to the inductor then has the maximum value when $\omega t = \pi/4, 3\pi/4, \ldots$, and

$$p_{\max} = V_m I_m \cos \pi/4 \sin \pi/4 = V_m I_m/2 = VI = (115 \text{ v})(0.15 \text{ amp}) = 17 \text{ w}$$

(d) The maximum energy stored in the inductor is found by integrating the power over that part of the cycle in which v and i are in the same direction, as seen in Figure 37-10d. Therefore,

$$U_L(\max) = \int_0^{T/4} p \, dt = V_m I_m \int_0^{T/4} \cos \omega t \sin \omega t \, dt$$

$$= V_m I_m/2\omega = \frac{VI}{\omega} = (115 \text{ v})(0.5 \text{ amp})/2\pi(60 \text{ cycles/sec}) = 0.045 \text{ joule}$$

(e) According to Equation 35-15, the maximum energy stored in the magnetic field is

$$U_L(\max) = \frac{1}{2}LI_m^2 = LI^2 = (2.0 \text{ h})(0.15 \text{ amp})^2 = 0.045 \text{ joule}$$

37-5 A-C circuit with capacitance only We wish to relate the current i in the circuit of Figure 37-11a to the sinusoidal voltage v applied across the capacitor plates. The instantaneous voltage across the plates and the instantaneous charge on the plates are related by

$$v = q/C$$

where C is the capacitance. Let us assume that the voltage oscillates sinusoidally such that

$$v = -V_m \cos \omega t \qquad [37\text{-}24]$$

as shown in Figure 37-11b. Then the instantaneous charge q on the plates will also oscillate with time at the same frequency and in phase with the

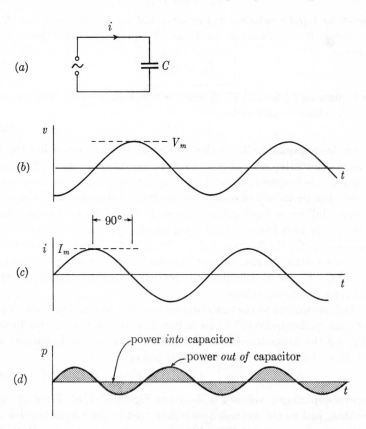

Figure 37-11. (a) A sinusoidal emf applied across a pure capacitance. As a function of time: (b) the applied voltage, (c) the current, and (d) the power delivered to the capacitor.

voltage v. Inasmuch as the current i is given by dq/dt, we find the instantaneous current to be

$$i = dq/dt = C \, dv/dt = \omega C V_m \sin \omega t = I_m \sin \omega t \qquad [37\text{-}25]$$

A graph of the current is shown in Figure 37-11c. The current i in the circuit oscillates with the same frequency as the oscillating voltage across the capacitor, but i and v are *not* in phase. As we see from Equations 37-24 and 37-25 or from Figure 37-11b and c, the *voltage across the capacitor lags the current by* $90°$. This is in contrast with the case of a pure inductor, in which the voltage *leads* the current by $90°$.

From Equation 37-25 we find the relation between the current amplitude I_m and voltage amplitude V_m:

$$I_m = (\omega C) V_m \qquad [37\text{-}26]$$

Inasmuch as $1/(\omega C)$ behaves in the same fashion as the resistance R in a pure resistor, it is convenient to define the quantity called the *capacitive reactance* as

$$\boxed{X_C = 1/\omega C} \qquad [37\text{-}27]$$

Using Equations 37-26 and 37-27 and the relations between rms values and maximum values, we can write

$$I = V/X_C \qquad [37\text{-}28]$$

We see from Equation 37-26 that the capacitive reactance has the same units as the inductive reactance and resistance, namely, ohms. The capacitive reactance is frequency-dependent, varying inversely as the frequency ω. Increasing the frequency of oscillation results in a decrease in the capacitive reactance, and for a fixed given voltage V, therefore an increase in the current I. For zero frequency, or open circuit, the current is zero. Figure 37-12a summarizes the frequency dependence of the effective resistance, the ratio of rms voltage to rms current, for the three separate circuit elements R, L, and C. Figure 37-12b gives the related frequency dependence of rms current for a fixed rms voltage.

In a fashion similar to that used in Section 37-3, to find the instantaneous and average power delivered to an inductor, it is a simple matter to find p and P_{av} for the capacitor circuit of Figure 37-11a. From Equations 37-24 and 37-25 we have, for the instantaneous power,

$$p = vi = (-V_m \cos \omega t)(I_m \sin \omega t) \qquad [37\text{-}29]$$

A graph depicting p versus t is shown in Figure 37-11d. From the figure we see that, just as the average power delivered to pure inductance is zero, so too the average power delivered to a pure capacitor is zero. Half of the time energy is being transferred from the external circuit to the capacitor; for the other half-time, the reverse takes place. There is, however, one significant

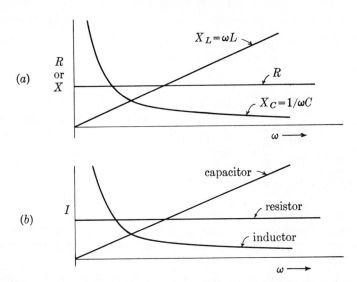

Figure 37-12. (a) The resistance or reactance as a function of frequency. (b) The rms current as a function of frequency through a capacitor, resistor, and inductor for a constant applied voltage.

difference between the capacitor circuit and the inductor circuit. Whereas energy is transferred *to* the inductor when v and i are in the *same* direction, energy is transferred to the capacitor when v and i are in *opposite* directions.

Example 3 A resistance R, capacitance C, and inductance L are separately connected, in turn, across the terminals of a 115 v 60-cycle/sec a-c source. For what values of R, C, and L will the rms current be 1.15 amp?

The resistance R is determined by Ohm's law:

$$R = V/I = (115 \text{ v})/(1.15 \text{ amp}) = 100 \text{ ohms}$$

Inasmuch as the current is to be the same for all three circuits, the capacitive reactance and inductive reactance must also be 100 ohms. By Equation 37-27 we have, then, for the capacitance,

$$C = 1/\omega X_C = 1/(377 \text{ rad/sec})(100 \text{ ohms}) = 27 \text{ } \mu\text{f}$$

When the inductor is connected across the terminals, the required inductance is, by Equation 37-21,

$$L = X_L/\omega = (100 \text{ ohms})/(377 \text{ rad/sec}) = 0.27 \text{ h}$$

37-6 RLC series circuit In this section we will be concerned with the circuit shown in Figure 37-13, consisting of a resistance R, an inductance L, and a capacitance C, connected in series and attached across an alternating voltage source varying sinusoidally with time according to

$$v = V_m \sin (\omega t + \phi) \qquad [37\text{-}30]$$

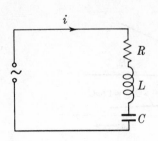

Figure 37-13. An *RLC* series circuit excited by a sinusoidally varying emf.

Thus, v oscillates between the values $\pm V_m$ at the frequency $\omega = 2\pi f$; the angle ϕ governs the phase of v at time $t = 0$:

$$v \ (\text{at } t = 0) = V_m \sin \phi$$

We wish to find the response of the series *RLC* circuit to the oscillating voltage. That is, we ask how the instantaneous current varies with time. Does it oscillate at the same frequency as v and, if so, what is the phase relation between the current and voltage? How is the amplitude of the current related to the amplitude of the voltage? What is the average power delivered to the circuit?

The basic principles governing the instantaneous behavior of this circuit are the same as those applying to d-c circuits, namely, Kirchhoff's rules, as follows.

(1) *Conservation of charge.* The instantaneous current i is the same at all points in the circuit. This is to say, if electric charge is to be conserved, no charge piling up at any point in the circuit, then the rate $dq/dt = i$ at which charge flows past any one point in the circuit must be the same as that at any other point. Thus, for the series circuit of Figure 37-13 the instantaneous current through any of the elements R, L, or C or through the energy source is the same.

(2) *Conservation of energy.* At every instant of time the net change in potential around the circuit loop is zero; alternatively, the emf across the energy source equals the sum of the potential drops across the circuit elements (here, R, L, and C). Since electric potential is the energy per unit charge, we see that energy is conserved in traversing the loop.

These Kirchhoff rules are, of course, easy to apply in the case of steady d-c circuits. In these the current, once established, is constant. The complications that arise in a-c circuits result from the fact that the impressed emf and the resultant current both vary sinusoidally with time. Furthermore, the potential difference across the three circuit elements are *not* in phase with one another or necessarily in phase with the common current. Thus, the voltage drops across R, L, and C do *not* reach their maxima at the same instant.

Applying rule 2 above to the series *RLC* circuit, we have

$$v = v_R + v_L + v_C \qquad [37\text{-}31]$$

The instantaneous voltage v across the generator is equal to the sum of the instantaneous voltage drops across the three circuit elements R, L, and C. Assuming a sinusoidal impressed voltage, we can write Equation 37-31 as

$$V_m \sin (\omega t + \phi) = Ri + L \, di/dt + q/C$$

or, using $dq/dt = i$,

$$V_m \sin (\omega t + \phi) = L \frac{d^2q}{dt^2} + R \frac{dq}{dt} + \frac{q}{c} \qquad [37\text{-}32]$$

The solution of this linear second-order differential equation can be written down immediately from the solution of an equivalent differential equation for a forced mechanical oscillator (Equation 17-23). Knowing q as a function of time gives also the current as a function of time. We will, however, find the current i in the RLC circuit by means of the rotating-vector diagrams discussed in the preceding sections.

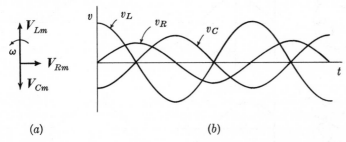

(a)   (b)

Figure 37-14. (a) Rotating vectors representing the voltages across the three circuit elements. (b) The corresponding variations in time of these voltages.

In Figure 37-14 are shown the instantaneous potential drops across the three elements of Figure 37-13, plotted as functions of time, where at the time $t = 0$ we have arbitrarily let $v_R = 0$. Also shown are the associated rotating vectors. We know by Kirchhoff rule 1 that the current in the series circuit is the same through all elements and, by Section 37-3 (see Figure 37-9), that whatever the common current i, it must always be in phase with v_R. Therefore, the voltage v_L across the inductor leads the voltage across R by 90° (as in Figure 37-10), and the voltage v_C across the capacitor lags v_R by 90° (as in Figure 37-11).

According to Equation 37-31 the applied instantaneous voltage v equals the sum of the drops across the three elements. Now, the instantaneous drop across any element is just the projection of the associated rotating vector onto the Y-axis, as illustrated in Figure 37-14a. Inasmuch as the sum of the projections of the rotating vectors V_{Rm}, V_{Lm}, and V_{Cm} is equal to the projection of the vector sum of these three vectors, we can compute the instantaneous voltage across all three circuit elements, which equals the impressed emf, by first adding the three vectors to obtain the resultant vector V_m and then taking the Y-projection of V_m.

Figure 37-15a gives the current i as a function of time, with the associated rotating vector I_m. Inasmuch as i is in phase with v_R, the equation for i as a function of time is

$$i = I_m \sin \omega t \qquad [37\text{-}33]$$

From the rotating vector diagram for the impressed voltage v we can write

$$v = V_m \sin (\omega t + \phi) \qquad [37\text{-}34]$$

which is shown in Figure 37-15b. The resultant voltage leads the current by the phase angle ϕ, and again the current oscillates at the same frequency

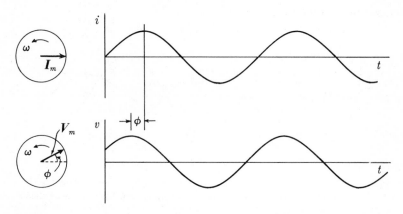

Figure 37-15. Instantaneous (a) current through and (b) voltage across a series RLC circuit. Angle ϕ gives the lag of the current behind the voltage.

ω as the impressed emf; see Figure 37-15. As we did in the cases of separate circuit elements, we now find the phase relation ϕ between v and i in terms of the characteristics of the circuit and also the relation between I_m and V_m.

Adding the three rotating vectors of Figure 37-14 as vectors we find:

$$V_m = V_{Rm} + V_{Lm} + V_{Cm}$$

The vector diagram representing this sum is shown in Figure 37-16. The magnitude of V_m is then

$$V_m = \sqrt{V_{Rm}^2 + (V_{Lm} - V_{Cm})^2} \qquad [37\text{-}35]$$

and the phase angle ϕ of V_m relative to I_m is determined by

$$\tan \phi = (V_{Lm} - V_{Cm})/V_{Rm} \qquad [37\text{-}36]$$

Just as we defined the ratios $(V_{Rm}/I_m) = R$, $(V_{Lm}/I_m) = X_L = \omega L$, and $(V_{Cm}/I_m) = X_C = 1/\omega C$, we now define the ratio of the maximum value V_m of the impressed voltage across the series circuit to the current amplitude I_m as the *impedance Z*,

$$Z = V_m/I_m = V/I \qquad [37\text{-}37]$$

where V and I are the rms values of v and i. The impedance, which gives a measure of the circuit elements' impedance to the flow of electric charge, plays the same rôle in a-c circuits as does the resistance, through the relation $V = RI$, in d-c circuits.

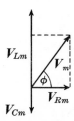

Figure 37-16. Vectors representing the instantaneous voltages across R, L, and C, and their vector sum, V_m.

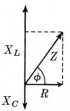

Figure 37-17. The impedance Z represented as the vector sum of the reactance and resistance.

Using Equation 37-35 along with the relation between voltage and current amplitudes across the separate elements, we can write Equations 37-37 and 37-36 as

$$Z = \sqrt{R^2 + (X_L - X_C)^2} = \sqrt{R^2 + \left(\omega L - \frac{1}{\omega C}\right)^2} \qquad [37\text{-}38]$$

$$\tan \phi = (X_L - X_C)/R = \left(\omega L - \frac{1}{\omega C}\right)\Big/ R \qquad [37\text{-}39]$$

For a series circuit, where the current is common to all elements, it is useful to represent the impedance on an impedance diagram, as shown in Figure 37-17. Note that, as one can see from Figures 37-14 and 37-15, the sum of the *instantaneous* potential drops is equal to the *instantaneous* impressed voltage across all three elements, but because of the differences in phase, the sum of the *maximum* values across the elements is *not* equal to the *maximum* value of the impressed voltage.

Finally, let us find the power delivered to the circuit. The instantaneous power is found by using Equations 37-34 and 37-33:

$$p = vi = V_m \sin(\omega t) + \phi\, I_m(\sin \omega t) \qquad [37\text{-}40]$$

Figure 37-18 shows the instantaneous power for an arbitrary RLC series circuit. There is more electric energy transferred to the circuit per cycle than transferred out of the circuit per cycle. Thus, the average power to the circuit is greater than zero. Using the trigonometric identity, we find

$$\sin(\omega t + \phi) = \sin \omega t \cos \phi + \cos \omega t \sin \phi$$

Equation 37-40 becomes

$$p = V_m I_m \cos \phi \sin^2 \omega t + V_m I_m \sin \phi \sin \omega t \cos \omega t$$

The time average of the second term is zero (see Equation 37-23 and arguments following that equation). By Equation 37-12 the average of the first

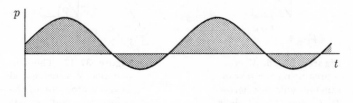

Figure 37-18. Instantaneous power delivered to an RLC circuit as a function of time. The average power is positive.

term is $\tfrac{1}{2} V_m I_m \cos \phi$. Thus we have, for the average power delivered to the RLC series circuit,

$$P_{\mathrm{av}} = \tfrac{1}{2} V_m I_m \cos \phi = VI \cos \phi \qquad [37\text{-}41]$$

or, using Equation 37-37 ($V = ZI$) and Figure 37-17 ($\cos \phi = R/Z$),

$$\boxed{P_{\mathrm{av}} = I^2 Z \cos \phi = I^2 R} \qquad [37\text{-}42]$$

All of the energy delivered to the circuit is dissipated as heat at the resistor at the average rate I^2R, where I is the rms current through the circuit.

The factor $\cos \phi$ appearing in Equation 37-42 is called the *power factor*. For a circuit consisting of a pure resistance, $\phi = 0$ and $P_{\mathrm{av}} = IV$. For a purely reactive circuit, whether capacitive or inductive, $\phi = \pm 90°$ and $P_{\mathrm{av}} = 0$. Furthermore, a more detailed analysis shows that Equation 37-41 gives the average power delivered to *any* a-c circuit, not merely the series circuit discussed here.

Example 4   An RLC series circuit is connected across the terminals of a sinusoidal energy source of 115 v rms and 60 cycles/sec. The circuit elements are $R = 50$ ohms, $C = 27$ μf, and $L = 0.13$ h. (a) Find the total impedance of the circuit. (b) What is the rms current through the circuit? (c) Find the rms voltage drops across each element separately and also across the inductor and resistor together. (d) How much power is transferred from the energy source to the circuit?

(a) The total impedance of the circuit is given by Equation 37-38:

$$Z = \sqrt{R^2 + (X_L - X_C)^2}$$

With $R = 50$ ohms, $X_L = \omega L = (377\ \text{rad/sec})(0.13\ \text{h}) = 50$ ohms, and $X_C = 1/\omega C = 1/(377\ \text{rad/sec})(27 \times 10^{-6}\ \text{f}) = 100$ ohms, we have

$$Z = \sqrt{(50\ \text{ohm})^2 + (50\ \text{ohm})^2} = 71\ \text{ohms}$$

(b) By Equation 37-37,

$$I = V/Z = (115\ \text{v})/(71\ \text{ohms}) = 1.6\ \text{amp}$$

(c) The rms voltages across the various circuit elements can also be obtained by using Equation 37-37, where Z is the impedance in that part of the circuit across which the rms voltage is desired. Thus,

$$V_R = Z_R I = (100\ \text{ohms})(1.6\ \text{amp}) = 160\ \text{v}$$
$$V_L = Z_L I = (50\ \text{ohms})(1.6\ \text{amp}) = 80\ \text{v}$$
$$V_C = Z_C I = (100\ \text{ohms})(1.6\ \text{amp}) = 160\ \text{v}$$

Note that these rms voltages, when added algebraically, do *not* give the rms voltage across the series combination.

The rms voltage across the resistor and inductor together is obtained in the same fashion:

$$V_{R.L} = Z_{R.L} I = \sqrt{R^2 + X_L{}^2}\, I = \sqrt{(50\ \text{ohms})^2 + (50\ \text{ohms})^2}\,(1.6\ \text{amp}) = 115\ \text{v}$$

Thus, an a-c voltmeter, when placed across R and L, will read the same voltage as when placed across all three circuit elements.

(d) The power to the circuit is given by Equation 37-42:

$$P_{\text{av}} = I^2 R = (1.6\ \text{amp})^2 (50\ \text{ohms}) = 130\ \text{w}$$

37-7 **Series resonance**   In this section we consider again an RLC series circuit like that of Figure 37-13. We assume that the rms voltage impressed across the circuit is of constant magnitude, while the frequency of oscillation is varied from zero to infinity. We wish to find the current, the phase between voltage and current, and the power delivered to the circuit, all as a function of the frequency.

The rms current is, by Equation 37-37,

$$I = V/Z = V/\sqrt{R^2 + (\omega L - 1/\omega C)^2} \qquad [37\text{-}43]$$

The current thus depends on frequency, according to Equation 37-43, where we assume all terms on the right-hand side to remain constant except ω.

The maximum I occurs when the denominator of Equation 37-43 is smallest, that is, when $\omega L - 1/\omega C = 0$. The frequency at which the current is greatest is then given by

[37-4] $$\omega_0 = 1/\sqrt{LC}$$ [37-44]

We recognize ω_0 to be the *natural frequency* at which the circuit oscillates in the absence of resistance and an impressed sinusoidal voltage. It is also that frequency for which energy is transferred from the energy source to the

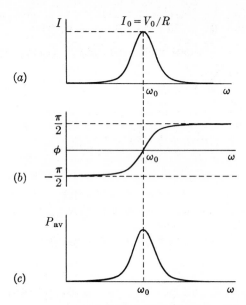

Figure 37-19. Resonance of a series RLC circuit: (a) current, (b) phase angle, and (c) power, all as a function of frequency.

circuit at a maximum rate. The source and circuit are in resonance, and ω_0 is called the *resonant frequency*. At resonance, Equation 37-43 becomes

$$I_0 = V/R$$

Decreasing or increasing the frequency from the resonant condition leads to a decrease in the rms current, because the impedance of the circuit increases to either side of the frequency ω_0. A plot of I as a function of the impressed frequency is shown in Figure 37-19a; this is merely a plot of Equation 37-43.

The phase between the impressed voltage and the current through the circuit also depends on the frequency. From Equation 37-39,

$$\tan \phi = (X_L - X_C)/R = (\omega L - 1/\omega C)/R$$

At resonance, $\omega = \omega_0$, $\tan \phi = 0$, and $\phi = 0$. At $\omega = 0$, $\tan \phi = -\infty$ and $\phi = -\pi/2$. At $\omega = \infty$, $\tan \phi = +\infty$ and $\phi = +\pi/2$. The behavior of the phase ϕ through the frequency range is shown in Figure 37-19b.

The power delivered to the circuit is given by

[37-42] $$P_{av} = I^2 R$$

Inasmuch as I depends on the frequency, so too must the power. The shape of the power-frequency curve is similar to the current-frequency curve, and is shown in Figure 37-19c. Note that the maximum rate of energy transfer occurs at resonance with $P_{av} \text{(max)} = I_0^2 R = V^2/R$.

37-8 Summary When an initially charged capacitor is connected across a resistanceless inductor, the charge and current in the circuit oscillate sinusoidally at the angular frequency ω of electric oscillations:

[37-4] $$\omega = \frac{1}{\sqrt{LC}}$$

The inductor shows inertia to a change in the current through it, and the capacitor tends to restore its charge state to electrical neutrality.

For a resistor R, inductor L, and capacitor C, all in series and connected across a sinusoidally varying emf of angular frequency ω, the maximum voltage V_m across and maximum current I_m through the series of three elements are related by

[37-37] $$V_m = ZI_m$$

where the impedance Z is

[37-38] $$Z = \sqrt{R^2 + (X_L - X_C)^2} = \sqrt{R^2 + \left(\omega L - \frac{1}{\omega C}\right)^2}$$

The inductive reactance is

[37-21] $$X_L = \omega L$$

and the capacitive reactance is

[37-27] $$X_C = 1/\omega C$$

The angle ϕ by which the phase of the alternating current lags behind the alternating emf is given by

[37-39] $$\tan \phi = (X_L - X_C)/R$$

The average power delivered to the circuit is

[37-41] $$P_{av} = \tfrac{1}{2} V_m I_m \cos \phi$$

The series RLC circuit is at resonance when the exciting frequency ω equals the natural oscillation frequency, $\omega_0 = 1/\sqrt{LC}$.

PROBLEMS

37-1 What capacitance must be used with an inductance coil of 4.0 h to cause the circuit to resonate at 60 cycles/sec?

37-2 By what factor does the capacitance in a resonant circuit in a radio receiver change, when the radio is tuned over the entire range of the broadcast band, from 500 kcycles/sec to 1.6 Mcycles/sec?

37-3 The dimensions of all circuit components in a resonant electric circuit are reduced by a factor of exactly 2. By what factor is the resonant frequency enhanced?

37-4 An electric oscillator consisting of a parallel-plate capacitor and a solenoid resonates at the frequency f. The capacitor plate separation distance is reduced by a factor 2, and the number of turns in the solenoid is increased by a factor 2. What is the new resonance frequency of the circuit?

37-5 ★ An initially charged capacitor is connected across the terminals of an inductor with *nonzero* resistance. (a) Write down the differential equation governing the charge q on one capacitor plate at any instant of time in terms of R, L, and C. (b) Show that the charge oscillates at the angular frequency $\omega = [(1/LC) - (R/2L)^2]^{1/2}$. (c) Show that if the resistance is relatively small, this oscillation frequency is the same as that of the electric oscillator without resistance. (d) Show that the amplitude of the oscillating charge decreases exponentially in time, the envelope of the q-t curve falling to $1/e$ of its initial value in the time $2L/R$. (e) Show that the total energy of the damped electric oscillator decays exponentially in time, the energy falling to $1/e$ of its initial value in the time L/R. (*Hint:* Consider the equivalent damped mechanical oscillator described in Section 17-5.)

37-6 A capacitor of 0.10 μf initially has a potential difference of 100 v across its terminals. The capacitor is then connected across a resistanceless inductor of 3.0 mh. (a) What is the total energy of the electric oscillator at any instant of time? (b) What is the maximum instantaneous current through the inductor?

37-7 The impedance of a certain inductance coil is 30 ohms at 100 cycles/sec and 60 ohms at 500 cycles/sec. What are (a) the inductance and (b) the resistance of the coil?

37-8 A leaky capacitor of 2.0 μf capacitance has an impedance of 54 ohms when excited by a sinusoidal emf of 10 kcycles/sec. What is the equivalent series resistance of the capacitor?

37-9 It is found that the current through a series RLC circuit lags the applied alternating emf. Must one increase or decrease the frequency of the applied emf, to bring the circuit to resonance?

37-10 A 60 cycle/sec 110 v (rms) alternating emf is applied across a series RLC circuit. A voltmeter reads 110 v (rms) when attached across any one of the three circuit elements. What are (a) R, (b) L, and (c) C?

37-11   It is found that when a 110 v (rms) emf of 60 cycles/sec is applied across the elements of a series RLC circuit, a current of 11 amp (rms) leads the applied emf by 20°. (a) What additional reactive circuit element, capacitive or inductive, must be added in series with the original circuit elements to make the phase angle zero? (b) What is the magnitude of the capacitance or inductance?

37-12   A series RLC circuit consists of a 5.0 ohm resistor, a 100 μf capacitor, and a 4.0 mh inductor. A sinusoidally varying emf of 20 v (rms) and of variable frequency is applied across the three circuit elements. (a) What is the impedance at 100 cycles/sec? (b) By what angle does the current lag the applied emf? (c) At what average rate is power dissipated in the circuit? (d) At what frequency is the maximum power dissipated? (e) What is the rms current at this resonance frequency?

37-13   The impedance of a certain series circuit elements increases with frequency over a certain frequency range in which the current lags the applied emf. If one adds additional capacitance in series with the original circuit elements, does the impedance for a given frequency increase or decrease?

37-14 ★ Assume that the resistance in a series RLC circuit is relatively small. (a) Show that the current in the circuit is half the current at resonance (for a fixed amplitude of applied emf) when the angular frequency ω differs from the resonance frequency ω_0 by $\Delta\omega = |\omega - \omega_0| = R/L$. (b) Show that the fractional change in frequency from the resonance frequency which reduces the average power absorbed by the circuit at resonance to one half is given by $\Delta\omega/\omega_0 = R/\omega_0 L$. (The reciprocal of this ratio, $\omega_0/\Delta\omega = \omega_0 L/R$, gives a measure of the Q, or quality, of the resonance circuit. The higher the Q, the more narrow the width of the frequency range to which the circuit responds in absorbing power; that is, a sharply tuned resonance circuit has a high Q.)

THIRTY-EIGHT

MAXWELL'S EQUATIONS

It is an extraordinary fact that *all* of classical electromagnetism can be summarized in four fundamental equations. These mathematical relations, which describe how the electric and magnetic fields are related to one another and to electric charge, are known as Maxwell's equations. We have already discussed these equations and the fundamental laws they express: Coulomb's law (or its equivalent, Gauss's law for electricity), Gauss's law for magnetism, Faraday's law, and Ampère's law. In this chapter we wish to review the experimental bases of Maxwell's equations and thereby assemble in one place the fundamental ideas of classical electromagnetism. First, however, we must deal once more with Ampère's law, which is incomplete as formulated thus far. We generalize Ampère's law by considering the so-called displacement current, or the changing electric flux, which can generate a magnetic field in the same fashion as do moving charges.

38-1 Ampère's law and the displacement current According to Ampère's law a magnetic field is created by the electric current i, the line integral of the magnetic field around a closed loop being merely the current (multiplied by μ_0) crossing the bound surface:

[33-23] $$\oint \boldsymbol{B} \cdot d\boldsymbol{l} = \mu_0 i$$

As given above, Ampère's law recognizes only one source of a magnetic field: moving electric charges. There is, however, a second origin of a magnetic field: a changing electric field (or electric flux), also called a displacement current.

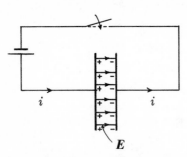

Figure 38-1. A parallel-plate capacitor being charged just after the switch in the circuit is closed. The current i is increasing with time.

To see how the so-called displacement current arises, consider the situation shown in Figure 38-1. Suppose that the switch in the circuit has just been closed. Initially the current rises from zero; very soon thereafter it falls to zero again, after the capacitor has been fully charged. We are interested in the time during which the current through the circuit is changing. Actually, to modify this statement slightly, we are interested in the time the current through the *conducting wire* is changing, since a real current does *not* exist at every point around the circuit loop. There is *no* current, apparently, at any time in the region between the two capacitor plates, inasmuch as no charged particles ever pass through this region.

This raises the question, How can we tell whether a current exists in an electric circuit? One fundamental procedure for finding out is to apply Ampère's law and test for the existence of a net current through any region of space simply by examining the associated magnetic field. Thus, we can check that a changing current exists along the connecting wire in the circuit of Figure 38-1 by using a device that detects the magnetic field loops surrounding the wire. Suppose, now, that we perform the same test in the region surrounding the charging capacitor. We find that there *is* a magnetic field here too, and that its magnitude and direction are precisely the same as that of the magnetic field arising from the real current in the circuit. In fact, if one were to infer the presence of an electric current solely by examining the surrounding magnetic field, one would conclude that a current exists at *every point* along the path of the circuit, the conducting wires and the charging capacitor being altogether indistinguishable. To put it differently, if the capacitor were enclosed in a black box, it would appear, on the basis of exterior magnetic-field measurements, that a straight conductor were running through the box. We conclude, then, that if one is always to attribute a magnetic field to a current, one must invoke, in addition to the real current through the circuit originating from moving charges, another type of current. We call this fictitious current the *displacement current*.

Now if we are to allow for contributions from the real current i and the displacement current i_d,† Ampère's law must be written as

$$\oint \boldsymbol{B} \cdot d\boldsymbol{l} = \mu_0(i + i_d) \qquad [38\text{-}1]$$

We thereby say that current exists at all points around the circuit loop: a real current i where charges flow in the conductors, and a displacement current i_d between the capacitor plates. For the simple situation in Figure 38-1,

$$i \ \ (\text{in conductor}) = i_d \ \ (\text{in capacitor}) \qquad [38\text{-}2]$$

What is it that is happening between the capacitor plates to which we can relate i_d? If there are no moving charges, what is it that generates the magnetic field? We shall see that i_d is related to the electric flux ϕ_E between the capacitor plates. By definition,

[27-3] $$\phi_E = \oint \boldsymbol{E} \cdot d\boldsymbol{S} \qquad [38\text{-}3]$$

The instantaneous current $i = dq/dt$ gives the rate at which charges pass any point in the conductor; dq/dt is also the rate at which charges accumulate on each of the capacitor plates. For the uniform electric field E between the plates of the parallel-plate capacitor, we know that

[27-10] $$E = \sigma/\epsilon_0 = q/\epsilon_0 A$$
$$q = \epsilon_0 E A = \epsilon_0 \phi_E \qquad [38\text{-}4]$$

Here we have identified EA, using Equation 38-3, as the electric flux ϕ_E through a transverse area parallel to the capacitor plates. From Equations 38-4 and 38-2, we have

$$i_d = i = dq/dt$$
$$i_d = \epsilon_0 \, d\phi_E/dt \qquad [38\text{-}5]$$

The displacement current i_d through any chosen area is the time rate of the electric flux through that area multiplied by ϵ_0. Using Equation 38-5 in Equation 38-1 gives

$$\oint \boldsymbol{B} \cdot d\boldsymbol{l} = \mu_0(i + \epsilon_0 \, d\phi_E/dt) = \mu_0 i + \epsilon_0 \mu_0 \, d\phi_E/dt \qquad [38\text{-}6]$$

† We include in the real current i the equivalent magnetization current i_m used to describe the properties of magnetic materials; see Section 36-2.

This is the generalized form of Ampère's law.† It implies that a magnetic field may be produced by a changing electric flux, even in the absence of electric charges. Note that, whereas B may come from *either* a steady *or* a changing current, B comes from a displacement current only if the electric flux is *changing*. Although we have derived the generalized form of the Ampère law from the rather special case of a charging parallel-plate capacitor, this relation is altogether general, holding for *any* changing electric flux.

When no real current exists and a magnetic field is generated entirely by a changing electric flux in space, Equation 38-6 becomes

$$\oint B \cdot dl = \epsilon_0 \mu_0 \, d\phi_E / dt \qquad [38\text{-}7]$$

This relation is similar in form to Faraday's law:

$$[34\text{-}9] \qquad \oint E \cdot dl = -d\phi_B / dt \qquad [38\text{-}8]$$

In the first instance a changing electric flux produces a magnetic field; in the second, a changing magnetic flux produces an electric field. We merely replace E by B and ϕ_E by ϕ_B (and -1 by $\epsilon_0 \mu_0$).

In Figure 38-2a are shown the B loops surrounding a region in which ϕ_E changes, and in Figure 38-2b, the E loops surrounding the region in which ϕ_B changes. Note that the sense of the B loops is related to the direction in which the electric flux increases by the right-hand rule; this follows from Figure 38-1, where we note that the real (and displacement) current is in the *same* direction as that in which the electric field increases. In other words, we

† We have supposed that the capacitor of Figure 38-1 is immersed in a vacuum. Then there are surely no actual charges in motion between the capacitor plates. But if the capacitor is filled with a dielectric, the changing electric field between the plates is accompanied by a changing polarization of the dielectric's molecules. The electric charges in the induced dipoles are *displaced* as the electric field changes, and there is an actual current, a *displacement* current, within the dielectric medium. Nineteenth-century physicists believed that all space was pervaded by a massless transparent medium called the *ether*. The ether was thought to be a subtle dielectric filled with neutral ether molecules. Then, when the electric field changed through apparently empty space, the changing polarization of the ether was accompanied by a displacement current. We hasten to say that the ether hypothesis has proved to be untenable and has been discarded as an unnecessary ingredient in electromagnetic theory. A displacement current—that is, a changing electric flux—may exist in truly empty space.

The term electric *displacement* for the field vector D is similarly related to the displacement of charges by an electric field. Indeed, an alternative way of writing Equation 38-6, with $i = 0$, is

$$\oint H \cdot dl = d\phi_D / dt = \int (dD/dt) \cdot dS$$

Here we use the facts that, for empty space, $B = \mu_0 H$ (Equation 36-20) and $D = \epsilon_0 E$ (Equation 36-9). Clearly, when written in this form, the displacement current is the rate at which the displacement flux $\phi_D = \oint D \cdot dS$ changes.

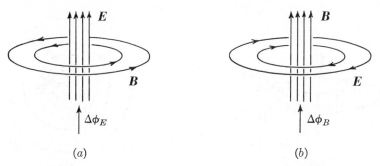

(a)   (b)

Figure 38-2. (a) Magnetic field loops surrounding a region in which the electric flux is increasing. (b) Electric field loops surrounding a region in which the magnetic flux is increasing. Notice the *different* senses of the field loops.

may treat the increasing electric flux as an electric current, in applying the right-hand rule to find the sense of the associated magnetic field loops. On the other hand, as we saw earlier in Figure 34-14b, the E loops surround a region in which ϕ_B increases in the opposite sense (a consequence of Lenz's law). This difference in the sense of the field loops is reflected in Equations 38-7 and 38-8: one has a plus sign, and the other a minus sign.

Because of the close parallel between Equations 38-7 and 38-8, essentially all of the conclusions we drew earlier from Faraday's law concerning the E field accompanying a change in ϕ_B (Section 34-5) hold equally well for the B field accompanying a change in ϕ_E. For example, the line integral $\oint B \cdot dl$ of the magnetic field depends only on the rate of change of the *total* electric flux enclosed by the path about which we evaluate the line integral, *not* upon whether there is flux at every interior point within the loop. Thus, if we choose concentric circular paths of various radii *outside* a region in which the electric flux is changing, the integral $\oint B \cdot dl$ is the same for all such closed paths. This implies that the magnitude of B varies inversely as r, where r is the radius of the path and the distance from the center of the region of changing electric flux, and this result corresponds exactly to the fact that the magnetic field from a long straight wire varies inversely as the distance from the wire.

Example 1   Suppose that we have a parallel-plate capacitor with circular plates of radius R which are being charged at a constant rate. We assume that the electric field is confined entirely to the region between the capacitor plates and that it changes in magnitude at a constant rate; see Figure 38-3a. What is the magnitude of the magnetic field B at any distance r from the center of the capacitor plates?

We worked an exactly analogous problem with Faraday's law in Section 34-5 (Figures 34-11 and 34-12), so that we need not work it again in detail. Comparing

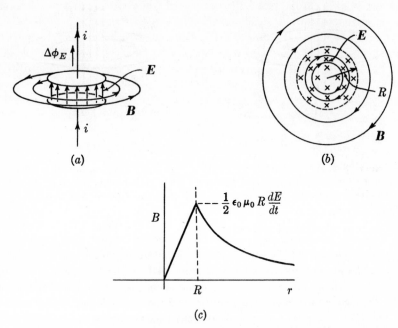

Figure 38-3. (a) A parallel-plate capacitor with circular plates of radius R being charged at a uniform rate. (b) The circular magnetic field loops in the plane perpendicular to the changing electric field. (c) The magnitude of the magnetic field as a function of r, the distance from the center of the capacitor.

Equations 38-7 and 38-8, we see that we merely need interchange E and B and introduce the additional factor $\epsilon_0\mu_0$. The results are shown in Figure 38-3c: the field B increases linearly with r for $r < R$, and decreases inversely as r for $r > R$. At $r = R$, $B = \tfrac{1}{2}\epsilon_0\mu_0 R\, dE/dt$.

What is the magnitude of the magnetic field induced by the changing electric flux? Suppose that the capacitor plate radius R is 10 cm and that the electric field changes at the rate $dE/dt = 10^{10}$ v/m-sec (this corresponds to. a change in electric potential difference across the capacitor of 10,000 v/μsec when the capacitor plates are separated by 1 mm). Then the maximum magnetic field (at $r = R$) is

$$B = \tfrac{1}{2}\epsilon_0\mu_0 R\, dE/dt$$
$$= \tfrac{1}{2}(8.9 \times 10^{-12}\ \text{coul}^2/\text{nt-m}^2)(4\pi \times 10^{-7}\ \text{weber/amp-m})(0.10\ \text{m})(10^{10}\ \text{v/m-sec})$$
$$= 5.6 \times 10^{-9}\ \text{weber/m}^2 = 0.056\ \text{milligauss}$$

Even for the relatively large rate of electric flux change in this example, the induced magnetic field is very small indeed. This is in contrast to the induced electric fields produced by a changing magnetic flux, where emf's of the order of volts are relatively easily obtained.

38-2 Maxwell and the displacement current Historically, the displacement current was not first found by experiment; the generalization of Ampère's law did not come initially from direct observation. Rather, it was a brilliant theoretical conjecture by J. C. Maxwell (1831–1879) in 1865.

Maxwell proposed the displacement current on two grounds, symmetry and the equation of continuity for electric charge. We have already seen that, in the absence of real currents, Faraday's law (Equation 38-8) is exactly analogous to Ampère's law (Equation 38-7) only if one introduces the displacement current, or changing electric flux.

The argument on the basis of continuity is a little more subtle. See Figure 38-4; here is a circular path around a conducting wire. We are to apply Ampère's law to this loop. If we choose a flat area whose boundary is the circular path, then clearly there is a real current penetrating this surface and producing a magnetic field around the closed path. Although simple, this flat surface is not the only one we may choose. Ampère's law relates to the current through the loop, *without* specifying the nature of the surface bounded by the loop; that is, we may choose a surface of *any* shape in applying the law. In every case the total current through the

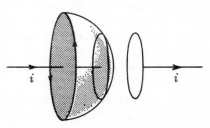

Figure 38-4. A charging capacitor. The loop for applying Ampère's law surrounds the conducting wire; one surface bounded by this loop is flat, the other is hemispherical.

surface determines the magnetic field around the loop. Now, if the circular path in Figure 38-4 is the boundary of a hemispherical surface which passes through the region between the charging capacitor plates, we have *no* current through the hemispherical surface. Another way of saying the same thing is this: if we take Ampère's law as the fundamental test of whether a current exists, a current must exist in the region between the charging capacitor plates. Otherwise, the basic equation of continuity for electric charge,

[30-8]
$$\oint \boldsymbol{j} \cdot d\boldsymbol{S} = -\partial/\partial t \int \rho_q \, dv$$

is incomplete. The left-hand term in this relation gives the surface integral of the current density $\boldsymbol{j}$, which is just the real current i. We may then generalize the equation of continuity by adding the displacement current,

[38-5]
$$i_d = d\phi_E/dt = d/dt \oint (\epsilon_0 \boldsymbol{E} \cdot d\boldsymbol{S})$$

to the left side; we then have

$$\oint (j + \epsilon_0 \, dE/dt) \cdot dS = -\partial/\partial t \int \rho_q \, dv \qquad [38\text{-}9]$$

How was the correctness of Maxwell's hypothesis concerning the displacement current tested? We have already seen that the magnitude of the magnetic field induced by a changing electric flux is relatively small and, therefore, not easily detected directly. The crucial test of the generalized Ampère law came from Maxwell's theoretical prediction that an electromagnetic disturbance, once excited in empty space, can be self-generating. That is, an electromagnetic disturbance can become detached from electric charges and propagate through space as an *electromagnetic wave*. A simple form of the theoretical argument is given in Section 41-1. The direct observation of electromagnetic waves (short-wave radio waves) by Heinrich Hertz vindicated Maxwell's prediction.

38-3 Maxwell's equations We have discussed Maxwell's contributions to electromagnetic theory through his hypothesis of the displacement current. Maxwell played an even more significant role in bringing together into one unified electromagnetic field theory the hitherto disparate facts of electric and magnetic phenomena. It was Faraday who invented the field concept as a useful and picturesque means of visualizing electric and magnetic effects. Maxwell took the electric and magnetic fields seriously and developed the mathematical expressions for their properties and interrelations. These fundamental relations, which say everything there is to say about classical electromagnetism, are called *Maxwell's equations*.

Before writing and discussing the four Maxwell equations we must be clear on the definitions of the electric field E and the magnetic flux density B. From the so-called Lorentz equation, which gives the total force on an electric charge arising from electric and magnetic fields, we have

[32-8] $F = q(E + v \times B)$

This equation defines E and B. That part of the force, $qv \times B$, which depends on the charge's velocity is the magnetic force; the remaining part, qE, is the electric force.

Table 38-1 lists the four Maxwell equations and gives the common name and the primary experimental evidence for each.

GAUSS'S LAW FOR ELECTRICITY Gauss's law for electricity implies that electric field lines are continuous and that the net electric flux through any closed volume depends only on the net charge q within:

[27-3] $\epsilon_0 \oint E \cdot dS = q$

We derived Gauss's law (Section 27-2) from Coulomb's law; indeed Gauss's law for electricity is merely an alternative way of saying that the force between point-charges varies inversely as the square of the distance between them. Gauss's law is confirmed by experiments showing that the Coulomb

Table 38-1

NAME	EQUATION		EXPERIMENTAL EVIDENCE
Gauss's law for electricity (Coulomb's law)	$\epsilon_0 \oint \boldsymbol{E} \cdot d\boldsymbol{S} = q$	[27-3]	Electric force is inverse-square; no charge on interior of hollow charged conductor
Gauss's law for magnetism	$\oint \boldsymbol{B} \cdot d\boldsymbol{S} = 0$	[33-22]	No isolated magnetic poles
Faraday's law	$\oint \boldsymbol{E} \cdot d\boldsymbol{l} = -d\phi_B/dt$	[34-9]	Electromagnetic induction effects
Ampère's law	$\oint \boldsymbol{B} \cdot d\boldsymbol{l} = \mu_0 i$ $+ \epsilon_0 \mu_0 \, d\phi_E/dt$	[38-6]	Magnetic force between current-carrying conductors; electromagnetic waves

force is inverse-square. But a more precise verification of Gauss's law comes from the observation that there is never any net charge within an empty hollow conductor (Section 27-5).

GAUSS'S LAW FOR MAGNETISM   The physical content of Gauss's law for magnetism is that the net magnetic flux through any closed volume is always zero:

[33-22]
$$\oint \boldsymbol{B} \cdot d\boldsymbol{S} = 0$$

If it were not zero, one would have "magnetic charges," or single magnetic poles, upon which the magnetic field lines would terminate. Gauss's law for magnetism is based on the observation that isolated magnetic poles do not exist in nature. One can always account for apparent pairs of magnetic poles, as in the case of a permanent magnet, by circulating or spinning electric charges.

FARADAY'S LAW   Faraday's law is the law of electromagnetic induction, which says that a changing magnetic flux generates electric field loops:

[34-9]
$$\oint \boldsymbol{E} \cdot d\boldsymbol{l} = -d\phi_B/dt$$

Faraday's law is confirmed by all the electromagnetic induction effects, for example, by the induced current in a conducting loop arising from a near-by separate conducting loop through which the current is changing.

AMPÈRE'S LAW   According to Ampère's law, as generalized to include the displacement current, a magnetic field has *two* origins: moving electric charge, or electric current i, and a changing electric flux, or displacement current:

[38-6] $$\oint \boldsymbol{B} \cdot d\boldsymbol{l} = \mu_0 i + \epsilon_0 \mu_0 \, d\phi_E/dt$$

The magnetic force between parallel current-carrying conductors, varying inversely as the separation distance, is a direct experimental test of the magnetic field originating from moving charges. The most convincing evidence that a magnetic field is generated also by a changing electric flux comes from the observed properties of electromagnetic waves.

The equations for Ampère's law and Faraday's law are very nearly symmetrical, but not quite. We do not have in Faraday's law a term corresponding to the current i. This merely reflects the fact that, since isolated magnetic poles do not exist, one cannot have a "magnetic current" arising from magnetic poles in motion. Since all electromagnetic phenomena can be accounted for *without* magnetic monopoles, we see that in this instance Nature chose economy over symmetry.

It should be noted that such relations as Ohm's law, or the relations between the several field vectors E, D, P, and B, H, M (Equations 36-5 and 36-18) are *not* regarded as fundamental. Ohm's law describes the properties of certain conducting materials, and the equations for the field vectors serve merely to describe electric and magnetic materials.

THIRTY-NINE

WAVES ON A STRING

Suppose that one wishes to transfer mechanical energy from one point in space to another. One might send a particle, energy being transferred as the kinetic energy of the particle. There is, however, another way to transfer mechanical energy, one in which *no* single particle travels from a first to a second location. This is *wave motion*, the topic of the next several chapters. The study of waves is crucially important in physics. Such phenomena as sound and light are wave phenomena. Even more importantly, from the point of view of the quantum theory, particles exhibit wave characteristics in *all* phenomena at the level of the atomic and nuclear physics.

In this and the next chapter we shall be concerned with mechanical waves, waves that involve the coupling together of a series of particles and which have their origin in the elastic properties of the medium transmitting them. First we shall deal exclusively with a simple type of wave, a wave traveling in one dimension along a string. Many of the results we find for this familiar type of wave behavior can be carried over, essentially unchanged, to more complicated types of mechanical waves.

We consider the origin of wave behavior from basic principles, and the dependence of the wave speed on the properties of the string. The general wave equation is developed. We then treat the superposition, interference, and reflection of wave pulses. The important special case of a sinusoidal wave generated by a simple harmonic oscillation is then introduced. The power of a sinusoidal wave is derived. We discuss the phenomenon of beats. Then we treat the phenomena of standing waves, the characteristic oscillation modes of a string attached at both ends, and resonance. Finally, we consider briefly the characteristics of linearly and circularly polarized transverse waves.

39-1 Basic wave behavior Consider a uniform perfectly flexible string, under tension and attached at its right end. Suppose that the left end is suddenly displaced laterally and then returned to its initial position. A

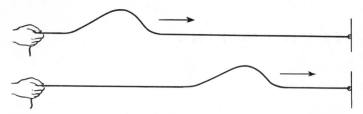

Figure 39-1. A wave pulse traveling along a stretched string.

wave pulse is produced, which travels to the right at constant speed with unchanged shape, as shown in Figure 39-1. Each particle along the string undergoes, in turn, a transverse motion and returns to its initial position. The shape of the wave as a whole moves to the right.

This is a commonplace observation. Yet, on further thought, the phenomenon of wave propagation is truly remarkable in that each of the string's particles "knows enough" to return precisely to its initial position, while the shape of the wave pulse is unaltered as the disturbance travels along the string. Actually, the behavior of mechanical waves can be deduced quite directly from Newton's laws and the ideas of reference frames, as we shall see.

We now suppose that a flexible string of constant linear density ρ (mass per unit length) and under constant tension F_t is threaded through a smooth tube, as shown in Figure 39-2. Clearly, if the taut string is at rest with respect to the tube, it will touch the tube at point A. On the other hand, if the string, still under tension F_t, is pulled to the left through the tube at a uniform high speed, the string's inertia will cause it to strike the tube at the higher point, B. There must be an intermediate speed at which the string can be reeled through the tube, touching neither A nor B. Let us find it.

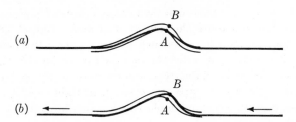

Figure 39-2. A tube with a taut string (a) at rest and (b) reeled through at a very high speed.

We concentrate on the small string segment shown in Figure 39-3a. This segment is assumed to be so short that we may regard it as a circular arc of radius of curvature R, the angle θ, subtended by the segment about the center of curvature, being small. Now, if the speed c of this segment is just right, it will not touch the tube, and the only external forces acting on it will be the tension forces at the ends, both of magnitude F_t. These forces are tangent to the ends of the segment, since the string is assumed to be perfectly flexible. As Figure 39-3b shows, the resultant force on the segment points to the center of curvature and has the magnitude $2F_t \sin (\theta/2)$. Applying Newton's second law yields

$$\Sigma \, \mathbf{F} = m\mathbf{a}$$

$$2F_t \sin (\theta/2) = (\rho R\theta)(c^2/R)$$

where we have used the fact that the segment of length $R\theta$ and mass $\rho R\theta$ travels with constant speed c in a circular arc of radius R and therefore undergoes a radial acceleration c^2/R. Since θ is small, $\sin (\theta/2) \simeq \theta/2$. Then the equation above reduces to

$$F_t = \rho c^2$$

$$\boxed{c = \sqrt{F_t/\rho}} \qquad\qquad [39\text{-}1]$$

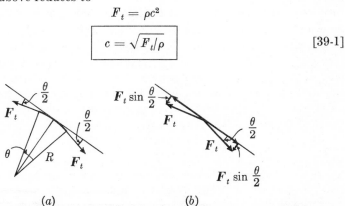

Figure 39-3. (a) Forces on a small string segment. (b) The resultant force is $2F_t \sin (\theta/2)$.

When the string is drawn through the tube at the speed $\sqrt{F_t/\rho}$, the small string segment does not touch the tube at A or at B. Indeed, *no* segment of the string touches the tube, inasmuch as the speed c is independent of R and θ. Thus, if the string is reeled through the tube at just the right speed, the tube may be removed and the string will maintain its shape, each particle of string following the tube's shape as it passes from right to left! Then, *any shape*, once established, will stand in place as long as the speed of the string is that given by Equation 39-1.

Note the assumptions: the string is uniform and perfectly flexible, the vertical displacements are small enough so that the tension is the same at all points along the string, and there are no sharp corners, which would preclude the assumption that $\sin(\theta/2) \simeq \theta/2$.

Now let us view this behavior from another reference frame, one in which the *string* (to the left and right of the disturbance) remains *at rest*. If we travel to the left at the same speed c as does the string relative to the tube, then in this new reference frame we see a wave disturbance, unchanged in shape, moving to the right at the speed c, as in Figure 39-1.

Our derivation for the wave speed did not depend on the direction in which the string was moving through the tube. Thus, if the string were reeled through the tube with the speed c in the opposite direction, the wave disturbance would be seen to travel to the left in the reference frame in which the string is at rest.

We can express these results more formally. First recall the Galilean coordinate transformation relations (Equations 6-1) for two reference frames in relative motion. The coordinate x measured in a reference frame traveling to the right (along the $+X$-axis) at speed c, relative to a reference frame in which the coordinate is x', is given by $x = x' - ct$, or $x' = x + ct$. (The time t is zero in both frames at the instant their origins coincide.) By the same token, if our moving reference frame travels to the left at speed c, and x again represents the X-coordinate in this "moving" frame, then $x' = x - ct$. Now let $y = F(x')$ represent the shape of the disturbance (and of the tube), whatever it may be, as seen in the reference frame of the tube. Then, if the *string* travels to the *left* at speed c relative to the wave pulse, the wave *pulse* must travel to the *right* as seen from the reference frame of the string. The shape is given, in general, by

$$\text{Wave to } right: \quad y = F(x - ct) \qquad \text{[39-2a]}$$

$$\text{Wave to } left: \quad y = F(x + ct) \qquad \text{[39-2b]}$$

The coordinate y giving the transverse displacement of a particle on the string depends, of course, both on the position x along the direction of

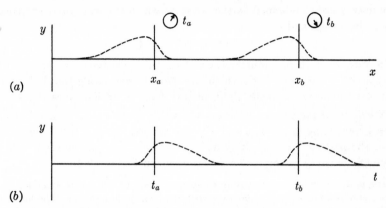

Figure 39-4. (a) The transverse displacement (a) as a function of x for two times and (b) as a function of t for two locations.

wave propagation and on the time t. But, whatever the shape of wave disturbance, the variables x and t must occur in the combinations $(x \mp ct)$. For example, $y = \sin A(x - Bt)$ represents a wave to the right, and $y = e^{-C(x+Dt)^2}$ is a wave to the left, where A, B, C and D are constants. Such a function as $y = E(x - Ft^2)$ *cannot*, however, depict a disturbance traveling with unchanged shape at constant speed.

Figure 39-4a shows the transverse displacement y of a wave pulse as a function of x for *two different times* of observation, t_a and t_b; that is, Figure 39-4a is a snapshot of the wave at two different times. Figure 39-4b shows y as a function of time t for *two different locations*, x_a and x_b (these are, of course, *not* snapshots). Note that, apart from a left-right reversal and change in horizontal scale, the shapes of the curves $y(x)$ at a fixed time t and $y(t)$ at a fixed position x are alike. The essence of wave behavior is seen in these curves: whatever one sees at point x_a, one sees in the same form at point x_b, but at a later time; equivalently, whatever the variation in time at point x_a, one finds the same variation in time at a more distant point, x_b.

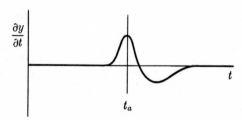

Figure 39-5. The transverse velocity of a particle of the string as a function of time at a particular location, as derived from Figure 39-4b.

The *wave speed* c is defined as the speed at which the *wave form* propagates along the string, and is

$$c = (x_b - x_a)/(t_b - t_a)$$

In wave motion one must clearly distinguish between two speeds: the *wave speed* c, the speed with which the *shape* travels along the X-direction, and the transverse velocity $\partial y/\partial t$ at any fixed x, which gives the *velocity of a particle of the string.* Whereas the wave speed $c = \sqrt{F_t/\rho}$ is constant for a given string (a given ρ and F_t), the particle speed is not. Figure 39-5 gives the particle velocity $\partial y/\partial t$ as a function of time, as derived from the slope of the curve giving y as a function of t in Figure 39-4b.

Example 1   A uniform 10 m string having a mass of 490 gm is attached at its upper end and has a mass of 50 kg suspended from its lower end. The lower end of the string is suddenly displaced horizontally. How long does it take for the wave pulse which is produced to travel to the upper end?

Denoting the string length by L, we can write the time t for the pulse to travel this length as $t = L/c$. From Equation 39-1, $c = \sqrt{F_t/\rho} = \sqrt{Mg/(m/L)}$, where M is the suspended mass and m is the mass of the string. Therefore,

$$t = \frac{L}{c} = \frac{L}{\sqrt{Mg/(m/L)}} = \sqrt{\frac{mL}{Mg}}$$

$$= \sqrt{\frac{(0.490 \text{ kg})(10 \text{ m})}{(50 \text{ kg})(9.8 \text{ m/sec}^2)}} = 0.10 \text{ sec}$$

We have ignored the 1 per cent difference in tension between the top and bottom string ends, arising from the nonzero weight of the string itself. Strictly, the wave speed at the top, where the tension is largest, exceeds that at the bottom by 0.5 per cent.

Here is an alternative derivation for the wave speed c given in Equation 39-1. Consider the simple wave shape shown in Figure 39-6a. All particles in the sloped portion of the string are moving upward with the same particle speed v, while the wave shape advances to the right with the speed c. Clearly, the slope of the wave shape is $(v \,\Delta t)/(c \,\Delta t) = v/c$. The change in transverse momentum

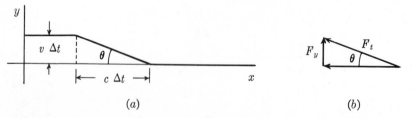

(a)   (b)

Figure 39-6. (a) An idealized wave pulse traveling to the right at speed c. (b) The force components.

of the sloped portion, whose length for small θ is close to $c\,\Delta t$, is

$$\Delta(mv) = (\rho c\,\Delta t)v$$

The transverse force F_y producing this momentum change in the time Δt is, from Newton's second law,

$$F_y = \Delta(mv)/\Delta t = \rho cv \qquad [39\text{-}3]$$

We see from Figure 39-6b that the vertical force component F_y of the string tension F_t is given by

$$F_y/F_t = \sin\theta$$

For small displacements, $\sin\theta \simeq \theta \simeq v/c$; therefore,

$$F_y = (v/c)F_t$$

Substituting this result in Equation 39-3 gives

$$F_t(v/c) = \rho cv$$

[39-1]
$$c = \sqrt{F_t/\rho}$$

Note that the wave speed $\sqrt{F_t/\rho}$ is constant and independent of the wave shape only under the condition that the string displacement is small, that is, that θ is small. This implies, in turn, that the particle speed v is much less than the wave speed c; that is, $v/c \ll 1$.

39-2 The wave equation We wish to find the general form of the differential equation describing wave propagation in one dimension. From the arguments of the last section we know that the wave disturbance must have the mathematical form

[39-2]
$$y(x, t) = y(x \mp ct)$$

where the minus and plus signs apply, respectively, to waves traveling to the right and to the left. For a transverse wave along a string, the wave function y denotes, of course, the actual transverse displacement y of a particle of the string. For other types of waves, however, the function y has other meanings. Thus, for a compressional wave through a solid, y represents the longitudinal displacement of particles; for a sound wave through a gas, the wave function y may denote the pressure change arising from the wave disturbance; for electromagnetic waves, the function y may represent the electric or magnetic field; and for the matter waves of quantum mechanics, the wave function is the so-called probability amplitude. Whatever the differences in the nature of the wave disturbance, *all* waves traveling at constant speed along X must satisfy the equation given above.

We take a first partial derivative of y with respect to x, maintaining t constant:

$$\partial y/\partial x = y' \qquad [39\text{-}4a]$$

Inasmuch as y varies with both x and t, we use the partial differential operator ∂ to symbolize the partial variation of y with one variable, the other variable being fixed. The symbol y' denotes the exact derivative of y with respect to, say, z, where $z = x \mp ct$.

The first time derivative, with x held constant, is

$$\partial y / \partial t = \mp c y'$$ [39-4b]

Eliminating y' between Equations 39-4a and 39-4b gives

$$\partial y / \partial t = \mp c(\partial y / \partial x)$$ [39-5]

Equation 39-5 shows that the "space shape" $\partial y / \partial x$ and the "time shape" $\partial y / \partial t$, are the same, as illustrated in Figures 39-4a and 39-4b. We see, furthermore, that the ratio of the particle speed to the wave speed, $(\partial y / \partial t)/c$, is simply the slope $\partial y / \partial x$ of the curve representing a snapshot of the wave. Therefore, if the wave disturbance is to be small, with $\partial y / \partial x$ small, as our derivation for the speed c required, the particle speed must always be *much less* than the wave speed.

The second partial derivatives of Equations 39-4a and 39-4b are, respectively,

$$\partial^2 y / \partial x^2 = y''$$

$$\partial^2 y / \partial t^2 = c^2 y''$$

Eliminating y'' from these equations yields

$$\partial^2 y / \partial x^2 = (1/c^2)(\partial^2 y / \partial t^2)$$

or, in terms of a general wave function F,

$$\boxed{\frac{\partial^2 F}{\partial x^2} = \frac{1}{c^2} \cdot \frac{\partial^2 F}{\partial t^2}}$$ [39-6]

This is the *wave equation* for waves propagated along X. It is a *linear* second-order partial differential equation. Its linearity insures that, if each of two distinct wave functions, F_1 and F_2, satisfies Equation 39-6 separately, their sum, $F_1 + F_2$, is also a proper solution. We shall explore the implications of this superposition of wave functions in the next section.

The wave equation may be interpreted quite directly in physical terms for a wave on a string. The quantity $\partial^2 y / \partial x^2$ is a measure of the string's curvature at any point and therefore also of the resultant force arising from the string's tension. The quantity $\partial^2 y / \partial t^2$ is the acceleration of a small string segment at the same location. Equation 39-6, then, shows that for wave propagation the resultant force must be proportional to the acceleration for any small transverse displacement y. Only if there are coupled particles (here, joined string segments), each one of which obeys this proportionality, can a wave be propagated.

39-3 The superposition principle and interference Suppose that

two wave disturbances traveling in opposite directions along the same string are allowed to "collide." The results of observation are shown in Figure 39-7. As the two pulses merge, the resultant disturbance at each point along the string and at any instant of time, is found merely by adding algebraically, or superposing, the separate wave disturbances. By the *principle of superposition*, the resultant transverse displacement is just the

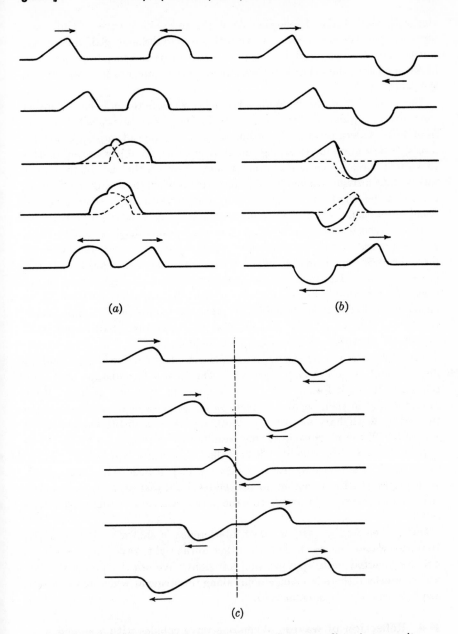

(a)

(b)

(c)

Figure 39-7. The "collision" of wave pulses traveling in opposite directions: (a) constructive interference, (b) destructive interference. (c) As the pulses interfere, a single point on the string remains undisplaced at all times.

algebraic sum of the displacements of the individual waves. Thus, any wave will pass through another wave with *unchanged* shape. Said differently, there is no wave-wave interaction; each wave carries away from the "collision" precisely the energy and transverse linear momentum it carried into the "collision."

The superposition principle for wave displacements reminds us of another superposition principle, that for forces. In fact, wave superposition results from force superposition. According to the principle of superposition for forces, two or more forces acting simultaneously on an object are equivalent to a single force which is their vector sum. Now, in the case of transverse waves along a string, an accelerating force arises when the string is deformed, the string deformation, as measured by the curvature of a small segment, being proportional to the deforming force. As long as this proportionality holds, superposing forces is equivalent to superposing displacements. Thus, for mechanical waves, superposition applies only for *small* deformations (here, small string displacements). If the string were displaced great distances, or were deformed with sharp corners, or if the tension were not constant, the approximations made in deriving Equation 39-1 would no longer apply. Then the principle of superposition would be inapplicable. In all that follows we shall assume that the wave disturbances are small enough for the superposition principle to hold strictly.

The superposing of separate wave displacements, to arrive at the resultant displacement, is known as *interference*. (The term is an unhappy one, since the separate wave forms really do not interfere with one another; they interfere only in their separate effects *on the particles* of the string.) When two waves both have positive (or both negative) y displacements, as in Figure 39-7a, the magnitude of their resultant displacement is greater than that of each wave separately. This is called *constructive interference*. On the other hand, when two waves of opposite y displacements are superposed, as in Figure 39-7b, the magnitude of the resultant displacement is less than that of each wave separately, and the waves are said to show *destructive interference*.

One rather special case of wave interference is shown in Figure 39-7c. Here two waves, one to the left, the other to the right, have identical shapes but are inverted both up-down and left-right. We see that when the two waves interfere, there is a single point along the string at which the resultant displacement *always* remains zero.

39-4　Reflection of waves　When one wave collides with a second wave on the same string nothing happens to either wave. What happens when a wave collides with a boundary, a point at which the medium propagating the wave (here, the string) changes?

First imagine a string attached firmly to a very massive wall, as in Figure
39-8a. Since the wall cannot move, we may describe this situation formally
by saying that the displacement y must always be zero at the point where
the string joins the wall. Now, if a wave pulse is propagated to the right,
we find it reflected to the left from the boundary. After reflection, the shape

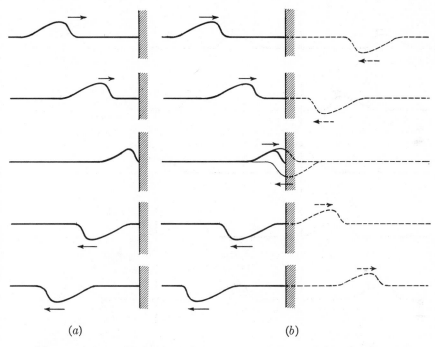

(a)   (b)

Figure 39-8. (a) Reflection of a wave pulse at an infinitely massive
boundary. (b) The reflection of (a) in terms of virtual waves (compare
with 39-7c).

is reversed left-right; the initial leading edge of the pulse is still the leading
edge after reflection. In addition, the sign of the wave is reversed; that is,
the wave is inverted up-down, a positive transverse displacement becoming
negative upon reflection, and conversely.

One can give a physical basis for this behavior. When the leading edge
of the wave disturbance arrives at the boundary, the tension of the string
produces an upward force on the infinitely massive, and therefore essentially
immovable, wall. By Newton's third law, the wall applies an equal downward force on the string. This force is, in fact, of greater magnitude than
that of the force applied by an adjoining segment of string in the absence
of the wall, because the string, being fixed vertically at the boundary,

undergoes a larger change in curvature at that point. The force of the wall on the string is so great that it does not merely return it to $y = 0$; the wall pulls so hard on the string that the string is brought below the line $y = 0$. Thus, an inverted wave to the left is generated.

We can view the reflection of a wave pulse in a different, but equivalent, way. First note that the displacement must always be zero at the boundary.

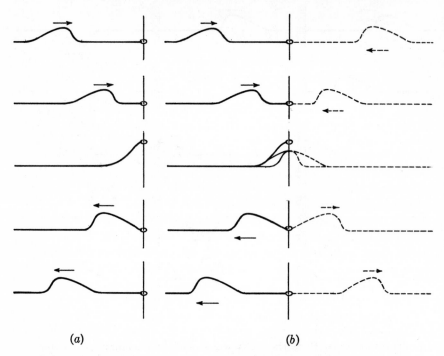

(a) (b)

Figure 39-9. (a) Reflection of a wave pulse from a free end. (b) The reflection of (a) in terms of virtual traveling waves.

This is exactly what occurs in Figure 39-7c. Comparing Figure 39-7c with Figure 39-8a and 39-8b, it is clear that we can imagine the incident wave to continue past the boundary to the right as a fictitious, or "virtual," wave, while the reflected wave corresponds to the emergence of a virtual wave traveling to the left through the boundary. The boundary condition, $y = 0$, is thereby satisfied at all times.

We now imagine that the end of the string, rather than being tied down, is perfectly free to move in the transverse direction. For definiteness, we suppose that the string is terminated with a small ring that can slide freely along a smooth vertical post. The results of a reflection are shown in Figure 39-9a. Again there is a left-right shape reversal, as the direction of propagation is changed from right to left. There is, however, *no* change in the sign of the wave shape. An upright incident wave is reflected as an upright wave. Figure 39-9b shows the reflection in terms of the interference between two waves traveling in opposite directions. A simple physical basis also can be given for reflection from a free boundary. Since there is no string to the right of the free end to provide a downward force component through the tension, the string overshoots as the disturbance reaches the end.

We have treated two extreme cases of reflection: a string attached to an infinitely massive second medium and a string attached to a massless second medium. Now consider the more general case in which one string with linear density ρ_1 is connected to a second string of linear density ρ_2. The tension F_t is the same in both strings. If $\rho_2 > \rho_1$, we see from Equation 39-1 that the wave speed c_1 in the first string exceeds the wave speed c_2 in the second string. Figure 39-10a shows what happens when a wave pulse incident from the left with speed c_1 encounters the boundary. The wave is partially transmitted into the second medium and partially reflected back into the first medium. Here, the boundary moves as the waves reach it. As we would expect, the transmitted wave undergoes no change in sign; on the other hand, the reflected wave is reversed. Moreover, the transmitted wave shape is compressed longitudinally by virtue of the decreased speed c_2. That the reflected wave is reversed in sign follows from the behavior found earlier for reflection from an infinitely massive second medium. The second medium here is not infinitely massive, but its inertia is greater than that of the first. Consequently, a reversal in polarity occurs upon reflection. As Figure 39-10b shows, the polarity is not reversed for an incident wave from the more massive string into the less massive string.

The relative amplitudes of the reflected and transmitted waves depend on the speed ratio c_1/c_2. The energy carried by the waves reflected and transmitted at the boundary must, of course, equal the energy carried by the incident wave. Complete reflection occurs for $c_1/c_2 = 0$ or ∞; complete transmission, for $c_1/c_2 = 1$. The boundary conditions are these: if y_1 and y_2 represent the displacements for the two media, then at the boundary $y_1 = y_2$ at any time (that is, the string ends must be joined together) and $dy_1/dt = dy_2/dt$ at any time (that is, the string ends must move together with the same velocity).

39-5 Sinusoidal waves Thus far our discussion of waves on a string has been quite general. We have not been concerned with the specific wave shape, that is, with the mathematical relation giving the displacement y of a particle on the string as an explicit function of time t and position x. Here we do this for the special case of continuous sinusoidal waves generated by a simple harmonic oscillator. The special importance of sinusoidal waves

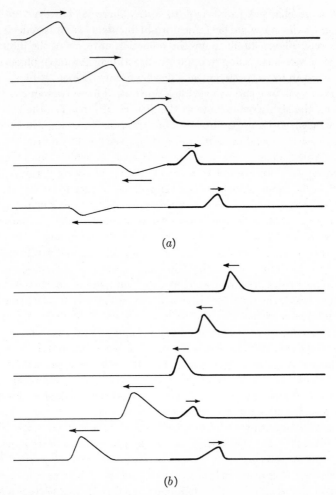

Figure 39-10. Reflection and transmission of a wave pulse incident upon (a) a string of greater linear density and (b) a string of lesser linear density.

is not merely that their generators are common but, more especially, that *any* wave shape can be regarded as the superposition of sinusoidal waves of various frequencies.

Suppose that the left end ($x = 0$) of a very long string under tension is moved up and down in simple harmonic motion with amplitude A and frequency f (and period T, where $T = 1/f$). Then (Section 17-3) the transverse displacement at this point is given by

$$y(x, t) = y(0, t) = A \sin \omega t$$

where $\omega = 2\pi f = 2\pi/T$. From the arguments of Section 39-1 and Figure 39-4 we know that the displacement of any other point on the string to the right will show exactly the same variation with time, but with a delay, or phase lag, δ:

$$y(x, t) = A \sin (\omega t - \delta)$$

Since the wave disturbance travels along the X-direction at a constant speed, the phase lag δ is proportional to x, and we may write

$$\delta = kx \qquad\qquad [39\text{-}7]$$

where k is known as the *wave number* (for reasons soon to be seen). The transverse displacement $y(x, t)$ can then be written

$$\boxed{\text{Wave to } right: \qquad y(x, t) = A \sin (\omega t - kx)} \qquad [39\text{-}8a]$$

This is one important form of the equation for a traveling sinusoidal wave. It gives the transverse displacement y as a function of both the coordinate x along the direction of propagation and the time t for a wave traveling to the right. If the wave were to travel to the left, the displacement at point x would *lead*, rather than lag, the displacement at $x = 0$. Then the equation for the traveling wave would be written

$$\boxed{\text{Wave to left:} \qquad y(x, t) = A \sin (\omega t + kx)} \qquad [39\text{-}8b]$$

The displacement y varies sinusoidally with time for every point along the string. Equation 39-8 also shows that, for any time t, y varies sinusoidally with x; that is, a snapshot of a wave generated by a simple harmonic oscillator is a sine or a cosine, as shown in Figure 39-11.

Points along the wave having the same displacement, velocity, and acceleration are in the same phase; for example, the dots of Figure 39-11. The distance between any two such adjacent points is known as the *wavelength*, λ. Thus, if x changes by λ, the phase must change by 2π or, from Equation 39-7,

$$k\lambda = 2\pi$$
$$k = 2\pi/\lambda \qquad\qquad [39\text{-}9]$$

The wave number k gives the number of wavelengths per 2π length; that is, k is the rate of change in phase with distance.

Using the definition $\omega = 2\pi/T$, we may write Equation 39-8a in another form:

$$y(x, t) = A \sin 2\pi \left(\frac{t}{T} - \frac{x}{\lambda}\right) \qquad\qquad [39\text{-}10]$$

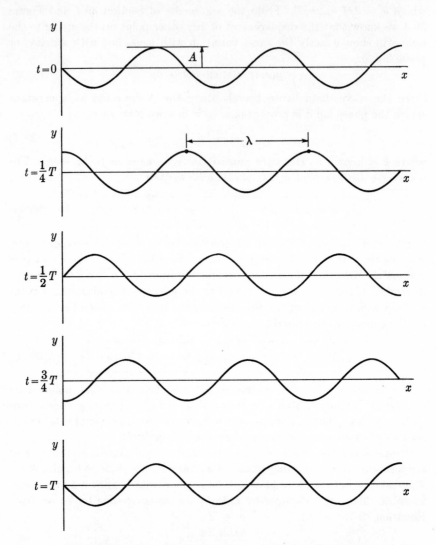

Figure 39-11. A sinusoidal wave for several different times.

Equation 39-10 applies for a wave traveling to the right; as before, a wave to the left is represented by the same equation, but a plus sign replaces the minus sign.

Clearly, a change in time t of the duration of one period T is equivalent to a change in space along X of one wavelength λ. That is, in the time T, during which the wave generator and each particle on the string complete one cycle, the wave shape advances a distance λ. This permits us to write the wave speed c as

$$c = \lambda/T \qquad [39\text{-}11]$$

or, since $1/T = f$,

$$\boxed{c = f\lambda} \qquad [39\text{-}12]$$

An alternate form of the relation is $c = (2\pi f)(\lambda/2\pi) = \omega/k$. Since the phase of oscillation advances along the propagation direction at the same rate as does the wave shape, it is appropriate to call the wave speed the *phase speed*.

The phase speed for a wave on a string depends only on the elastic and inertial properties of the string (the tension and linear density), not on the form of the wave. It follows, then, from Equation 39-12 that high-frequency oscillations generate waves of relatively short wavelength, while low-frequency oscillations generate long wavelengths, the product of f and λ always remaining constant.

We may write the equation for a traveling wave in still another form by using Equation 39-12 in Equation 39-8a:

$$y = A \sin 2\pi\left(\frac{t}{T} - \frac{x}{\lambda}\right) = A \sin \frac{2\pi}{\lambda}\left(\frac{\lambda}{T}t - x\right)$$

$$y(x, t) = A \sin \frac{2\pi}{\lambda}(ct - x)$$

Using Equation 39-9 and the fact that $\sin(-\theta) = -\sin\theta$, we have

$$y(x, t) = -A \sin k(x - ct) \qquad [39\text{-}13]$$

again for a wave propagated along positive X. We note that the quantities x, c, and t appear in Equation 39-13 in the combination $x - ct$, as required by the very general arguments leading to Equation 39-2.

The three forms of the equation for a traveling sinusoidal wave given in Equations 39-8, 39-10, and 39-13 are, of course, equivalent. They differ only as to which of the quantities k, λ, ω, T, f, and c appear. We have assumed, however, that the displacement y is zero when $x = 0$ and $t = 0$. To allow for an initial displacement at $x = 0$ and $t = 0$, we need merely incorporate a phase constant ϕ, writing

$$y(x, t) = A \sin[k(x - ct) - \phi]$$

Example 2   A sinusoidal wave is generated along a rope that has a linear density of 70 gm/m and is under a tension of 10 nt from a transverse simple harmonic oscillator at the point $x = 0$. The oscillator executes 4.0 oscillations per second with an amplitude of 2.0 cm. (a) What is the wave speed? (b) What is the wavelength? (c) Assuming that the oscillator is at the upper amplitude position at time $t = 0$, write the equation for the traveling sinusoidal wave as a function of x and t. (d) What is the magnitude of the maximum transverse linear momentum of a segment of string 1.0 mm long? (e) What is the magnitude of the maximum resultant force on such a segment?

(a) From Equation 39-1,

$$c = \sqrt{F_t/\rho} = \sqrt{(10 \text{ nt})/(0.070 \text{ kg/m})} = 12 \text{ m/sec}$$

(b) From Equation 39-12,

$$\lambda = c/f = (12 \text{ m/sec})/(4.0 \text{ sec}^{-1}) = 3.0 \text{ m}$$

(c) The transverse displacement y is *not* zero initially; therefore, we must include a phase constant ϕ:

$$y(x, t) = A \sin [k(x - ct) - \phi]$$

Since $y = A$ at $t = 0$ and $x = 0$,

$$A = A \sin (-\phi) = -A \sin \phi$$

or

$$\phi = -\pi/2$$

Then

$$y(x, t) = A \sin [k(x - ct) + \pi/2]$$

or

$$y(x, t) = A \cos k(x - ct)$$

Recalling that $k = 2\pi/\lambda$, we have

$$y(x, t) = A \cos \frac{2\pi}{\lambda} (x - ct) = (2.0 \times 10^{-2}) \cos \frac{2\pi}{3} (x - 12t)$$

where y and x are in meters and t is in seconds.

(d) To find the maximum transverse linear momentum of a small rope segment we must find the maximum transverse speed $(\partial y/\partial t)_{\max}$ and multiply it by the mass of the 1.0 mm segment, which is $(0.070 \text{ kg/m})(1.0 \times 10^{-3} \text{ m}) = 7.0 \times 10^{-5}$ kg. The length of the segment is so small compared with the wavelength (1 in 300), that we may properly regard all parts of the small segment as having the same speed. Taking the time derivative of y (with x held constant), we have, from the equation in part (c),

$$\partial y/\partial t = kcA \sin k(x - ct) = \omega A \sin k(x - ct)$$

Therefore, $(\partial y/\partial t)_{\max} = (2\pi \times 4.0 \text{ sec}^{-1})(2.0 \times 10^{-2} \text{ m}) = 0.50 \text{ m/sec}$

The magnitude of the maximum transverse linear momentum of the 7.0×10^{-5} kg segment is

$$p_{\max} = m(\partial y/\partial t)_{\max} = (7.0 \times 10^{-5} \text{ kg})(0.50 \text{ m/sec}) = 3.5 \times 10^{-5} \text{ kg-m/sec}$$

(e) To find the magnitude of the maximum resultant force on the small rope segment we first compute the maximum transverse acceleration $\partial^2 y/\partial t^2$:

$$\partial^2 y/\partial t^2 = -(kc)^2 A \cos k(x - ct) = -\omega^2 A \cos k(x - ct)$$
$$(\partial^2 y/\partial t^2)_{\max} = (2\pi \times 4.0 \text{ sec}^{-1})^2 (2.0 \times 10^{-2} \text{ m}) = 13 \text{ m/sec}^2$$

The magnitude of the maximum resultant force is

$$(F_y)_{\max} = m(\partial^2 y/\partial t^2)_{\max} = (7.0 \times 10^{-5} \text{ kg})(13 \text{ m/sec}^2) = 9.1 \times 10^{-4} \text{ nt}$$

Note that the maximum transverse force is much less than the rope's tension of 10 nt, as it must be, since only the vertical components of the rope tension enter here.

39-6   Energy considerations in wave motion   Wave motion represents a mode of energy transport. Energy goes from the oscillating source, through the medium, and to a distant point where energy may be extracted from the medium. No particle actually moves from the initial source to the final absorber; rather, it is the *state of motion*, and therefore the transverse linear momentum and the energy, that move along the propagation direction.

Let us analyze this energy transfer in more detail. We imagine that one end of a taut string is moved up and down in simple harmonic motion by an external agent. The agent does work continuously on the particle at the string's end. This particle acquires kinetic energy and potential energy, the kinetic energy being a maximum when the particle passes through the equilibrium position $y = 0$ and the potential energy being a maximum at the amplitude position $y = A$. Despite the fact that work is done on it, the total energy of the oscillating particle is unchanged. This means that the particle loses energy to neighboring particles by doing work on them at precisely the same rate at which it gains energy from the external agent. The energy travels along the string at the wave speed c. Energy is finally removed from the string, and the wave is at least partially absorbed if the string is attached to a movable object which is set in oscillatory motion by the string.

Let us compute the power, the time rate at which energy passes any point along the direction of propagation, for a sinusoidal wave. Each point on the string executes simple harmonic motion at the same angular frequency $\omega = 2\pi f$ and with the same amplitude A. Designating the mass of each particle m, we find the total mechanical energy E of each oscillating particle:

$$[17\text{-}14] \qquad E = \tfrac{1}{2}k'A^2 = \tfrac{1}{2}(\omega^2 m)A^2$$

where the quantity k' is used here to represent the equivalent force constant.

The total energy E_λ of all oscillating particles in a segment of string one wavelength long and having a total mass $\rho\lambda$ is, then,

$$E_\lambda = \tfrac{1}{2}\omega^2 \rho\lambda A^2$$

All of the energy originally contained in such a segment will have left the segment in a time of one period T, as shown in Figure 39-12. Therefore,

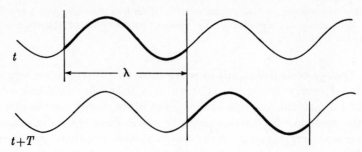

Figure 39-12. The energy contained within a segment of length λ leaves this segment in a time of one period.

the power is

$$P = \frac{E_\lambda}{T} = \frac{\tfrac{1}{2}\omega^2\rho\lambda A^2}{T}$$

$$\boxed{P = \tfrac{1}{2}\omega^2 A^2 \rho c} \qquad [39\text{-}14]$$

As one would expect, the rate of energy flow is proportional to the wave speed c. The power is also proportional to the *square* of both the angular *frequency* ω and the *amplitude* A. Thus, a high-frequency, or short-wavelength, disturbance can carry appreciable power even though its amplitude is relatively small.

39-7 Superposition of sinusoidal waves Here we treat the superposition of sinusoidal waves traveling in the same direction along a string. We find the resultant displacement, following the superposition principle, by adding the component displacements algebraically.

First, consider the case of two waves of the same amplitude and wavelength (and frequency), but having various fixed values of relative phase angle ϕ. Several examples are shown graphically in Figure 39-13. One finds that the resultant wave form is always a sine wave of the *same wavelength* as its component waves. The amplitude A_r and phase ϕ_r of the resultant wave depend, however, on the relative phase ϕ between the component waves. In Figure 39-13a the two waves are exactly in phase; $\phi = 0$. The resultant wave then has the same phase and twice the amplitude of the individual waves: $A_r = 2A$ and $\phi_r = 0$. This is an example of complete *constructive interference*. In Figure 39-13b the two waves are out of phase by one half-wavelength, or by $\phi = 180°$, the amplitude A_r is zero, and there is no resultant wave. The two waves now annul one another, and we have complete *destructive interference*. Figure 39-13c shows the waves superposed with $\phi = 60°$. The resultant wave here differs in phase by 30° from each of

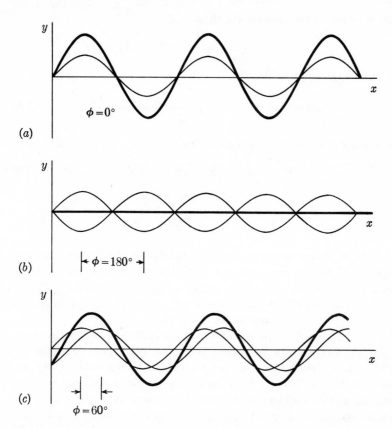

Figure 39-13. Superposition of two sinusoidal waves of equal amplitude and wavelength for relative phase differences: (a) 0°, (b) 180°, and (c) 60°.

the two component waves. Note that, although Figure 39-13 portrays snapshots of the waves (y as a function of x for some instant of time), the variation of y in time at any point along the string is of exactly the same form.

Now we find the resultant wave analytically, choosing the time $t = 0$ for simplicity. Using Equation 39-13, the component waves may be represented by

$$y_1 = A \sin kx$$

$$y_2 = A \sin (kx - \phi)$$

In time the wave y_2 reaches its peak *before* y_1; therefore, y_2 *leads* y_1 by ϕ in time.

The resultant displacement y is then

$$y = y_1 + y_2 = A \sin kx + A \sin (kx - \phi)$$

Using the trigonometric identity

$$\sin a + \sin b = 2 \cos \left(\frac{a - b}{2} \right) \sin \left(\frac{a + b}{2} \right) \qquad [39\text{-}15]$$

we can write the equation for y above as

$$y = [2A \cos (\phi/2)] \sin (kx - \phi/2) \qquad [39\text{-}16]$$

$$y = A_r \sin (kx - \phi_r)$$

where

$$A_r = 2A \cos (\phi/2) \qquad \text{and} \qquad \phi_r = \phi/2$$

We see from Equation 39-16 that the amplitude of the resultant wave is $2A \cos (\phi/2)$, that its wavelength, $\lambda = 2\pi/k$, is the same as that of the component waves, and that its phase relative to the y_1 wave is $\phi/2$. The results given in Figure 39-13a, b, and c are easily confirmed by putting ϕ equal, respectively, to $0°$, $180°$, and $60°$ in Equation 39-16.

The general case for superposition of sinusoidal waves is that in which the component waves differ in wavelength (and frequency), amplitude, and relative phase. Then the resultant wave pattern is usually quite complicated; see Figure 39-14a. An interesting example of such superposition is shown in Figure 39-14b, where the superposing of three sine waves of frequencies f, $3f$, and $5f$ (with appropriate amplitudes and phases) leads to a resultant wave closely approximating a square wave of frequency f. By the same token, a square wave is altogether equivalent to superposed sine waves with frequencies in the ratios of the odd integers. This illustrates a general rule: *any* (periodic) wave form, simple or complicated, can be arrived at by superposing pure sinusoidal wave forms of appropriate frequency, phase, and amplitude. Conversely, any wave shape may be decomposed into a series (a so-called Fourier series) of sinusoidal waves. This remarkable fact, which is demonstrated rigorously in Fourier's theorem, means that in treating sinusoidal wave behavior one is able to treat *all* other types of periodic wave forms through the superposition principle.

39-8 Beats As another example of wave superposition consider the superposition of two waves of equal amplitude (for convenience) but of *different* frequencies. We choose to examine the variation with time of the resultant displacement at a particular position in space (of course, the space variation for a given time is similar).

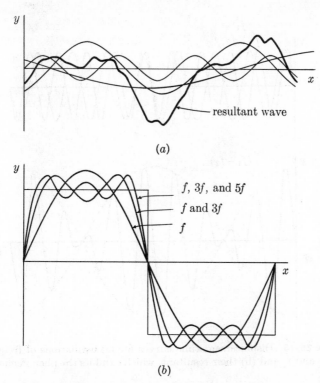

(a)

(b)

Figure 39-14. (a) Superposing sinusoidal waves of different frequencies may yield a complicated resultant wave. (b) A square wave is closely approximated by superposing sinusoidal waves of frequencies f, $3f$, and $5f$.

The results are shown graphically in Figure 39-15 for two waves of nearly equal frequency. We see that the component waves at first interfere constructively, to give a large resultant amplitude. As time passes, the component waves become increasingly out of phase until they interfere destructively. This behavior is repeated. The resultant wave form shows rapid oscillations with an "amplitude," or envelope, which varies slowly.

We can deduce this analytically. For definiteness we choose to look at the time variations at the point $x = 0$. Using Equation 39-8 we write the component oscillations as

$$y_1 = A \sin 2\pi f_1 t$$
$$y_2 = A \sin 2\pi f_2 t$$

where $f_1 \neq f_2$. The resultant displacement is

$$y = y_1 + y_2 = A(\sin 2\pi f_1 t + \sin 2\pi f_2 t)$$

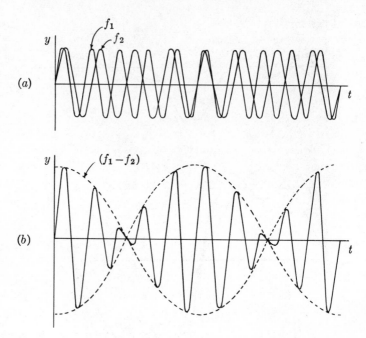

Figure 39-15. Displacement-time curves for (a) oscillations of frequencies f_1 and f_2 and (b) their resultant, which exhibits the phenomenon of beats.

Again using the trigonometric identity, Equation 39-15, we may rewrite this equation as

$$y = \left[2A \cos 2\pi \left(\frac{f_1 - f_2}{2} \right) t \right] \sin 2\pi \left(\frac{f_1 + f_2}{2} \right) t \qquad [39\text{-}17]$$

$$= A_r \sin 2\pi f t$$

Equation 39-17 shows that y can be thought of as the product of two sinusoidal functions, $A_r = 2A \cos 2\pi[(f_1 - f_2)/2]t$, the "amplitude," which oscillates at the frequency $(f_1 - f_2)/2$, and $\sin 2\pi[(f_1 + f_2)/2]t$, which oscillates more rapidly in time at the average of the two frequencies, $f = (f_1 + f_2)/2$. Now, if $f_1 \simeq f_2$, the average frequency $(f_1 + f_2)/2$ appearing in the second factor is essentially the same as f_1 or f_2. Then, the envelope varies very slowly with time at the frequency $(f_1 - f_2)/2$.

This phenomenon is known as *beats*. The number of times the *magnitude* of the "amplitude" of the resultant wave reaches a maximum per unit time is defined as the number of beats per unit time. Since any sinusoidal oscillation has *two* extreme values over one cycle—one a maximum, the other a minimum—the number of beats per unit time is $|f_1 - f_2|$. That is, the beat frequency is the absolute value of the frequency difference between the two component frequencies:

$$\boxed{\text{Beat frequency} = |f_1 - f_2|}$$ [39-18]

The higher the beat frequency, the greater the frequency difference. Thus, one may measure the frequency difference between two waves or oscillators by "beating" one against the other and measuring the time variation of the resultant amplitude. If the two component oscillators have the same frequency, the beats disappear, since the resultant wave form then has a constant amplitude.

Beats are perceived directly by the ear as pulsations in loudness, when one hears two simultaneous oscillations of nearly equal frequency. The ear is sensitive to energy variations, which are proportional to the *square* of the displacement of the wave disturbance, but not to the sign of the displacement. Therefore, the ear hears a frequency $f_1 - f_2$ rather than $(f_1 - f_2)/2$. The method of beats is used frequently to tune musical instruments, especially the piano.

39-9 Standing waves When two or more sinusoidal waves traveling in the *same* direction at the same speed are superposed, the resultant wave form travels with the wave speed of the component waves. Now consider the superposition of two sinusoidal waves of the same wavelength and amplitude but traveling in *opposite* directions at the same speed. The results are shown graphically in Figure 39-16, where the two traveling waves, together with their resultant, are shown for a succession of times.

First, we note that there are certain times at which the two waves fall exactly on top of one another, namely at $t = 0$ or $t = \frac{1}{2}T$, where T is the period. There are other times at which the waves give complete destructive interference, namely at $t = \frac{1}{4}T$, $\frac{3}{4}T$, etc. Figure 39-16 shows, further, that there are certain *points* along the string at which the two traveling waves always interfere destructively. These points, at which the string never undergoes a displacement, are known as nodal points, or *nodes*. The string has its largest amplitude of oscillation at locations, known as *loops*, midway between adjoining nodes. Clearly, *adjacent nodes* (or antiloops) are *separated by one half-wavelength* ($\frac{1}{2}\lambda$); (likewise) *adjacent loops are separated by* $\frac{1}{2}\lambda$. The resultant oscillating disturbance is called a *standing wave*, or *stationary wave*. These terms are appropriate, since no resultant wave form is seen traveling left or right, and no energy is transferred left or right. The particles of the string oscillate, but the pattern stands still in the sense that the loops and nodes are fixed along the X-axis.

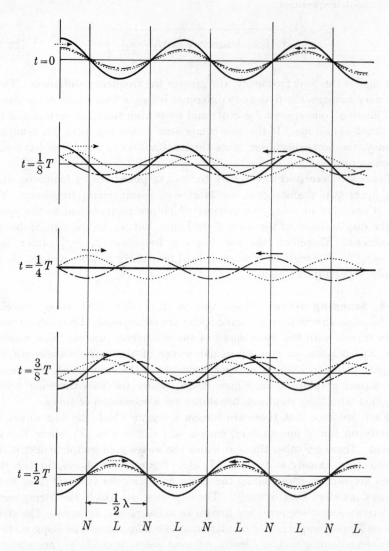

Figure 39-16. Standing waves. The resultant wave form for two waves travelling in opposite directions for a succession of times. Adjacent nodes (*N*) and adjacent loops (*L*) are separated by one-half a wavelength.

Let us derive these results analytically. Using Equation 39-8 to represent the waves traveling to the right and left, we have, for the resultant displacement,

$$y = A \sin (\omega t - kx) + A \sin (\omega t + kx)$$

Using Equation 39-15 this can be rewritten as

$$y = 2A \cos kx \sin \omega t$$

$$y = 2A \cos \frac{2\pi x}{\lambda} \sin \omega t \qquad\qquad [39\text{-}19]$$

which is the equation for a standing wave.

Equation 39-19 shows that every particle on the string oscillates at the angular frequency $\omega = 2\pi f = 2\pi/T$. The oscillation amplitude varies, however, with the position x, according to $\cos (2\pi x/\lambda)$. The displacement y is *always* zero for positions for which $\cos (2\pi x/\lambda)$ is zero, that is, when $2\pi x/\lambda$ is an odd multiple of $\frac{1}{2}\pi$ radians. Therefore, nodes occur at the positions

$$\frac{2\pi x}{\lambda} = n\left(\frac{\pi}{2}\right), \qquad \text{where } n = 1, 3, 5, \dots,$$

$$\text{Nodes:} \qquad x = \frac{\lambda}{4}, 3\frac{\lambda}{4}, 5\frac{\lambda}{4}, \dots$$

Note that adjacent nodes are separated by $\lambda/2$.

Loops are found at those positions for which the amplitude has its maximum value, $2A$. This occurs when $\cos (2\pi x/\lambda) = \pm 1$, that is, when $(2\pi x/\lambda)$ is an integral multiple of π. Thus, loops are found at the positions

$$2\pi x/\lambda = m\pi, \qquad \text{where } m = 0, 1, 2, \dots$$

$$\text{Loops:} \qquad x = 0, \frac{\lambda}{2}, \lambda, \dots$$

Adjacent loops are separated by $\lambda/2$ and lie midway between nodes.

How can one produce two similar sinusoidal waves traveling in opposite directions and thus obtain standing waves? One can, of course, place transverse simple harmonic oscillators, or wave generators, at both ends of a string. Even more simply, one can reflect an incident sinusoidal wave at a boundary to produce a reflected wave traveling in the opposite direction. As we saw in Section 39-4, any wave form is reflected completely at an infinitely massive boundary. The reflected wave is inverted both up-down and left-right with respect to the incident wave. When one changes the sign of y for a sinusoidal wave, inverting it up-down, one makes every wave crest a wave trough, and conversely; that is, the *phase* of the wave is *shifted* 180°. Thus, when a sinusoidal wave on a string is reflected from a

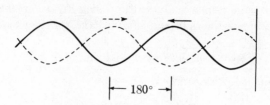

Figure 39-17. A sinusoidal wave reflected from a hard boundary undergoes a 180° shift in phase.

hard boundary, it undergoes a phase shift of 180° relative to the incident
wave; see Figure 39-17. (By the same token, a wave on a string reflected
from an infinitely "soft" boundary, as in Figure 39-9, is *not* shifted in phase.)
One can, therefore, generate a standing-wave pattern on a string by oscillating one end laterally while keeping the other end fixed, as shown in Figure
39-18. This effect is strikingly demonstrated by using a tuning fork or
other mechanical oscillator; the oscillations are typically so rapid that one
sees only the envelope of the standing-wave pattern.

Standing waves can, in fact, be produced when *both* ends of the string
are fixed. The standing-wave pattern must, however, fit between the two
ends of the string; that is, the string length L must be an integral multiple
of half-wavelengths, if the *boundary conditions* at the string ends, $x = 0$
and $x = L$, are to be satisfied. The allowed wavelengths and frequencies
for standing waves on a string fixed at both ends are given by

$$n(\lambda/2) = L, \quad \text{where } n = 1, 2, 3, \ldots$$

$$f = c/\lambda = n\left(\frac{\sqrt{F_t/\rho}}{2L}\right) \qquad [39\text{-}20]$$

where we have used Equation 39-1 for the wave speed c.

The lowest frequency, called the *fundamental* frequency, occurs for $n = 1$.
We designate this frequency f_1. Then standing waves can be produced for
the frequencies

$$f = nf_1 = f_1, 2f_1, 3f_1, \ldots$$

all allowed frequencies being integral multiples of the fundamental, as shown

Figure 39-18. An arrangement for demonstrating standing waves on a
string. One string end is attached to a vibrating tuning fork; the other
end is attached to a weight and hung over a pulley.

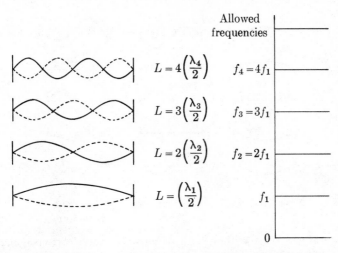

$$L = 4\left(\frac{\lambda_4}{2}\right) \qquad f_4 = 4f_1$$

$$L = 3\left(\frac{\lambda_3}{2}\right) \qquad f_3 = 3f_1$$

$$L = 2\left(\frac{\lambda_2}{2}\right) \qquad f_2 = 2f_1$$

$$L = \left(\frac{\lambda_1}{2}\right) \qquad f_1$$

Figure 39-19. Allowed oscillations for a string attached at both ends.

in Figure 39-19. The lowest frequency is often denoted the *first harmonic*. The second harmonic is $2f_1$, the third harmonic is $3f_1$, etc. The term *harmonic* is used only when the characteristic frequencies are *integral* multiples of the fundamental frequency.

An alternative argument leading to the conditions for standing waves is the following. Imagine a wave incident to the right on a boundary. The reflected wave may be considered to be the incident wave "folded" backward to the left. This folded, or reflected, wave then strikes the left boundary, is folded once more, and again proceeds to the right. Now, this twice-reflected wave will destructively interfere with the initial wave to the right (really, its own tail end) unless the distance ($2L$) it has traveled in one round trip between the boundaries is exactly an integral multiple of *whole* wavelengths. See Figure 39-20. The wave will then, so to speak, con-structively interfere with itself, provided $2L = n\lambda$, or $n(\lambda/2) = L$, as in Equation 39-20. (Although a 180° phase change occurs upon reflection from a hard boundary, the argument is unchanged, since *two* such phase shifts are made in one round trip.) Thus, a standing wave may be thought of as a traveling wave of infinite extent folded upon itself an infinite number of times, the wavelength being such as to insure that the boundary conditions are met, namely, that an integral multiple of half-wavelengths fits between the ends.

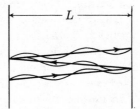

Figure 39-20. A traveling wave undergoing multiple reflections at boundaries.

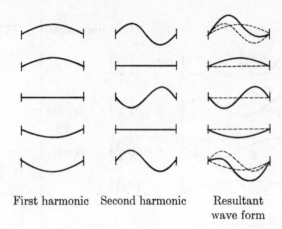

First harmonic　　Second harmonic　　Resultant
　　　　　　　　　　　　　　　　　　　wave form

Figure 39-21. Wave pattern for a succession of times corresponding to
the simultaneous excitation of the first and second harmonics.

According to the superposition principle, several waves may exist simultaneously on a string without their disturbing one another in any way.
The waves pass through one another without interaction. Thus, two or
more standing waves of *different* frequencies and wavelengths may exist
simultaneously on a single string with fixed ends. See Figure 39-21, which
shows the resultant wave pattern on a string for simultaneous excitation
of the first and second harmonics. Conversely, *any* periodic disturbance
on a string—any oscillations of a string which persist in time—must consist
of one or more standing waves. On the other hand, any wave disturbance
which is not at one of the allowed frequencies—any oscillation which does
not correspond to one of the allowed *modes* of oscillation—must, through
the arguments of the last paragraph, quickly die out, because such a wave
destructively interferes with itself, the energy being dissipated at the
boundaries. Thus, when a string is struck or bowed, as in the piano or
violin, it can oscillate simultaneously in one or more of the allowed frequencies. Typically, the amplitude of the fundamental exceeds that of higher
harmonics. The higher harmonics are sometimes referred to as "overtones";
they have a frequency "over" that of the fundamental. For a string with
fixed ends, the second harmonic is the first overtone, etc.

In musical terminology, the frequency of the fundamental is a measure
of the "pitch" of the oscillating string, whereas the "tone," which allows
the ear to discriminate between a violin and a piano playing the same note,
is a measure of the relative amplitudes of the harmonics present. The
frequency spectra of two tones of the same pitch are shown in Figure 39-22.

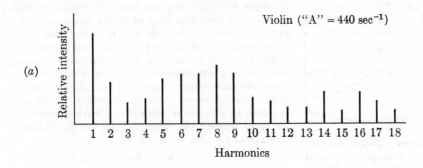

(a)

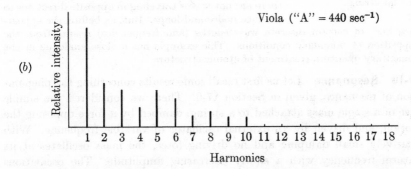

(b)

Figure 39-22. Frequency spectra for (a) a violin string and (b) a viola string having the same fundamental frequency, or pitch.

Note that, although the two tones have the same fundamental frequency, or pitch, they differ in the relative intensity of harmonics.

Example 3 A string 2.0 m long is held fixed at both ends. It is found that if a wave pulse is generated near one end, it takes 0.10 sec for the pulse to travel one round trip to the far end and return. What are the allowed frequencies of oscillation for this string?

The wave speed c is the distance traveled by the wave pulse divided by the elapsed time, $(4.0 \text{ m})/(0.10 \text{ sec}) = 40 \text{ m/sec}$. The allowed standing-wave patterns are those for which the string length L is an integral multiple of one half-wavelength: $L = n(\lambda/2)$. Thus,

$$f = c/\lambda = nc/2L = n(40 \text{ m/sec})/2(2.0 \text{ m})$$
$$= n(10 \text{ sec}^{-1}) = 10, 20, 30, \ldots, \text{sec}^{-1}$$

We can arrive at the same result through another argument: With the string oscillating in its fundamental mode, a sinusoidal wave will travel one round trip between the boundaries in a time of one period, because only then will it constructively interfere with itself in further reflections. Thus, the period of the first harmonic is 0.10 sec and its frequency is 10 cycles/sec. The higher harmonics are integral multiples of 10 sec^{-1}. Note that string length and wave speed do *not* enter here.

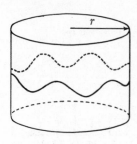

Figure 39-23. An al-lowed mode ($n = 4$) of oscillation of a stretched circular string.

Example 4 What are the allowed modes of oscil-lation for a stretched loop of string fitted around a right circular cylinder, the string undergoing trans-verse displacements along the cylindrical surface?

The situation is shown in Figure 39-23. The string ends are now not attached to a second medium, but rather to each other. Thus, the boundary condition here is that the string ends join smoothly, which is to say that an integral number of *full* wavelengths must be fitted around the circumference of the cylinder. The allowed modes are given by

$$n\lambda = 2\pi r$$

This is *not* a standing wave of the usual sort, since there are not waves traveling in opposite directions to produce nodes and loops. But, as before, the appear-ance here of certain discrete wavelengths (and frequencies) results from the imposition of boundary conditions. This example has a close analogue in the elementary quantum treatment of atomic structure.

39-10   Resonance   Let us first recall some results concerning the phenom-enon of resonance, given in Section 17-6. There we considered the simple case of a single mass attached to a spring, damped by a force opposing the motion, and driven by an external oscillator of variable frequency. With relatively small damping and no driving force, the mass oscillates at its natural frequency with a slowly decreasing amplitude. The oscillations die out. When the driving force is applied, the mass always oscillates at the same frequency as the driving force, but its oscillation amplitude reaches a sharp maximum when the frequency of the applied force is equal to the oscillator's natural frequency. That is, energy is transferred from the driver to the oscillator at a maximum rate, and *resonance* is achieved, when the oscillator is driven at its natural frequency.

Now consider a string fixed at its ends. It has many natural frequencies of oscillation, not just one. It has, in fact, an infinite number of characteristic frequencies and characteristic, or normal, modes of oscillation. The resonant frequencies are given by Equation 39-20; they are the frequencies corre-sponding to the existence of standing waves. All oscillations of a string are, of course, damped, either by friction with the surrounding air or by internal friction arising from the stretching of the string. If a string is excited by an external driving force, for example, by variations in the air pressure from a sound wave, it may exhibit resonance; the oscillation amplitude will be large if the exciting frequency is one of the string's natural frequencies. Note that, although there exist an infinite number of resonant frequencies for a given string (corresponding to the infinite number of string particles), these frequencies are not distributed continuously, but rather are in the ratio of integers, as shown in Figure 39-19.

The fact that waves on a string, or other waves trapped between reflecting boundaries, have a set of discrete frequencies and characteristic modes of oscillation has important consequences in the quantum theory. Indeed, the stability and structure of atoms, molecules, and nuclei can be understood on the basis of the wave properties one must attribute to such particles as electrons, protons, and neutrons.

Example 5   A violin with a string 31.6 cm long, of linear density 0.65 gm/m, is placed near a loudspeaker fed by an audio-oscillator of variable frequency. It is found that as the frequency of the sound waves reaching the violin string is varied continuously over the range of 500 to 1500 cycles/sec, the string is set in oscillation only at the frequencies 880 and 1320 cycles/sec. What is the tension in the string?

The violin string, fixed at both ends, oscillates in resonance at its characteristic frequencies, which are in the ratio of the integers 1, 2, 3, ... The ratio of the resonance frequencies here is 1320/880 = 3/2. Therefore, the two resonances correspond to the string oscillating in its second and third harmonics. (If the two harmonics were, for example, the fourth and sixth, their ratio would again be 3/2, but one would then find, in addition, a resonance at the fifth harmonic, 1100 sec^{-1}.) Consequently, the fundamental, or first harmonic is 440 cycles/sec; this corresponds to "A" above "middle C" on the concert scale. The length of the string for this frequency is one half-wavelength:

$$L = \frac{\lambda}{2} = \frac{c}{2f} = \frac{\sqrt{F_t/\rho}}{2f}$$

$$F_t = 4f^2L^2\rho = 4(440 \text{ sec}^{-1})^2(0.316 \text{ m})^2(6.5 \times 10^{-4} \text{ kg/m}) = 50 \text{ nt}$$

39-11   Polarization   Up to this point we have assumed implicitly that, for a wave disturbance on a string, the displacements lie entirely within a single plane, any one particle oscillating *along a straight line*. Such a wave is said to be *linearly polarized;* the *plane of polarization* of a linearly polarized wave is that in which the oscillations take place. Through the superposition principle, a string can, of course, transmit two or more waves simultaneously with *different* planes of polarization. For this more general case, the superposition principle requires that the resultant displacement of a particle on a string be the *vector* sum, rather than the algebraic sum, of the displacements arising from the separate wave disturbances. Any *transverse* wave—one in which the wave disturbance is at right angles to the wave's direction of propagation—exhibits *polarization*. Of great importance for light and other forms of electromagnetic radiation, the fundamental polarization effects are simply illustrated for transverse waves on a string.

Figure 39-24 shows two linearly polarized waves with perpendicular planes of polarization propagated simultaneously along a string. For simplicity, the two waves are assumed to have the same amplitude and frequency, one wave being produced by simple harmonic oscillations along the

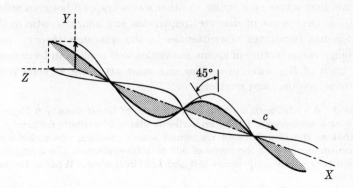

Figure 39-24. Superposition of two linearly polarized waves generated by oscillators in phase.

Y-axis and the other wave by oscillations along the Z-axis *in phase* with the first. Except for the plane of polarization, the two waves are identical. We find the resultant displacement at any point along the X-axis, the direction of propagation, by summing the Y- and Z-components as vectors. Thus, the two oscillations are equivalent to a single oscillation at an angle of 45° between the positive Y- and Z-axes, and the resultant wave disturbance consists of a linearly polarized wave whose plane of polarization lies at 45° between the XY- and XZ-planes.

Now suppose that the two component oscillators are *not* in phase, but differ by 90°, as given by

$$y = A \sin \omega t$$
$$z = A \cos \omega t$$

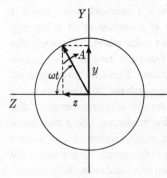

We recognize these equations as the component equations for uniform circular motion in the YZ-plane at the angular frequency ω in the clockwise sense (when viewed from the positive X-axis); see Figure 39-25. The string's end then moves in a circle of radius A at the angular frequency ω. So does every other particle of the string. As in every wave disturbance, the phase at a more distant point is delayed relative to the phase at $x = 0$. Thus, at any instant the form of the string is a *helix*, as shown in Figure 39-26. As time goes on, the helix turns in the clockwise sense,

Figure 39-25. Uniform circular motion in the YZ plane is equivalent to simple harmonic oscillations along Y and Z out of phase by 90°.

as viewed looking from the positive X-axis *toward* the origin. Any particle on the string moves in uniform clockwise circular motion, and the wave is said to be a *right circularly polarized* wave. A left circularly polarized wave corresponds to rotation in the opposite sense.

The most general sort of wave disturbance on a string always may be resolved into two mutually perpendicular disturbances, such as $y(x, t)$ and $z(x, t)$; that is, *any* wave disturbance, not merely a circularly polarized wave, may be regarded as the superposition of linearly polarized waves in the XY- and XZ-planes.

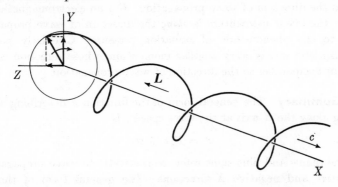

Figure 39-26. A circularly polarized wave.

A wave on a string transmits energy. Such a wave also transmits *transverse* linear momentum, since the particles of the string are in motion in the transverse direction, and the wave can exert a transverse force on an absorber. A *circularly polarized* wave *transmits angular momentum* from the wave source to a more distant point, and such a wave impinging on an absorber can impart a torque, or twist, to the absorber. For the so-called right (or clockwise) circularly polarized wave of Figure 39-26, the angular momentum vector, $L = r \times mv$, points in a direction opposite to that of wave motion. If the two linearly polarized oscillators of Figure 39-25 were 90° out of phase in the opposite sense, the particles of the string would move in circular motion in the counterclockwise sense. Then the wave disturbance would be a left circularly polarized wave, and the angular momentum vector would point in the same direction as that of wave propagation.

For Y and Z oscillators of the same frequency, 90° out of phase, but of *unequal* amplitudes, each particle of the string moves in an ellipse, with its symmetry axis along Y or Z. The wave is then said to be *elliptically* polarized. Elliptical polarization may be produced as well with Y and Z oscillators out of phase by an angle different from 90°. Then the axis of the ellipse is inclined relative to Y or Z.

There are two ways in which one can transmit energy, linear momentum, and angular momentum from one point in space to a second point: (a) by a particle that moves directly from the first to the second point, and carries with it energy and linear and angular momentum, and (b) by a transverse wave, in which no single particle moves along the line connecting the first and second point, but which transmits energy and linear and angular momentum equally well through the coupling of the particles of the medium. Electromagnetic waves are transverse waves in the sense that the electric and magnetic fields which comprise the wave disturbance oscillate at right angles to the direction of wave propagation. For an electromagnetic wave, however, the linear momentum is *along* the direction of wave propagation, leading to the phenomenon of radiation pressure. Circularly polarized electromagnetic waves carry angular momentum, whose direction is either parallel or antiparallel to the direction of wave propagation.

39-12 Summary The general form of the function F describing a wave, traveling along the X-axis at the wave speed c is

[39-2] $$F = F(x \mp ct)$$

where the minus and plus signs refer, respectively, to wave propagation in the positive and negative X-directions. The general form of the wave equation is

[39-6] $$\frac{\partial^2 F}{\partial x^2} = \frac{1}{c^2} \cdot \frac{\partial^2 F}{\partial t^2}$$

For a transverse wave on a stretched uniform string the wave function F is the transverse displacement y, and the wave speed is

[39-1] $$c = \sqrt{F_t/\rho}$$

where F_t is the tension in the string and ρ is its linear density.

A sinusoidal wave, generated by a simple harmonic oscillator of amplitude A, angular frequency ω, and period T, and traveling along the positive X-axis, may be represented in any of the following equivalent forms:

[39-8] $$y = A \sin (\omega t - kx)$$

[39-10] $$y = A \sin 2\pi\left(\frac{t}{T} - \frac{x}{\lambda}\right)$$

[39-13] $$y = -A \sin k(x - ct)$$

where the wavelength λ, the distance between two nearest points in the same phase, is related to the wave number k by $k = 2\pi/\lambda$. The product of the frequency f and wavelength λ is a constant, c, the phase speed.

[39-12] $$c = f\lambda$$

A transverse wave on a string carries energy, the time rate of the energy, or the power, of a sinusoidal wave being given by

[39-14] $$P = \tfrac{1}{2}\omega^2 A^2 \rho c$$

The superposition principle governs in situations in which waves interfere: the resultant wave disturbance is simply the vector sum of the component disturbances. There are no wave-wave interactions. Superposition of transverse waves on a string requires that the transverse displacements be small. Constructive and destructive interference refer, respectively, to situations in which the resultant disturbance is greater than or less than the component disturbances. At a boundary, or change in medium for wave propagation, the incident wave is partially transmitted and partially reflected. Reflection from a more massive second medium results in a 180° change; reflection from a less massive second medium produces no phase change.

Two examples of wave interference are beats with an amplitude beat frequency of $|f_1 - f_2|$ and standing waves which, for a string of length L fixed at both ends, leads to the allowed frequencies $nc/2L$.

When all parts of a string transmitting a wave oscillate in a single plane, the wave is said to be linearly polarized. A wave in which every particle of the string undergoes transverse uniform circular motion and the shape of the string at any instant is a helix, is said to be circularly polarized. A circularly polarized wave carries angular momentum in the direction of wave propagation or in the opposite direction.

PROBLEMS

39-1 A string under a tension of 10 nt is to generate a wave traveling at the speed of 4.0 m/sec. What must be the string's linear density?

39-2 The leading edge of a wave pulse on a string has a slope of 0.010. The wave speed is 5.0 m/sec. What is the transverse particle speed at the leading edge of the pulse?

39-3 A flexible wire made of material having a volume density ρ_v and Young's modulus Y is stretched so that its length, originally L, is increased by ΔL. Show that the speed of a transverse wave along the stretched wire is given by $\sqrt{Y \, \Delta L/\rho_v L}$. Note that if one were to measure the wave speed along a stretched wire of known ρ_v, Y, and L, one could, using this relation, compute the elongation.

39-4 A traveling wave is described by the equation

$$y = \exp\left\{ -az^2 - bt^2 - 2\sqrt{ab}\, zt \right\}$$

(a) In what direction is the wave traveling? (b) What is the wave speed?

39-5   A uniform rope 10 m long and having a weight of 25 nt hangs vertically
under its own weight. What is the speed of a transverse pulse at (a)
the midpoint of the rope and (b) a point close to the upper end?

39-6   A rope hangs vertically under its own weight. Show that the wave
speed at a distance y from the lower end is given by $\sqrt{gy}$. Note that
the wave speed is independent of the rope's linear density; hence,
this relation applies even if the rope is *not* uniform.

39-7   Figure 39-27 shows a snapshot of the wave shape $y(x)$ at one instant of
a pulse's traveling to the left. Sketch curves showing the transverse

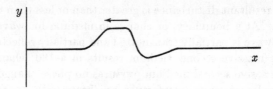

Figure 39-27

(a) displacement, (b) velocity, and (c) acceleration, all as a function of
time.

39-8 ★ Show that the total transverse linear momentum carried by *any* wave
pulse (a disturbance in which the transverse displacement is zero at
both the leading and trailing edges) is zero.

39-9   Transverse waves may travel in two dimensions along the surface of a
flexible membrane under tension. Show that the wave speed of such
waves is given by $\sqrt{T/\sigma}$, where T is the surface tension (Section 18-2)
of the membrane and σ is its areal density (mass per unit area). (*Hint:*
Consider the membrane to be in uniform motion between a pair of
curved but parallel plates, and use arguments like those in Section
39-1.)

39-10   Two wave pulses traveling in opposite directions completely annul
each other at one instant. What has become of the energy carried by
each wave pulse?

39-11   A wave pulse is propagated along a string having both ends fixed.
Draw curves, in the fashion of Figures 39-8b and 39-9b, for the waves
traveling continuously to the left and right and existing as virtual
waves beyond the string ends. Show that the periodicity in space of
both of the traveling wave forms is $2L$.

39-12   A traveling transverse wave is described by the equation

$$y = (0.0030) \cos (20x + 200t)$$

where y and x are in meters and t is in seconds. Find (a) the wave
speed, (b) the wavelength, (c) the frequency, (d) the amplitude, and
(e) the transverse particle speed at $x = \pi/10$ m and $t = \pi/400$ sec.

39-13   Figure 39-28 shows a sinusoidal traveling wave for three different
times. What are (a) the (minimum) wave speed, (b) the amplitude,
(c) the frequency, and (d) the wavelength? (e) In what direction does
the wave travel? (f) Write an equation for this traveling wave.

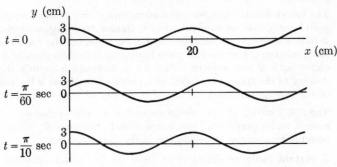

Figure 39-28

39-14   The transverse displacement at a certain crest of a sinusoidal wave is
4.00 mm. The nearest point from this crest having a displacement of
2.00 mm is 3.00 cm from the first at the same instant of time. What is
the wavelength?

39-15   A requirement for the applicability of the superposition principle is
that the wave speed be large compared with the transverse speed of a
particle. Show that, for a sinusoidal wave, this requirement implies
that the amplitude be small compared with the wavelength.

39-16   A sinusoidal wave carrying a power of 0.10 w is to be produced by a
harmonic oscillator, with an amplitude of 0.50 mm, attached to a
string of linear density 0.040 kg/m and under 100 nt of tension. What
is the frequency of the oscillator?

39-17   A simple harmonic oscillator with an amplitude of 3.0 mm and
frequency of 400 cycles/sec generates a sinusoidal wave along a string
with a linear density of 20 gm/m and under a tension of 200 nt. (a)
What is the power of the traveling wave? (b) What is the power of the
wave when the frequency is increased to 4000 cycles/sec, the amplitude
unchanged?

39-18   A sinusoidal wave on a string encounters a boundary with a second
string of different linear density. The reflected wave has half the
amplitude of the incident wave. What fraction of the incident power
is transmitted into the second string?

39-19 ⋆ Two strings with linear densities ρ_1 and ρ_2 are joined together and are
under the same tension. (a) If a wave has a wavelength of 2.0 cm in
string *1*, what is the wavelength in string *2*? (b) If the frequency is
100 sec^{-1} in string *1*, what is the frequency in string *2*? (c) If the
amplitude of a wave incident on the boundary from string *1* is 4.0 mm
and the transmitted wave in string *2* has an amplitude of 2.0 mm,
what is the amplitude of the reflected wave?

39-20   As Figure 39-14b shows, a traveling square wave is closely approximated by superposing sine waves of frequencies f, $3f$, and $5f$ with relative amplitudes of 1, 1/3, and 1/5, respectively. What is the relative power carried by the three component sinusoidal waves?

39-21   The linear density of a certain nonuniform string changes so gradually with length that an incident wave is transmitted without reflection as it passes along the nonuniform string, even though the wave speed and shape change. A sinusoidal wave having an initial amplitude A travels along such a nonuniform string for a distance in which the linear density of the string is reduced by a factor of 4. What is the amplitude of the emerging wave? (*Hint:* The energy of the wave is constant.)

39-22   The "A" string of one violin oscillates at 440 cycles/sec. When a second violin plays "A," one hears 5 beats per second. What are the possible frequencies of oscillation of the second string?

39-23   A certain radio oscillator is to have its frequency adjusted to one megacycle/sec to within 0.1 per cent by comparison with a standard oscillator having a frequency of exactly one megacycle/sec. What is the minimum permissible beat frequency between the two oscillators?

39-24   Two transverse sinusoidal waves of frequencies 20 sec^{-1} and 22 sec^{-1} are propagated simultaneously along a string for which the wave speed is 10 m/sec. What is the distance between adjacent maxima in the envelope of the resultant wave pattern?

39-25 ★   Simple harmonic motion may be represented as the projection along a diameter of a vector A_1 rotating at the constant angular speed ω_1. If a particle undergoes simultaneously two simple harmonic motions, one may represent the resultant displacement as the projection along a line passing through the origin of the vector sum of two vectors A_1 and A_2 rotating at frequencies ω_1 and ω_2, respectively, about a common origin. Assuming $\omega_2 > \omega_1$, show that the number of beats per second is given by the number of times per second that rotating vector A_2 overtakes vector A_1.

39-26   A wire with a linear density of 10 gm/m and under a tension of 36 nt is to resonate in its fundamental mode at a frequency of 200 sec^{-1}. What must be the distance between the two fixed ends of the wire?

39-27   When attached at both ends, a certain string under a tension of 450 nt and having a linear density of 0.050 gm/cm is resonant at the frequency of 420 sec^{-1}. The next highest frequency at which it resonates is 490 sec^{-1}. What is the string's length?

39-28   In an arrangement like that shown in Figure 39-18, a tuning fork oscillating at a frequency of 1000 cycles/sec causes six half-wavelength segments to be fitted in the 3.0 m between the ends of the string. A mass of 1.0 kg hangs from the pulley. What mass must be hung from the pulley to yield a pattern with seven segments?

39-29   A piano string is wound with wire so that its linear density is quadrupled. By what factor are the characteristic oscillation frequencies of the string decreased?

39-30   A string fastened at both ends is to be resonant with wavelengths of 0.64 m and of 0.72 m. What is the minimum string length?

39-31   A string fixed at its ends oscillates in the normal modes corresponding to its first and third harmonics. Both modes have the same amplitude. Sketch the resultant wave pattern for several instants of time in the fashion of Figure 39-21.

39-32   Confirm by direct substitution that Equation 39-19, giving $y(x, t)$ for a standing wave, is a solution of the general wave equation, Equation 39-6.

39-33   A string has one end fixed and is attached at its other end to a second string whose linear density is much less than that of the first string. (a) Draw the allowed standing-wave patterns in the first string, imposing the requirement that the boundary between the two strings occur at a loop while the fixed end is a node in the standing-wave pattern. (b) What are the allowed frequencies of the resonating string in terms of its length L and wave speed c?

39-34   A string attached at both ends is pulled aside at its center and then released. What harmonics are expected to be present in the ensuing oscillations? (Note that, because the string initially has its largest displacement at the midpoint, those modes having nodes at the midpoint of the string will not be excited.)

39-35   A violin string is tightened so that its tension increases by 20 per cent. By what factor is the fundamental resonant frequency increased?

39-36 ★ The temperature of a wire, initially stretched an amount ΔL over its unstretched length L_0 and fixed at both ends, is changed by Δt. The wire's linear coefficient of thermal expansion is α and its stretch modulus (Young's modulus) is Y. Show that the ratio of the fundamental frequency of the oscillating wire at the lower temperature to that at the higher temperature is $\left[1 + \dfrac{\alpha\,\Delta t L_0}{\Delta L} \right]^{1/2}$.

39-37   An oscillating string is damped by a force which is proportional to the transverse velocity of the string. Show that the higher-frequency modes of a struck or plucked string are damped out more rapidly than the fundamental. (This effect can be heard, particularly in bass notes of stringed instruments: the tone quality changes with time, the fundamental becoming relatively more important as the overtones are quickly damped.)

39-38   The following sets of equations for $y(t)$ and $z(t)$ describe the transverse oscillations at one point of a string: (a) $y = -A \cos \omega t$, $z = A \sin \omega t$; (b) $y = A \sin \omega t$, $z = B \cos \omega t$; (c) $y = A \cos \omega t$, $z = A \cos \omega t$; (d) $y = A \sin \omega t$, $z = A \sin (\omega t + \pi/6)$; (e) $y = A \sin \omega t$, $z = B \sin (\omega t + \pi/6)$. Describe the nature of the polarization of the wave generated in each case.

39-39 ⋆ Show that when a right circularly polarized wave is reflected from an infinitely massive boundary, the reflected wave is a *left* circularly polarized wave traveling in the opposite direction.

39-40 A point along a string is moved transversely in uniform circular motion centered about the equilibrium position of the string, thereby generating waves traveling in opposite directions along the string. What is the total (vector) angular momentum of the waves?

39-41 Show that the angular momentum associated with a circularly polarized wave is *spin* angular momentum rather than orbital angular momentum, because the angular momentum of the wave is independent of the choice of an axis for computing angular momentum.

39-42 Show that any linearly polarized wave may be regarded as the superposition of left and right circularly polarized waves in phase and having equal amplitudes and frequencies.

39-43 A right circularly polarized wave interferes with a right circularly polarized wave of the same amplitude and wavelength traveling in the opposite direction. (a) What is the resultant polarization of the wave? (b) What is the resultant polarization, if the second is *left* circularly polarized?

39-44 ⋆ Show that the power of a circularly polarized wave is given by $4\pi^2f^2A^2\rho c$, where A is the radius of the circle and the other symbols have their usual meanings.

39-45 ⋆ Show that the rate of transfer of angular momentum along the direction of propagation of a circularly polarized wave is given by $dL/dt = \omega A^2\rho c$. (*Hint:* The magnitude of the angular momentum of a particle of mass m relative to its undisplaced position is, from the definition of angular momentum, Equation 15-1, $L = r \times mv$, given by $mAv = mA^2\omega$, where A is the radius of the circle in which it moves and ω is its angular frequency.)

FORTY

ELASTIC WAVES

This chapter deals with longitudinal, or compressional, elastic waves through a solid, liquid, or gas. There is a close parallel between the wave characteristics, developed in the last chapter, for transverse waves on a stretched string and those for longitudinal waves. Happily, all of the phenomena (except polarization) discussed earlier—superposition, reflection, standing waves, resonance—apply, essentially without modification, to compressional waves. The chief difference is this: the property describing the wave disturbance is now not a transverse displacement, but rather a longitudinal displacement, a density variation or a pressure variation.

After considering some general properties of longitudinal waves, we derive formulas for compressional wave speeds through solids, liquids, and ideal gases. Then we treat other phenomena directly analogous to those discussed earlier for transverse waves. We derive an expression for the intensity of an elastic wave. We treat briefly other types of mechanical waves: transverse waves in a solid, torsional waves, bending waves on a rod, surface waves on a stretched membrane, and surface waves on a liquid. Finally, some elementary aspects of sound and acoustics are discussed.

40-1 Longitudinal waves Figure 40-1 shows a simple structure for propagating longitudinal elastic waves. Here a number of identical masses are coupled together by springs to form a chain. Each spring is assumed to follow Hooke's law for small elongations or compressions. The equilibrium position of each mass is that for which the resultant force on it is zero.

When any one mass is displaced longitudinally, the springs attached to it are stretched or compressed; these deformations not only produce a force on the displaced mass but also on the neighboring masses. Thus, neighboring masses are set in motion and, when the mass at the left end of the chain is suddenly displaced to the right, a compressional disturbance is found to be

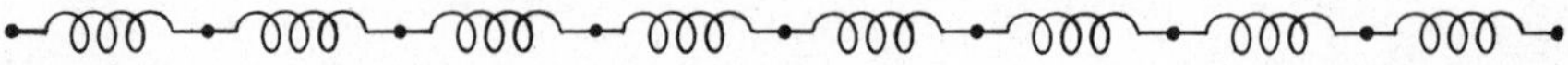

Figure 40-1. A simple model for longitudinal waves.

propagated to the right along the chain. Each mass undergoes, in turn, a longitudinal displacement and then returns to its equilibrium position, as a *longitudinal*, or *compressional*, wave travels along the chain. Energy is transported longitudinally—along the line of the mass's motion—as the kinetic energy of the masses and the elastic potential energy of the deformed springs. In addition, a traveling longitudinal wave carries linear momentum *along* the direction of wave propagation. (Recall that a transverse wave on a stretched string carries linear momentum at right angles to the direction of energy propagation.) Longitudinal waves do not, of course, exhibit polarization effects; these occur only for transverse waves.

The essential condition for the existence of longitudinal waves is that the *medium*, in this case the chain of masses and springs, possess *inertia* and be *elastically deformable*. Clearly, if there were no coupling between masses (if the springs were infinitely weak), displacing one mass would not influence neighboring springs or masses, and a wave would not be produced. On the other hand, if the medium were perfectly rigid (if the springs were infinitely stiff), displacing one mass would cause *all* of the other masses to be displaced *simultaneously*. Again, a wave traveling at finite speed would not be produced. With an elastic medium, however, an external force initially deforms and sets in motion only a portion of the medium, and this deformed portion, through its coupling with adjoining portions, sets them in motion.

For simplicity, suppose that one end of the chain in Figure 40-1 is moved longitudinally in simple harmonic motion. All of the masses will eventually be set in simple harmonic motion with the same amplitude and frequency as that of the source, each oscillating mass having a phase lag relative to the source which is proportional to its distance from it. Thus, we have a longitudinal sinusoidal wave. How do we represent such a wave graphically and describe it analytically?

The coordinate x gives the equilibrium location of each mass in the chain relative to, say, the left end. Let us use y to represent the *longitudinal* displacement of a particle from *its* equilibrium position along the X-axis, the direction of wave propagation. Figure 40-2a shows the Y-displacements of the particles along the chain, and Figure 40-2b is a plot of y against x, both for a sinusoidal wave. Just as in the case of a transverse wave propagated along a stretched string, the function $y(x)$ for any given time t is a sinusoidal wave. This wave shape travels to the right at the wave speed, or

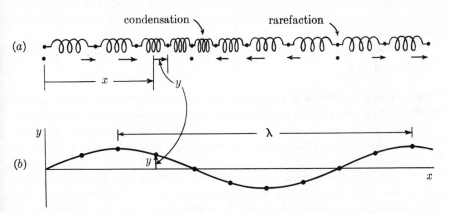

Figure 40-2. (a) A sinusoidal longitudinal wave. (b) The corresponding wave shape.

phase speed, c, and we may represent it analytically by any of the relations (Equations 39-8, 39-10, or 39-13) describing a traveling sinusoidal wave. For example,

[39-8a] $$y = A \sin (\omega t - kx)$$ [40-1]

where A is the longitudinal oscillation amplitude, $\omega = 2\pi f$, and $k = 2\pi/\lambda$. As before, the wavelength λ is the distance between adjoining oscillators having the same phase, and the phase velocity is given by $c = f\lambda$.

It must be emphasized that Figure 40-2b, which graphs the wave shape $y(x)$, is *not* a snapshot of the longitudinal wave at any instant, as was the case of a transverse wave on a string. We may, however, use exactly the same mathematical expressions to describe longitudinal waves, if it is understood that the particle displacement y is now a *longitudinal* displacement. The regions in Figure 40-2a (a snapshot) in which the particles are crowded together, the regions where the medium has its greatest density, are known as *condensations*. Regions in which the particles have their greatest relative separation, corresponding to points of minimum density, are called *rare-factions*. Rarefactions and condensations travel in the direction of wave propagation at the wave speed c. In fact, a longitudinal wave in a deformable medium may be described as a disturbance for which the propagated property, or wave function, is the density variation of the medium.

Our model for a longitudinal wave consists of discrete masses coupled by identical springs. A still simpler physical arrangement for longitudinal waves is that of a single long stretched helical spring. Here the mass is distributed continuously throughout the length of the spring, rather than concentrated in regularly spaced masses. The displacment y then gives the shift from its equilibrium position of any turn of the spring, and a longitudinal wave is seen as compressed or elongated segments traveling along the spring.

40-2 Longitudinal wave speeds We wish to derive the relation giving the speed of propagation of a longitudinal wave through an elastic medium in terms of the inertial and elastic properties of the medium.† We first restrict our considerations to waves traveling through a solid or liquid in one direction only.

We know that the molecules of a solid or liquid are subject to intermolecular forces which, for small displacements, obey Hooke's law, the intermolecular restoring force being proportional to the molecule's displacement from equilibrium position (Section 17-1). Consequently, macroscopic deformations of a solid or liquid also follow Hooke's law, the strain being proportional to the deforming stress. Thus, the simple model of masses and springs shown in Figure 40-1 represents quite faithfully the actual situation for a deformable solid or liquid. The discrete masses are now to be thought of as atoms or molecules, and the springs correspond to the interatomic or intermolecular forces, see Figure 40-3. Of course, for a three-dimensional medium any one molecule is coupled to *all* molecules that immediately surround it.

We imagine a continuous medium of undeformed density ρ to be confined inside a pipe of cross-sectional area S. A piston at the left end of the pipe is imagined to be displaced suddenly to the right, thereby compressing the medium immediately adjoining it and generating a compressional wave pulse; see Figure 40-4. For simplicity, we suppose that the piston has set all particles comprising the pulse (shown shaded) in motion to the right with the same longitudinal particle speed v (where $v = \partial y/\partial t$). Thus, after a time Δt has elapsed, the trailing edge of the wave pulse, which immediately adjoins the piston, has advanced a distance $v\,\Delta t$. During this same time

† The derivation here is similar to that given in small type at the end of Section 39-1 for transverse waves.

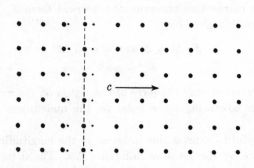

Figure 40-3. An elastic wave pulse traveling through a solid.

interval the leading edge of the wave pulse has advanced a distance $c \, \Delta t$, where c is the *wave* speed. (Note that $c > v$; that is, the wave speed exceeds the speeds of the particles.)

All of the material originally at rest within the volume $V = (c \, \Delta t)S$ and having an *undeformed* density ρ, now moves with the speed v. The mass of this material in motion is approximately $\rho V = \rho c S \, \Delta t$. Therefore, the change in momentum, $\Delta(mv)$, associated with the wave pulse is

$$\Delta(mv) = (\rho c S \, \Delta t) v$$

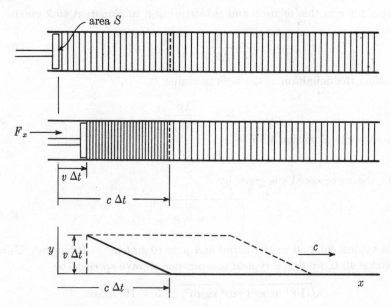

Figure 40-4. A wave pulse produced in an elastic medium.

By the impulse-momentum theorem, the average force F_x producing this momentum change is given by

$$F_x \, \Delta t = \Delta(mv) = \rho c v S \, \Delta t$$

$$F_x = \rho c v S \qquad [40\text{-}2]$$

The force F_x gives, not only the force of the piston on the medium, but also the force of the advancing wave pulse on the undeformed medium lying ahead of it.

It is more useful to express this in terms of the longitudinal stress F_x/S, which we denote by the pressure difference Δp. The delta symbol (Δ) is employed here to emphasize that the longitudinal stress, or pressure, is that arising from the wave disturbance and is in addition to any constant stress that may exist in the medium; equivalently, Δp represents the gauge pressure, not the absolute pressure. Then Equation 40-2 can be written:

$$\Delta p = \rho c v \qquad [40\text{-}3]$$

The undeformed volume of the wave pulse is $V = cS \, \Delta t$; the change in volume arising from the deformation is $\Delta V = -vS \, \Delta t$. The minus sign implies that a positive stress produces a compression, a *decrease* in volume. Then,

$$-\Delta V/V = v/c \qquad [40\text{-}4]$$

Solving for v in this relation and substituting it in Equation 40-3 yields

$$\frac{\Delta p}{-\Delta V/V} = \rho c^2 \qquad [40\text{-}5]$$

Recalling the definition of the bulk modulus B,

$$[17\text{-}6] \qquad B = \frac{\Delta p}{-\Delta V/V}$$

we may write Equation 40-5 as

$$B = \rho c^2$$

Thus, the wave speed c is given by

$$\boxed{c = \sqrt{B/\rho}} \qquad [40\text{-}6]$$

For a typical solid, $B \simeq 10^{11}$ nt/m^2 and $\rho \simeq 10$ gm/cm^3 $= 10^4$ kg/m^3. Using Equation 40-6, we find a typical compressional wave speed to be

$$\sqrt{(10^{11} \text{ nt/m}^2)/(10^4 \text{ kg/m}^3)} \simeq 3 \times 10^3 \text{ m/sec}$$

For a frequency of 10^3 sec^{-1}, the wavelength is 3 m.

A long solid rod will propagate a longitudinal wave when struck at one end. Equation 40-6 does not, however, apply for this situation. Young's modulus Y (Equation 17-4), which relates the rod's undeformed length L and change in length ΔL to the longitudinal stress Δp through the definition $Y = (\Delta p)/(-\Delta L/L)$, must be used. Here $V = LS$ and $\Delta V = (\Delta L)S$, so that the left side of Equation 40-5 is now the Young modulus. Then the wave speed is given by

$$c = \sqrt{Y/\rho} \qquad\qquad\qquad [40\text{-}7]$$

When a long rod is stretched, its cross-sectional area is reduced, and conversely. Thus, a compressional wave along a rod is manifest, not only in longitudinal deformations and changes in density, but also in transverse deformations of the rod. Therefore, such a wave can be generated by stroking the rod to induce the transverse deformations as well as by striking the rod at its end.

Equations 40-6 and 40-7 are of the general form:

$$\text{wave speed} = \sqrt{\text{elastic property/inertial property}}$$

All types of mechanical waves follow a relation of this type. It is illustrated, not only by Equations 40-6 and 40-7, but also by our earlier formula $c = \sqrt{F_t/\rho}$ (Equation 39-1), for the wave speed of a transverse wave on a stretched string, where the elastic and inertial properties are, respectively, the string's tension and linear density.

As Figure 40-4 shows, the particle speed v is less than the wave speed c. Indeed, a requirement for propagation of waves at a constant speed, independent of the particular wave "shape," is $v \ll c$. Let us prove it. Hooke's law describes deformations only when the elastic parameters (B or Y) are truly constants; this requires that the deformations be small. Equation 40-4 shows that the relative deformation $\Delta V/V$ is small only if $v/c \ll 1$, or $v \ll c$. This inequality must also be fulfilled if the principle of superposition is to apply to compressional waves. One can, of course, conceive of situations in which the particle speed is comparable to or exceeds the wave speed. For example, suppose that the piston of Figure 40-4 is moved to the right at a greater speed than c. The disturbance is then a so-called shock wave (Section 42-5). Its shape changes as the disturbance spreads through the medium; it is not, therefore, a wave in the strict sense.

Although we have restricted our treatment to elastic waves traveling in a single direction in a deformable medium, it is possible for a number of longitudinal waves, traveling in various directions in three dimensions, to exist simultaneously within a solid (in addition, there are the transverse elastic waves to be discussed in Section 40-7). Such a collection of elastic waves, having a broad range of frequencies and traveling in random directions, corresponds to (most) of the thermal-energy content of a solid (electrons make a minor contribution). Heretofore (Section 23-1), we spoke of the internal thermal energy of a solid or liquid as consisting (mainly) in the kinetic and potential energies of the atoms of a solid undergoing disordered oscillations. When any one atom oscillates, it causes neighboring atoms to oscillate as well, thereby transferring disordered, or thermal, energy to, and receiving such energy from, neighboring atoms. Now we can describe this situation in a different but equivalent way. When any one atom oscillates (typically with $f \simeq 10^{13} \sec^{-1}$), it generates elastic waves ($\lambda \simeq 3 \times 10^{-10}$ m) through the solid, and the *thermal energy* of the material may be said to consist of the *energy carried by elastic waves traveling in the solid*. Thermal waves, although they may have frequencies extending into the usual range of audible sound and are, in fact, acoustic waves, have such low amplitude as actually to be inaudible. When a solid undergoes a macroscopic deformation that generates an elastic wave, this wave is superposed on the ever-present thermal elastic waves.

40-3 Waves through a gas Elastic waves through a gas are, of course, responsible for sounds that reach the ear. What is the wave speed through an ideal gas? Clearly, here we do not have a collection of particles coupled together in the fashion of the molecules of a solid or liquid. The molecules are in random thermal motion, interacting only during collisions. There are no elastic forces acting constantly. But, if one portion of a gas is suddenly compressed, and gas molecules are thereby crowded together in a condensation, the molecules will, because of the higher pressure, tend to move to adjoining portions of the gas where the pressure and density are lower. A compressional wave for a gas, then, corresponds to density changes, in exactly the same fashion as for solids and liquids, superposed on the random molecular motion. We may apply Equation 40-6

$$[40\text{-}6] \qquad\qquad c = \sqrt{B/\rho} \qquad\qquad [40\text{-}8]$$

to find the wave speed through a gas, provided that the bulk modulus B is that appropriate for an ideal gas, one following the relation

$$[20\text{-}7] \qquad\qquad pV = nRT$$

where p is the pressure (in the absence of a wave), V the gas volume, n the number of moles, R the general-gas constant, and T is the absolute temperature.

A gas may be compressed in a number of ways. For example, it may be compressed isothermally, in which case thermal energy must be extracted from the gas to maintain its temperature constant. Or, it may be compressed adiabatically, in which case the temperature rises upon compression because no thermal energy may leave the gas. Still other more complicated processes can take place. For sound waves through a gas—waves having frequencies in the audible range, roughly 20 to 20,000 vibrations per second—the compressions and expansions are essentially adiabatic. That is to say, the oscillations in gas density take place so rapidly, and the thermal conductivity of the gas is so low, that there is not enough time for the thermal energy to flow from a condensation to a rarefaction, from a region of high density and temperature to one of low density and temperature. To compute the speed of sound waves through an ideal gas we must use the bulk modulus $B = \Delta p/(-\Delta V/V)$ under *adiabatic* conditions.

An adiabatic process for an ideal gas is described by the relation

[21-23] $pV^\gamma = K$ [40-9]

where $\gamma = C_p/C_v$, the ratio of the specific heats at constant pressure and volume, and $K = $ a constant. Taking the differential of Equation 40-9 yields

$$(\Delta p)V^\gamma + \gamma p V^{\gamma-1}\,\Delta V = 0$$

$$\frac{\Delta p}{-\Delta V/V} = \gamma p$$

Thus, the adiabatic bulk modulus B for a gas is γp, and Equation 40-8 becomes

$$c = \sqrt{\gamma p/\rho} \qquad\qquad [40\text{-}10]$$

Had the compressions been assumed isothermal, the bulk modulus would be found to be p, and the wave speed would then be given by $c = \sqrt{p/\rho}$.

Equation 40-10 may be written in another useful form by recognizing that the number of moles n is M/w, where M is the mass of gas and w is the atomic weight of the molecules, and that the density ρ is M/V. Then we have, using $p = nRT/V = MRT/wV$,

$$c = \sqrt{\frac{\gamma(MRT/wV)}{M/V}}$$

$$\boxed{c = \sqrt{\gamma RT/w}} \qquad\qquad [40\text{-}11]$$

The speed of sound through an ideal gas varies directly as the square root of the absolute temperature and inversely as the square root of the atomic weight (for an unchanged γ). For air at $0°$ C, $w = 28.8 \times 10^{-3}$ kg and $\gamma = 1.40$ (Section 21-7). Equation 40-11 then gives

$$c = \sqrt{\gamma RT/w} = \sqrt{(1.40)(8.31 \text{ joule/K}°)(273° \text{ K})/(28.8 \times 10^{-3} \text{ kg})}$$
$$= 331 \text{ m/sec} = 1{,}087 \text{ ft/sec} = 742 \text{ mi/hr}$$

The measured speed of sound through air at $0°$ C is 331 m/sec. Thus, the assumed adiabatic character of compressional waves through a gas is confirmed. As one would expect, the speed of sound through a gas is comparable to the rms speeds of the molecules (see Problem 40-13).

As Equation 40-11 shows, the speed of sound through a gas depends on the temperature, not the pressure. The wave speed does, however, depend on the type of gas; that is, c depends on the specific-heat ratio γ and on the molecular weight w. Since the ratio γ depends, in turn, upon whether the molecules of a gas undergo rotation and vibration (Section 21-7), and since a measurement of c for any gas permits γ to be computed, one may decide whether the molecules of a particular gas are in rotation or vibration or both, simply by measuring the speed of sound!

40-4   Pressure variations for elastic waves   We may write the equation for a traveling sinusoidal wave through a compressible medium as

[40-1] $$y = A \sin (\omega t - kx)$$

where it is understood that y gives the *longitudinal* displacements of the particles. For a gas, y would represent the displacement of a gas molecule arising from a wave. It is more meaningful, however, to describe a traveling wave through a gas in terms of the pressure variations Δp, particularly because it is pressure changes that are detected and measured for sound waves. Note that Δp gives the pressure *difference* arising from the wave motion.

From the definition of the bulk modulus B and Equation 40-4 we have

$$\Delta p = -B(\Delta V/V) = -B(v/c) \qquad \text{[40-12]}$$

We find the speed ratio v/c by examining the plot of y versus x in Figure 40-4. It is clear from this figure that the slope $\partial y/\partial x$ is equal to

$$\frac{\partial y}{\partial x} = \frac{v \, \Delta t}{c \, \Delta t - v \, \Delta t} \simeq v/c$$

since $v \ll c$. Then Equation 40-12 can be written

$$\Delta p = -B(\partial y/\partial x) \qquad \text{[40-13]}$$

From Equation 40-1 above,

$$\partial y/\partial x = -kA \cos (\omega t - kx)$$

and from Equation 40-6,

$$B = c^2\rho$$

Therefore, Equation 40-13 becomes

$$\Delta p = -c^2\rho kA \cos(\omega t - kx)$$

which we may write more simply as

$$\Delta p = -\Delta p_0 \cos(\omega t - kx) \qquad [40\text{-}14]$$

where

$$\Delta p_0 = c^2\rho kA = \omega A\rho c \qquad [40\text{-}15]$$

Equation 40-15 relates the pressure amplitude Δp_0 to the corresponding displacement amplitude A.

A compressional wave may be described as a displacement wave (following Equation 40-1) or a pressure wave (following Equation 40-14). We see

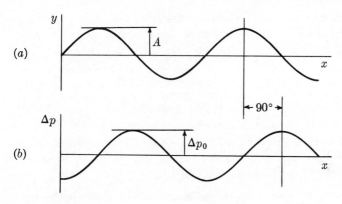

Figure 40-5. (a) Longitudinal displacements y and (b) the corresponding pressure variations Δp for a sinusoidal elastic wave.

that Δp depends upon the cosine of $\omega t - kx$, whereas y depends on its sine. Thus, the *pressure variations* are *90° out of phase* with respect to the *displacement variations*; that is, the pressure is greatest (and least) at those points where the particles undergo no displacement, as shown in Figure 40-5. This is evident also from Figure 40-2b, which shows that the condensations and rarefactions—the regions of respective maximum and minimum pressure (and density)—occur at those locations where the particles are momentarily at their equilibrium positions.

40-5 Intensity of a sound wave By the *intensity* of a sound wave or any sort of wave is meant the energy passing per unit time through a unit area oriented at right angles to the direction of wave propagation; that is, the intensity I is the power P of the wave per unit transverse area S:

$$I = P/S \qquad [40\text{-}16]$$

We recall that the power of a transverse wave on a string is given by

[39-14] $\qquad\qquad P = \tfrac{1}{2}\omega^2 A^2 \rho_l c \qquad\qquad [40\text{-}17]$

where ρ_l denotes the *linear* density of the string. Although derived originally for a transverse wave on a string, we may use this relation to find the intensity of a sound wave, provided we reinterpret the symbols in terms of longitudinal waves.

First, A must now represent the longitudinal oscillation amplitude. Dividing both sides of Equation 40-17 by the transverse area S yields

$$I = P/S = \tfrac{1}{2}\omega^2 A^2 (\rho_l/S)c \qquad [40\text{-}18]$$

The quantity ρ_l/S now represents the *volume* density ρ of the gas. From Equation 40-15, the displacement amplitude is given by $A = \Delta p_0/\omega\rho c$. Using this in Equation 40-18 gives

$$I = \tfrac{1}{2}\omega^2 (\Delta p_0/\omega\rho c)^2 \rho c$$

$$\boxed{I = \Delta p_0{}^2/2\rho c} \qquad [40\text{-}19]$$

The intensity is proportional to the *square* of the pressure difference. Surprisingly, perhaps, the intensity when written as in Equation 40-19, is *independent* of the frequency or wavelength.

Example 1   At 1000 cycles/sec the faintest sound detectable by the human ear and the loudest tolerable sound—the so-called "threshold of hearing" and the "threshold of feeling"—correspond to sound intensities of 10^{-16} w/cm^2 and 10^{-4} w/cm^2, respectively (the ear is remarkably sensitive over an enormous range of intensities). What are the pressure and displacement amplitudes of the sound waves for these extremes?

From Equation 40-19,

$$\Delta p_0 = \sqrt{2I\rho c}$$

Taking the density of air as 1.29 kg/m^3 and the speed of sound as 344 m/sec, we have, at the threshold of hearing, at which $I = 10^{-12}$ w/m^2,

$$\Delta p_0 = \sqrt{2(10^{-12} \text{ w/m}^2)(1.29 \text{ kg/m}^3)(344 \text{ m/sec})}$$

Hearing threshold: $\qquad = 3.0 \times 10^{-5}$ nt/m^2 = 3×10^{-10} atm

The intensity is 10^{12} times larger at the threshold of feeling, so that,

Feeling threshold: $\qquad \Delta p_0 = 30$ nt/m^2 = 3×10^{-4} atm

We find the corresponding displacement amplitudes at $f = 1000$ sec^{-1}, using Equation 40-15:

$$A = \Delta p_0/\omega\rho c = \Delta p_0/2\pi f\rho c$$

$$A = (3.0 \times 10^{-5}\text{ nt/m}^2)/(2\pi \times 10^3\text{ sec}^{-1})(1.29\text{ kg/m}^3)(344\text{ m/sec})$$

Hearing threshold: $A = 1.1 \times 10^{-11}$ m $= 0.11$ Å

Feeling threshold: $A = 1.1 \times 10^{-5}$ m

Note that the ear is so sensitive that it can detect oscillations corresponding to molecular displacements of less than one tenth of an atomic diameter, which is 100 times smaller than the molecular mean-free-path at atmospheric pressure. If it were just slightly more sensitive, the ear would "hear" thermal vibrations as noise.

40-6 Superposition, reflection, and standing waves The first thing to be said about superposition, reflection, and standing waves, as they apply to elastic waves, is that these phenomena are altogether similar to the corresponding effects found earlier in transverse waves on a stretched string. The wave property simply is different: now it is a longitudinal displacement, or a pressure or density change, rather than a transverse displacement.

The superposition principle for wave motion applies to compressional waves; that is, two or more wave disturbances propagated through the same medium yield a resultant wave disturbance according to the following rule: the separate longitudinal displacements at any time or place are added algebraically to give the resultant displacement. Thus, two wave pulses traveling in opposite directions pass through one another, each pulse emerging with unchanged shape. The rule is exactly that found for transverse waves on a string. Again, the superposition principle applies, however, only if the deformation of the medium is *linear*, that is, if the deformation is directly proportional to the deforming force. Two waves are said to interfere constructively when the displacement (or density or pressure) is enhanced by the superposition of the separate displacements, whereas destructive interference takes place when the two separate waves have displacements of opposite sign.

As in the case of the transverse wave on a string, compressional waves are reflected whenever the medium through which they travel changes. Inasmuch as the wave speed is controlled, according to Equations 40-6, 40-7, and 40-10, by the medium's inertia and elasticity, a change in the character of the medium implies a change in the wave speed. At a boundary, the following takes place: the wave is partially transmitted into the new medium, with a change in wave speed (and, for a sinusoidal wave, a change in the wavelength), and the wave is partially reflected back from the boundary. The energy originally carried by the incident wave is divided between the transmitted and the reflected waves.

Suppose that a deformable medium is terminated by an infinitely hard and massive second medium. The second medium is not deformable, and when a compressional wave reaches the boundary, the particles there cannot be displaced longitudinally. Therefore, a wave cannot be propagated into the second medium: the wave is completely reflected. In mathematical terms, since the boundary is infinitely hard, the longitudinal displacement y must be zero at the boundary. There is, therefore, a *displacement node* at the boundary between a deformable medium and a nondeformable medium. The boundary condition can equally well be given in terms of the compressional stress for a solid or liquid, or the pressure difference Δp for a compressional wave through a gas. We recall that the displacement and pressure variations are 90° out of phase for a traveling sinusoidal elastic wave. Thus, if the resultant displacement y is zero at the boundary, Δp must be a maximum at such a boundary. A *pressure loop*, or antinode, must exist at the boundary. This follows also from the fact that the particles will tend to pile up at the boundary, since the hard medium cannot be deformed, thereby producing a high density and pressure at this point. On the other hand, if the deformable medium is terminated with a less dense medium—for example, a solid terminated by air—so that no deformable medium adjoins the boundary, the displacement y will be a maximum, or loop, and the pressure Δp will be a minimum, or node, at this boundary. As before, a wave undergoes a 180° change in phase when reflected from a boundary leading to a second medium in which the wave speed is less, but no phase change occurs with waves traveling in the reverse direction.

Let us recall the circumstances under which a standing wave can exist in a medium propagating a wave disturbance. One has waves of the same wavelength traveling in opposite directions. The resultant disturbance consists of a standing wave, with displacement nodes and loops distributed alternately along the medium. Adjacent loops and adjacent nodes are separated by half-wavelengths. The standing waves may be thought of as a traveling wave trapped between two reflecting boundaries, the standing-wave pattern being such as fits the standing-wave segments properly at the boundaries. We can best see these ideas applied in specific examples.

Example 2   A sound wave is propagated through a pipe closed at one end. What are the allowed oscillation modes and characteristic frequencies?

The boundary conditions are as follows. At the closed end there is a displacement node or pressure loop; at the open end there is a displacement loop or pressure node. The allowed oscillation modes, or standing-wave patterns, are shown in Figure 40-6 (the actual displacement node lies somewhat beyond the open end of the pipe). Note particularly that the quantity plotted here is the longitudinal particle displacement y; if one were to plot the pressure variations along the tube, the loops and nodes would be reversed.

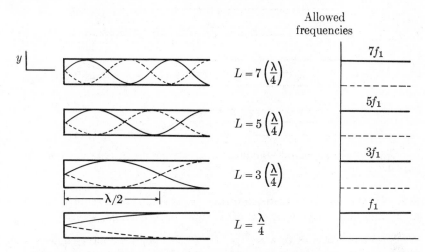

Figure 40-6. Allowed oscillation modes and characteristic frequencies for sound waves in a pipe closed at one end and open at the other. Note that the standing wave patterns the longitudinal displacements, rather than the pressure variations.

Clearly, the length L of the tube must always be an odd multiple of $\frac{1}{4}\lambda$; $L = n(\lambda/4)$, where $n = 1, 3, 5, \ldots$. The allowed frequencies are $f = c/\lambda = n(c/4L) = nf_1 = f_1, 3f_1, 5f_1, \ldots$. The overtones are harmonics of the fundamental frequency f_1, but only *odd* harmonics. There may, of course, be two or more characteristic oscillation modes existing simultaneously, and any disturbance persisting in time must consist of a superposition of allowed modes.

If the length of the closed pipe is 0.50 m, roughly the length of a clarinet, the fundamental frequency is

$$f_1 = c/4L = (344 \text{ m/sec})/4(0.50 \text{ m}) = 172 \text{ sec}^{-1}$$

roughly at the center of the audible range.

Figure 40-6 shows a number of standing-wave patterns for a pipe of fixed length. If one has a pipe of variable length, excited by a constant oscillation frequency, there are a number of tube lengths, as shown in Figure 40-7, which correspond to resonance between the tube and the sound source. The tube is set in resonance every time the length of the tube is increased by $\frac{1}{2}\lambda$. Knowing the exciting frequency f and finding the wavelength λ from two successive resonances, one can very easily compute the speed of sound through air by the relation $c = f\lambda$.

Example 3 A sound wave is propagated through a pipe open at both ends. What are its allowed oscillation modes and characteristic frequencies?

Now, the boundary conditions are these: a displacement loop, or pressure node, must exist at each of the two open ends. The allowed oscillation modes are shown in Figure 40-8. The tube length is always an integral multiple of $\frac{1}{2}\lambda$; the allowed frequencies consist of *all* harmonics of the fundamental.

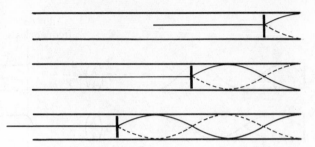

Figure 40-7. Resonant standing-wave patterns for a pipe of variable length.

40-7 Other types of mechanical waves

In this section we treat briefly and qualitatively several other types of mechanical waves.

TRANSVERSE WAVES IN A SOLID   Up to this point we have concentrated on longitudinal waves within a deformable medium. An elastic solid can, in addition, propagate transverse waves, the particles undergoing displacements at right angles to the direction of wave propagation; see Figure 40-9. Such a deformation in a solid involves a shearing of the material rather than a compression and change in density; therefore, the wave speed depends (in part) on the shear modulus (Section 17-2). Inasmuch as the elastic constants differ for transverse and longitudinal elastic waves, the two wave types propagate at *different* wave speeds. Typically, the transverse wave speed exceeds the longitudinal wave speed by a factor of 1.5 to 2.0.

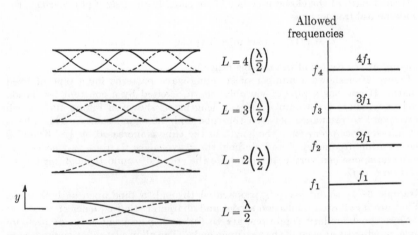

Figure 40-8. Allowed oscillation modes and characteristic frequencies of sound waves in a pipe open at both ends.

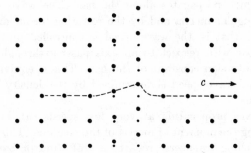

Figure 40-9. Particle displacements for a transverse elastic wave in a solid.

There are, in fact, *two* transverse waves possible for a given direction of propagation. If the wave progresses along X, then there may be transverse displacements in the YZ-plane both along Y and along Z. *Any* other transverse displacement can be resolved into displacements along these two directions. Thus, when an earthquake or tremor is produced within the Earth's crust, both a longitudinal wave and a transverse wave are produced; by virtue of the difference in the transverse and longitudinal wave speeds, their arrival at a distant point is registered on a seismograph at *different* times.

Transverse waves *cannot* be propagated through a nonviscous fluid, that is, through a perfect liquid or through a gas. These media are characterized by a zero shear modulus.

TORSIONAL WAVES Consider a deformable bar, as shown in Figure 40-10a, which has, through an applied twist or torque, undergone a rapid angular displacement at one end. The deformation is now an *angular*

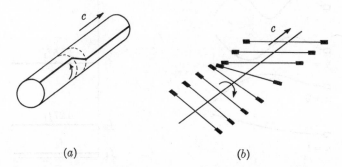

(a)   (b)

Figure 40-10. Torsional wave disturbances: (a) in a torsion rod and (b) in a band with transverse rods.

displacement which propagates along the bar. The wave speed is determined by the angular inertia and by the restoring torque arising from the elastic medium; that is, the wave speed is controlled by the moment of inertia of the bar with respect to an axis passing through its symmetry axis and by the torsion constant of the bar. This is equivalent to saying that the torsional wave speed is determined by the density of the bar and its shear modulus.

Torsional waves propagating at very low speeds can be produced by greatly increasing the moment of inertia of the medium. This can be accomplished by attaching transverse rods to a stiff band or bar, as shown in Figure 40-10b. Such a device is often used to demonstrate wave phenomena.

BENDING WAVES Consider a bar which is clamped at one end and deformed by bending, as in the case of the tines of a tuning fork. Waves will travel along the bar and be reflected both at the free and the attached ends. Standing-wave patterns are produced. It is significant, however, that the frequencies of the overtones are *not integral* multiples of the fundamental frequency; that is, the overtones are not harmonics of the fundamental. See Figure 40-11. This illustrates an important rule concerning the characteristic oscillation frequencies of a deformable object: although the characteristic frequencies can always be identified with standing-wave patterns involving the reflection of waves at boundaries, only in the simplest cases (for example, waves on a stretched string, compressional waves in a

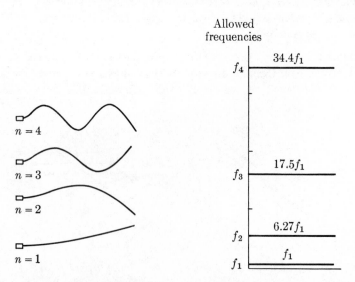

Figure 40-11. Allowed oscillation modes and characteristic frequencies of bending waves on a rod fixed at one end.

pipe) will the allowed frequencies be integral multiples of the fundamental. In general, the overtones are not harmonics.

WAVES ON A MEMBRANE   Consider a membrane under tension, such as a drumhead or a stretched rubber sheet. If some small portion of the membrane is displaced out of the equilibrium plane, then restoring forces will act on this patch to return it to the plane. Consequently, a transverse wave disturbance can be propagated along the surface of the membrane. The

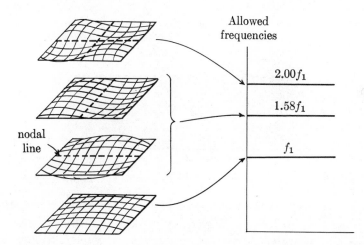

Figure 40-12. Allowed oscillation modes and characteristic frequencies for surface waves on a stretched rectangular membrane.

wave travels in any direction lying in the plane of the undisplaced membrane. If the membrane is bounded by clamped edges, the wave disturbance is reflected at these boundaries. Several allowed modes of oscillation and the corresponding characteristic frequencies are shown in Figure 40-12 for a square membrane. Note that again the allowed frequencies are not harmonic. We see, further, that two distinct oscillation modes have the *same* characteristic frequency. Such oscillations are said to be *degenerate*. For such a two-dimensional surface wave one speaks of the undisplaced portions of the membrane as *nodal lines*. With a different geometry at the membrane's boundaries—a clamped circular membrane, for example—the oscillation modes and frequencies are quite different.

SURFACE WAVES   Waves traveling along the surface of a liquid are perhaps the most familiar example of wave motion, and such waves are used frequently to demonstrate wave phenomena in a "ripple tank." Water waves are, in general, fairly complicated: the liquid is not compressed and the motion of the particles is neither entirely transverse nor longitudinal, as in other mechanical waves. The wave disturbance is influenced primarily by the difference in hydrostatic pressure, at a given horizontal level within the liquid, which arises when the liquid surface is displaced above or beneath the equilibrium level; see Figure 40-13. Surface waves are influenced to a lesser extent by the liquid's surface tension, which causes the surface to act as a membrane.

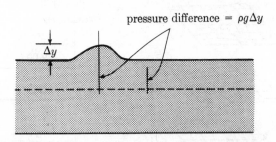

Figure 40-13. Disturbance giving rise to a wave at a liquid surface.

Analysis shows that the wave speed of water waves through a shallow liquid of depth h (with $h \ll \lambda$) is given by $c = \sqrt{gh}$, the speed decreasing as the depth is decreased. That the hydrostatic pressure difference Δp is responsible for surface wave propagation is seen by writing this relation as $c = \sqrt{\rho g h / \rho} = \sqrt{\Delta p / \rho}$, where ρ is the liquid density.

40-8 Sound and acoustics Mechanical vibrations over the audible frequency range, from 20 to 20,000 cycles/sec (a factor of 10^3), and with intensities lying between 10^{-16} and 10^{-4} w/cm², are perceived by a typical human ear as sound. (The eye detects electromagnetic vibrations only over a frequency range of factor 2.) Nonperiodic variations in the air pressure correspond to noise. The ear finds sinusoidal oscillations to be more pleasant. Indeed, simultaneous oscillations at different frequencies in the ratios of simple integers are recognized as musical tones.

By the *pitch* of a musical tone is meant the lowest, or fundamental, frequency. The relation of pitch to fundamental frequency is not precise, however, since an oscillation of unchanged frequency but increasing intensity appears to go "flat." The *loudness* of the tone is a measure of the sound intensity. The tonal *quality*, by which the ear can distinguish, for example, between a violin and a clarinet playing the same note, is a measure of the relative amplitudes of the overtones excited simultaneously with the fundamental oscillation.

Musical instruments usually involve arrangements whereby the characteristic overtones are harmonics, or integral multiples of the fundamental frequency. This is illustrated by oscillating strings in string instruments and oscillating air columns in pipes, such as in the woodwind and brass instruments. Since the wavelength of sound through air at 400 cycles/sec, roughly the center of the audible range, is about 0.8 m, wind instruments are expected to be, and are found to be, roughly this size.

The acoustic spectrum is shown in Figure 40-14. Note that frequencies alone are given; the wavelengths depend on the medium—that is, on the wave speed—through which the elastic vibrations travel.

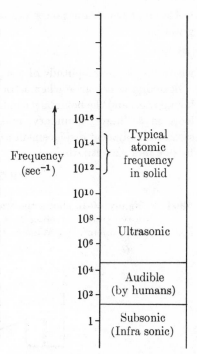

Figure 40-14. The acoustic spectrum.

40-9 Summary In a longitudinal wave disturbance the particles oscillate along the same direction as that in which the energy and linear momentum of the wave travel. The superposition principle applies when the elastic deformations follow Hooke's law.

The wave speeds of longitudinal waves through a solid or liquid, a long solid bar, and an ideal gas are given, respectively, by

[40-6]   Solid or liquid: $c = \sqrt{B/\rho}$

[40-7]   Long solid bar: $c = \sqrt{Y/\rho}$

[40-10], [40-11]   Ideal gas: $c = \sqrt{\gamma p/\rho} = \sqrt{\gamma RT/w}$

where B is the bulk modulus, Y is Young's modulus, ρ is the density, p is the pressure, γ is the specific heat ratio, T is the absolute temperature, and w is the atomic weight. Solids can also propagate transverse and torsional waves.

The pressure variations for a longitudinal wave through a compressible medium are 90° out of phase with the longitudinal particle displacement.

The intensity I, the power per unit transverse area, of an elastic wave is given by

[40-19] $$I = \Delta p_0{}^2/2\rho c$$

where Δp_0 is the amplitude of the pressure difference.

Standing waves arise when a traveling wave is trapped between reflecting boundaries, and the boundary conditions—a displacement node, or a pressure loop, at a "hard" boundary, and the reverse at a "soft" boundary—are satisfied. Adjacent displacement and pressure nodes and loops are separated by one half-wavelength.

PROBLEMS

40-1   Figure 40-15 shows the wave shape at one instant for a longitudinal wave pulse traveling at 4.0×10^3 m/sec through a solid of density 8.0 gm/cm^3. (a) What is the longitudinal particle speed at the wave

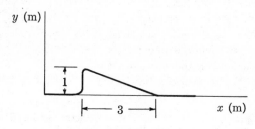

Figure 40-15

pulse? (b) What change in pressure is associated with this pulse? (c) By what fraction is the density of the solid changed at the pulse?

40-2   For a certain longitudinal wave, the particle speed at a wave pulse is 0.10 of the wave speed. By what factor is the density of the material increased or decreased at the pulse?

40-3 ★ Consider the structure of Figure 40-1. The particles, each of mass m, are separated by L, where L is the relaxed length of each spring of force constant k. Show that the longitudinal wave speed is $L(k/m)^{1/2}$.

40-4 ★ A long helical spring having a relaxed length L_0, a force constant k, and a total mass M, is stretched until its length is L. Show that the wave speed of a longitudinal wave pulse along the spring is

$$\sqrt{kL_0(L - L_0)/M}$$

40-5   Longitudinal sound waves travel through water at 20° C at the speed 1450 m/sec. What is the bulk modulus for water?

40-6   The volume of a certain solid shrinks by 2 parts in 10^6 when it is subject to an external hydrostatic pressure of 1 atm. The density of the solid is 8.0 gm/cm^3. What is the speed of a longitudinal wave through this material?

40-7 In the sonar method of measuring distances under water a sound pulse travels from the generator to a distant object and is reflected back to the location of the generator. The distance is computed by measuring the time interval between the transmission and reception of the pulse. Taking the bulk modulus of water as 2.0×10^9 nt/m^2 and the density of water as 1.0×10^3 kg/m^3, what is the time interval for a sonar pulse striking an object 50 m distant from the transmitter?

40-8 * A certain solid shows departures from Hooke's law when its volume is changed by 2 parts in 10^3 by external hydrostatic pressures. Thus, the principle of superposition will not apply for deformations produced by compressional waves which exceed this limit. Assuming that waves are generated with a displacement amplitude of 0.40 mm, what is the minimum frequency at which departures from linear wave superposition will appear? The speed of sound through the solid is 5.0×10^3 m/sec.

40-9 A certain long thin rod with Young's modulus Y, density ρ, and cross-sectional area A is under tension F_t. What is the ratio of the speed of a transverse wave along the rod to the speed of a longitudinal wave through the rod?

40-10 Roughly how long does it take for an earthquake tremor to pass through the Earth? (Choose order-of-magnitude values for the physical constants involved.)

40-11 A rod of length 1.0 m and density 7.8 gm/cm^3 is set into resonant longitudinal oscillation in its fundamental mode at the frequency 2,500 sec^{-1} by being struck at one end. The rod is clamped at its center and free at its ends. (a) What is the wavelength of the oscillations in the rod? (b) What is Young's modulus for this solid?

40-12 Show that for relatively low Celsius temperatures t_C the speed of sound through air is given closely by the relation $v = (331.4 + 0.6t_C)$ m/sec.

40-13 Show that the ratio of the rms molecular speed of a gas to the speed of sound through the gas is given by $(3/\gamma)^{1/2}$.

40-14 Show that the wave speed through all monatomic gases is $\sqrt{5RT/3w}$, where w is the molecular weight.

40-15 An observer fires a shot and hears its echo from a surface 150 m distant 0.86 sec later. What is the temperature of the air?

40-16 Confirm that the isothermal bulk modulus for an ideal gas is the pressure p.

40-17 The measured speed of sound through molecular hydrogen (H$_2$) gas at 0° C is 1.26×10^3 m/sec. (a) Are the hydrogen molecules undergoing rotation at this temperature? (b) Are they undergoing vibration?

40-18 A listener hears a sound pulse arriving through a railroad track made of iron (Young's modulus, 9.1×10^{10} nt/m^2; density, 7.8 gm/cm^3) and then 5.6 sec later hears the same sound pulse arrive through air at 0° C. How far away is the listener from the sound source?

40-19 ★ Since a sound wave through air (at atmospheric pressure) consists of adiabatic compressions and expansions, not only do condensations and rarefactions correspond, respectively, to regions in which the density of air is larger than and less than that of undisturbed air, but also to regions in which the temperature is above and below that of the undisturbed air. By how much does the temperature at a condensation exceed that of room temperature (20° C) for a sound wave for which the pressure amplitude is 2.0 nt/m²?

40-20 (a) The condition for the existence of sound waves in a gas is that the wavelength be large compared with the mean free path of the gas molecules, because only then can the gas be regarded as a compressible fluid. For air at room temperature the mean free path is 7×10^{-8} m. Compute the frequency of sound waves for which the wavelength is equal to the mean free path. (b) The condition that the wavelength be large compared with the mean free path is equivalent to the condition that the frequency of the wave oscillations be small compared with the molecular collision frequency. Confirm this equivalence.

40-21 The pressure variations of a certain sound wave are described by the relation $\Delta p = (2.0) \cos (200t - 6.3x)$, all quantities being given in mks units. What are (a) the pressure amplitude, (b) the frequency, (c) the wavelength, and (d) the wave speed?

40-22 Figure 40-16 shows a plot of the pressure Δp as a function of time for a wave traveling along the positive X-axis. Sketch curves giving

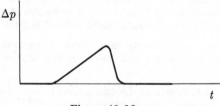

Figure 40-16

(a) the longitudinal displacement y as a function of time, (b) the longitudinal velocity $\partial y / \partial t$ as a function of time, and (c) the wave shape, $y(x)$.

40-23 A loudspeaker having a diaphram of 2.0 cm diameter oscillating at a frequency of 100 cycles/sec is to generate sound waves for which the pressure amplitude is 0.010 atm. (a) What is the required displacement amplitude? (b) What is the acoustic power output of the loudspeaker? (c) Assuming for simplicity that the generated sound waves travel outward in a single direction, what is the intensity of the sound beam?

40-24 A certain explosion releases 1.0 w of acoustic power. The sound travels outward uniformly in all directions through air. (a) What is the intensity of the sound at a distance of 100 m from the source? (b) What is the pressure amplitude at this point?

40-25 A certain loudspeaker with a diaphram of 5.0 cm radius is to generate acoustic radiation of 1000 cycles/sec with a power of 20 w. What is the minimum oscillation amplitude of the diaphram?

40-26 A pipe, open at both ends, is set in resonance only at the frequencies of 800 sec^{-1} and 1000 sec^{-1} when an exciting audio-oscillator is varied in frequency over the range of 700 to 1100 sec^{-1}. What is the length of the pipe?

40-27 A pipe, initially open at both ends, oscillates at the frequency of 840 sec^{-1} (not necessarily its fundamental frequency). When one end is closed, its oscillation frequency is 210 sec^{-1}. What is the minimum pipe length satisfying these conditions?

40-28 The speed of sound is measured with a tube, open at one end and fitted at the other end with a movable piston. Resonance oscillations are excited by a tuning fork of frequency 880 cycles/sec placed near the open end. It is found that the sound intensity exhibits peaks when the piston is at the positions 9.2 cm, 28.3 cm, and 47.2 cm. What is the speed of sound?

40-29 A trumpeter extends the upper range of notes that he can achieve by replacing the air in his instrument (and lungs) with helium, a monatomic gas with atomic weight 4. By what factor will the frequencies be increased?

40-30 A 12-inch $33\frac{1}{3}$-rpm phonograph record can reproduce sound with frequencies of up to 16,000 cycles/sec. (a) What is the maximum separation distance in the record groove (near the beginning of the record) between the oscillations corresponding to the highest frequency? (b) What is the corresponding separation distance on a magnetic tape played at the speed of $7\frac{1}{2}$ inches/sec?

40-31 Since the ear is sensitive to sound over an enormous range of intensities, from 10^{-16} to 10^{-4} w/cm^2, it is convenient to measure the loudness of sound on a logarithmic scale. The sound level in *decibels* (db) of an intensity I is given by $10 \log_{10} (I/I_0)$, I_0 being the minimum detectable intensity, 10^{-16} w/cm^2. What is the noise level in decibels of (a) ordinary conversation, which corresponds to 10^{-10} w/cm^2, and (b) the threshold of pain, 10^{-4} w/cm^2?

40-32 In the musical *diatonic scale*, the "fifth" has a frequency which is 3/2 times that of the tonic ("G," 396 sec^{-1}, as compared with "C," 264 sec^{-1}, for example). Indeed, all the tones in the major scale are in the ratio of simple integers. In the *well-tempered scale*, on the other hand, any two adjoining tones of the twelve half-tones comprised in one octave differ in frequency by the factor $2^{1/12} = 1.0595$. (a) What is the ratio of the fifth (the seventh half-tone) to the tonic on the well-tempered scale? That is, what is the factor $2^{7/12}$? (b) By what fraction do the fifths on the diatonic and well-tempered scale differ?

FORTY-ONE

ELECTROMAGNETIC WAVES

Up to this point we have been concerned with mechanical waves, waves in which material particles undergo displacements as the wave form travels through a deformable medium. In this chapter we treat a very different sort of wave phenomenon, electromagnetic waves. Electric and magnetic fields, unattached to electric charges or currents, move through empty space at the speed of light. Our starting point is Maxwell's equations, from which we derive quite directly the principal features of electromagnetic waves in space. We prove that the speed of light, or of any other electromagnetic wave, is given by $1/\sqrt{\epsilon_0\mu_0}$. We then derive relations giving the energy density and intensity of electromagnetic radiation. We treat the radiation force and pressure produced by electromagnetic waves impinging upon a material, and the linear momentum that must be ascribed to electromagnetic fields in space. We then consider accelerating electric charges as generators of electromagnetic waves, together with sinusoidal electromagnetic oscillations and the electromagnetic spectrum. Finally, we discuss briefly a number of methods of measuring the speed of light.

41-1   Fundamental properties of electromagnetic waves   We wish to show that electromagnetic waves—electric and magnetic fields unattached to any electric charges—can exist in space and that an electromagnetic wave travels at the speed of light. The fundamentals are these:

(1) A changing magnetic field (strictly, a changing magnetic flux) generates an electric field following *Faraday's law*:

$$[34\text{-}9] \qquad \oint E \cdot dl = -\frac{d\phi_B}{dt} \qquad [41\text{-}1]$$

(2) A changing electric field (strictly, a changing electric flux) generates a magnetic field following the *generalized Ampère law*:

$$[38\text{-}7] \qquad \oint B \cdot dl = \epsilon_0 \mu_0 \frac{d\phi_E}{dt}$$

Note that the conduction current i is zero, since we are considering fields in the absence of real currents.

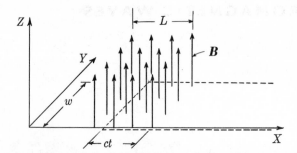

Figure 41-1. Traveling magnetic pulse.

We assume that a rectangular pulse of magnetic field with flux density B is moving along the X-axis at the speed c, as shown in Figure 41-1. This field is imagined to move through empty space, far from any electric charges or currents. How such a magnetic field can be separated from charges and currents will be discussed later. The flux density is assumed to have a constant magnitude B at all points along the Z-axis over the space interval of width L along the X-axis. The width of pulse along the Y-axis is infinite. Outside this interval B is zero.

We consider a fixed imaginary rectangular loop, lying in the XY-plane, whose width along the Y-direction is w and whose length in the X-direction is indefinitely long. Then, if the leading edge of the magnetic pulse passes the left end of the loop at the time $t = 0$, it will, after a time t has elapsed, have progressed a distance ct into the loop. We evaluate the electric field induced in the loop by the passing magnetic pulse from Faraday's law.

The flux through the loop at time t is

$$\phi_B = BA = B(wct)$$

When $t = L/c$, the trailing edge of the pulse has entered the loop; thereafter ϕ_B is constant. The rate of flux change while the pulse passes the left end of the loop is, from Equation 41-1,

$$\frac{d\phi_B}{dt} = Bwc \qquad [41\text{-}2]$$

The only contribution to the integral $\oint E \cdot dl$ taken around the loop is along the left side, where the integral yields Ew. Here we assume the induced electric field to be in the Y-direction. Thus,

$$\oint E \cdot dl = Ew \qquad [41\text{-}3]$$

Substituting Equations 41-2 and 41-3 into Equation 41-1 gives

$$Ew = Bwc$$
$$E = Bc \qquad [41\text{-}4]$$

We omit the minus sign here since we are interested in magnitudes only. Equation 41-4 gives the magnitude of the electric field induced in an imaginary loop in space, which is to say, it gives the magnitude of the electric field produced in empty space. What about the direction of E? We find this from Lenz's law. As the magnetic pulse passes into the loop, the magnetic flux through the loop increases in the $+Z$-direction. Consequently, an induced emf and an induced electric field are set up to oppose the increase in magnetic flux. This requires that the direction of E in the left side of the loop be inward, that is, in the $+Y$-direction. As long as the magnetic pulse passes the left end of the loop, there will exist an electric field E, in the $+Y$-direction, of magnitude Bc. At any time that the pulse is *not* passing the left end of the loop, there is *no* electric field there. Thus, the original transverse magnetic pulse is accompanied by a transverse electric pulse, the two fields being perpendicular to each other and to the direction of propagation of both fields; see Figure 41-2.

Let us review what has been done so far. We began with a magnetic pulse and showed, using Faraday's law, that an electric pulse must accompany it. The magnitudes of E and B are related by Equation 41-4. Now we do just the reverse. We begin with an electric pulse and show that a magnetic pulse must accompany it.

In a fashion similar to that employed for the magnetic pulse in Figure 41-1, we consider a rectangular pulse of electric field E, as shown in Figure 41-3. The field is in the direction of the $+Y$-axis and travels at speed c

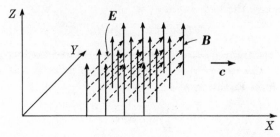

Figure 41-2. Electric field accompanying the magnetic field of Figure 41-1.

along the $+X$-axis. We now consider an imaginary rectangular loop lying in the XZ-plane, whose width in the Z-direction is l. We evaluate the magnetic field produced in this loop by the passing electric pulse from Ampère's law:

[38-7] $$\oint \boldsymbol{B} \cdot d\boldsymbol{l} = \epsilon_0 \mu_0 \frac{d\phi_E}{dt} \qquad [41\text{-}5]$$

The only contribution to the integral $\oint \boldsymbol{B} \cdot d\boldsymbol{l}$ is along the left end of the loop, where the direction of $\boldsymbol{B}$ is taken as along the Z-axis:

$$\oint \boldsymbol{B} \cdot d\boldsymbol{l} = Bl \qquad [41\text{-}6]$$

The electric flux $\phi_E = EA$ through the loop at time t is

$$\phi_E = EA = E(lct)$$

After $t = L/c$, the trailing edge of the moving pulse has passed the left end of the loop, and the flux within the loop is constant thereafter. While the flux changes,

$$\frac{d\phi_E}{dt} = Elc \qquad [41\text{-}7]$$

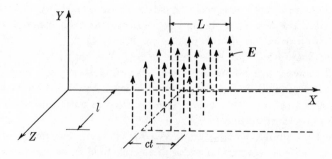

Figure 41-3. Traveling electric pulse.

Substituting Equations 41-6 and 41-7 into Equation 41-5 yields

$$Bl = \epsilon_0 \mu_0 Elc$$

$$B = \epsilon_0 \mu_0 Ec \qquad [41\text{-}8]$$

The direction of B at the left end of the loop is out of the paper (in the $+Z$-direction). This is so because the displacement current (electric flux change) is in the $+Y$-direction; the accompanying magnetic field surrounding this current follows from the right-hand rule. Thus, a transverse magnetic pulse accompanies the electric pulse. When the electric field is zero, so is the magnetic field; see Figure 41-4. The combined electric and magnetic fields are the same as shown in Figure 41-2. The relative directions of E, B, and c are exactly the same as we found before!

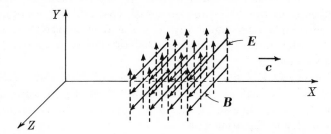

Figure 41-4. Magnetic field accompanying the electric field of Figure 41-3.

Beginning with a magnetic pulse one finds an accompanying electric pulse; beginning with an electric pulse one finds an accompanying magnetic pulse. The directions of the fields are self-consistent. In addition, the magnitudes of E and B, given by Equations 41-4 and 41-8, must be self-consistent. Substituting Equation 41-4 into Equation 41-5 gives

$$B = \epsilon_0 \mu_0 Bc^2$$

$$\boxed{c = \dfrac{1}{\sqrt{\epsilon_0 \mu_0}}} \qquad [41\text{-}9]$$

By experiment, it is found that

[25-6] $\epsilon_0 = 8.85 \times 10^{-12}$ coul²/nt-m²

and, by arbitrary choice (Section 33-2), that

[33-2] $\mu_0 = 4\pi \times 10^{-7}$ weber/amp-m $= 12.56 \times 10^{-7}$ nt/amp²

Substituting the values for the electric and magnetic constants, ϵ_0 and μ_0, into Equation 41-9 gives

$$c = 1/\sqrt{(8.85 \times 10^{-12} \text{ coul}^2/\text{nt-m}^2)(12.56 \times 10^{-7} \text{ nt/amp}^2)}$$

[41-9]
$$c = 3.00 \times 10^8 \text{ m/sec}$$

Thus, an electromagnetic disturbance can travel through empty space, but it must travel at the unique speed $c = 3.00 \times 10^8$ m/sec. This is exactly the same as the measured speed at which light travels. Light is, in fact, just one form of electromagnetic radiation. Discovering this is the greatest triumph of classical electromagnetic theory. We shall discuss several methods of measuring the speed of electromagnetic radiation in Section 41-7; suffice it to say here that the speed predicted by electromagnetic theory is in complete agreement with that found by a variety of measurements. Hereafter in this chapter the symbol c shall denote the speed of light through a vacuum.

Figures 41-3 and 41-4 show that the directions of the E and B fields must be perpendicular to each other and to the direction of propagation. What are the relative magnitudes of E and B? We find this by using the results of Equation 41-9 in Equation 41-8:

$$B = \frac{E}{c} \qquad \text{[41-10]}$$

For any electromagnetic wave the magnitude of the magnetic field is smaller than that of the electric field which accompanies it, by the very large factor c (in the rationalized mksa system of units).

In terms of the magnetic field intensity (Equation 36-18) $H = B/\mu_0$, we have, from Equations 41-9 and 41-10,

$$\sqrt{\mu_0} H = \sqrt{\epsilon_0} E$$

In our derivation the electric and magnetic fields change with time, but in a simple way: the fields are "turned on and off" abruptly at the leading and trailing edges of the pulse. We shall, of course, wish to consider waves in which the electric and magnetic fields change continuously with time, particularly sinusoidally. Nothing new need be done, however, in treating such waves, inasmuch as it has been shown above that whenever the electric field changes magnitude in space so does the magnetic field accompanying it. Moreover, through the superposition principle, which applies without restriction to electromagnetic waves, we may add, or superpose, any number of pulses to approximate a sinusoidal wave.

We add a few historical notes concerning the prediction and discovery of electromagnetic waves and their identification with visible light as an electromagnetic wave disturbance. The theoretical foundation was put forth in 1864 by J. C. Maxwell, who showed that the existence of electromagnetic waves having the properties just described were a logical consequence of what have become known as Maxwell's equations, the equations summarizing all electromagnetic effects. The direct experimental confirmation of the existence of electromagnetic waves was made by H. Hertz in 1887. Hertz used an oscillator of the sort described in Section 37-1. This oscillator generated high-frequency radio waves which were detected by a similar resonant circuit removed from the generator by a distance which was so great that the oscillating currents in the receiver could not be attributed to the induced fields of the generator; it had to be assumed that the generator produced an electromagnetic wave which traveled to the receiver and was absorbed there.

Before Maxwell, it was known that light consists of waves, although it was not known that light consists, in fact, of *electromagnetic* waves. That light is a wave phenomenon of any sort was not recognized, however, for many years. The reasons for this lie in the sublety of the characteristic wave phenomena (Chapters 45 and 46) exhibited by waves having a wavelength as small as that of light ($\sim 10^{-3}$ mm). Moreover, a particle model for light is in accord with many experimental observations concerning light (Chapter 43).

Thus far we have not raised the question of what the medium is through which light is propagated. Nineteenth-century physicists, thoroughly grounded in the then well-known properties of mechanical waves, could not conceive of any wave without a medium. For them, all waves had to consist of some type of mechanical wave arising from a disturbance in a medium. Thus, they imagined an electromagnetic wave to be a disturbance in a massless medium pervading all space, called the *ether*. The wave speed was thought to be c only when measured by an observer at rest in the ether; for an observer in motion relative to the ether, the speed of light was thought to be different from c. That the ether concept is neither useful nor necessary and that the speed of light through a vacuum is the *same* for *all* observers, whatever the state of their motion, were shown in the historic experiment of Michelson and Morley in 1887 (Section 45-8). One now thinks of an electromagnetic wave as traveling through empty space in the absence of a medium of any kind. The failure of the ether concept and the observed constancy of the speed of light for all observers were the starting point for the special theory of relativity.

41-2   Electromagnetic energy density, intensity, and the Poynting vector   First recall that the energy density u_E of an electric field of magnitude E is given by

[29-16] $u_E = \frac{1}{2}\epsilon_0 E^2$ [41-11]

and that the magnetic energy density u_B is

[35-16] $u_B = \frac{1}{2\mu_0} B^2$ [41-12]

Of course, if the E and B fields vary with time, so do the energy densities u_E and u_B. These relations give the *instantaneous* energy densities at any point in space. Using Equation 41-10 in Equation 41-12, we have

$$u_B = \frac{1}{2\mu_0}\left(\frac{E}{c}\right)^2 = \frac{\epsilon_0\mu_0}{2\mu_0}E^2 = \frac{1}{2}\epsilon_0 E^2$$

Comparing this with Equation 41-11 we find that

$$u_B = u_E \qquad [41\text{-}13]$$

The energy densities of the electric and the magnetic fields of an electromagnetic wave are *equal*; that is, the energy carried by an electromagnetic disturbance is shared equally by the electric and magnetic fields.

Now the total energy density u, or energy per unit volume, of an electromagnetic wave is

$$\boxed{u = u_E + u_B = 2u_E = \epsilon_0 E^2} \qquad [41\text{-}14]$$

The energy density is proportional to the *square* of the electric field (equivalently, we may write $u = 2u_B = B^2/\mu_0$).

The intensity I of any wave is defined as the energy flow per unit time (the power P) across a unit area oriented at right angles to the direction of wave propagation; that is,

$$I = P/A \qquad [41\text{-}15]$$

where A is the transverse area through which the energy flows. The intensity is sometimes referred to as the *energy flux*. We wish to find an expression for the intensity I in terms of the energy density u of a wave traveling in one direction only and having the wave speed c. Consider a cylinder of cross-sectional area A and length L through which electromagnetic radiation is propagated along the direction of the cylinder's axis, as shown in Figure 41-5 (the cylinder's volume is assumed to be so small that the energy density u is constant throughout). The length can be written as $L = ct$, where c is the speed of light and t is the time required for a wave to travel from one end of the cylinder to the other. Therefore, in the time t, all the energy originally contained in the cylinder's volume $AL = Act$ will have passed through the area A. We can write

$$\text{intensity} = \frac{\text{energy}}{\text{area} \times \text{time}} = \frac{(\text{energy/volume}) \times (\text{volume})}{\text{area} \times \text{time}}$$

$$I = \frac{u \times Act}{At}$$

$$\boxed{I = uc} \qquad [41\text{-}16]$$

We have not used the explicit form for the energy density u; therefore, Equation 41-16 is a general relationship applying to *any* type of wave. For

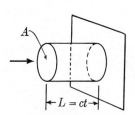

Figure 41-5. Electromagnetic energy flux through the area A.

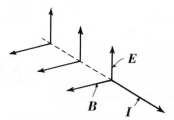

Figure 41-6. The relative directions of **E**, **B**, and **I** for an electromagnetic wave.

an electromagnetic wave, we have, using Equation 41-14,

$$I = \epsilon_0 E^2 c \qquad [41\text{-}17]$$

We may write the relation for the intensity differently by using Equations 41-9 and 41-10 in Equation 41-17:

$$I = \epsilon_0 E^2 c = \epsilon_0 E(Bc)c = \frac{\epsilon_0 EB}{\epsilon_0 \mu_0} = EB/\mu_0$$

$$I = E\left(\frac{B}{\mu_0}\right) = EH$$

Recall that for an electromagnetic wave, the electric field **E** and the magnetic induction **B** are perpendicular to each other and to the direction of wave, or energy, propagation, as shown in Figure 41-6 (and earlier in Figures 41-2 and 41-4). In fact, the direction of the cross product **E × B** is the direction of wave propagation (the thumb of the right hand points in the direction in which the electromagnetic energy flows when we turn the **E** vector into the **B** vector through 90° with the right-hand fingers).

Thus, we can assign a *direction* to the intensity I and regard it as a *vector* pointing in the direction of the electromagnetic energy flux. We write the last equation in the vector form

$$I = E \times \frac{B}{\mu_0}$$
$$I = E \times H$$

[41-18]

The vector intensity I is referred to as the *Poynting vector*, named for J. H. Poynting (1852–1914). If we wish to find the electromagnetic energy flow per unit time, or the power P, through a surface having an element dS we merely integrate $I \cdot dS$ over the entire surface:

$$P = \int I \cdot dS$$

[41-19]

Example 1 A beam of light has an intensity of 100 w/m². (a) What is the electromagnetic energy density for this radiation? (b) What are the magnitudes of the electric and magnetic fields for this light beam?

(a) From Equation 41-16,

$$u = I/c = (100 \text{ w/m}^2)/(3 \times 10^8 \text{ m/sec}) = 3.3 \times 10^{-7} \text{ joule/m}^3$$

(b) Using Equation 41-14, we have

$$E = \sqrt{u/\epsilon_0} = \sqrt{(3.3 \times 10^{-7} \text{ joule/m}^3)/(8.85 \times 10^{-12} \text{ coul}^2/\text{nt-m}^2)}$$
$$= 1.9 \times 10^2 \text{ nt/coul} = 190 \text{ v/m}$$

and from Equation 41-10,

$$B = E/c = (1.9 \times 10^2 \text{ nt/coul})/(3.0 \times 10^8 \text{ m/sec})$$
$$= 6.5 \times 10^{-7} \text{ weber/m}^2 = 6.5 \times 10^{-3} \text{ gauss}$$

The magnitude of the magnetic field of an electromagnetic wave is *much* less (by the factor c) than that of the electric field. So small a magnetic field as 10^{-3} gauss cannot easily be detected; an electromagnetic wave is detected in absorption by the much larger effects of the electric field.

It should be noted that all of the relations derived in this exercise apply for a point in space and an instant of time. If the electric and magnetic fields were to vary with time, as would be the case of visible light, then the values of E and B computed above are strictly the root-mean-square values (Section 41-5). It is significant, however, that *all* of the above formulas apply without regard to the time variation, or frequency, of the electromagnetic wave; that is, the magnitudes of E and B for a 100 w radio beam are the same as for a 100 w light beam.

Example 2 Show that the energy dissipated per unit time in a conductor with a current i and having a resistance R is i^2R, by using the Poynting vector to find the electromagnetic energy flux into the conductor.

See Figure 41-7, which shows a cylindrical conductor of radius a and length L. Also shown are the electric field lines in the interior of the conductor, pointing in the direction of the current i, as well as the magnetic field lines surrounding the conductor in circular loops and having their origin in the current i. We see that the direction of the Poynting vector I is radially inward at all points on the cylindrical surface; that is, electromagnetic energy flows continuously into the conductor. Since I, E, and B are mutually perpendicular, the power P may be written simply as

$$P = \int I \cdot dS = I(2\pi a L) = \frac{EB}{\mu_0}(2\pi a L)$$

where $2\pi a L$ is the cylindrical surface area.

We find the magnitude of B at the outside surface of the conductor by applying Ampère's law to a circular loop of radius a at the cylinder's surface:

[33-23]

$$\oint B \cdot dl = \mu_0 i$$

$$B(2\pi a) = \mu_0 i$$

$$B = \mu_0 i / 2\pi a$$

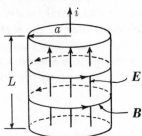

Figure 41-7. Electromagnetic energy flux into a cylindrical conductor.

The uniform electric field E within the conductor is related to the potential drop V across its ends by $E = V/L$, where $V = iR$; therefore,

$$E = iR/L$$

Substituting the values of B and E in the equation for the power P given above gives

$$P = i^2 R$$

What a remarkable result! We can find the power dissipated in a resistor by computing the energy entering it from the electromagnetic field. Indeed, *all* problems involving the flow of electric or magnetic energy (for example, the charging of a capacitor) can be solved by applying the Poynting vector. There is, however, a restriction. The electric and magnetic fields must be related; that is, they cannot arise from independent sources of charge and current. Thus, there may be mutually perpendicular electric and magnetic fields, as in the case of the velocity selector (Section 32-4), but there is *no* energy flux associated with these fields, inasmuch as they have independent origins. In the case of the conductor here, however, the electric and magnetic fields *are* related; that is, the electric field drives charges through the conductor, producing an electric current, and this electric current in turn generates the magnetic field. These fields are not, however, those of an electromagnetic wave traveling at the speed c through empty space.

41-3 Radiation force and pressure: the linear momentum of an electromagnetic wave

An electromagnetic wave carries energy. It is easy to show that an electromagnetic wave also has *linear momentum* in the direction of propagation and that such a wave can exert a force, or *radiation pressure*, on a material upon which it impinges. The first measurement of the pressure of light was made by P. N. Lebedev (1866–1912) in 1901.

We first assume that an electromagnetic wave strikes a material which absorbs all the energy striking it, reflecting and transmitting none. This implies that the electric field E must do work on a charged particle within the material, the energy removed per unit time from the electromagnetic wave being exactly the power absorbed by the material. Note that we say, the work done by the *electric* field. The magnetic force, since it always acts at right angles to a charged particle's velocity, does *no work*.

Consider the situation shown in Figure 41-8. Here an electromagnetic wave travels along the positive Z-axis, the electric field E being along the positive X-axis and the magnetic field B being along the positive Y-axis. We are interested in the forces produced by E and B on an electron within the material. The electric force $F_e = qE$ on the electron has a magnitude $F_e = eE$. This force acts in the direction opposite to that of E, and accelerates the electron in a direction transverse to that of the wave propagation.

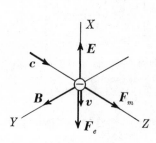

Figure 41-8. The electric force F_e and magnetic force F_m, arising from an electromagnetic wave, on an electron.

What is the effect of the magnetic field? We assume the electron to be moving with speed v along the negative X-axis. The field B is along the positive Y-axis. In general, the direction and magnitude of the magnetic force is given by $F_m = qv \times B$. In this case, the magnitude of F_m is evB and its direction is along the positive Z-axis. The electromagnetic wave produces a *force* on the electron (and, therefore, also on the material to which the electron is bound) *along the direction of wave motion*! In short, when an electromagnetic wave impinges on an electric charge, the E field accelerates the charge in the transverse direction and does work on it, while the B field, acting on the moving charge, produces a longitudinal force.

We wish to find relations for the radiation force and pressure, and the linear momentum of the electromagnetic field, in terms of such quantities as the intensity I and power P of the wave. We found that the radiation force F_r is given by

$$F_r = evB \qquad [41\text{-}20]$$

Since the magnitudes of E and B are related by $B = E/c$, Equation 41-20 may be rewritten as

$$F_r = \frac{(eE)v}{c} \qquad [41\text{-}21]$$

But eE is just the magnitude of the electric force, F_e, the force that does work. In general, the rate of doing work, or the power P, is given by

[11-21] $$P = Fv$$

where F is the force doing work and v is the speed of the particle acted on. Then Equation 41-21 may be written

$$F_r = \frac{F_e v}{c}$$

$$\boxed{\text{Total absorption}: F_r = \frac{P}{c}} \qquad [41\text{-}22]$$

The radiation force of an electromagnetic wave on a material that *absorbs it completely* is simply the power of the wave divided by the speed of light.

Of course, the electrons in an absorbing material are *not* at rest until acted upon by the impinging electromagnetic wave; they are in constant motion, although bound to the material. Nevertheless, the simple derivation for the radiation pressure given above still applies. The forces arising from the electric and magnetic fields of the electromagnetic wave are in addition to any other forces present. Even if the electric and magnetic fields vary with time, the relations hold at each instant.

We have found that a longitudinal force P/c is exerted by an electromagnetic wave on a material absorbing it completely. It follows that when a material *emits* radiation of power P in one direction, the emitter must recoil under the action of a recoil radiation force of magnitude P/c. We can see this most easily by noting that emission is, so to speak, absorption run backward in time. That is, in emission accelerating charges within the material *lose* energy and create an outgoing electromagnetic wave. With time reversal the directions of the electric field E, the electric force F_e, and the radiation force F_r are *the same*; but the direction of the *velocity* v is reversed, as is also the direction of the *magnetic field* B. Thus, under time reversal, that is, with emission rather than absorption, the direction of the Poynting vector is reversed and energy now flows away from the material rather than toward it.

What is the radiation force on a material which reflects all the radiation striking it, absorbing none? We imagine the reflection process to take place in two stages: absorption of the incident radiation followed by re-emission in the reverse direction. Since a radiation force of magnitude P/c acts on the material both in absorption and in emission, the radiation force for complete reflection is

$$\boxed{\text{Complete reflection}: F_r = 2P/c} \qquad [41\text{-}23]$$

The fact that the radiation force for complete reflection is twice that for complete absorption has an exact analogue in mechanics. When a particle with initial momentum $+mv$ strikes and sticks to an object, the linear momentum transferred to the struck object is $+mv$, but when a particle with initial momentum $+mv$ is "reflected" from the struck object, rebounding with the same speed, the particle's final momentum is $-mv$, its momentum having been changed by $\Delta(mv) = mv - (-mv) = 2mv$. Thus, for reflection the struck object acquires a momentum $2mv$, just *twice* the momentum acquired in absorption. Equivalently, the (average) force on the struck object is twice as great for reflection as for absorption.

The radiation force given in Equations 41-22 and 41-23 applies for radiation which is incident in a direction *perpendicular* to the absorbing or reflecting surface. For oblique incidence, with an angle θ between the direction of wave propagation and the normal to the plane of the absorber or reflector, the radiation force is found by multiplying F_r by the factor $\cos \theta$.

Example 3 A 3 w beam of electromagnetic radiation shines on, and is completely absorbed by, a black object. (a) What is the radiation force on the absorber? (b) What is the recoil force on the source emitting the beam?

(a) For complete absorption,

$$F_r = P/c = 3 \text{ w}/(3 \times 10^8 \text{ m/sec}) = 10^{-8} \text{ nt}$$

which is a very small force indeed.

(b) The source emitting the 3 w beam, whether it be a source of light or a radio transmitter, will, as long as the emitted waves travel outward in a single direction, recoil under the action of a force of 10^{-8} nt. Thus, a very elementary form of a rocket consists of a flashlight emitting light.

It is useful to write relations giving the *radiation pressure p_r*, the radiation force F_r per unit transverse area A, for absorption and reflection. Since the pressure p is, by definition, F/A, we have for complete absorption,

$$p_r = F_r/A = P/cA$$

The intensity I is given by $I = P/A$. Therefore,

$$\boxed{\begin{array}{ll} \text{Complete absorption:} & p_r = I/c \\ \text{Complete reflection:} & p_r = 2I/c \end{array}} \qquad \text{[41-24]}$$

Example 4 The intensity of all electromagnetic radiation from the Sun at the Earth's surface is 1400 w/m². What is the radiation pressure of the Sun's radiation (including sunlight) shining on an object at the Earth's distance from the Sun? Assume complete absorption.

From Equation 41-24,

$$p_r = I/c = (1.4 \times 10^3 \text{ w/m}^2)/(3.0 \times 10^8 \text{ m/sec})$$
$$= 4.7 \times 10^{-6} \text{ nt/m}^2 = 1.8 \times 10^{-9} \text{ ounce/cm}^2$$

For any sources of moderate intensity or power the radiation pressure and force are extraordinarily small. Yet the radiation force and pressure can be measured with a torsion pendulum, the same instrument used to measure the extremely small gravitational force between laboratory-size objects in the Cavendish experiment (Section 16-2). The results are found to be in exact agreement with the predictions of electromagnetic theory. Moreover, the radiation force may equal or exceed the gravitational force in stellar phenomena, as witness an exploding star, or supernova.

Clearly, if electromagnetic radiation can exert a force and transfer linear momentum to an object upon which it impinges, one must associate linear momentum with the electromagnetic field itself. It is easy to derive the expression for the momentum M of an electromagnetic wave (we use the symbol M for linear momentum, rather than the conventional symbol p, to avoid confusion with the pressure p and the power P). By definition, the force F is related to the momentum M by

$$F = dM/dt$$

Similarly, the power P is the rate of doing work, or the time rate of the energy:

$$P = (d/dt)(\text{energy})$$

From Equation 41-22

$$F_r = P/c$$

$$dM/dt = (1/c) \times (d/dt)(\text{energy})$$

We use the relation for the radiation force in *absorption* since we wish to count the energy transfer only *once*. Integrating yields

$$\boxed{M = (\text{electromagnetic energy})/c} \qquad [41\text{-}25]$$

The magnitude of the linear momentum of an electromagnetic wave is the energy of the wave divided by c; the direction of the momentum is along the direction of energy propagation, that is, along the direction of the intensity vector I.

Example 5   A 100 w beam of light is turned on for 10 sec. What is the linear momentum of this beam?

We first find the energy of the beam as $(100 \text{ w})(10 \text{ sec}) = 10^3$ joules. From Equation 41-25, the electromagnetic linear momentum is

$$(10^3 \text{ joules})/(3 \times 10^8 \text{ m/sec}) = 3.3 \times 10^{-6} \text{ kg-m/sec},$$

roughly the linear momentum of a high-speed mosquito. Note that an electromagnetic wave of 1 w turned on for 10^3 sec would carry the same linear momentum, but the "length" of the beam would be 3×10^{11} m, rather than 3×10^9 m.

It is interesting to write Equation 41-25, which connects the linear momentum with the energy of an electromagnetic wave, in the form suggested by classical mechanics. It is perhaps natural to take the energy of the electromagnetic field as kinetic energy (rather than potential energy), since it corresponds to energy in motion. Then, if we associate a mass m and a speed v with the radiation, Equation 41-25 becomes

$$mv = \frac{\frac{1}{2}mv^2}{c}$$

We have already shown that the speed of radiation is $v = c$, so that we must say

two equals one

This is clearly a contradiction, and something is basically wrong. It is *not* Equation 41-25. Rather, from the point of view of the theory of relativity, it is improper to attempt to apply the customary Newtonian relations for linear momentum and kinetic energy to objects traveling at speeds close to that of light, and certainly improper for light itself (more is said about this in Chapter 2, *Elementary Modern Physics*, Weidner and Sells).

We have seen that one can and must attribute energy and linear momentum to an electromagnetic wave. One can also attribute *angular* momentum (actually, *spin* angular momentum) to circularly polarized electromagnetic waves. It will be shown in Section 47-6 that the magnitude of the electromagnetic angular momentum of a circularly polarized wave of frequency f is the energy of the wave divided by $2\pi f$ and that the direction of the angular momentum vector is parallel or antiparallel to the direction of wave propagation.

41-4 Accelerating charges and electromagnetic waves In our

derivation of the speed $(1/\sqrt{\epsilon_0\mu_0})$ of an electromagnetic wave in Section 41-1 we assumed the electric and magnetic fields to exist in space unattached to any charges. We then showed that such an electromagnetic disturbance in space was self-generating, that is, it was an electromagnetic *wave*. But how is such a wave launched? How can the electric and magnetic fields become detached from the electric charges which produce them? The subject of the generation of electromagnetic waves can, of course, be treated by applying Maxwell's equations, a rather complex analysis lying beyond the scope of this book. What shall be done here is to give qualitative and plausible arguments to show how an accelerating electric charge generates an electromagnetic wave.

Note that we say an *accelerating* electric charge. If one views an electric charge from an inertial frame in which it is at rest, one sees radiating outward from the charge a static electric field only. On the other hand, if one views the charge from an inertial frame in which the charge moves with constant velocity, the electric charge has, in addition to the electric field, an accompanying field which encircles it; see Figure 41-9. As long as the electric charge has a *constant* velocity, zero or nonzero, the electric and magnetic fields are unchanged and remain attached to the charge.

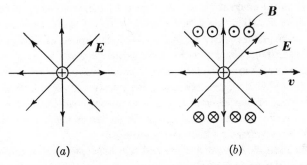

(a)   (b)

Figure 41-9. Electric and magnetic fields surrounding an electric charge (a) at rest and (b) in motion at constant velocity.

Now let us consider the behavior of the electric lines of force from a single accelerating positive charge. It is proper to regard the electric lines surrounding it as rigidly attached to the charge. Consider what happens when the electric charge is accelerated. Figure 41-10 shows a positive charge q originally at rest at point A, then accelerated, and finally brought to rest at B. When the charge is at rest at A, electric lines extend outward in all directions in straight lines from A. One such line is E_A. Further,

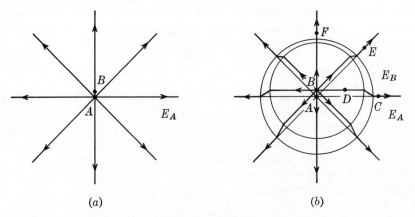

(a)   (b)

Figure 41-10. Electric-field lines surrounding an electric charge (a) before being displaced and (b) after being displaced from A to B.

after q has come to rest at B, the electric lines *near the charge* q again extend outward, the corresponding line being shown as E_B. But the far electric line E_A and the near electric line E_B are the *same* line of force! We know that this is true because the electromagnetic effects produced by an accelerated charge travel outward from the charge with a *finite* speed c. Thus, a small charge q_C at point C will not have "known" that q has accelerated from A to B at the instant shown in Figure 41-10, because q_C is still experiencing the field E_A. The kink in the electric line of force, that is, the transverse component, is traveling toward q_C with the speed of light and reaches it at some later time. On the other hand, a charge q_D at point D has already experienced a transverse electric force arising from the acceleration of q. A charge q_E at E will experience a smaller transverse electric force than q_C, because the kink in the electric line is less pronounced than at C. Finally, a charge q_F at F, which lies along the direction of the acceleration (from A to B) of q experiences *no* transverse force.

At a point such as E, both before and after the passage of the transverse kink, a small charge is acted upon only by a *radial* electric field, whose strength varies inversely as the *square* of the distance AE (or BE), in accordance with Coulomb's law. The radial electric field is the *static* electric field, always attached to the accelerated charge; the transverse electric field is the *radiated* electric field, which becomes detached from the charge and moves outward from it. The magnitude of the transverse electric field can be shown (see below) to vary inversely as the distance AE. Therefore, at large distances from the charge q, the radial component (varying as $1/r^2$) is negligible compared with the transverse component (varying as $1/r$). Although both the static and radiation fields fall off with distance, the radiation field survives over the static field at great distances from the charge. In the derivation given below it will be shown that the electric field E at a distance r from an electric charge q having an acceleration a is given by

$$E \propto \frac{qa \sin \theta}{r} \qquad [41\text{-}26]$$

where θ is the azimuthal angle, the angle between the direction of the charge's acceleration and that of the radius vector r; see Figure 41-11a.

Since the magnitude of the radiated electric field varies as $\sin \theta$, the radiated energy is a maximum in the equatorial plane (perpendicular to the direction of the charge's acceleration) with no radiation along the polar axis. The intensity I of an electromagnetic field is, from Equation 41-17, proportional to E^2. Therefore, from Equation 41-26,

$$I \propto \frac{a^2 q^2 \sin^2 \theta}{r^2} \qquad [41\text{-}27]$$

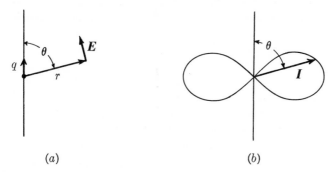

(a)

(b)

Figure 41-11. (a) Electric field radiated from an accelerated charge. (b) Radiation pattern giving the variation in intensity *I* from an accelerated electric charge with the azimuthal angle θ.

The radiated intensity falls off inversely as the square of the distance *r* from the accelerating charge and varies with direction according to $\sin^2 \theta$.

The angular variation is shown in Figure 41-11b, which is a polar diagram showing the intensity *I* as a function of the azimuthal angle θ. The curve is so drawn that the length of the vector *I* for a given angle θ is proportional to the intensity of the radiation in that direction (following $\sin^2 \theta$). The pattern is, of course, symmetrical with respect to an axis along the direction of the charge's acceleration.

We wish to derive from an elementary argument the results stated in Equation 41-26. Consider Figure 41-12, which shows a charge moved from point *A* to point *B*, in the fashion shown earlier in Figure 41-10.

The charge is initially at rest at *A* at time $t = 0$. It is then given a constant acceleration *a* during a very short time δt and acquires a velocity *v* long before it reaches point *B*. The particle arrives at point *B* after the time *t*. Therefore,

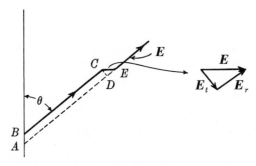

Figure 41-12. One electric field line from an accelerated electric charge.

the transverse kink at this time is a distance $r = AD \simeq BC = ct$ from the charge. We have assumed that the disturbance travels outward at the speed c. We know that

$$v = a\,\delta t \quad \text{and} \quad AB = vt$$

From the geometry of Figure 41-12,

$$CD = AB \sin \theta = vt \sin \theta = (a\,\delta t)t \sin \theta$$

$$DE = c\,\delta t$$

Resolving the electric field at CE into a transverse component E_t and a radial component E_r, we have the following proportionality:

$$\frac{E_t}{E_r} = \frac{CD}{DE} = \frac{(a\,\delta t)t \sin \theta}{c\,\delta t}$$

The radial component E_r is given by Coulomb's law as

$$E_r = kq/r^2$$

Therefore,

$$E_t = E_r \frac{at \sin \theta}{c}$$

$$= \frac{kqat \sin \theta}{r^2 c}$$

Using the fact that $r = ct$, we have, finally,

$$E_t = \frac{ka \sin \theta}{c^2 r}$$

in accord with Equation 41-26.

We have focussed our attention on the electric field radiated by an accelerated electric charge. Because the charge is in motion, there is, in addition, an associated magnetic field, transverse to the electric field and also traveling outward from the accelerated charge at the speed of light. We know, of course, that any electromagnetic disturbance carries energy. The radiated energy arises from the fact that an external agent does work on the charge in accelerating it. This acquired energy does *not*, however, appear as energy residing in the *static* fields. It leaves the charge and travels through space. When the radiation is absorbed, the electric force of the electromagnetic wave does work on a charge in the absorber.

41-5 Sinusoidal electromagnetic waves We have discussed a pulse of electromagnetic radiation arising from a single accelerated charge. Let us now turn to the more interesting and useful situation in which a continuous electromagnetic wave having a well-defined frequency and wavelength is produced. A common source of sinusoidal electromagnetic radiation is an electric-dipole oscillator, represented schematically in Figure 41-13a. An applied voltage varying sinusoidally produces an alternating current in the two straight-line conductors (an antenna). At one end of the wire the charge is alternately positive and negative; at the other end, the charge similarly

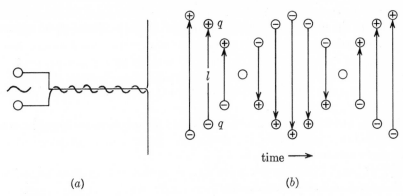

(a)   (b)

Figure 41-13. (a) Electric dipole oscillator. (b) Equivalent oscillating electric charges.

alternates, but is 180° out of phase. We can think of this behavior in terms of the motion of two equal but opposite electric charges undergoing simple harmonic motion along the axis of the antenna at the same frequency as that of the alternating-current source, as in Figure 41-13b. Such a pair of oscillating charges constitute an oscillating electric dipole. The intensity pattern from each charge is that of Figure 41-11. Therefore, the radiation pattern of an oscillating electric dipole is also that shown in Figure 41-11.

Figure 41-14 is a representation of the electric and magnetic fields produced by such an electric dipole oscillator at one instant of time. We can see several features in this figure.

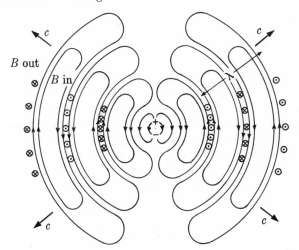

Figure 41-14. Electric and magnetic fields generated by a sinusoidally varying electric dipole.

(1) At short distances from the dipole the electric lines extend from the positive to the negative charge of the dipole. At large distances the electric lines have become detached from the dipole and form closed loops. These electric field loops are formed in space because, at great distances from the antenna, the electric lines do not have enough time (because the speed of light is finite) to collapse into the oscillator as the electric dipole moment alternates.

(2) The electric field E and the magnetic induction B are perpendicular to one another and also to the direction (outward) of propagation of the radiated electromagnetic waves.

(3) At great distances the wave fronts, surfaces of constant phase, are spheres centered about the dipole.

(4) The wave is *linearly* polarized; that is, the transverse electric field at any point in space oscillates along a fixed straight line, this direction being called the direction of polarization of the wave (we shall have more to say about the polarization properties of electromagnetic waves in Chapter 47).

(5) The radiation pattern is symmetrical about the axis of the dipole, in accord with Figure 41-11b.

(6) The wavelength λ of the electromagnetic wave is the distance between two adjacent wave fronts in the same phase. As the oscillator completes one oscillation cycle, a wave front travels outward a distance λ. The frequency f of the oscillator is precisely the frequency of the electromagnetic wave. Therefore, as for other types of waves,

[39-12] $c = f\lambda$ [41-28]

The radiation pattern of Figure 41-11b applies only when the distance r is large compared with the wavelength.

The variation in space at an instant of time of the electric and magnetic fields of a sinusoidal electromagnetic wave is shown in Figure 41-15a. Here, in the customary fashion, the relative spacing of the electric and magnetic field lines indicates the sinusoidal variation. An alternate representation is used in Figure 41-15b. Here the *length* of the lines representing the electric and magnetic fields is used to indicate the strength of the fields.

For a monochromatic (single-frequency) electromagnetic wave propagated along the positive X-direction, with the electric field oscillating sinusoidally along the Y-axis (linearly polarized along Y) and the magnetic field necessarily varying sinusoidally in phase along the Z-axis, we can write

$$E_y = E_0 \sin 2\pi\left(\frac{x}{\lambda} - ft\right)$$

$$B_z = B_0 \sin 2\pi\left(\frac{x}{\lambda} - ft\right)$$

[41-29]

where we have used the form of the equation for a traveling sinusoidal wave given in Equation 39-10. E_0 and B_0 represent, respectively, the amplitudes of the electric and magnetic fields. From Equation 41-10 these field amplitudes are related by $B_0 = E_0/c$.

The expressions for the instantaneous intensity I and energy density u derived earlier involve the *square* of the electric field, E^2. If the electromagnetic fields vary, we must take E^2 to mean the *time average*, or $\overline{E^2}$.

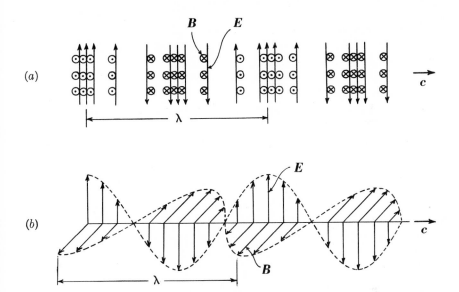

Figure 41-15. Representations of the electric and magnetic fields of a sinusoidal electromagnetic wave: (a) the field lines; (b) the sinusoidally varying amplitudes.

Then I and u give the time average of the intensity and energy density. When the fields vary sinusoidally and $E = E_0 \sin \omega t$, where $\omega = 2\pi f$, we must find the time average of $\sin^2 \omega t$. As was shown in Section 37-2, the average of $\sin^2 \omega t$ or $\cos^2 \omega t$ over one period (or over any integral number of periods) is $\frac{1}{2}$, therefore,

$$\overline{E^2} = \tfrac{1}{2}E_0{}^2 \qquad\qquad [41\text{-}30]$$

Then we may replace E^2, wherever it appears in our earlier relations, by by $\frac{1}{2}E_0{}^2$ when dealing with sinusoidally varying electromagnetic waves.

Example 6   A radio wave having an intensity of 1.5×10^{-10} μw/m^2 is incident upon a 1.0 m antenna oriented along the direction of the electric field of the electromagnetic wave. What is the maximum instantaneous potential difference across the ends of the antenna?

From Equations 41-17 and 41-30, we have

$$I = \tfrac{1}{2}\epsilon_0 c E_0{}^2$$

$$E_0 = \sqrt{2I/\epsilon_0 c}$$

$$= \sqrt{2(1.5 \times 10^{-16}\ \text{w/m}^2)/(8.85 \times 10^{-12}\ \text{coul/nt}^2\text{-m}^2)(3.0 \times 10^8\ \text{m/sec})}$$

$$= 3.4 \times 10^{-7}\ \text{v/m}$$

Across the 1 m conductor the maximum potential difference is a mere 0.34 μv.

41-6 The electromagnetic spectrum   *All* electromagnetic waves, whatever the frequency and wavelength, travel at the speed $1/\sqrt{\epsilon_0\mu_0}$ through a vacuum and have the fundamental properties we have already discussed. The complete spectrum of electromagnetic radiation is shown in Figure 41-16, where the frequency and wavelength are plotted on a logarithmic scale.   At the time of Hertz's experiments in 1887, which confirmed

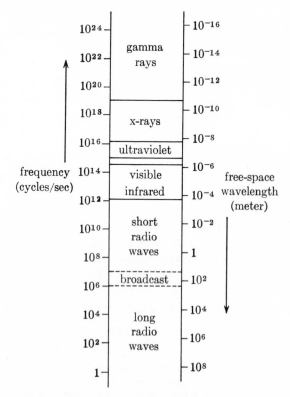

Figure 41-16. The electromagnetic spectrum.

Maxwell's electromagnetic theory of light, only two types of radiation were recognized, visible light and radio waves. Now it is known that other types of radiation exist; they differ in wavelength and frequency as well as in the origin of the radiation and their effects on substances upon which they impinge.

The waves of lowest frequency (and longest wavelength) are radio waves; such waves are generated by oscillating electric currents. The short-wavelength radio waves, or microwaves, have wavelengths comparable to those of audible sound through air. Infrared radiation is produced by heated solids or the molecular vibrations and rotations in gases and liquids. Visible light is produced by rearrangements of the outer electrons in atoms. The very narrow range of wavelengths, from 4000 Å (1 Å $= 10^{-10}$ m) to 7000 Å (from red to violet light) to which the human eye is sensitive corresponds, in musical terminology, to slightly less than one octave (a factor of 2 in frequency) and is to be compared with the enormous frequency range (20 to 20,000 cycles/sec) to which the human ear is sensitive. Ultraviolet radiation immediately adjoins the visible spectrum. X-rays have wavelengths of the approximate size of atoms, and they originate in the rearrangement of innermost electrons of atoms. Gamma rays are the electromagnetic waves of the highest frequency and lowest wavelength; they originate in rearrangements in the particles within the atomic nucleus.

The boundaries between the adjoining regions are not sharply defined. For example, one cannot distinguish between a short-wavelength x-ray and a long-wavelength gamma ray. The various types of electromagnetic radiation differ in their effects on materials. For example, materials which are opaque to visible light are transparent to x-rays.

In Chapters 45 and 46 we shall discuss procedures for measuring the wavelengths of electromagnetic radiation, particularly for relatively short-wavelength radiation, such as visible light. Suffice it to say here that a wavelength measurement requires an arrangement in which some characteristic dimension is of the same order of magnitude as the wavelength.

41-7 Measurements of the speed of light Nothing travels faster than light or any other form of electromagnetic radiation. In fact, light's speed is so great that it appears to the casual observer to move at an infinite speed. It takes considerable insight to raise the question whether the propagation of light is *not* instantaneous and considerable experimental ingenuity and finesse to measure light's speed of propagation with precision. A variety of methods have been developed over the past three hundred years to measure the fundamental constant c. Although differing in many respects, all methods have this in common: one must either measure the time for light to travel a very large distance, so as to make the time interval reasonably large (or, with smaller distances, one must measure the very short time interval with great precision), or else one must somehow combine the velocity of light with another high velocity in an effect depending upon their vector combination.

ROEMER METHOD   The first rough measurement of c was made in 1666 by the Danish astronomer, Ole Roemer (1644–1710). Consider Figure 41-17; here we see the Earth and planet Jupiter in their respective orbits around the Sun. The period of Jupiter is about 12 (Earth) years, so that

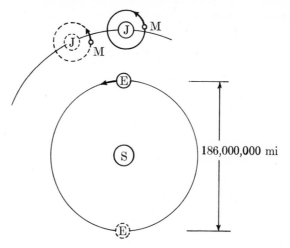

Figure 41-17. Roemer's measurement of the speed of light. The Sun (*S*), Earth (*E*), Jupiter (*J*), and moon (*M*) of Jupiter.

during the time that the Earth orbits through 180°, Jupiter turns through only 15°. Jupiter has a number of satellites, four of which were easily seen by Roemer. One particular moon of Jupiter has a period of 42 hours. This can be easily determined by watching for the eclipse of the moon as it passes behind the planet. (The orbits of the Earth and Jupiter about the Sun and of the moon of Jupiter about the planet all lie in essentially the same plane.) Now, the period of any satellite is nearly constant, so that the orbital motion of the moon of Jupiter may be used as a clock; that is, one should be confident of finding the moon emerging from its eclipse once every 42 hours.

This is, however, *not* what is seen. As the distance between the Earth and Jupiter increases, the period of the Jupiter moon increases, or appears to increase; that is, the moon falls progressively behind schedule in emerging from eclipse. Roemer recognized that this could not be attributed to an actual slowing of the moon's orbital motion, but rather to the fact that the light from Jupiter to the Earth must travel an increasingly larger distance at a noninfinite speed. The cumulative amount of time by which the planet is "behind schedule" over a period of six months is close to 1000 sec. During this time the separation distance between the Earth and Jupiter has increased by 186,000,000 miles, the Earth's orbital diameter. One concludes then, that light travels at the speed $c = (186 \times 10^6 \text{ mi})/(10^3 \text{ sec}) = 186{,}000$ mi/sec.

STELLAR ABERRATION   In this method, first employed by the astronomer James Bradley (1692–1762) in 1725, the velocity of light is combined vectorially with the large velocity with which large-scale apparatus move relative to the fixed stars, the orbital velocity, 3×10^4 m/sec, of the Earth around the Sun.

The principles on which this method is based were treated in Example 3 of Chapter 6. We review them briefly. Suppose first that one is to catch raindrops falling vertically to the bottom of a long tube. Of course, the tube must be held vertical. If the tube is now set in motion horizontally, it must be tilted or aligned at an angle θ relative to the vertical to prevent the raindrops from striking the sides on their way to the bottom. When the speed of the tube is v and the speed of the raindrops is c the required angle θ is given by $\tan \theta = v/c$. This is precisely the situation arising when an astronomer views a distant star. His tube, a telescope, is to catch light from a distant "fixed" star. The telescope, however, is moving relative to the fixed stars; it is attached to the Earth, which moves at the speed 3×10^4 m/sec relative to the Sun and fixed stars, by virtue of its orbital motion around the Sun; see Figure 41-18.

Thus, when a star at the zenith is being viewed, the telescope must be tilted through the angle θ when the Earth is in position a, Figure 41-18. Six months later, when the Earth is traveling in the opposite direction relative to the fixed stars, the telescope must be tilted in the opposite sense. The change in telescope orientation 2θ can be measured, and from it the speed of light c can be computed. The effect is known as *stellar aberration*. The angle 2θ is a mere 41 sec of arc.

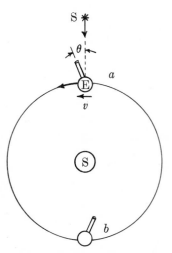

Figure 41-18. Inclination of a telescope arising from stellar aberration.

FIZEAU METHOD   The most obvious way of measuring the speed of light is to time its travel in a round trip from some starting point to a more or less distant mirror and back. One must, of course, now have pulses of light rather than a continuous train, and one can use the same device which chops the continuous light beam into pulses to measure their total travel time t, where $c = 2d/t$, d being the distance from the light source to the mirror. Figure 41-19 shows the simple arrangement used by A. H. L. Fizeau (1819–1896) in 1849. A rotatable wheel has regularly spaced openings along its rim. When the wheel is at rest, the light can pass through an opening, travel to the distant mirror, and return to pass through the *same* opening. With the wheel is in rotation, however, the light will be prevented

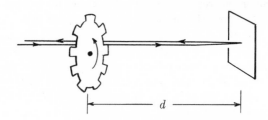

Figure 41-19. Arrangement used by Fizeau in measuring the speed of light.

from entering the telescope on return, unless the wheel has turned fast enough for the adjoining opening to be in the position of the opening through which the light first left the light source. It is then an easy matter to compute the time for the round trip from the measured speed of rotation and the angular separation between adjacent openings. In Fizeau's experiment, $d \simeq 9$ km, and thus $t \simeq 6 \times 10^{-5}$ sec. Present-day techniques allow the measurement of time intervals to a fraction of a nanosecond (10^{-9} sec).

A modification of Fizeau's method was used by J. B. L. Foucault (1819–1868) in 1849 to measure the speed of light through air and also through water. Foucault found that the speed of light through water was *less* than through air (2.3×10^8 m/sec, rather than 3.0×10^8 m/sec). This result had profound influence on the development of the theory of light. If light and other electromagnetic radiation is assumed to consist of waves, the speed of light is expected to be less through a refracting material, such as water, than through air. On the other hand, if light is assumed to consist of particles, its speed through a refracting medium is expected to exceed its speed through air (more about this in Section 43-6).

RESONANCE METHOD   One need not use visible light to measure its speed. Any electromagnetic radiation will do. Indeed, the most recent precision measurements of c have come mostly from measurements with microwaves, radiation having wavelengths of a few centimeters. One can readily produce monochromatic microwave radiation of precisely measurable frequency; the wavelengths can be measured to a fraction of the wavelength *of visible light*. One can then measure c by using the relation $c = f\lambda$.

Consider Figure 41-20. Here we have microwaves being propagated between two reflecting mirrors, one movable. Their separation is adjusted to produce standing waves and resonance. The method is altogether similar to that used commonly to measure the speed of sound.

Again we wish to find the time t required for a wave to travel a round trip between the two positions separated by the distance d. We compute c

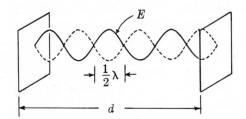

Figure 41-20. Simplified representation of an arrangement for measuring c by the microwave resonance method.

by using the relation $c = 2d/t$. Suppose that a wave of frequency f and wavelength λ has made one round trip. Then, if the same wave is not to interfere destructively with its own tail end upon starting the second trip, the time t must be equal to an integral multiple of the period of the wave, that is, $t = nT$, where $n = 1, 2, 3, \ldots$, and $T = 1/f$. Substituting this result, we find

$$c = 2d/t = 2d/nT$$

$$d = n(cT/2) = n(\lambda/2) \qquad [41\text{-}31]$$

The condition is simply that the distance between the two reflectors be an integral multiple of half-wavelengths. For a standing electromagnetic wave to be produced, an integral number of half-wavelengths must be fitted between the ends. In this method c is measured by using monochromatic electromagnetic waves, their wavelength λ and frequency f being measured simultaneously. The resonance is very narrow, that is, the microwaves will oscillate in resonance only if the length meets the requirement of Equation 41-31. The frequency is measured by comparing the frequency of the microwave oscillator with a standard oscillator which is calibrated, in turn, against the time standard. The microwave measurements permit c to be known to within 3×10^{-7} per cent.

The presently accepted best value for c, the speed of electromagnetic waves through a vacuum, based on a large number of independent measurements by various methods, is

$$c = (2.9979 \pm 0.0001) \times 10^8 \text{ m/sec}$$

the uncertainty in its value being only 3×10^{-3} percent.

Why is it desirable to know the speed of light with such high precision? First, of course, we thereby confirm the electromagnetic theory of light in finding that the computed value of $c = 1/\sqrt{\epsilon_0 \mu_0}$ based on electrical measurements of ϵ_0 is in agreement with the measured value. There are other compelling reasons, however. If one knows c with high precision, then one can reverse the procedure; that is, by timing a light pulse in a round trip one can measure astronomical and large terrestial distances with precision. Thus, the distance to the Moon or to Jupiter can be measured precisely by radar timing of radio pulses. Furthermore, the speed of light plays a dominant role in the theory of relativity and in the quantum theory of atomic and nuclear structure. One can make precise comparisons between theory and experiment only if c is known precisely.

Although one important motivation for knowing c with high accuracy was first that of confirming the electromagnetic theory of light, the correctness of this theory is now so well established that one can use the relation $c = 1/\sqrt{\epsilon_0 \mu_0}$ in reverse; that is, from the measured value of c and the arbitrarily chosen value for μ_0 (Section 33-2), one can *compute* the value of ϵ_0 and give its value to much higher accuracy than from measuring ϵ_0 directly through the electric interactions.

41-8 Summary   Maxwell's equations predict, and experiment shows, that electromagnetic radiation has the following properties.

The radiation is produced by accelerated electric charges; the charges lose energy which is carried in the electromagnetic field. Simple harmonic oscillations of electric charge produce sinusoidal electromagnetic waves.

Electromagnetic waves travel through a vacuum at the speed of light:

[41-9] $$c = \frac{1}{\sqrt{\epsilon_0 \mu_0}} = 3.00 \times 10^8 \text{ m/sec}$$

The instantaneous intensity (the Poynting vector), the electromagnetic power per unit transverse area, is given in both direction and magnitude by

[41-18] $$\boldsymbol{I} = \boldsymbol{E} \times \frac{\boldsymbol{B}}{\mu_0}$$

The E and B fields are perpendicular to each other and also perpendicular to the direction of propagation of the electromagnetic energy. The relative magnitudes of the E and B fields are related by

[41-10] $$B = E/c$$

The energy density u and linear momentum density M/v of an electromagnetic wave are given by

[41-14] $$u = \epsilon_0 E^2$$
[41-25] $$M/v = u/c$$

where E is the instantaneous electric field.

A completely absorbed electromagnetic wave of power P and intensity I exerts a radiation force F_r and radiation pressure p_r on its absorber, given by

[41-22] $$F_r = P/c$$
[41-24] $$p_r = I/c$$

For complete reflection, the force and pressure are doubled.

PROBLEMS

41-1 An electromagnetic wave is traveling along the negative Y-axis. The electric field at one instant is along the positive Z-axis and has a magnitude of 100 v/m. What are (a) the direction and (b) the magnitude of the magnetic induction at this instant?

41-2 Show in detail that $1/\sqrt{\epsilon_0 \mu_0}$ is 3.00×10^8 m/sec.

41-3 The intensity, or energy flux, is related to the energy density by the relation $I = uc$. If a beam consists of particles, all of velocity v and having a *particle flux* of N particles per second through a unit transverse area, what is the number density of the particles in the beam?

41-4 A parallel-plate capacitor is being charged. Show that the direction of the energy flux, as found from the Poynting vector, is radially into the space between the capacitor plates. (*Hint:* The magnetic induction arises from a displacement current.)

41-5 The expression giving the power P of an electromagnetic wave, $P = IA = \epsilon_0 c E^2 A$, is of the same form as the relation $P = (1/R)V^2$, giving the power dissipated in a resistor R with a potential difference V. Comparing these equations, one may identify the quantity $(1/\epsilon_0 c)$ as having the dimensions of resistance; this quantity, which enters in radiation problems, is, in fact, known as the "impedance of the vacuum." Show that $1/\epsilon_0 c$ is 377 ohms.

41-6 A beam of plane waves has a power P. Show that the energy per unit length along the direction of wave propagation is P/c.

41-7   Show that the linear momentum density (the linear momentum per unit volume) of an electromagnetic wave is equal to the wave's energy density divided by c.

41-8   A 10 kw light source is turned on for 10 sec and produces a beam of plane wave fronts. What are (a) the energy of the beam, (b) the linear momentum of the beam, (c) the recoil force acting on the light source while it is turned on, and (d) the distance between the leading and trailing edges of the beam?

41-9   A thin perfectly reflecting sheet of 50 mg mass is to be made to float near the Earth's surface by shining an electromagnetic beam on its lower surface. What is the minimum power of the beam?

41-10   A space ship, initially at rest and far from any other bodies, navigates by the radiation force produced by an emitted electromagnetic beam (a "photon rocket"). Assume the space ship's mass to be 2000 kg and the power output of the photon rocket to be 10 Mw. If the rocket is turned on for 1000 sec, what are (a) the linear momentum of the emitted radiation and (b) the final recoil speed of the space ship?

41-11   An evacuated spherical shell, black on its inside and having an isotropic 10 Mw point source of electromagnetic radiation at its center, is subject to atmospheric pressure (1.0×10^5 nt/m^2) at its exterior. For what radius will the shell have equal interior and exterior pressures?

41-12   What is the radiation force of a 1.0 kw beam of light on a surface which absorbs 75 per cent of the incident radiation and reflects the remainder?

41-13 ★   An electromagnetic beam of power P is incident normally on a perfectly reflecting square sheet of edge length L hinged at one edge. What is the radiation torque?

41-14 ★   A horizontal electromagnetic beam having a constant intensity of 10 Mw/m^2 is incident upon a perfectly absorbing rectangular sheet of area 1.0 m^2 which hangs freely and rotates about a horizontal axis at its top edge. The sheet's mass is 50 gm. At what angle with respect to the vertical does the sheet remain in equilibrium?

41-15   A beam of radiation of power P is incident at an angle of 45° upon a perfectly reflecting plane sheet. What are (a) the magnitude and (b) the direction of the radiation force on the sheet?

41-16   When a certain beam of light is completely absorbed by an object, the temperature rise over a period of 1.0 min is the same as that produced by heating the object with 15 cal. What is the radiation force of this beam on the absorber?

41-17   In emitting visible light, an atom is typically radiating for a time of 10^{-8} sec. (a) What is the total length of such a wave train? (b) How many wavelengths of 5000 Å light are contained in this wave train?

41-18   What is the average intensity of a sinusoidal electromagnetic wave in which the amplitude of the magnetic induction is 1.0 gauss?

41-19   Light has been observed from galaxies as far as 10^9 light-years away. What is the distance in meters to such a galaxy?

41-20   (a) Show that the electromagnetic power radiated from a sinusoidal electric dipole oscillator varies as the fourth power of the oscillation frequency. (b) An electric dipole emits radio waves of 10 Mcycles/sec with an amplitude of the oscillating charges of 0.10 m. What must be the oscillation amplitude of an atomic radiator emitting light of 5000 Å wavelength and having the same power output?

41-21   The presently accepted value for the speed of light is in error by no more than 3 parts in 10^6. Suppose that the radar method is used to determine the distance to the Moon (3.8×10^8 m). To what fraction of a second must one measure the time for a pulse of electromagnetic radiation to complete a round trip to the Moon, if one is to exploit fully the precision in the known value of the speed of light?

41-22   Galileo proposed (and tried, without success) the following method of measuring the speed of light. He and an assistant, each equipped with a lantern which could be shuttered or exposed, were separated by a large distance. At the instant that the assistant saw Galileo's light source first exposed, he was to expose his own; then Galileo was to observe the elapsed time by watching for the light from his assistant's light source. The human reaction time, approximately 0.1 sec, precludes a meaningful measurement for all moderate distances. By what distance would Galileo's assistant have to have been separated from him for a measurement of the speed of light to be in error by no more than 1 per cent, assuming no errors apart from those arising from the finite reaction times?

41-23   In Fizeau's experiment, the distance between the rotating toothed wheel and the mirror was 5.4 miles. What was the time interval for the light to travel a round trip?

41-24   Using a modification of the Fizeau method, in 1927 A. H. Michelson measured the speed of light by timing the flight of a light beam on a round trip between Mount Wilson and Mount San Antonio, 22 miles away. This distance was measured to within $\frac{1}{5}$ inch. What is the maximum allowable error in the time interval for one round trip, if the errors in the distance and time measurements are to be alike?

41-25   In a certain microwave measurement of the speed of "light," accurate to one part in 3×10^5, radiation having a frequency of 10 kMcycles/sec was used. What error, in terms of the number of wavelengths of 6000 Å light, is permissible in the measurement of wavelength?

FORTY-TWO

WAVES IN TWO AND THREE DIMENSIONS

Heretofore we have considered wave motion in which the energy is propagated along a single direction in space. In this chapter we treat the propagation of waves, both elastic and electromagnetic, in two and three dimensions. We first consider the wave fronts and rays of plane, cylindrical, and spherical waves, and find the variation of the intensity with distance for these three geometries. Next, we discuss the Huygens construction, through which the advance of a wave front may be charted. The Doppler effect, whereby the frequency of a wave is apparently influenced by the state of motion of the wave source or of the observer relative to the medium transmitting the wave, is then treated. We discuss briefly the special case of shock waves. Finally, we consider a general principle governing wave motion, the principle of reciprocity (optical reversibility).

42-1 Wave fronts and rays The simplest configuration for wave propagation is shown in Figure 42-1. Here the wave source is spread over a plane, as in the case of an oscillating flat diaphragm generating sound waves.

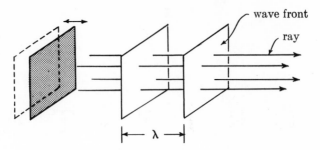

Figure 42-1. Plane wave source and plane wave fronts.

The waves progress to the right in a single direction. We may indicate the direction in which waves radiate from the source by straight lines, or *rays*. A *wave front* is defined as a surface on which all points have the same phase of oscillation. The wave front of a plane wave source consist of planes at right angles to the rays. In a periodic wave disturbance there are many wave fronts in the same phase, following one another. The perpendicular distance between adjoining wave fronts is the wavelength. Since the wave speed is also the phase speed, surfaces of constant phase, or wave fronts, advance from the source at the phase speed c.

A familiar special example of cylindrical wave fronts is that of a surface wave at a liquid surface, where circular wave fronts advance from a point in the liquid generating the waves. In the more general situation of three dimensions, a line source generates cylindrical wave fronts centered about it, as shown in Figure 42-2. The rays again intercept the wave fronts at right angles and radiate outward from the line source in planes perpendicular to the axis of the source. An example of cylindrical waves is that of electromagnetic waves generated by an oscillating electric current in an infinitely long straight conductor.

Now consider Figure 42-3, which shows waves emanating in three dimensions from a point source. An example is a small source of light or, more generally, any wave source viewed from a distance which is large compared with the size of the source. Thus, all stars (except the Sun) are effectively

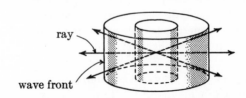

Figure 42-2. Line-source and cylindrical wave fronts.

point sources to an observer on Earth. The wave
fronts are spheres centered about the point
source. The rays radiate outward from the
source and are perpendicular to the wave fronts.
In general, rays are always perpendicular to the
associated wave fronts, even when the fronts are
not planes, cylinders, or spheres.

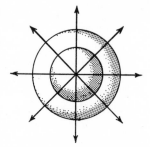

Any small portion of a cylindrical or spherical
surface is very closely a plane; that is, over a
small solid angle, a cylindrical or spherical wave
front closely approximates a plane wave front.
Thus, one can achieve a nearly plane wave from

Figure 42-3. Point-source
and spherical wave fronts.

a line source or point source simply by restricting the emitted waves to a
small solid angle to form a pencil of radiation.

42-2   Intensity variation with distance from source   The intensity,
or energy flux, of any wave is defined as the energy passing per unit time
through a unit cross-sectional area. That is, the intensity I is the power P
per unit transverse area A:

[41-15] $$I = P/A$$

In Section 41-2 it was shown that the energy density u is related to the
intensity I by

[41-16] $$\boxed{I = uc}$$ [42-1]

For a sinusoidal electromagnetic wave having an electric field amplitude
E_0 (see Equations 41-14 and 41-30),

$$u_{EM} = \tfrac{1}{2}\epsilon_0 E_0{}^2$$
$$I_{EM} = \tfrac{1}{2}\epsilon_0 E_0{}^2 c$$

For an elastic wave with pressure amplitude Δp_0 traveling through a material
of density ρ,

[40-19] $$I_{el} = \Delta p_0{}^2/2\rho c$$

and, therefore, from Equation 42-1 the corresponding energy density is

$$u_{el} = \Delta p_0{}^2/2\rho c^2$$

Every type of wave generated by a sinusoidal oscillator has an intensity I
and energy density u which is proportional to the *square* of the wave function, the physical property which characterizes the wave disturbance. The
wave function of electromagnetic waves may be chosen to be the electric

field E (or the magnetic field B); for elastic waves it is the pressure difference Δp. This result is hardly surprising. The total energy of any simple harmonic oscillator is proportional to the square of the oscillator's amplitude.

We wish now to consider how the intensity of a wave varies with distance from the source in the cases of three simple configurations of wave fronts, plane, cylindrical, and spherical. In a plane wave there is no divergence of the rays; the wave fronts are parallel planes. Therefore, the same energy from the source passes through any transverse area. The intensity is *constant*, independent of distance from the source.

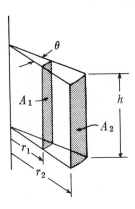

With cylindrical waves the situation is different. The energy carried by the wave is diluted in space as the expanding cylindrical wave fronts increase their surface area with time. Consider one angular segment, shown in Figure 42-4. The energy passing through the area A_1 with radius r_1 is exactly the same as the energy passing later through the area A_2 with radius r_2. Clearly, $A_1 = r_1\theta h$ and $A_2 = r_2\theta h$, or $A_1/A_2 = r_1/r_2$. Since the intensity varies inversely with the transverse area and $A = r\theta h$, the intensity of a cylindrical wave varies inversely as the distance r from the line source.

Figure   42-4. Angular segment for cylindrical wave fronts.

In the case of a spherical wave propagated from a point source, all the energy within the small cone having angles θ_1 and θ_2 passes, in turn, through areas A_1 and A_2, as shown in Figure 42-5. But $A_1 = r_1{}^2\theta_1\theta_2$ and $A_2 = r_2{}^2\theta_1\theta_2$; that is, the surface area of a given solid angle varies directly as the square of the sphere's radius. Thus, the intensity of waves from a point source varies inversely as the square of the distance from the source. In summary,

Plane waves:	$I = \text{constant}$
Cylindrical waves:	$I \propto 1/r$
Spherical waves:	$I \propto 1/r^2$

[42-2]

Waves on a surface from a point source, such as water waves, are a special case of cylindrical waves, and the intensity of these circular waves follows a $1/r$ dependence. In arriving at the results given in Equation 42-2 we have merely applied fundamental ideas of geometry and energy conservation.

We have *not* assumed that the intensity is the same in all directions from a line source or a point source. A point source radiating energy uniformly in all directions—a so-called isotropic radiator—would, of course, follow the

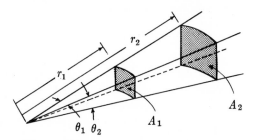

Figure 42-5. Angular segment for spherical wave fronts.

inverse-square rule for intensity, but exactly the same rule would also hold for a nonisotropic radiator, one in which the intensity is *not* the same for all points at the same distance from the source. Consider, for example, the electric dipole oscillator which we treated in Section 41-5. We found there that the magnitude of the transverse component of the electric field, in any direction θ with respect to the axis of oscillation of the electric charges, varied according to $E \propto \sin \theta$, a maximum field being radiated in the equatorial plane ($\theta = 90°$) and no electric field being radiated along the direction of acceleration of the charges ($\theta = 0$). Since $I \propto E^2$, the intensity varies with angle according to $I \propto \sin^2 \theta$; moreover, for *any* direction θ the intensity varies inversely as r^2. Therefore, the spatial dependence of the intensity for a dipole oscillator is given by

$$I \propto \frac{\sin^2 \theta}{r^2}$$

in agreement with Equation 41-27.

It is convenient to portray the angular dependence of the intensity in a *polar diagram*, as shown in Figure 42-6. In such a diagram the radius vector is proportional to the intensity I. Note that the intensity from a point source varies inversely as r^2 for *any* angular dependence.

It is interesting to compare the density of the electric energy associated with an electric point-charge at rest with the energy density arising from an accelerated electric charge radiating electromagnetic waves. We know from Coulomb's law that the electric field for a point-charge at rest (or one moving with constant velocity) is given by

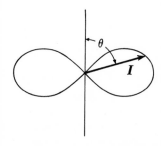

Figure 42-6. Intensity pattern for an electric dipole oscillator.

[26-3] $E = kq/r^2$

Therefore, the energy density associated with

a *static* electric field varies with distance according to

$$\text{Static charge:} \qquad u_E \propto 1/r^4$$

since the electric energy density is proportional to E^2. The static electric energy density falls off inversely as the *fourth* power of the distance from the charge. On the other hand, the energy density of an electromagnetic wave radiated by an accelerated charge varies with distance according to

$$\text{Radiating charge:} \qquad u_E \propto 1/r^2$$

since $u_E \propto I$, following Equation 42-1. At great distances from an accelerated charge only the radiation energy is important; static energy falls off with distance much more rapidly.

Example 1   A point source radiates isotropically at the rate of 10 kw. What is the intensity of the radiation at a distance of 10 m from the source?

The intensity I at a radius r from a point source is given by the power P through a spherical area $A = 4\pi r^2$:

$$I = \frac{P}{A} = \frac{P}{4\pi r^2} = \frac{(1.0 \times 10^4 \text{ w})}{4\pi(10 \text{ m})^2} = 8.0 \text{ w/m}^2$$

Example 2   The energy carried by a surface wave on a liquid is proportional to the square of the crest height h. How does the crest height vary with distance for a point source?

We are given that

$$h^2 \propto E$$

But $E \propto I \propto 1/r$; therefore, $h \propto 1/\sqrt{r}$.

42-3 Huygens' principle   Given one wave front for a progressing wave, how does one find a future wave front? If the waves are electromagnetic, it is possible, of course, to solve this problem by applying Maxwell's equations, and if they are elastic, or mechanical, one may use Newton's laws. There is, however, a remarkably simple geometrical procedure, *Huygens' principle*, that may be used to chart the progress of a wave front through a medium. Devised by C. Huygens (1629–1695) in 1678, this principle asserts that each point on an advancing wave front may be regarded as a new point source generating spherical *Huygens wavelets* in the forward direction of wave propagation. Thus, to find the wave front at a time t later, one draws circular arcs of radius ct centered at points along the wave front; the new wave front at time t is merely the envelope of these wavelets; see Figure 42-7. Thus a plane wave front generates another plane wave front; a spherical wave front generates another spherical wave front, of larger radius, about the same point source.

The Huygens construction is a geometrical procedure, not a physical method. Clearly, if one is to find a wave front at some *future* time, one must know the direction in which the wave front is advancing. That is, one must draw the envelope of the wavelets along the *leading*, rather than the trailing, side of the wave front. Huygens' method gives only the *possible* wave fronts at some future time; it does not give the distribution of energy over these wave fronts. A. J. Fresnel (1788–1827) showed, through a rather complex analysis, that there is, in fact, no energy on the trailing side of a wave front; that is, Fresnel showed that the Huygens construction corresponds realistically to the physical situation.†

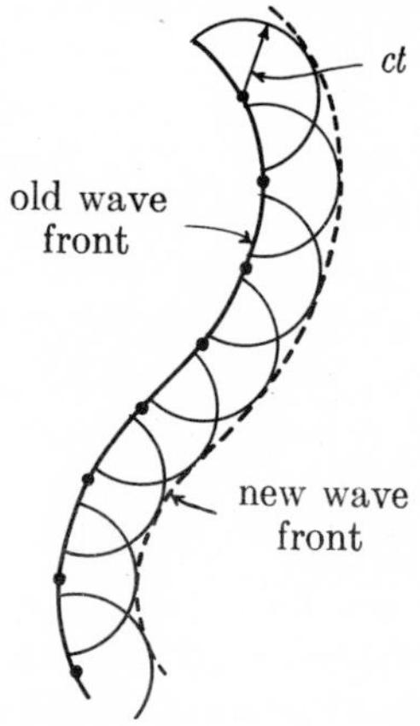

42-4   The Doppler effect   It is a common observation that the frequency of a wave source changes, or appears to change, when an observer of the wave disturbance or the source of the waves is in motion relative to the medium propagating the waves. Everyone is familiar, for example, with the change in the pitch of an automobile horn when the listener, or the horn, or both, are in motion relative to the medium (air) through which the wave propagates. This wave phenomenon, which also implies a change in the color of light emitted by a source moving relative to the observer, was first pointed out by C. J. Doppler (1803–1853) in 1842; it is known as the *Doppler effect*. We shall first consider elastic waves, or sound waves, propagated through a medium such as the air.

MOVING OBSERVER   We consider the case in which the wave source is at rest in the medium and the observer or listener is in motion. For a point source the wave fronts (in two dimensions) consist of circles concentric about the source and progressing outward with the wave speed c, as shown in Figure 42-8. We imagine the observer to be in motion at the speed v_0 relative to the medium.

Figure 42-7. Huygens' construction for advancing wave fronts.

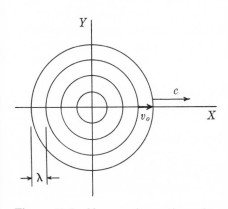

Figure 42-8. Observer in motion relative to a medium and a wave source.

† Fresnel's analysis showed that the amplitude of the Huygens wavelet depends upon the angle θ measured from the forward normal to the envelope, according to the *obliquity factor* $(1 + \cos \theta)$. The amplitude decreases as θ increases and becomes zero in the reverse direction ($\theta = 180°$).

We assume $v_o < c$. For simplicity, we consider only the special case in which the observer moves along a line which passes through the source, in this case to the left or right. Clearly, when the observer *recedes* from the wave source and travels in the same direction as the expanding wave fronts, he intercepts *fewer* wave crests per unit time; therefore, the *frequency* of arrival of wave crests at his ear is *reduced*. A listener receding from a sound source hears a lower pitch. Conversely, when he *approaches* the source, traveling in the opposite direction to that of the waves through the medium, he intercepts *more* wave crests per unit time, and the *frequency* of arrival of wave crests at his ear is *increased*.

We wish to find the frequency f_o measured by a *moving observer* in terms of the frequency of oscillations f_s of the wave *source*, the wave speed c, and the observer's speed v_o relative to the medium. We first write an equation describing the sinusoidal traveling wave relative to a reference frame in which the wave source is at rest; then, through the Galilean coordinate transformation relations we find the corresponding equation for the traveling wave as seen in a second "moving" reference frame. For definiteness, we assume the observer to be in motion to the right along the positive X-axis. An equation describing an elastic wave traveling to the right is

[39-10]
$$\Delta p = \Delta p_0 \sin 2\pi (f_s t - x/\lambda) \qquad \text{[42-3]}$$

where x is the coordinate measured in the reference in which both the generator and the medium are at rest. By definition, $c = f_s \lambda$.

How does an observer traveling to the right describe the same wave disturbance? We label the X-coordinate as measured by the moving observer x'; that is, x' is the coordinate relative to the reference frame in which the observer is at rest. Then from the Galilean coordinate transformations or from Figure 42-9.

[6-1]
$$x' = x - v_o t$$

or,
$$x = x' + v_o t \qquad \text{[42-4]}$$

Replacing x in Equation 42-3 by its value from Equation 42-4, we have

$$\Delta p = \Delta p_0 \sin 2\pi \left[f_s t - \frac{x' + v_0 t}{\lambda} \right]$$

$$= \Delta p_0 \sin 2\pi \left[\left(f_s - \frac{v_0}{\lambda} \right) t - \frac{x'}{\lambda} \right] \qquad \text{[42-5]}$$

Equation 42-5 describes the traveling wave as seen by the moving observer. It is of the form

$$\Delta p = \Delta p_0 \sin 2\pi \left(f_0 t - \frac{x'}{\lambda} \right) \qquad \text{[42-6]}$$

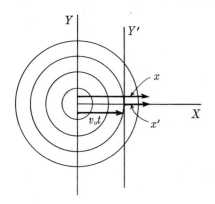

Figure 42-9. Coordinates for reference frames at rest relative to the medium x and the moving observer x'.

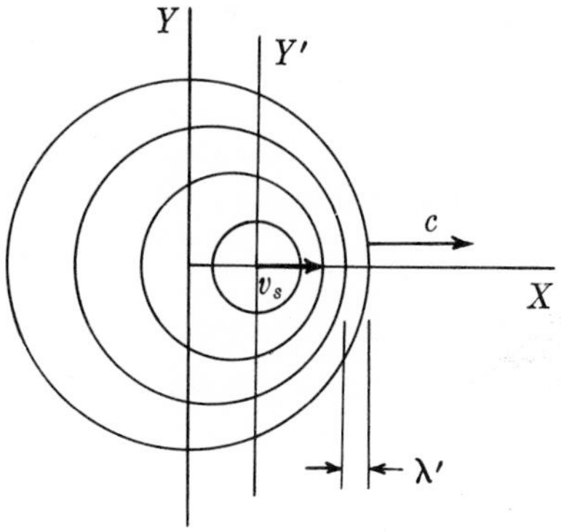

Figure 42-10. Source in motion relative to the medium.

Comparing Equations 42-5 and 42-6 it is clear that the observed frequency f_o is

$$\text{Observer receding from source:} \quad f_o = f_s - \frac{v_o}{\lambda} = f_s - \frac{f_s v_o}{c}$$

$$= f_s\left(1 - \frac{v_o}{c}\right) \qquad [42\text{-}7]$$

If the observer approaches the source with speed v_o, we must replace the velocity v_o by $-v_o$, and the observed frequency is then

$$\text{Observer approaching source:} \quad f_o = f_s\left(1 + \frac{v_o}{c}\right) \qquad [42\text{-}8]$$

Equations 42-7 and 42-8 apply, of course, only when $v_o < c$.

MOVING SOURCE   Now suppose that the source is in motion with the speed v_s relative to the medium propagating the wave. We again have wave fronts expanding outward at the wave speed c in the medium, but these wave fronts (nearly circular for $v_s \ll c$) are *not* concentric. Since the source is in motion relative to the medium, the wave fronts are crowded together in front of the traveling source and spread apart behind the source, as shown in Figure 42-10. The perpendicular distance between adjacent wave fronts is *no longer* given by c/f_s. An observer at rest in the medium and located to the right of the source measures a smaller wavelength; one to the left, a larger wavelength. Since all wave fronts travel at the speed c through the medium, a fixed observer on the right measures a higher frequency, and one fixed on the left measures a lower frequency, as compared with the single frequency f_s found when the wave source is at rest in the medium.

We wish to find the observed frequency f_o when the wave source is motion at the speed v_s. Our procedure is, as before, that of considering the wave propagation from two reference frames, that in which the medium (and observer) is at rest and that in which the wave source is at rest. Relative to a reference frame traveling *with the source*, the wave fronts move to the right with respect to the medium at the speed $c - v_s$; the frequency in this reference frame is f_s and the wavelength is λ'. Therefore,

$$c - v_s = f_s \lambda' \qquad [42\text{-}9]$$

On the other hand, relative to a reference frame fixed in the medium, the wave fronts advance to the right with the speed c. The frequency is now f_o, and the wavelength is again λ'. Thus,

$$c = f_o \lambda' \qquad [42\text{-}10]$$

Eliminating λ' between Equations 42-9 and 42-10 yields

$$\text{Source approaching observer:} \qquad f_o = \frac{f_s}{1 - v_s/c} \qquad [42\text{-}11]$$

For an observer located to the left of the moving source we have, replacing v_s by $-v_s$,

$$\text{Source receding from observer:} \qquad f_o = \frac{f_s}{1 + v_s/c} \qquad [42\text{-}12]$$

We can combine Equations 42-7, 42-8, 42-11, and 42-12 into a single equation:

$$\boxed{f_o = f_s \frac{(1 \pm v_o/c)}{(1 \mp v_s/c)}} \qquad [42\text{-}13]$$

The upper signs apply for relative approach of the source and observer; the lower signs, for relative recession.

If the speed v_s is much less than c, Equation 42-11 is closely approximated by $f_o \simeq f_s(1 + v_s/c)$; similarly, Equation 42-12 becomes $f_o \simeq f_s(1 - v_s/c)$. Thus, with $v \ll c$, Equations 42-11 and 42-12 for a moving source are of the same form as Equations 42-7 and 42-8. We may, in fact, summarize all of these equations by a single approximate relation:

$$\text{For } v \ll c, \qquad \frac{\Delta f}{f} = \frac{v}{c} \qquad [42\text{-}14]$$

where Δf is the change in frequency, or Doppler shift, $f_o - f_s$, and v represents the relative velocity between the source and the observer. Thus, for relative motion at speeds much less than c, the fractional change in frequency equals the relative speed divided by the wave speed. When the separation distance between the source and observer is decreased by their relative motion, the observed frequency is increased, and conversely.

For sound waves through air, or more generally, for elastic waves through any medium, there exists a *unique* reference frame in which the *speed* of the waves is the same in all directions, quite apart from the motion of the source. This unique reference frame is that in which the medium is at rest. Thus, when one is *at rest in the medium* transmitting the wave disturbance, the wave speed is *always* found to be c (although the motion of the source may change the frequency and wavelength). On the other hand, if an observer is in motion relative to the medium, he finds the wave *speed* to be different from c. Suppose, for example, that some observer knows the wave speed of sound through air to be 1100 feet/sec. This observer measures the frequency and wavelength of waves from the source in motion relative to him, and finds them to be 300 sec^{-1} and 4.0 feet, respectively. Therefore, the speed of waves relative to the reference frame in which the observer resides is 1200 feet/sec. The observer concludes that he is *not* at rest in the medium transmitting the sound waves (there is a wind, or an apparent wind, blowing).

This may appear to be a rather formal and pedantic point. It is, however, precisely on considerations of this kind that some profound differences are found concerning the propagation of electromagnetic waves, differences that led to the special theory of relativity.

Example 3 Sound waves of frequency 1000 cycles/sec travel through air at 330 m/sec. The waves strike and are reflected from a surface approaching the sound source at the speed 10.0 m/sec. The sound source is at rest with respect to air. What is the frequency of the reflected waves as observed at the site of the sound source?

We can solve this problem most readily by regarding it in two steps. First, the number of wave crests per second striking a reflector moving at speed v is the same as the frequency measured by a moving observer approaching the fixed sound source at speed v. Therefore, from Equation 42-8,

$$f_r = f_s\left(1 + \frac{v}{c}\right)$$

where f_s is the frequency of the source and f_r is the frequency at which the waves impinge upon the moving reflector.

The frequency of waves leaving the reflector is also f_r, and we may now regard the reflector as a moving source traveling at speed v toward the original sound source. From Equation 42-11, we have, for the frequency f' of the wave arriving at the original fixed source,

$$f' = \frac{f_r}{(1 - v/c)} = f\frac{(1 + v/c)}{(1 - v/c)}$$

$$f' \simeq f\left(1 + 2\frac{v}{c}\right) = (1000 \text{ sec}^{-1})\left[1 + \frac{2(10.0 \text{ m/sec})}{330 \text{ m/sec}}\right]$$

$$f' \simeq 1060 \text{ sec}^{-1}$$

DOPPLER EFFECT FOR LIGHT   Our results for the Doppler frequency shift apply, of course, not only to a sound wave through air, but to any wave which is propagated through a medium. We found that there is an increase in frequency when the source is at rest in the medium and the observer approaches it. Likewise, there is a frequency increase when the observer is at rest in the medium and the source approaches him. Suppose that the relative speed of source and observer in these two situations is the same speed v. Then, for the source at rest and the observer moving at speed v, we have

[42-8] f_o (an approaching observer) $= f_s(1 + v/c)$ [42-15]

For the observer at rest and the source moving at speed v,

[42-11] f_o (an approaching source) $= \dfrac{f_s}{1 - v/c}$

$$= f_s\left[1 + \frac{v}{c} + \frac{v^2}{c} + \cdots + \right] \qquad [42\text{-}16]$$

where we have used the binomial expansion. Clearly, the frequencies for f_o in Equations 42-15 and 42-16, although closely the same for $v \ll c$, are never precisely equal. The Doppler shift for elastic waves in a medium depends on whether it is the source or the observer that moves relative to the medium.

What is the situation with light or any other form of electromagnetic wave? No medium is required for the propagation of electromagnetic waves through empty space. Moreover, very delicate experiments show that the speed of light through a vacuum is precisely the same whether the observer, or the light source, or both are in motion. Said differently, there exists no unique reference frame, or medium (ether), in which the speed is c. The speed of light is exactly c in *all* reference frames. A profound consequence of this (apparently) bizarre phenomenon is that the Galilean transformation relations, on which our derivations for the Doppler effect in sound were based, do not properly describe the propagation of light. This implies, in turn, that the apparently self-evident properties of space and time on which the Galilean transformations are based are, in fact, invalid. These matters are corrected in the special theory of relativity.

An important consequence for electromagnetic radiation is the following. Since the speed of light is found to be the same by all observers, quite independent of the state of motion of the source or observer, one cannot distinguish between the situation in which a source of light is at rest and an observer in motion and that in which the observer is at rest and the light source in motion. The two are indistinguishable and equivalent. Thus, there can be but a *single* relation for the relativistic Doppler shift. As can be shown from the theory of special relativity, this relation is

$$f' = f_s \frac{(1 + v/c)}{\sqrt{1 - (v/c)^2}} \qquad [42\text{-}17]$$

where v is the relative speed of approach between source and observer, f_s is the source frequency, and f' is the observed frequency. It is easy to show that the frequency f' in Equation 42-17 differs from the frequency f_o given in either Equation 42-15 or Equation 42-16. If the speed v is small, the differences between Equations 42-15, 42-16, and 42-17 are slight, but if v becomes comparable to c, 3×10^8 m/sec, the relativistic Doppler effect *can* be distinguished from the classical Doppler effect. The relativistic Doppler effect has been observed, and Equation 42-17 has been confirmed, for the light from very high-speed ($\sim 10^6$ m/sec) hydrogen atoms emitted in the direction of their motion and in the opposite direction. That the observed frequency shift is in accord with Equation 42-17 constitutes one compelling experimental proof of the special theory of relativity.

Since the color of visible light is a measure of the wavelength and frequency of the light, the Doppler effect implies that an approaching light source appears "bluer" and a receding light source "redder" that the same light emitted when the source is at rest relative to the observer. The characteristic frequencies, or spectral lines emitted by excited atoms from distant stars thus serve as a means of measuring the speeds of the stars relative to the Earth. The Doppler shifts observed with light from certain very distant galaxies imply that such bodies are receding from our galaxy at speeds of up to one sixth the speed of light! An astronomer, whether studying visible electromagnetic radiation with an ordinary telescope or radio waves with a radio telescope, is restricted to observations of the directions, intensity, and frequencies of the electromagnetic radiation from distant objects. The Doppler effect is the most direct means of measuring the speeds of stellar objects through a measurement of frequency.

The Doppler effect is also responsible for the broadening of otherwise "sharp" (monochromatic) spectral lines. When atoms of a gas are in motion at any finite temperature, the radiating atoms have various velocity components along the direction of propagation of light which enters the detecting instrument. Thus, the observed frequency undergoes Doppler broadening.

Since the molecular velocities are determined by the temperature of the gas through the relation $\frac{1}{2}mv^2 = \frac{3}{2}kT$, the breadth of the spectral line may be used to deduce the gas's temperature. For typical molecular velocities, $v \ll c$. Then Equation 42-14 shows that the Doppler frequency breadth Δf of the observed radiation will be given by

$$\Delta f/f = v/c$$

Example 4 The H_α line of atomic hydrogen has a wavelength of 6565 Å. The measured wavelength of this radiation from a distant star is 6585 Å. What is the velocity of the star relative to the Earth?

Since the wavelength is increased and the frequency decreased, we know that the star must be receding from the Earth. The change in wavelength is 20 Å. The fractional change in wavelength and in frequency is small; therefore, the speed v of the receding star is much less than c, and we may write, using Equation 42-14,

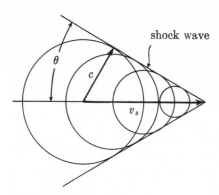

shock wave

$$\frac{\Delta\lambda}{\lambda} = \frac{\Delta f}{f} = \frac{v}{c}$$

$$v = \frac{\Delta\lambda}{\lambda} c = \frac{20 \text{ Å}}{6565 \text{ Å}}(3.0 \times 10^8 \text{ m/sec})$$

$$v = 9.1 \times 10^5 \text{ m/sec}$$

Figure 42-11. A shock wave.

42-5 Shock waves Consider the situation in which the speed v_s of a wave source through an elastic medium *exceeds* c, the speed of waves through the same medium. The circular wave fronts generated at a succession of times are then as shown in Figure 42-11. The envelope of these wavefronts is a cone centered about the velocity of the moving object with the source of the disturbance at its apex. The energy is concentrated at the expanding surface of the cone. There is, of course, energy within the cone, but because of the superposition of all wave fronts, the energy density is high along the cone. This concentration of energy is called a *shock wave*. Examples are these: the bow wave produced by a boat traveling along a body of water at a speed that exceeds that of the water waves along the surface, and shock waves produced by bullets or high-speed aircraft exceeding the speed of sound; see Figure 42-12.

When electrically charged particles pass through a medium at a speed which exceeds the speed of light *in that medium*, electromagnetic radiation, called *Cerenkov radiation,* is emitted in a cone surrounding the moving particle. The effect here arises from the polarization, or charge displacement, of the charges within the material as the swiftly moving particle traverses

Figure 42-12. Shock wave from a bullet through air. (Courtesy Ballistic Research Laboratories, Aberdeen Proving Ground, Maryland.)

the medium. The Cerenkov radiation, named for its discoverer, P. A. Cerenkov (1904–   ), is visible as bluish light when a source of high-speed particles, such as a nuclear reactor, is immersed in a refracting medium, such as water.

From the geometry of Figure 42-12 it is clear that the angle θ of the cone relative to its symmetry axis is given by

$$\sin \theta = c/v_s$$

[42-18]

The cone is narrow when the speed of the source is high. Indeed, one can measure the speed of the traveling source of the shock wave if one knows the speed of wave propagation in the medium and measures the angle θ. Thus, one may find the speed of a boat by measuring the angle of its bow wave; similarly, through the Cerenkov effect, one can find the speed of very high-speed particles by measuring the angle at which the Cerenkov radiation is emitted.

Strictly, an *elastic* shock wave is not a true wave in the sense that the shape of a traveling disturbance is unchanged as the disturbance advances through the medium. Recall (Section 40-2) that the requirement for the applicability of the superposition principle was that the particle speed be much *less* than the wave speed. Clearly, this is not the case in shock "waves."

Therefore, the shock disturbance travels outward from the conical surface at the speed c, but its shape changes with time.

42-6   The reciprocity principle for waves   Suppose that we view a motion picture of a wave phenomenon, perhaps a wave traveling along the surface of a liquid, as in a ripple tank. Assume, for simplicity, that there is no dissipation of energy as the wave progresses through the medium. Now, if the motion picture is run backward—that is, if we view the wave motion with time reversed—we see the wave fronts moving in the opposite directions, the directions of rays associated with these wave fronts having been reversed. Both wave motions, the first one with time running forward and the second with time reversed, are *possible* motions. Both are consistent with the

(a) (b)

Figure 42-13. Example of "optical" reversibility: a parabolic reflector as a transmitter and as a receiver.

laws governing wave motion. Thus, if we know the "path" of a wave from one point to a second point from the configuration of the ray (or rays) connecting the two points, the reverse path, from the second to the first point, is found simply by reversing the arrows on the rays. In short, if a ray goes from A to B, a ray also goes from B to A by the same route. This is the *reciprocity principle*, which asserts that any two points connected by a ray are reciprocal in the sense that the directions of wave propagation may be interchanged with no alteration in the pattern of the wave fronts. This principle is also termed the principle of *optical reversibility*. It applies to *all* nondissipative wave motion, not merely visible light.

Consider Figure 42-13. Here we see a portion of the wave fronts and their corresponding rays, which radiate from the point source and reflect off a parabolic reflector (the remaining waves emitted by the point-source continue to expand outward as spherical waves). As we shall see in Section 43-9, the beam consists of plane waves. Thus, a parabolic reflector changes diverging rays into parallel rays; as it were, it changes a point source into a plane wave source. Reversing the ray directions (imagining time to run backwards), we see that a beam of plane wave fronts incident upon the parabolic reflector is brought to a focus, all the rays intersecting at a single point. Thus, a parabolic reflector serves equally well as a transmitter or receiver of a parallel beam. By the same token, if we know the radiation pattern of a transmitting antenna, which gives the intensity radiated as a function of direction, we thereby know as well the behavior of the same antenna used as a receiver of radiation incident upon it; see Figure 42-14.

Another example of reciprocity is shown in Figure 42-15. Here light from a point source passes through a lens to form an image of the source. Upon ray (or time) reversal, the image becomes the source, and the source becomes the image. Strictly, the arrows on the rays are *not* necessary, except to indicate for convenience which of the two possibilities is under consideration.

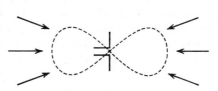

Figure 42-14. A receiving antenna has the same radiation pattern as a transmitting antenna.

The essential requirement for reciprocity, or reversibility, in wave motion is the absence of dissipation. We know from the second law of thermodynamics (Section 22-2) that a mechanical system can be reversed in time

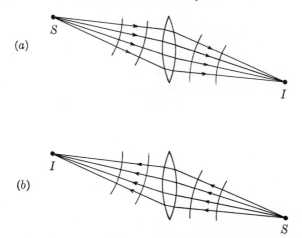

Figure 42-15. (a) A source S forms an image I when rays pass through a lens. (b) Reversing ray directions interchanges the source and image.

without any violation of the fundamental physical laws, provided that ordered energy is not degraded into disordered energy, or thermal energy. In any actual or real system, comprised of a large number of interacting particles, time's arrow points invariably to the future, because ordered energy is invariably degraded. Thus, if all the very many objects upon which a broadcast radio wave impinges were to oscillate in precisely the right way, these very many absorbers would act as radio transmitters, sending waves back to converge upon the broadcasting station's antenna and be absorbed there. This *is* a possible situation. It is also a very improbable one, essentially ruled out by the second law of thermodynamics.

42-7 Summary Wave fronts are surfaces of constant phase. Rays indicate the direction of wave propagation and are always at right angles to the wave fronts. Plane, line, and point sources generate, respectively, plane, cylindrical, and spherical wave fronts.

The energy density u of any wave is related to its intensity I by

[42-1] $$I = uc$$

where u is proportional to the square of the wave function.

The variation with distance of the intensity follows the rules:

[42-2]
Plane waves:	$I = \text{constant}$
Cylindrical waves:	$I \propto 1/r$
Spherical waves:	$I \propto 1/r^2$

In using Huygens' principle to construct future wave fronts one imagines each point on the present wave front to act as a point source of Huygens wavelets, the future wave front being the envelope of such wavelets.

In the Doppler effect the observed frequency f_o is related to the frequency f_s of the source by

[42-13] $$f_o = f_s \frac{(1 \pm v_o/c)}{(1 \mp v_s/c)}$$

where v_o is the speed of the observer and v_s is the speed of the source, both relative to the medium transmitting the waves, and the upper signs apply for approach and the lower for recession. In electromagnetic radiation the Doppler shifts do *not* arise by virtue of motion relative to a medium; they depend on the relative motion between source and observer only.

A shock wave is produced when the speed v_s of a wave source exceeds c, that of the wave through the medium. The angle θ of the shock wave is given by

[42-18] $$\sin \theta = c/v_s$$

According to the principle of reciprocity, one may imagine time to be run backward; that is, one may reverse the direction of the rays and the directions of motion of wave fronts, to arrive at a possible wave behavior.

PROBLEMS

42-1 What is the minimum power output of an isotropic point source of sound that will produce an intensity of 10^{-16} w/m^2 (the minimum threshold of hearing) at the ear of a listener 1.0 km distant from the source?

42-2 A 10 w isotropic point source radiates monochromatic electromagnetic waves. What are (a) the amplitude of the electric field and (b) the amplitude of the magnetic induction, at a distance of 10 km from the source?

42-3 What is the total output of electromagnetic radiation emitted by the Sun, given that the intensity of the Sun's radiation at the Earth's surface is 1.4 kw/m^2 and the Earth-Sun distance is 1.49×10^8 km?

42-4 What is the total radiation force of the Sun on the Earth? The Sun radiates electromagnetic energy at the rate of 4.0×10^{26} watt. Assume the radiation to be totally absorbed. The Earth's radius is 6.4×10^6 m; the Earth-Sun distance is 1.5×10^{11} m.

42-5 ★ A 1000 kg space ship near the Sun is attracted by a gravitational force and repelled by a radiation force. Assume that such a space ship has a perfectly absorbing "sail" oriented at right angles to the rays from the Sun. The mass of the sail is negligible. What is the minimum area of the sail that will permit the space ship to "float" at *any* distance from the Sun? The intensity at the Earth's surface of the Sun's radiation is 1.4 kw/m^2, the Sun's mass is 1.97×10^{30} kg, and the Earth-Sun distance is 1.5×10^{11} m.

42-6 ★ A perfectly absorbing sphere having a density of 4 gm/cm^3 is to be made to "float" when placed near the Sun. The Sun attracts the sphere gravitationally, but repels it through the radiation force. What is the maximum radius of such a sphere that will enable it to float? The intensity at the Earth's surface of the Sun's radiation is 1.4 kw/m^2, the Sun's mass is 1.97×10^{30} kg, and the Earth-Sun distance is 1.5×10^{11} m.

42-7 A certain radio telescope can detect a signal having an electric field amplitude of 10^{-6} μv/m. If such a signal is received from a star 10^4 light-years away, what is the electromagnetic power output of this star at this frequency?

42-8 The intensity from an electric dipole oscillator at a distance of 1.0 km and in a plane perpendicular to that of the dipole's axis is 1.0 w/m^2. If one measured the same intensity along a direction 30° from the axis of the dipole, at what distance would one be from the oscillator?

42-9 A camera with an aperture of 25 mm diameter ("$f/2$" for 50 mm focal-length lens) takes a photograph of a 50 w light source 100 m distant with an exposure time of $\frac{1}{100}$ sec. What is the energy of the light incident upon the film?

42-10 At one instant of time a certain wave front has the shape of an S. Sketch the wave fronts for later times.

42-11   An Earth satellite carries a radio transmitter operating at exactly 100 Mcycles/sec. What is the maximum change in frequency observed when the satellite is in orbit at a speed of 18,000 mi/hr relative to the observer?

42-12   A fixed observer hears a frequency of 1100 cycles/sec as a moving sound source approaches him, and a frequency of 1080 cycles/second as the same source recedes from him. Take the speed of sound through air as 1100 feet/sec. (a) What is the speed of the moving source? (b) What is the frequency of the source?

42-13   A moving observer hears a frequency of 1080 cycles/sec when approaching a fixed source of sound, and a frequency of 920 cycles/sec when receding from the same source. Take the speed of sound through air as 1100 feet/sec. (a) What is the speed of the moving observer? (b) What is the frequency of the source?

42-14   Show that the Doppler frequency shift for a source receding from a fixed observer is the same for supersonic $(v > c)$ and subsonic $(v < c)$ speeds.

42-15 ★ Observers A, B, and C all have wave generators operating at the same frequency f_o when the three observers are together and at rest relative to one another. Suppose that observer A moves west at the speed v, observer B remains at rest, and observer C moves east at the speed v, all relative to the medium transmitting the waves at the speed c. What is the frequency observed by A of (a) the waves generated by A and (b) the waves generated by C? What is the frequency observed by B of (c) the waves generated by A and (d) the waves generated by C?

42-16   Sound from a fixed 1000-cycle/sec source strikes a reflecting surface approaching the source. The interference between the incident and reflected sound produces beats of 30 cycles/sec. Take the speed of sound as 330 m/sec. What is the speed of the reflector?

42-17   A police "radar" device for measuring the speeds of vehicles compares the frequency of the transmitted radio wave with the frequency of the wave reflected from the moving vehicle. If the radio transmitter operates at 10.00 Mcycles/sec, what is the received frequency of waves reflected from an automobile receding at a speed of 60 miles/hr?

42-18   A source of sound with a frequency of exactly 10 kcycles/sec is traveling east at a speed of 100 feet/sec. An observer also moves to the east at 100 feet/sec. The speed of sound through air is 1100 feet/sec. What is the frequency of the source as measured by the moving observer when (a) he is traveling ahead of the source and (b) he is traveling behind the source?

42-19   A sound source fixed on the Earth oscillates at the frequency of 10,000 cycles/sec. The speed of sound through air is 330 m/sec. A wind of velocity of 20 m/sec is blowing from the east. What is the frequency heard by an observer fixed on Earth (a) to the west of the source and (b) to the east of the source?

42-20 ★ An observer stationed at one sound source of frequency f hears beats at a frequency f_b from a second identical source separated from and moving toward the first at speed v_2. A wind is blowing from the second toward the first source at a speed v_w. Derive an expression giving the wind velocity v_w in terms of f, f_b, v_2 and c, the speed of sound through still air.

42-21 (a) An observer is at rest in a medium. Sketch the curve of the observed frequency f_o versus the velocity of the source v_s (represent approach as to the right, recession as to the left) in the interval $-c \leq v_s \leq +c$. (b) With the source at rest in the medium, show on the graph of part (a) the curve of the observed frequency f_o versus the velocity of the observer in the interval $-c \leq v_o \leq +c$.

42-22 Relative to a reference frame attached to a source of frequency f and moving at the speed v_s through a medium transmitting an elastic wave at the speed c, the pressure variations are written as

$$\Delta p = \Delta p_o \sin 2\pi (ft - x'/\lambda')$$

where x' is the coordinate in the moving frame and λ' is the wavelength. Since the speed of the waves traveling along the positive X'-axis relative to this moving frame is $c - v_s = f\lambda'$, we may write

$$\Delta p = \Delta p_o \sin 2\pi [ft - fx'/(c - v_s)]$$

Use the Galilean coordinate transformations to write the corresponding equation for the pressure variations as measured by an observer at rest in the medium, and show thereby that the frequency measured by the fixed observer when the source recedes from him is given by $f/(1 + v_s/c)$, Equation 41-12.

42-23 The variable period of the moon of Jupiter, which is the basis of the measurement of the speed of light in Roemer's method, may be regarded as arising from a Doppler effect. The period of the orbital motion of one of Jupiter's moons is 42 hours. The orbital speed of the Earth about the Sun is 3.0×10^4 m/sec. What is the maximum change in the period (sec) of this moon as observed from Earth?

42-24 At what speed must a distant galaxy recede from the Earth so that green light ($\sim$5300 Å) emitted from it appears as yellow light ($\sim$5600 Å) upon its arrival at Earth?

42-25 The light from a member of the cluster of galaxies of Hydra shows a Doppler shift corresponding to a recession rate from our galaxy of 6.1×10^7 m/sec. Thus, ultraviolet light (light with a wavelength of less than 4300 Å, the violet limit of the visible spectrum) from this source can be "seen." What wavelength of light, measured relative to the source, would become visible at Earth at the violet limit of the visible spectrum?

42-26 The red shift of light from distant galaxies supports the model of the expanding universe, according to which the velocities of recession of distant galaxies is proportional to their distance. Given that light from the galaxy of Hydra, 10^9 light-years distant, shows a Doppler shift corresponding to 6.1×10^7 m/sec (one fifth the speed of light!), what is the limit of the observable universe in meters?

42-27 Show that for low speeds, $v/c \ll 1$, the relativistic Doppler relation, reduces to the classical Doppler relation. (Use the binomial expansion to show that Equation 42-17 reduces to Equation 42-15 or 42-16.)

42-28   The *Mach number* N gives the speed of an object, such as an aircraft, relative to the speed of sound in the medium through which the object travels. Show that the angle θ of a shock wave produced by an object with a Mach number N is given by $\sin^{-1}(1/N)$.

42-29   The Cerenkov effect is used to measure the speed of a particle through a medium in which the speed of light is 2.00×10^8 m/sec. If the angle between the direction of the particle's velocity and the wave front of the emitted Cerenkov radiation in the medium is $45°$, what is the speed of the particle?

42-30 ★ A plane wave is incident upon a converging lens like that shown in Figure 42-15. The wave comes to a focus at a distance f from the lens. Before passing through the lens, the wave's intensity is I_o, a constant. How does the intensity along the lens axis vary with the distance x from the lens after the wave has passed through the lens?

FORTY-THREE

REFLECTION AND REFRACTION

In this chapter we shall deal with waves traveling in two or three dimensions and encountering the boundaries between media. In respect to waves whose wavelength is small compared with the size of obstacles or apertures, the only phenomena occurring at the interfaces are reflection and refraction. Happily, these effects can be understood and the progress of a wave can be charted by a simple geometrical procedure, that of ray-tracing. Thus, in this chapter we shall be concerned with ray optics, or geometrical optics, and we shall exclude such distinctive wave effects as interference and diffraction.

Besides treating the rules of reflection and refraction of both elastic and electromagnetic waves, we shall briefly discuss reflection, refraction, and dispersion of electromagnetic waves from an atomic point of view. We shall discuss the reflection properties of pseudovectors. Finally, we shall treat Fermat's principle, an alternative general procedure for understanding reflection and refraction.

43-1   Ray optics and wave optics   An opaque object with a sharp boundary casts a sharp shadow when illuminated with visible light from a small source. Light travels, or appears to travel, strictly along a straight line. It is not obvious, certainly not to the casual observer, that light is, in fact, an electromagnetic *wave* phenomenon. Indeed, the rectilinear propagation of light through a uniform medium suggested to early physicists that light consists of particles, or corpuscles. Let us see under what conditions light, or any other wave disturbance, can be considered to follow

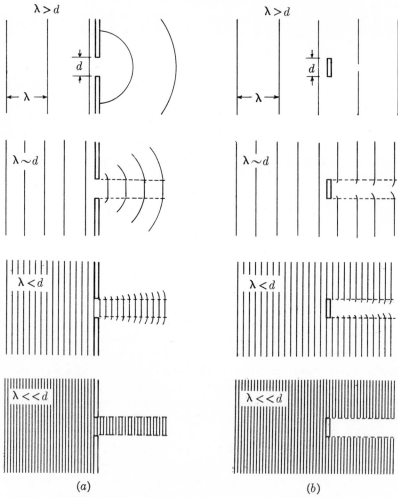

(a)   (b)

Figure 43-1. (a) Waves of decreasing wavelength λ encountering an aperture of size d. (b) Waves of decreasing λ encountering an obstacle of size d.

the "paths" given by the rays associated with wave fronts; that is, let us note under what conditions one may ignore the distinctive wave effects.

Figure 43-1a shows waves of various wavelengths impinging on an opaque object with a circular aperture of width d. When $\lambda > d$, the waves spread outward from the aperture in all directions, and the wave fronts are circular. In the case of shorter wavelengths, the spreading, or diffraction, of the waves beyond the limits of the geometrical shadow is less pronounced. Finally, when $\lambda \ll d$, the wave fronts remain straight lines as they pass through the aperture, and the wave disturbance lies strictly within the limits of the "shadow" of the opening. Said differently, any ray which enters the opening continues through the opening without a change in direction.

A similar behavior is seen in waves encountering an isolated opaque object, as shown in Figure 41-1b. When the wavelength is relatively large compared with d, the rays are bent and the wave fronts are curved by diffraction with the object. When $\lambda \ll d$, however, the object casts a sharp shadow, the diffraction effects are so small as to be negligible, and we may draw any ray as undeviated if it does not make a direct encounter with the object. In the remainder of this chapter we shall assume that the condition $\lambda \ll d$ is always met; the diffraction effects with $\lambda \simeq d$ will be dealt with in Chapter 46.

Under what conditions, then, may we treat visible light by the procedures of ray, or geometrical, optics rather than wave, or physical, optics? The wavelengths of visible light are somewhat less than 0.001 mm. Therefore, ray optics will suffice in the analysis of visible light as long as we deal with objects or openings of ordinary size, that is, much larger than 10^{-3} mm (several thousand Angstroms). The requirement for ray "optics" applies equally well to other wave types. Thus, an audible sound wave through air with a frequency of 1000 cycles/sec and a wavelength of 30 cm *cannot* ordinarily be treated by the procedures of ray optics. Similarly, the rays of microwave electromagnetic waves, whose wavelengths are also typically of the order of several centimeters, cannot be traced by geometrical optics unless the microwaves strike objects whose characteristic dimensions are much larger than a few centimeters.

Although we shall deal with wavelengths which are much shorter than the width of apertures and obstacles, it will always be assumed that the wavelength is large compared with the microscopic objects responsible for the reflection and refraction effects. For example, it is the individual atoms and their associated electrons in a solid or liquid that cause visible light to be reflected and refracted; but the spacing between adjacent atoms, a few Angstroms typically, is much less than several thousand angstroms. By the same token, a sheet of ordinary chicken wire, porous to visible light, acts as an opaque reflector for radio waves of several meters in wavelength.

43-2   Rules of reflection and refraction   We have already seen (Section 39-4) that when an elastic wave traveling in one dimension encounters a boundary between two media, the incident wave is partially transmitted into the second medium and partially reflected back into the first medium. This is exactly what happens when waves in two and three dimensions encounter a boundary: partial reflection and partial transmission take place. Since the transmitted wave is, in two or three dimensions, usually bent, or refracted (except for normal incidence), at the interface, we shall call it the *refracted* ray, or wave front, rather than the transmitted ray or wave front.

We first state the rules for reflection and refraction, and later we shall show how they follow simply from fundamental principles. Figure 43-2

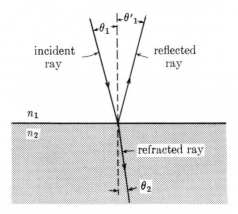

Figure 43-2. Reflection and refraction at an interface.

shows a ray incident at the interface between two media; for example, a narrow pencil of light is entering water from air. The directions of the incident ray θ_1, of the reflected ray θ_1', and of the refracted ray θ_2 are, by convention, measured relative to the normal to the interface.

(1) Both the reflected ray and the refracted ray lie in the plane defined by the incident ray and the normal.

(2) The angle of incidence equals the angle of reflection.

$$\boxed{\theta_1 = \theta_1'}$$ [43-1]

(3) For a given frequency of the wave, the angles of incidence, θ_1, and of refraction, θ_2, are related by

$$\boxed{n_1 \sin \theta_1 = n_2 \sin \theta_2}$$ [43-2]

where n_1 and n_2 are constants characteristic of media 1 and 2, respectively. This relation is known as Snell's law, after its discoverer W. Snell (1591–1626). The constants, called *indices of refraction*, will be related to the wave speeds and wavelengths in the respective media in Section 43-6. According to the principle of reciprocity, we may reverse the ray directions; thus, the designation of one angle as that of "incidence" and the other as that of "refraction" is actually arbitrary.

This is the long and the short of ray optics. Given a table listing the values of n for various materials, one may, in principle, trace the rays in complete detail as they pass through a whole succession of surfaces. In *specular* reflection, as that from the polished surface of a flat or curved mirror, irregularities in the surface are not large compared with the wavelength. Even in *diffuse* reflection, which occurs when the surface is not smooth, the law of reflection holds exactly at any portion of the surface which is small enough to be regarded as smooth. Although Figure 43-2 shows the interface between the media as a straight line, one may apply these rules to curved surfaces merely by choosing the interface small enough for it to be regarded as a plane. Although the program of ray optics is simple in principle, involving nothing more than geometrical constructions following the rules given above, the actual design of optical systems, such as lenses, or collections of lenses, or radar antennas, is, except for certain special situations, rendered extraordinarily difficult by the fact that one must trace an extremely large number of rays. Indeed, the computations are so involved that a thoroughgoing analysis of lens design can be carried out only by the use of large-capacity high-speed computers. (The simpler elements of the theory of refraction from curved surfaces and of lens design are discussed in Chapter 44.)

There is one aspect of reflection and refraction at an interface that *cannot* be treated by the methods of ray optics. This is the matter of determining the relative intensities of the reflected and transmitted beams. The reflection-transmission ratio can, in fact, be computed from the n_1/n_2 ratio by applying Maxwell's equations to electromagnetic waves, or applying energy and momentum conservation to elastic waves. We shall omit considerations of the intensity ratios, except for one important case: that in which the incident wave is *totally* reflected from the interface (Section 43-8).

43-3 Reflection Figure 43-3 shows a succession of plane wave fronts incident upon a plane surface, the angle of each wave front *relative to the surface* being the angle of incidence θ_1. We find the reflected wave fronts from Huygens' principle (Section 42-3), taking the envelope of the Huygens wavelets generated along the wave front to find a future wave front. Although we used the Huygens wavelets only on the *leading* side of a wave

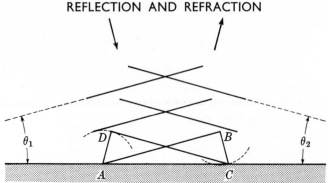

Figure 43-3. Plane wave fronts incident upon a plane reflecting surface.

front in charting a wave's progress through a uniform medium, here we must use the Huygens wavelets generated at the interface in the *backward* direction. There is a physical basis for this construction: when an elastic wave impinges upon a boundary, it sets the particles at the boundary in motion, and these oscillating particles act as wave generators, sending waves both into the interior of the medium and backward into the first medium. When an electromagnetic wave travels through a medium, the electric field of the wave sets electrons in forced oscillation. These electric oscillators generate electromagnetic waves traveling both forward *and* backward within the refracting medium. The intensity of the radiation in the backward direction is, however, zero. But at the boundary to a refracting medium there is no longer the symmetry required to cancel the backward wave; therefore a reflected as well as a refracted wave is generated.

As Figure 43-3 shows, the left end A of the wave front touches the surface at the instant that the right end of the wave front B is a distance BC away from the surface. After a time t has elapsed, where $t = c/BC$ (c being the wave speed), the right end of the wave front has reached point C. At this same instant the left end is at D, where $DB = ct$. Therefore, $AC = DB$, and $\theta_1 = \theta_1'$.

Note that it is not necessary to assume the surface to consist of a continuous distribution of material. As long as the individual sources of reflected waves are separated by a distance which is small compared with the wavelength, a collection of discrete scatterers of incident waves is equivalent to a continuous distribution.

Now consider spherical wave fronts from a point source S and incident on a plane surface, as shown in Figure 43-4. We find the reflected rays and the reflected wave fronts, their orthogonal trajectories, by applying the rule $\theta_1 = \theta_1'$ to each ray. The reflected wave fronts are still spherical wave fronts (or circular wave fronts in two dimensions), and the reflected rays diverge, or appear to diverge, from a single point I. To an observer viewing the reflected rays only, these rays seem to come from the *image I* rather than from their true origin, the source S. The human eye is naïve in that it interprets all rays reaching it as having always traveled in unbroken straight lines. Thus, to the eye (or a camera) it would appear that the source is located at the location of the image, which, from the geometry of Figure 43-4, is symmetrically located with the source relative to the reflecting boundary midway between them. This image is said to be *virtual*, inasmuch as the rays appear to, but do not actually, pass through the location I.

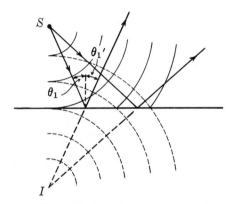

Figure 43-4. Spherical wave fronts striking a plane reflecting surface and forming an image I.

We treat the important case of reflection of a plane wave from a parabolic mirror (in two dimensions, or by a paraboloidal mirror in three dimensions) in Section 43-9 by the elegant methods of Fermat's principle. Reflection from a spherical surface is treated in Section 44-5.

Example 1 An object is placed near two plane mirrors at right angles to one another. What images of the object are seen in the mirrors?

See Figure 43-5a, where the object is represented by O and the eye by E. Applying the rule $\theta_1 = \theta_1'$ at each reflection, we find that there are *three* virtual images: image I_1 formed by reflection from mirror 1, image I_2 formed by reflection from mirror 2, and image I_{12} formed by reflections from both mirrors. Image I_{12} can be said to be the image in mirror 2 of the image I_1. The object and the three images are located symmetrically with respect to the lines representing the mirrors.

Note that the ray reaching the eye from image I_{12} is *parallel* to the same ray leaving the object O; that is, a ray undergoing two reflections at a corner mirror always emerges parallel to the ray leaving the object. This same behavior is seen when billiard balls make two "reflections" upon colliding with a corner of a billiard table. When one has *three* mutually perpendicular mirrors forming a corner reflector, any ray undergoing a reflection from each of the three mirrors will

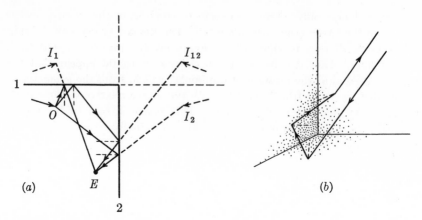

Figure 43-5. (a) Images formed by reflections from two mirrors at right angles. (b) A corner mirror.

emerge parallel to the incident ray, as shown in Figure 43-5b. Thus, *any* ray, whatever its direction, encountering a corner mirror is reflected back undeviated in direction (but displaced laterally). A number of corner reflectors, usually made of red glass, are used for example, on the rear fenders of bicycles; any light shining on them is returned toward the light source. Large-scale corner reflectors are in common use as "targets" for radar signals.

43-4 Reflection properties of pseudovectors In this section we digress to consider some fundamental properties of vector quantities which are most vividly exhibited in their reflection properties.

We delineate two types of vectors: ordinary (or polar) vectors, and so-called *pseudovectors* (or axial vectors). The pseudovector P is defined as the cross product of two ordinary vectors V_1 and V_2:

$$P = V_1 \times V_2 \qquad [43\text{-}3]$$

Ordinary vectors and pseudovectors *differ* in their reflection properties. A consideration of this difference allows us to state in formal terms why it is that we see our left and right sides reversed in a mirror image, but not our head and feet or front and back. More importantly, the distinction between ordinary vectors and pseudovectors has important consequences in the properties of physical quantities and wave functions in the quantum theory.

Some physical examples of pseudovectors are these: the angular momentum of a particle, $L = r \times p$ (Equation 15-1); the magnetic field generated by a moving charge, $dB = (\mu_0 q_1/4\pi r^3)v_1 \times r$ (Equation 33-3). In each instance we follow the *right*-hand rule to relate the direction of P to those of V_1 and V_2, as shown in Figure 43-6; that is, we *rotate* V_1 into V_2 through the smaller angle with the right-hand fingers to find the direction of P.

As we know, the rules for vector addition hold for both V and P. Therefore, we may always replace either V or P with its rectangular components. Moreover, multiplication of either V or P by a scalar changes the magnitude of the vector but not its direction.

We wish to inquire into the three operations translation, rotation, and reflection, in which we change the direction of V and of P. Figure 43-7 shows the translation and rotation of V and P. There is no change in the magnitude or direction of either V or P under translation. Under rotation, the magnitudes are unchanged, while the direction changes.

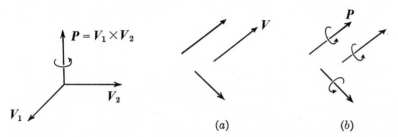

(a)   (b)

Figure 43-6. A pseudo-vector $P = V_1 \times V_2$.

Figure 43-7. (a) Ordinary vectors and (b) pseudovectors under translation and rotation.

Consider reflection. We imagine the vector V to be an object whose image V' is found on the reverse side of a mirror by the rules of reflection. (This operation is related to the so-called *parity* operation in which we change the signs of the coordinates of a vector to find its vector pair.) As Figure 43-8a shows, the magnitudes of the image vectors V_1', V_2', and V_3' are equal, respectively, to the magnitudes of their object vectors. On the other hand, any vector (or component) *perpendicular* to the mirror *changes direction*, while vectors (or components of vectors) parallel to the mirror do not. Symbolically,

$$V_\perp' = -V_\perp$$
$$V_\parallel' = V_\parallel \qquad\qquad [43\text{-}4]$$

The reflection rules for pseudovectors are *not* the same as those given in Equation 43-4, as Figure 43-8b shows. The reflection properties of each of the vectors V_1, V_2, and V_3 follow from Equation 43-4. The reflection property of the pseudovector $P_\perp = V_2 \times V_3$ then becomes, according to the rules given in Equation 43-4,

$$P_\perp' = P_\perp \qquad\qquad [43\text{-}5a]$$

In similar fashion we find that the pseudovector $P_\parallel = V_1 \times V_2$ is given by

$$P_\parallel' = -P_\parallel \qquad\qquad [43\text{-}5b]$$

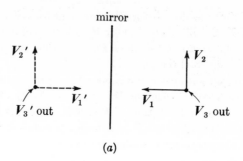

(a)

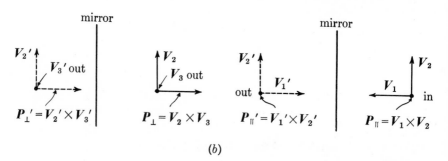

(b)

Figure 43-8. Reflection properties of (a) ordinary vectors and (b) pseudo-vectors.

The reflection rules for pseudovectors, given in Equation 43-5, are just the *reverse* of the reflection rules (Equation 43-4) for ordinary vectors.

Now consider the pseudovector P,

$$P = F \times U$$

where F is the vector *front* and U is the vector *up*. What is the meaning, directionally speaking, of P? See Figure 43-9. The direction of P is *right*. In fact, this is how we define "right": cross "forward" into "up" (using the

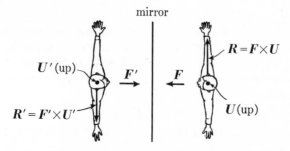

Figure 43-9. Reflection properties of "up," "right," and "front."

right-hand rule). On the other hand, the direction of P', P's mirror image, is *left*. Left and right are interchanged in mirror reflection because right and left are pseudovectors; up and down are not interchanged in reflection because these ordinary vectors are oriented *parallel* to the mirror; front and back are *reversed* (we do not see our back in a mirror image), because F is an ordinary vector perpendicular to the mirror. For the man looking into a mirror in Figure 43-9, the direction right (a pseudovector) is in the *same* direction as his six-fingered hand. For the reflection image, the direction right is in the direction of his four-fingered hand.

A pseudovector, ordinarily represented as a directed line segment in the same fashion as an ordinary vector, can be represented more properly

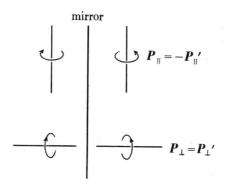

Figure 43-10. Axial (pseudo) vectors represented by a curl and their reflection properties.

without an arrowhead giving its direction. (An ordinary vector, a *polar* vector, has an arrow; a pseudovector, an *axial* vector, merely an axis.) One may use instead a curl to give the rotational sense of the cross product, as shown in Figure 43-10. Note that the reflection properties given in Equation 43-5 are preserved, if we replace the direction with the rotational sense.

In all physical situations in which a pseudovector, or a cross product, enters, the assignment of the rotational sense by a *right*-hand rule, rather than a *left*-hand rule, is actually of no consequence. By convention we use the right-hand rule to find the direction of the magnetic field from the relation $d\boldsymbol{B} = (\mu_0 q_1/4\pi r^3)\boldsymbol{v}_1 \times \boldsymbol{r}$. The right-hand rule also enters in finding the magnetic force through the relation $\boldsymbol{F}_m = q_2\boldsymbol{v}_2 \times \boldsymbol{B}$. If we had chosen the left-hand rules there would be *no* change in the direction of the magnetic *force* between two electric charges in relative motion. When cross products appear in physical laws, they always appear in *pairs* or in even numbers.

Thus, the choice of right or left for the cross-product convention does *not* enter into any physical result.

One would, therefore, conclude that if any event in physics is imagined to be reflected in a mirror, that is, if we watch the phenomenon after reflection in a mirror, as well as directly, it would be impossible to tell whether the "real" events or the "mirror" events corresponded to the real world. Either of the two should be equally possible. (In formal terms in physics this state of affairs is described by saying that "parity is conserved.") It is, therefore, an extraordinary fact that in certain phenomena in radioactive decay only one, not both, of the events on the two sides of the mirror are actually found to occur in our universe. In such events parity is *not* conserved. More specifically, since the labels "north" and "south" are merely convenient names to keep straight the direction of the pseudovector $d\boldsymbol{B}$, needed later to find the magnetic force direction, one would expect there to be no essential difference between north and south, that is, between a magnet (or a circular loop of current-carrying conductor) and its mirror image. The experiments in beta decay show, however, that elementary particles can, in fact, tell a difference, and will be emitted in beta decay preferentially along *one* direction in a magnetic field.

43-5 Index of refraction We first recognize that when a wave travels from medium 1, in which its wave speed is c_1, to a second medium 2, in which the wave speed is c_2, the *frequency f* of the wave is *unchanged*. Thus, if the wavelengths in the two media are, respectively, λ_1 and λ_2, we may write

$$c_1 = f\lambda_1$$
$$c_2 = f\lambda_2$$

[43-6]

The wavelength is greater in the medium with higher wave speed.

We shall hereafter denote the wave speed of electromagnetic radiation traveling *in a vacuum* by the symbol c. It is then useful to specify the wave speed in any medium by an *index of refraction n*, which gives the ratio of c to that of the wave speed in the medium. Therefore,

$$c_1 = c/n_1$$
$$c_2 = c/n_2$$

[43-7]

where n_1 and n_2 are called the indices of refraction for media 1 and 2. By definition, the index of refraction of a vacuum, or empty space, is exactly 1. Light and other types of electromagnetic wave travel through all other media at a *lower* speed than c. Therefore, the indices of refraction are always greater than 1. For example, the speed of light through water is found to be

2.25 $\times$ 10^8 m/sec, so that the water's index of refraction for visible light is $n = (3.00 \times 10^8 \text{ m/sec})/(2.25 \times 10^8 \text{ m/sec}) = 1.33$. The index of refraction for air near the Earth's surface is found to be 1.00029. Thus, the speed of electromagnetic waves in air is, to four significant figures, the same as in a vacuum, 3.00×10^8 m/sec, and $n_{air} \simeq 1$.

Table 43-1 lists indices of refraction to three significant figures for some common transparent materials.

Table 43-1

MATERIAL	REFRACTIVE INDEX
Diamond	2.42
Ethyl alcohol	1.36
Glass (crown)	1.52
Glass (light flint)	1.60
Ice	1.31
Quartz (fused)	1.46
Sodium chloride	1.54
Stibnite (Sb_2S_3)	4.46
Water	1.33

The *relative* index of refraction of medium 2 to medium 1, represented by n_{21}, is given by

$$n_{21} = n_2/n_1 \qquad [43\text{-}8]$$

which, from Equation 43-7, is equivalent to

$$n_{21} = c_1/c_2$$

It follows, of course, that

$$n_{21} = 1/n_{12}$$

In the next section we shall see that the index of refraction, here defined as the ratio of wave speeds in two media, is the same as the refractive index defined by Snell's law, Equation 43-2. Thus, one can measure the value of the refractive index quite directly by observing the refraction of waves at an interface. The wavelengths in two media can be related to the respective indices of refraction from Equations 43-6 and 43-7;

$$\lambda_1/\lambda_2 = n_2/n_1 \qquad [43\text{-}9]$$

If the index is large, the wavelength is small. For example, when blue light of wavelength 4000 Å (in free space) enters glass having an index of refraction of 1.500, the wavelength of this *blue* light in glass is *less*, namely (4000 Å)/1.500 = 2667 Å. The *color* of visible light is a measure of the *frequency* of the radiation (for blue light, 7.5×10^{14} sec^{-1} in *any* medium), not of the wavelength, which is a maximum for free space and less in media. It is customary, however, to characterize a particular color of visible light by its *wavelength in free space*, rather than by its frequency, simply because the wavelength can be measured directly, whereas the frequency is computed from a knowledge of the wave speed.

In the case of elastic waves one can give only relative indices of refraction for a pair of media; there is no unique "medium" corresponding to free space for electromagnetic waves, in which the index of refraction is 1.

Figure 43-11. Change in wavelength arising from a change in wave speed in a ripple tank. (From PSSC PHYSICS, D. C. Heath and Company.)

For small deformations the wave speed of elastic waves through any given medium depends on the elastic and inertial properties of the medium (Section 40-2) but *not* on the wave shape. Elastic waves, whatever their wavelengths or frequencies, travel through a given medium at nearly the *same* speed. Measurements show, however, that the relative index of refraction for elastic waves in a given medium is *dependent* on the frequency. This is also the case of electromagnetic waves. The index of refraction of a material transparent to visible light rays usually *increases* with frequency. Thus, violet light travels through glass at a lower speed (approximately 1 per cent) than does red light, of longer wavelength and lower frequency. Whereas all the component frequencies of white light travel through a vacuum at the same speed c, the speeds of the various colors differ as the white light enters a refracting medium. Table 43-2 shows the refractive indices for several wavelengths (in air) through quartz.

Table 43-2

Wavelength, in air (Å)	Refractive index, quartz
4000	1.470
5000	1.463
6000	1.458
7000	1.455

The surface waves of a liquid show a behavior similar to that of light waves. The wave speed decreases as the depth of the water is reduced. Thus, in the ripple tank one sees the wave fronts compressed, corresponding to a decrease in wavelength, as the waves enter a region in which the depth is reduced; see Figure 43-11.

43-6 Refraction Figure 43-12 shows wave fronts incident from medium 1, in which the wave speed is c_1, the wavelength is λ_1, and the index of refraction is n_1 into medium 2, where the corresponding quantities are c_2, λ_2, and n_2. The angle of incidence θ_1 is also the angle between the incident

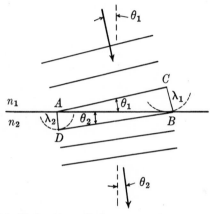

Figure 43-12. Refraction of plane wave fronts at an interface.

wave fronts and the interface; similarly, the angle of refraction θ_2 can be measured between the boundary and the wave fronts in medium 2. We see from the figure that, in the time interval in which the right end of the wave front advances one wavelength λ_1 in medium 1, the left end of the same wave front has advanced one wavelength λ_2. From the geometry of Figure 43-12, we have for triangle ABC

$$\sin \theta_1 = CB/AB = \lambda_1/AB$$

and for triangle ABD

$$\sin \theta_2 = AD/AB = \lambda_2/AB$$

Eliminating AB gives

$$\frac{\sin \theta_1}{\sin \theta_2} = \frac{\lambda_1}{\lambda_2}$$

which can be written, by using Equation 43-9,

[43-2] $$n_1 \sin \theta_1 = n_2 \sin \theta_2$$ [43-10]

This is Snell's law.

An alternative form of Snell's law, in which the relative index of refraction is used, is

$$\frac{\sin \theta_1}{\sin \theta_2} = n_{21} = 1/n_{12} \qquad [43\text{-}11]$$

We have seen that the refraction of a ray at the interface of two media arises from a change in the wave speed, and we may compute the relative wave speeds in two media simply by applying Snell's law to find the relative refractive index. In 1862 J. B. L. Foucault performed an experiment highly significant in the history of the theory of light, when he showed that the speed of visible light through water is *less* than through air.

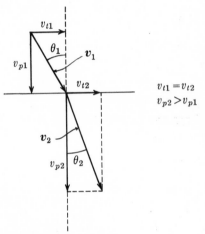

$$v_{t1} = v_{t2}$$
$$v_{p2} > v_{p1}$$

Figure 43-13. Change in velocity of "particles" of light at an interface. The tangential and perpendicular velocity components are v_t and v_p, respectively.

In deriving Snell's law we have assumed light to be a *wave* phenomenon. Snell's law, however, was recognized as a mere empirical relation for describing the change in direction of light at an interface, long before the wave theory of light was accepted in the early nineteenth century. At that time the indices of refraction were taken as mere parameters characterizing the media and were not then recognized as giving the relative wave speeds. Indeed, light was first thought to consist of particles. The particle model is consistent with the rectilinear propagation of light and the sharp shadows cast by point sources: the rays are the paths of the light corpuscles. It also can account for the inverse-square diminution in intensity from a point source: the particles radiate outward from the source passing through increasingly larger transverse areas. The equality of angles of incidence and reflection is easily interpreted: the particles collide elastically, in the fashion of small billiard balls, with a hard surface, momentum and energy conservation insuring that $\theta_1 = \theta_1'$.

The particle model can, in fact, account for Snell's law, but only if it is assumed that particles move through a refracting medium at a *greater* speed than through air. Here one imagines that the component of the particle's velocity parallel to the interface remains unchanged as the particles enter the second medium, while the perpendicular velocity component *increases* at the interface as particles enter a dense medium; see Figure 43-13. One may argue that in passing through a uniform medium the particles of light, being surrounded on all sides by the particles of the medium, are subject to no net force; but at the interface the particles are attracted, and accelerated, toward the more "dense" medium, their perpendicular velocity component thereby increasing in the optically dense medium. The particle model of light—at least, the naïve particle model described above—must be rejected for several compelling reasons: The wave speed in a refracting medium is *less* than in a vacuum; there is no simple mechanism determining which of the incident particles will be *completely* reflected or completely transmitted into the second medium, and there is no basis for predicting the

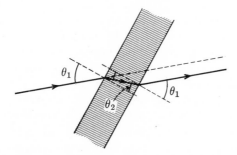

Figure 43-14. Refraction of a ray through a plate with parallel faces.

relative intensities of the reflected and transmitted beams; the particle model cannot account for such distinctive wave effects as diffraction, interference, and polarization.

Consider Figure 43-14, which shows a ray incident on a slab of refracting material with parallel faces. Since Snell's law governs the refraction at both interfaces and the interior angles θ_2 are the same at both, the emerging ray is exactly parallel to the incident ray. The ray is displaced laterally by an amount which depends on the thickness of the slab and its refraction index, without deviation from its initial direction. Thus, objects viewed through a window of glass with parallel surfaces are not distorted but merely displaced laterally by the refraction of light rays. Because the lateral displacement depends on the index of refraction, violet light is displaced slightly more than red light, although all emerging rays are undeviated.

A ray is deviated from its original direction when it passes through a slab of refracting material with *nonparallel* faces. Such a device is known as a *prism*; see Figure 43-15. The angle of deviation φ between the incident and emergent rays depends, for a given incident angle θ_1, upon the index of refraction of the material of the slab. Thus, if white light is incident upon

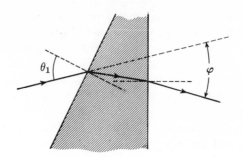

Figure 43-15. Refraction of a ray through a prism.

a glass prism, the various frequency components are deviated by different angles, or dispersed, since the refractive index varies with frequency. The index n is greatest for high frequencies (violet) and least for low frequencies (red); consequently, violet light is deviated most and red least, all intermediate colors of the visible spectrum lying between.

It was Sir Isaac Newton who first observed the dispersion of the visible spectrum by a prism and noted that one single color, such as green, *cannot* be further resolved into component colors. He also saw that two prisms can be used first to disperse and then to reunite the various components into white light; see Figure 43-16.

A prism is commonly used in a device, known as a prism spectrometer, for analyzing visible light into its component wavelengths; see Figure 43-17. Light from the source goes through a narrow slit and thence through the prism. If the emitted light is not continuous over a range of frequencies but rather consists of certain discrete frequencies, as does light emitted from excited atoms in the gaseous state, the eye sees, or a photographic film records, a succession of "lines," each line being an image of the slit at a particular frequency. One cannot make absolute determinations of wavelength with a prism spectrometer, but only relative measurements. One

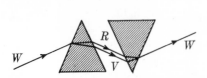

Figure 43-16. Dispersion of white light by a prism and its (approximate) recombination in a second prism.

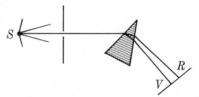

Figure 43-17. Simple elements of a prism spectrometer.

requires an independent determination of wavelength, as is possible with a diffraction-grating spectrometer (Section 46-7), to calibrate the prism spectrometer.

43-7   Refraction of light, atomic point of view   When light or any other type of electromagnetic radiation impinges on a material, the primary effect is that the wave's transverse electric field accelerates the electrons in the material. A secondary effect is that its transverse magnetic field produces a longitudinal radiation force (Section 41-3). If the electromagnetic wave varies sinusoidally with time, so does the electric force on the electrons. We can imagine the electrons to be bound to their parent atoms as if attached to a simple elastic spring (the actual details of the binding are more complicated, but this serves as a good approximate model). Thus, the electrons are set in motion at precisely the *same* frequency as that of the incident wave, a frequency which may differ from the natural frequency of the electrons. The natural frequency is that with which the electrons would oscillate if free of an external driving force (Section 17-6). Thus, an electromagnetic wave causes the electrons to oscillate in forced simple harmonic motion. As a consequence of their continuous acceleration, the electrons act as generators of electromagnetic radiation. In short, when radiation is incident upon a bound electric charge, the charge reradiates, or scatters, the radiation. Of course, if radiation is incident upon a material which absorbs radiation, only a portion of the energy is reradiated by the charges, the remainder appearing as thermal energy.

Reflection arises from the scattering of incident radiation back into the "medium" (the vacuum) from which it originated, with unchanged frequency. A detailed analysis of the scattering process occurring in reflection shows that the oscillating electrons are not only those located immediately at the surface of the reflector but also those well inside the surface.

Refraction is more complicated than reflection. First we note that, if any simple mechanical oscillator is driven at its natural, or resonance, frequency, its motion is exactly *in phase* with that of the driving oscillator. On the other hand, its motion is out of phase with that of the external driving agent if it is set in motion at a frequency which differs from its natural frequency. Now the natural frequencies of the outermost electrons of atoms, the weakly bound electrons which respond most readily to an external oscillating electric field, lie, for the most part, in the ultraviolet portion of the electromagnetic spectrum, that is, at frequencies which are *higher* than those of visible light. Consequently, when visible light is incident upon a transparent material, the electrons in it are set in oscillation *not* at their resonance frequencies, and in the scattered waves the electric field is *out of phase* with respect to the driving electric field of the incident wave.

We must recognize that, when visible light passes through a transparent medium, *on an atomic scale* electromagnetic waves are in actuality traveling through empty space. Apart from their encounters with widely separated charged particles, the electromagnetic waves always *travel at the speed c, their speed through a vacuum.* How, then, can one assert that light passes through a refracting medium at a lesser speed? The key is the fact that the scattered radiation is, for each encounter with an electron, *delayed in phase* relative to the incident radiation; see Figure 43-18. Consequently, the

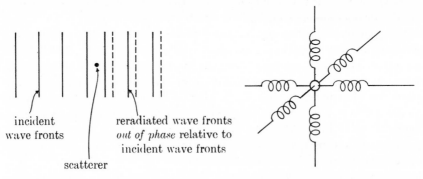

incident wave fronts

scatterer

reradiated wave fronts *out of phase* relative to incident wave fronts

Figure 43-18. An electron in a refracting material reradiates wave fronts which are *out* of phase relative to the incident wave fronts.

Figure 43-19. Mechanical model for an electron in an anisotropic refracting medium.

time it takes each *wave crest* to traverse the medium is reduced. The situation is, of course, further complicated by the fact that the scattered radiation travels in *all* directions, not merely in the forward direction of the incident beam, so that the problem of refraction, from an atomic point of view, is concerned not only with phase differences but also with the fact that each atomic radiator radiates in all directions. Suffice it to say that when these effects are taken into account through theoretical arguments, indices of refraction greater than 1 and a propagation of the electromagnetic energy through the medium at a speed *less* than c are found.

The phenomenon of dispersion now finds a ready explanation. If one excites the electrons of a refracting material with different frequencies (different colors), the phase lags differ according to the degree to which the exciting frequency differs from natural frequency; that is, the index of refraction for visible light depends on the color.

All that has been said above applies in the common, but nevertheless special, situation in which the natural frequency of oscillation of a bound electron is the same when it is displaced in any direction from its equilibrium position. That is, we have discussed refraction through *isotropic* refracting materials. Some materials, by virtue of their crystalline structure, are not isotropic, in the sense that the natural frequency of oscillation is different in different directions. Figure 43-19 shows a mechanical analogue of this situation. Here a particle is bound by several springs of different force constants; when the particle is displaced in one direction and released, it oscillates at a frequency which differs from what would be natural if it were displaced in another direction. We may then expect that anistropic materials will exhibit another phenomenon: the scattered radiation in one direction will differ in phase from the scattered radiation in another direc-tion. This implies that the electro-magnetic energy will travel at different speeds in different direc-tions. Anisotropic materials have (most commonly) *two* indices of re-fraction. Quartz, for example, has two indices of refraction, 1.544 and 1.553. This fact leads, in turn, to the observation of *two* images when light passes through a *doubly refracting* medium; see Figure 43-20. It is clear that the double-refraction effect

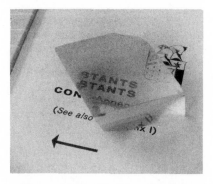

Figure 43-20. Double refraction.

is strongly dependent on the direction of the oscillating electric field of the incident radiation; that is, double refraction is intimately related to the state of *polarization* of the incident and refracted beams. We shall have a little more on this in Section 47-7.

43-8 Total internal reflection Typically, a beam incident upon the surface of a refracting medium is partially transmitted into the medium and partially reflected from it. There is, however, one situation in which the incident beam *cannot* be transmitted, and consequently the beam is *totally reflected*.

Consider Figure 43-21 which shows a series of rays traveling from an optically less dense medium to an optically more dense medium (from a medium with one value of n to a medium with a larger value of n). Clearly, the largest possible angle, θ_1, is 90°. It follows from Snell's law, that the corresponding angle for θ_2 is given by:

$$\frac{\sin \theta_1}{\sin \theta_2} = \frac{1}{\sin \theta_2} = \frac{n_2}{n_1}$$

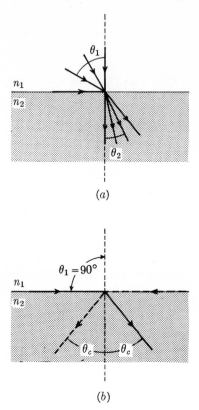

(a)

(b)

Figure 43-21. (a) The range of permitted refraction angles; (b) the critical angle θ_c.

We term the angle θ_2 under these conditions the *critical angle*, θ_c, where

$$\sin \theta_c = n_1/n_2 \qquad\qquad [43\text{-}12]$$

Here θ_c is the largest possible angle of refraction in medium 2.

Now consider all the directions of the rays in Figure 43-21 to be reversed, as in Figure 43-22. A ray incident upon the interface from medium 2 at the angle θ_c will emerge into medium 1 to travel along the interface. All rays incident at lesser angles will emerge in medium 1. But it is impossible for a ray to be refracted into medium 1 if its angle in medium 2 is greater than θ_c. Consequently, all rays incident at greater angles than the critical angle will be *totally reflected* back into the optically more dense medium. At an air-water interface, $\theta_c = \sin^{-1}(1/1.33) = 49°$.

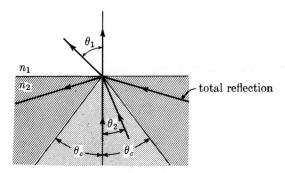

Figure 43-22. Total internal reflection for $\theta_2 > \theta_c$.

Thus, an observer located within an optically dense material such as water will see, when looking toward the surface, a transparent circular hole, through which all rays above the surface enter, surrounded by a mirror. The total internal reflection effect has a number of important applications. If light is incident upon a glass prism, as in Figure 43-23, at an angle which is greater than θ_c for the relative index of refraction for glass-to-air, the light is reflected from the interior face as from a perfectly reflecting mirror. Likewise, the particular brilliance of the light reflected from a prism of a gem, such as a diamond, arises from the very large index of refraction of crystalline carbon, the high dispersion in this material, and the multiple reflected rays. One can construct so-called *light pipes*, as shown in Figure 43-24, which trap the light within to follow bends in the pipe. The light strikes the sides of the pipe in such a manner that it is always totally reflected back into the pipe.

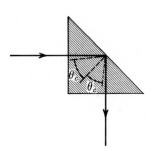

Figure 43-23. Total internal reflection from a 45–90–45° prism.

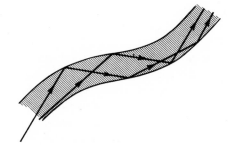

Figure 43-24. A light pipe.

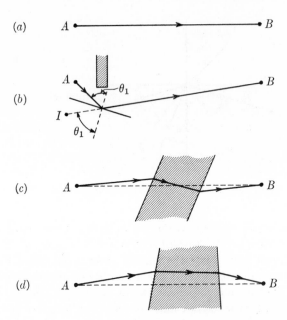

Figure 43-25. The permitted light paths from A to B for (a) a uniform medium, (b) reflection from a mirror, (c) refraction through a plate, and (d) refraction through a prism.

43-9 Fermat's principle Figure 43-25 shows a number of arrangements in which light starting at point A reaches point B. The light path, or ray, may be computed very directly from the laws of reflection and refraction. One can say that the light follows the paths shown in the figure because only these paths are consistent with the reflection and refraction laws. Only if the initial rays from A are "aimed" in the directions shown will they end up at B; in any other initial directions they will miss B.

There is, however, quite a different way of looking at this, a procedure in which we say that the light follows the indicated routes from A to B because, for these routes, the total travel time between A and B is a *minimum*. That is, the actual path followed by light (or by any other form of electromagnetic radiation or an elastic wave) differs from all other conceivable paths leading from A to B in that it corresponds to the path of *least time*. This remarkable principle, called the *principle of least time*, or *Fermat's principle*, was first propounded by P. Fermat (1608–1665) in 1650.

We can illustrate the least-time principle very easily with the rectilinear propagation of waves through a uniform medium. Light travels in a straight line between two points, as in Figure 43-25a, because this path represents the shortest distance, and also the least time, between two end points.

Similarly, the law of reflection follows directly from Fermat's principle. In Figure 43-25b the image I and the source A are located symmetrically with respect to the mirror. Then the total path length, from I to B, is the same as the path length from A to B via reflection at the mirror. But the path from A to B is a *minimum* in distance, and therefore also in time, since the line from I to B is a *straight* line.

The rectilinear propagation and reflection rules show that the actual path is one of *least distance*. The behavior of light rays in refraction clearly shows that the allowed path is that of least *time*. Note that in Figure 43-25c the actual path is *not* the shortest line between A and B. The light chooses the longer path because this path, although it involves a longer distance and time through air, corresponds to a path of shorter distance (and less time) through the refracting medium (in which the speed is, of course, less). The greater distance through air is exactly compensated for by the lesser distance through the refracting medium. Of course, if the incident ray were "aimed" still higher above the horizontal, the distance through the refracting medium would be still less, but this reduction in travel time would be more than compensated for by the greater travel time through the air. Figure 43-25d shows the allowed path, the one of least time, through a prism. In Example 2 we shall prove that, in general, the path of least time through a refracting medium is that specified by Snell's law. Thus, *all of ray optics is contained in Fermat's principle.*

Figure 43-26 shows a plane wave incident upon a curved reflector. The shape of this reflector is such that a plane wave front becomes, after reflection, a converging spherical wave front. The incident parallel rays converge

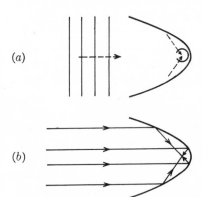

(a)

(b)

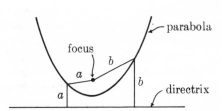

Figure 43-26. (a) Plane wave fronts incident upon a parabolic reflector; (b) parallel rays incident upon a parabolic reflector.

Figure 43-27. Geometrical properties of a parabola.

to intersect at a single point after reflection; that is, the plane waves are brought to a *focus*. It is tedious, but not fundamentally difficult, to prove, by applying the law of reflection to each ray incident upon a reflector, that the required reflector shape is a *parabola* (in two dimensions, or a paraboloid in three dimensions). By using Fermat's principle it is easy, however, to prove that only a parabolic reflector will give perfect focussing.

First recall that a parabola may be defined as that locus of points for which the distance to a point (the focus of the parabola) and the perpendicular distance to a fixed straight line (the directrix) are equal; see Figure 43-27. Now consider the plane wave front incident on a parabola in Figure 43-28. We know that this wave front shrinks into a point after reflection

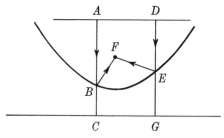

Figure 43-28. A wave front AD incident upon a parabolic reflector.

as it comes to the focus. Therefore, each point on the wave front must travel equal distances (and equal times) in reaching the focus. The point on the wave front at A travels to B and then to F. But the distance BC equals BF if the curve is a parabola. Similarly, the point at D goes to E and thence to F, where $EG = EF$. Indeed, all points on the wave front AD reach the focus F at the same instant, inasmuch as they would, if the parabola were not present, be found on a plane wave front CG at a later time.

The matter of focussing, which is illustrated by a parabolic reflector, exemplifies a further aspect of Fermat's principle: whenever a wave front is brought to a focus, *all* the paths, or rays, are paths of *least time*, since all such paths are paths of the same time. Thus, when a wave is focussed, there is not merely a single, allowed, least-time path leading from A to B; there are a number of possible paths, all of least time. See Figure 43-29, which shows the focussing of rays by a lens. Here all paths from the object O to the image I are of the same time. We may use the principle of least time to advantage (Section 44-4) to derive the focussing properties of spherically refracting surfaces.

We have spoken of light "choosing" the least-time path between two points as the "right" path. This seems to imply that the light actually had a choice available to it, that it could try the alternative paths, find them to be paths of greater time, discard such paths, and then move along the path of least time. Without such a preliminary testing of the alternatives we seem to be confronted with an extraordinary situation, in which the rays know in advance which path is the permitted path without actually having to test it. Is this what happens? Does the light really explore the alternatives and choose the path (or paths) of least time? The answer is "yes." Because of the diffraction, or spreading, of light, a beam is never actually restricted to a narrow pencil. In this way the light moves, in part, into the "forbidden" regions. The beam is established along the "true" path only after the short time has elapsed corresponding to the time required for the light (or other wave) to travel the complete path.

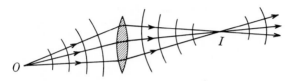

Figure 43-29. *All* paths from an object O, through a lens, to a focus at the image I are paths of least time.

Fermat's principle seems to differ radically in its spirit from that of ray optics, in which we follow the ray point by point to find its later paths. There seems to be nothing quite like Fermat's principle in mechanics, in which we use Newton's law to find the path of a particle by knowing the forces acting on the particle at each instant and thereby determine the particle's acceleration, velocity and, consequently, its path. As a matter of fact, there *is* a principle in mechanics, altogether analogous to Fermat's principle, called the *principle of least action*, which requires that the actual path of a particle differ from the alternative near-by paths, which it does *not* take, in being a path of minimum "action." We cannot, at this point, make clear the meaning in detail of the least action principle nor illustrate it as an alternative to Newton's laws, but we note one very special and simple example of it: a particle free of external forces moves in a straight line, not only because Newton's first law requires it, but also because the straight-line path is the only one that corresponds to the path of least action.

Now, if the mechanical analogue of Fermat's principle can be used as the basis of mechanics, it is implied that particles too have some means of exploring alternative paths and of rejecting them. Do they, as light, make use of diffraction? Are the particles of mechanics in some sense *waves*, exhibiting such wave characteristics as diffraction? If so, one would see the principles of least time and of least action to be the same principle, and therefore a fundamental one in all physics. The fantastic discovery made by the quantum theory, or wave mechanics, is that this is precisely the case: particles exhibit wave characteristics. These wave properties are manifest at the atomic level, where the dimensions of the "obstacles" and "apertures"—the atoms—are comparable to the particle's wave length.

When ordinary macroscopic dimensions are being dealt with, however, the wave lengths of the particles are so short that we treat their behavior by the methods of *ray optics*, that is, by the rules of ordinary Newtonian particle mechanics.

Example 2 Show that Snell's law is a consequence of Fermat's principle.

Figure 43-30 shows a ray from point A in medium 1, incident on the interface with medium 2 at point B and proceeding to point C. Points A and C are fixed, being perpendicular distances h_1 and h_2, respectively, from the interface. We regard the angles θ_1 and θ_2 (that is, the location of point B) as variable. The distance $DB + BE$ is a constant K. From the geometry of the figure it is clear that $AB = h_1/\cos\theta_1$ and $BC = h_2/\cos\theta_2$. Therefore, the total travel time t from A to B to C is

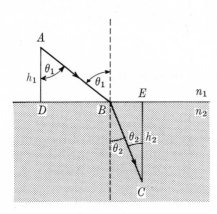

Figure 43-30

$$t = t_{AB} + t_{BC} = \frac{AB}{(c/n_1)} + \frac{BC}{(c/n_2)}$$

$$t = \frac{n_1 h_1}{c \cos\theta_1} + \frac{n_2 h_2}{c \cos\theta_2} \quad [43\text{-}13]$$

Furthermore, we have that

$$K = DB + BE$$
$$= h_1 \tan\theta_1 + h_2 \tan\theta_2 \quad [43\text{-}14]$$

According to Fermat's principle, the allowed light path is that for which the travel time t is a minimum or for which the differential dt is zero. From Equation 43-13,

$$c\,dt = n_1 h_1 \sec\theta_1 \tan\theta_1\,d\theta_1 + n_2 h_2 \sec\theta_2 \tan\theta_2\,d\theta_2 = 0 \qquad [43\text{-}15]$$

Since the distance K is a constant, we have, taking the differential of Equation 43-14,

$$0 = h_1 \sec^2\theta_1\,d\theta_1 + h_2 \sec^2\theta_2\,d\theta_2$$

$$d\theta_2 = -\frac{h_1 \sec^2\theta_1}{h_2 \sec^2\theta_2}\,d\theta_1$$

Substituting this result in Equation 43-15 gives

$$0 = n_1 h_1 \sec\theta_1 \tan\theta_1\,d\theta_1 - n_2 h_2 \sec\theta_2 \tan\theta_2 \frac{h_1 \sec^2\theta_1}{h_2 \sec^2\theta_2}\,d\theta_1$$

This simplifies to

[43-2] $$n_1 \sin\theta_1 = n_2 \sin\theta_2$$

which is Snell's law!

43-10 Summary In ray optics one ignores diffraction effects and is concerned only with the change in direction of rays at an interface arising from reflection and refraction. In reflection,

[43-1] $\theta_1 = \theta_1'$

and in refraction (Snell's law),

[43-2] $n_1 \sin \theta_1 = n_2 \sin \theta_2$

where the indices of refraction n_1 and n_2 are given by

[43-7] $c_1 = c/n_1$ and $c_2 = c/n_2$

[43-8] $n_{21} = n_2/n_1 = 1/n_{12} = \lambda_1/\lambda_2$

Refraction arises from the slowing down of waves in an optically dense medium.

The phenomenon of dispersion has its origin in the dependence on frequency of the refractive index. At the atomic level, refraction and dispersion arise from the oscillation of electrons in a refracting medium, forced by the electromagnetic radiation, at a frequency which differs from the electrons' natural oscillation frequency.

A ray is totally reflected internally when refraction cannot take place, the critical angle θ_c in medium 2 being given by

[43-12] $\sin \theta_c = n_1/n_2$

Fermat's principle, which embraces all of ray optics, requires that the actual rays between any two fixed end points correspond to paths of least time.

PROBLEMS

43-1   Many sensitive instruments involving the measurement of a small
angular displacement, such as the torsion pendulum in the Cavendish
experiment, have a mirror mounted on the object undergoing an angular displacement. Show that, if the mirror turns through an angle θ, a
light ray reflected from the mirror from a fixed light source is turned
through an angle 2θ.

43-2   Two sides and the floor of a room are covered with mirrors. What is the
maximum number of images that can be seen with this arrangement?

43-3   Two plane mirrors make an angle of 60°, as in
Figure 43-31. Find all images of the object O.

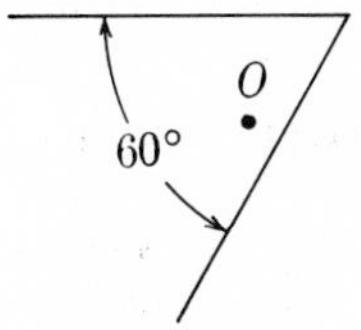

Figure 43-31

43-4   What is the minimum height of a mirror that will permit a person 6.0 feet tall to see himself from head to toe?

43-5   Choose arbitrary directions for the velocities of two electrons and find the direction of the magnetic force on each electron by using the right-hand rule in applying Equation 33-3, to find the magnetic field of one electron acting on the second, and when applying Equation 32-3 to find the magnetic force arising from the motion of the second electron in the magnetic field of the first. Now suppose that we choose the left-hand rule for obtaining the direction of the cross product. Show that the direction of the magnetic force is *not* changed under these circumstances.

43-6   What is the minimum thickness of an oil film for which the ratio of the number of wavelengths of red light (7000 Å) to blue (4000 Å) is an integral number? Assume that the index of refraction of oil is 1.30 for all wavelengths.

43-7   Show that the index of refraction of sound waves through an ideal gas at the Celsius temperature t_c, relative to that at 0°C, is given, for small t_c, by $n = 1 - t_c/(546 \text{ C}°)$.

43-8   A fish looks toward a water surface to see light reaching its eye at an angle of 30° relative to the normal. What is the angle between the ray in air and the surface of the lake? For water $n = 1.33$.

43-9   Light is incident at 45° upon a plate of glass 3.0 mm thick and having an index of refraction of 1.40. What is the lateral displacement of the emerging ray relative to the incident ray?

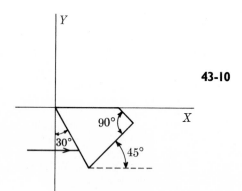

43-10   The material of which the object in Figure 43-32 is made has a refractive index of 1.50. Find the direction, relative to the positive X-axis, of the emergent ray. Ignore *partial* reflection.

Figure 43-32

43-11   Snell's law was known, in the approximate form $\theta_1/_2\theta$ = a constant, to Ptolemy in the first century A.D. Assuming the relative index of refraction to be 1.50, what per cent error will you obtain in the angle of refraction if you use Ptolemy's approximate form for angles of incidence of (a) 24°, and (b) 48°?

43-12   An opaque cylindrical tumbler having a diameter and height of 3.0 inches is first empty. A person sighting along an outside edge of the tumbler is just able to see the line dividing the opposite side from the bottom. To what height would the tumbler have to be filled with water ($n = 1.33$) if the observer were to be able to see, without moving his eye of a mark on the bottom 1.0 inch from the opposite side?

43-13   A swimming pool brim-full of water with refractive index 1.33, is a cube 8.0 feet on a side. What is the maximum distance from one side of the pool that a man, whose eyes are 5.50 feet above ground, can stand and see the lower edge of the pool's opposite side?

43-14   Figure 43-33 shows several parallel slabs of refracting material with indices of refraction $n_1 = 1.50$, $n_2 = 1.40$, and $n_3 = 1.30$. The angle of the incident ray upon the first surface is 30°. Trace the ray to the point at which it emerges from the refracting materials, ignoring all *partial* reflections, and find the angle of the emerging ray.

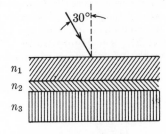

Figure 43-33

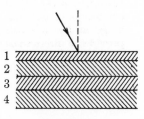

Figure 43-34

43-15   A ray of light passes through several parallel slabs of material with different refractive indices, as shown in Figure 43-34. Suppose that the order of the materials is changed; for example, 2, 1, 4, 3, rather than 1, 2, 3, 4. Assume, further, that total internal reflection does *not* occur. Show that the angle of emerging ray is *not* changed.

43-16   The "apparent depth" of an object immersed in an optically dense refracting medium is less than the true depth when viewed from directly above. Show that the apparent depth d' is related to the true depth d by $d' = d/n$, where n is the relative refractive index of the medium in which the object is immersed. See Figure 43-35. One may assume the angles to be so small that the sine of an angle can be replaced by the angle itself.

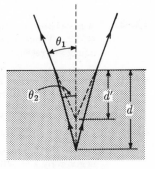

Figure 43-35

43-17   The apparent depth of an object within a refracting medium is smaller than its true depth by the factor n, where n is the refractive index in the optically dense medium (Problem 43-16). A microscope is focussed on a scratch made on the upper surface at the bottom of a small container. Water is added to the container to a depth of 3.00 mm. Through what vertical displacement must the microscope lens be raised, to bring the scratch into focus again?

43-18   The angle through which a ray passing through a prism is deviated depends, of course, on the angle of incidence of the ray with respect to the first surface, the angle of the prism, and its refractive index. There is, however one angle of incidence for which the deviation angle is a minimum. Show that for minimum deviation the angles of incident and emergent rays with respect to the front and back surfaces of the prism are *equal*. (*Hint:* Apply the reciprocity principle.)

43-19   When a ray is incident upon a prism having an angle φ in such a direction as to produce minimum deviation, the incident and emergent rays make the same angle with respect to the prism surfaces (Problem 43-18). Show that if the emergent ray is deviated through an angle δ under the conditions of minimum deviation, the refractive index of the prism is given by $n = \sin[(\delta + \varphi)/2] \sin(\varphi/2)$; see Figure 43-36. This provides a direct means of measuring the prism's index of refraction.

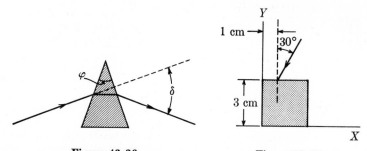

Figure 43-36   Figure 43-37

43-20   A ray enters a cube of refracting material ($n = 1.45$) as shown in Figure 43-37. What is the angle, relative to the positive X-axis, of the emerging ray?

43-21   All ocean waves reach a shore line which is reasonably smooth, by traveling normal to the interface between land and water. Explain this behavior.

43-22   Light travels from within a refracting material, whose index of refraction is $2/\sqrt{3}$, into a vacuum. The angle of incidence within the material is given by $\lambda = (4000\ \text{Å}) \cos(\theta/2)$, where λ is the wavelength of the light; that is, the various colors of the spectrum are incident upon the interface at different angles. What is the range of wavelengths which will be observed after the light has entered the vacuum?

43-23 Figure 43-38 shows two parallel rays, 1 and 2, incident upon a prism with angles of 45°, 45°, and 90°. The index of refraction for the glass is 1.5. Trace the rays to show that they emerge from the prism inverted. Of what practical use is a prism of this type?

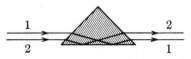

Figure 43-38

43-24 A light pipe made of plastic has an index of refraction of 1.60. What is the maximum angle between a ray within the plastic and the side of the tube that will prevent the light from leaving the light pipe?

45-25 (a) What is the critical angle for total internal reflection between a surface separating water ($n = 1.33$) and glass ($n = 1.50$)? (b) In what material must the light originate?

43-26 See Figure 43-39. A ray starting at point A reaches C after reflection from the surface at B. We assume at first that the angles θ_1 and θ_1' of the incident and reflected rays are *not* the same. Assume that both A and C are equal distances, h, from the reflecting surface. (a) Show that the total travel time from A to C in reflection from the surface is given by $h/\cos \theta_1 c + h/\cos \theta_1' c$. (b) Derive the law of reflection from Fermat's principle by finding the relation between θ_1 and θ_1' for a minimum travel time between A and C.

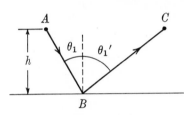

Figure 43-39

43-27 Use Fermat's principle to prove that the incident ray, reflected ray, refracted ray, and normal ray must all lie in a single plane.

43-28 Any curve can be approximated over a small region by a circular arc, the radius R of the circle being the radius of curvature of the curve, where $R = [1 + (dy/dx)^2]^{3/2}/d^2y/dx^2$. Show that the focus of a parabola lies at $\frac{1}{2}R$, where R is the radius of the circle fitting the parabola at its vertex. The equation of a parabola can be written as $x^2 = 2Py$, where P is the distance between the focus and the directrix of the parabola.

43-29 An ellipse can be defined as the locus of points the sum of whose distances from two fixed points (the foci of the ellipse) is constant. See Figure 43-40. Show that any wave disturbance originating at f_1 is focussed at f_2, and conversely.

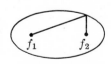

Figure 43-40

43-30   (a) Show that the intensity of the signal received at the focus of a parabolic reflector is proportional to the square of the radius R of the antenna; see Figure 43-41. (b) The radius of the parabolic mirror in a reflecting telescope or of the objective lens (the one closest to the object) in a refracting telescope determines the intensity of the image registered on a photographic plate. Assuming, for simplicity, that the power outputs of distant stars are all alike, how does doubling the radius of the mirror or objective lens affect the range of stars that can be "seen"?

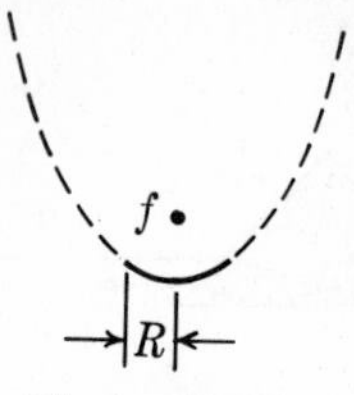

Figure 43-41

FORTY-FOUR

LENSES

This chapter is about lenses. First we deal with thin lenses and arrive at the simple graphical and analytical procedures for locating the image of an object. Next we consider briefly the most important types of lens aberration. Then we turn to combinations of lenses, illustrated by such optical devices as the telescope and microscope. Finally, we consider the general problem of refraction at the spherical interface between two media of different refractive indices.

44-1 Thin lenses The change in direction of a ray at any interface between two media is governed by Snell's law:

[43-11]
$$\frac{\sin \theta_1}{\sin \theta_2} = \frac{n_2}{n_1} = n_{21}$$

The angles between the rays and the normal to the surface in media 1 and 2 are θ_1 and θ_2, respectively; see Figure 44-1. The corresponding indices of refraction are n_1 and n_2, and the respective wave speeds are c/n_1 and c/n_2. When $n_2 > n_1$, then $\theta_1 > \theta_2$. Thus, when a ray enters a medium in which

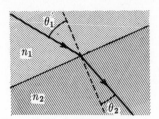

Figure 44-1. Refraction at an interface.

the wave speed is reduced, the ray is bent toward the normal. For example, a ray of light is bent toward the normal in entering glass from air; conversely, the ray's angle relative to the normal increases when a ray emerges from glass into air.

When a ray passes through a plate of glass with parallel surfaces, the ray is refracted at each interface, but the emerging ray is parallel to the incident ray, as shown in Figure 44-2a. The ray undergoes a lateral displacement, but it is *not* deviated in direction. On the other hand, when a ray enters a slab of glass with nonparallel faces (a prism), the emerging ray is deviated relative to the incident ray, as shown in Figure 44-2b. It is a simple, although somewhat tedious, matter to compute the total angle of deviation of the ray by applying Snell's law to each of the two refractions in turn. It is obvious that the angle of deviation increases as the angle between the faces increases.

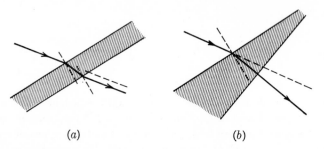

(a)   (b)

Figure 44-2. (a) Refraction through a slab with parallel faces results in a lateral displacement of the rays, but no deviation. (b) A ray is deviated by a prism.

Consider the structure shown in Figure 44-3, two prisms and a plate with parallel faces. A number of horizontal rays incident from the left pass through this rather crude lens. The rays intersect in a relatively small region to the right. The rays through the center are undeviated, while the rays through the top and bottom prisms are deviated down and up, respectively, both sets of rays emerging at a single deviation angle. We wish to devise a structure in which *all* of the parallel incident rays intersect at a *single point*. It is clear what is required: the rays' deviation must increase gradually upward (or downward) from the center of the lens, rather than abruptly, as in the figure. That is, the external surfaces must be smoothly

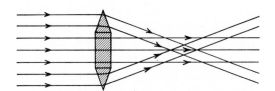

Figure 44-3. Focussing by a crude lens.

curved rather than flat. In practice, this is done by making lenses with *spherical* surfaces, because they are relatively easy to grind. Such a lens refracts parallel rays so that they intersect (almost) at a single point. It will be assumed in this section that the radii of curvature of the surfaces are large compared with the thickness of the lens at its center, as shown in Figure 44-4; that is, here we shall consider thin lenses only. (The more general case of thick lenses is treated in Section 44-5.)

Figure 44-5a shows a thin lens with *convex* spherical surfaces. After refracting through the lens, incident rays parallel to the axis now intersect at a single point, or at least in a very much smaller region than shown in Figure 44-3. This point is known as a *principal focal point*, or *principal focus*, of the lens. Thus, if a source is placed at an *infinite* (or very large) distance from the lens, so that the rays incident upon the lens are effectively parallel over a small solid angle, these parallel rays intersect at the principal focus after traversing the lens. The focussing arises from the fact that, in going upward (or downward) from the center, each ray is deviated slightly more than the one below (or above) it. The corresponding behavior for incident plane wave fronts is shown in Figure 44-5b. The wave fronts undergo a change in curvature at each of the two faces, and the emerging wave fronts consist of converging spherical wave fronts which collapse into

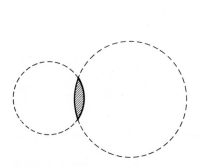

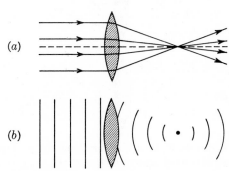

Figure 44-4. A thin lens with spherical surfaces.

Figure 44-5. (a) Parallel incident rays focussed by a lens. (b) Plane wave fronts focussed by a lens.

a point at the principal focus and then expand outward as diverging spherical waves. This behavior is easily understood when we note that the relatively thick central section of the lens slows a wave front more than do the thinner sections near the edges.

Any focus may be defined in several equivalent ways: (1) the point at which *all rays intersect*, (2) the point at which *wave fronts collapse into a point*, thereby changing from converging into diverging spherical wave fronts, (3) the point at which the *intensity* of the beam is a *maximum*. (4) Still another definition of a focus involves Fermat's principle, according to which a ray will always follow that path corresponding to the least time between the end points; that is, a focus represents that point for which *all* paths from the source are traveled in the *same time, all* paths to the focus being *paths of least time*.

Through the principle of reciprocity (or time reversal) we know that we can reverse the directions of rays (or imagine time to run backward) without changing the light paths. Thus, if a point source is placed at a principal focus, as in Figure 44-6, rays emerge from the lens as a beam of parallel rays. Stated equivalently, spherical wave fronts diverging from the principal focus and entering the lens emerge as plane wave fronts.

Now suppose that we reverse the thin lens, interchanging the two faces, and allow rays to pass through in the opposite direction. The incident parallel rays again converge to a focal point at the *same* distance from the

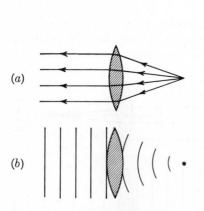

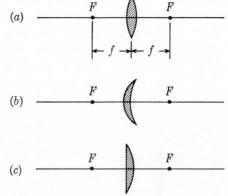

Figure 44-6. (a) Rays originating at the focal point emerge after refraction as parallel rays. (b) Diverging spherical wave fronts become plane wave fronts after refraction through the lens.

Figure 44-7. Three examples of converging lenses: (a) a double convex lens, (b) a concave–convex lens, and (c) a planoconvex lens.

lens' center. Thus, every lens has *two* principal focal points, one on each
side. Both principal foci, denoted by *F*, are at the same distance *f*, the
focal length, from the center of the thin lens; see Figure 44-7a.

This holds, not only for a thin lens with two convex surfaces, but also
for a lens, such as that shown in Figure 44-7b, with a concave and a convex
surface, or a planoconvex lens with one surface of infinite radius of curvature,
as in Figure 44-7c. The essential requirement is that the lens be very thin,
but thicker at its center than at its edges. (Clearly, the focal length depends
on the radii of curvature of the two surfaces and on the refractive index of
the lens material. The relation for *f* in terms of these parameters, Equation
44-20, is given in Section 44-5.)

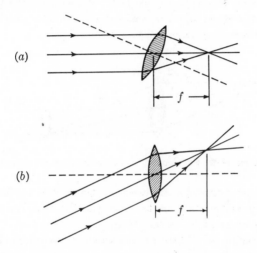

Figure 44-8. (a) Tilting the lens through a small angle does *not* change
the focal point. (b) Equivalently, oblique rays also come to a focus a
distance *f* from the lens.

Imagine, now, that the lens is tilted a little, as in Figure 44-8a, so that its
symmetry axis does not lie along the direction of incident parallel rays.
With a small tilt angle, there is no change: the rays are focussed at essentially
the same point as before, a distance *f* from the center of the lens. Now look
at the situation when the lens axis is horizontal, as in Figure 44-8b. We see
that with obliquely incident parallel rays, the focus is displaced transversely
from the lens axis. Clearly, the ray through the lens' center is undeviated,
since this ray passes, in effect, through two parallel surfaces. Thus, rays from
an infinitely distant source are brought to focus in a *plane*, the *focal plane*, a
distance *f* from the lens. This simple behavior is found, however, only if
the angle between the rays and the lens axis is small. Such rays, nearly

parallel to the lens axis, are called *paraxial rays*. We shall assume throughout our discussion that the lens is very thin and that the rays are paraxial.

The type of lens illustrated thus far is known as a *converging* lens. (Strictly, a lens thicker at its center than at its edges is a converging lens only if the material of which the lens is made is optically more dense than its surroundings, as in the case of a glass lens for visible light immersed in air.) Any converging lens increases the degree of convergence of rays and wave fronts passing through it, or decreases the degree of their divergence.

We can illustrate the convergence property of a converging lens for a source located at *any* location along the lens axis. Suppose that we have some luminous source, or object represented by *O*, located near a thin converging lens, as shown in Figure 44-9. We wish to find the place where the light from the upper tip of *O* comes to a focus after passing through the lens. We can trace three rays easily.

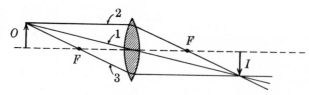

Figure 44-9. Formation of an image *I* by an object *O*.

(1) A ray passing through the center of the lens is *unchanged*, inasmuch as it is neither deviated (the lens faces are parallel here) nor displaced laterally (the lens is assumed to be very thin).

(2) A ray incident *parallel* to the lens axis is deviated by the lens through the principal focus *F* on the *far* side.

(3) A ray which passes through the *near principal focus F* is deviated to emerge *parallel* to the lens axis.

These three rays intersect, or focus, at a single point; indeed, *all* other paraxial rays from the upper tip of *O* intersect to form a point image of this point of the object. We have traced rays from the uppermost point of the object *O*. If we choose some other point on an extended object lying in the same transverse plane, we can again find the corresponding image point. Thus, for paraxial rays through a thin lens, we obtain the image *I* of the object *O*.

The method of ray construction is simple. All that we need is a prior knowledge of the lens' focal length *f*; then we may locate the image by drawing the three rays as in Figure 44-9. The geometrical procedure of ray-tracing is not, however, always practicable, and we wish to find the mathematical relation between the focal length *f*, the distance *s* of the object from the lens, and the distance s' of the image from the lens. Consider Figure 44-10, which is merely Figure 44-9 redrawn with identifying letters. The object distance s is AB, the image distance s' is $EH = DG$, and the focal length f is $CD = DF$. The object height h is $AJ = BD$; the image height h' is $GH = DE$. Triangles AJD and DGH are similar. Therefore,

$$AJ/JD = GH/DG$$
$$h/s = h'/s' \qquad [44\text{-}1]$$

The ratio of image-object *distances*, s'/s, is equal to the ratio of image-object *sizes*, h'/h. This ratio h'/h is known as the *lateral magnification*.

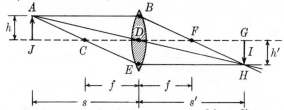

Figure 44-10. Geometrical relations among object distance s, image distance s', and focal length f.

Triangles BDF and FGH are similar. Therefore,

$$DF/BD = FG/GH$$
$$f/h = (s' - f)/h'$$

Through the use of Equation 44-1 this becomes

$$f/s = (s' - f)/s' = 1 - f/s'$$

Dividing by f and rearranging yields

$$\boxed{1/f = 1/s + 1/s'} \qquad [44\text{-}2]$$

This is the formula for locating images formed by a thin lens. Everything we can do with it in computing image or object distances can be done equally well by ray construction (that is how we derived Equation 44-2). For example, if $f = 12$ cm and $s = 50$ cm, we find, either by ray construction or by Equation 44-2, that $s' = 60$ cm. Moreover, the image size is 6/5 that of the object.

Note that if we place $s = \infty$ in Equation 44-2, we find $s' = f$. That is, the image of a very distant object is found at the principal focus. Conversely, if $s = f$, then $s' = \infty$.

The image shown in Figures 44-9 and 44-10 is said to be a *real* image, since the rays actually pass through this location. That is, if one were to place a sheet of paper at the distance s' from the lens, one would see an actual image focussed there. The image would be inverted in the transverse focal plane; that is, up and down would be interchanged relative to the object, as would be left and right. Equation 44-2 shows that as s increases, s' decreases, and conversely. That is, when the object is displaced along the lens axis, its image is displaced in the *same* direction. Thus, a three-dimensional object, although inverted in the transverse plane, is *not* inverted along the lens axis.

Let us apply the reciprocity principle to the object in Figures 44-9 and 44-10 and its real image. The rays are then reversed; our former image becomes the object, and our original object becomes the image. The two locations, one for s and one for s', are said to be *conjugate* points. When

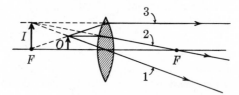

Figure 44-11. Formation of a virtual image.

we have $s = 2f$, we also have $s' = 2f$. For this special case, the lens serves only to invert the object without changing its size.

A number of optical devices are based on a converging lens forming a real image. The most familiar is the eye, which forms a real image on the retina. Here the image distance s' from the eye lens to the retina is fixed; objects at various distances from the eye are brought into focus on the retina when the eye muscles change the focal length f of the eye lens by changing the radii of curvature of the lens surfaces. A camera forms a real image in the focal plane of the photographic film. A projector forms a much enlarged and inverted image of a slide or film on the screen.

Now consider the situation arising when an object is placed closer to a converging lens than the principal focal point; see Figure 44-11. We locate the image geometrically by drawing exactly the same three rays as before. Ray 1 through the lens center is undeviated. Ray 2, initially parallel to the lens axis, passes through the far focal point. Ray 3 is so drawn that its direction after leaving the object is the same as that of a ray starting at the near focal point and passing through the top of the object; therefore, this third ray emerges from the lens parallel to the axis. These rays do *not* intersect. What sort of image is now formed? What does an eye see when looking from the right toward the lens?

The eye (or a camera) is naïve in that it interprets any ray reaching it as always having traveled strictly along a straight line. Said differently, the eye recognizes only the *final* direction of rays entering it. Thus, the three rays appear to have originated from that point on the left of the lens where their backward extensions intersect. The rays appear to come from a virtual image *I*. If a sheet of paper were placed at the location of *I*, *no* image would be seen on it. A person viewing the object through the lens would see an *erect, enlarged*, and *virtual* image. Used in this fashion, with an object closer to the lens than the focal length, a converging lens is a *magnifying glass*, or *simple magnifier*.

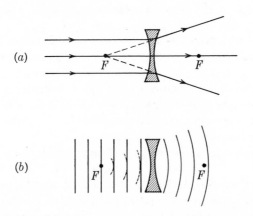

Figure 44-12. Divergence of (a) the rays and (b) the wave fronts by a diverging lens.

Exactly the same lens equation, Equation 44-2, can be used to compute the image distance s', when s and f are given, if the image distance s' is taken to be negative. (This can be proved in detail by analyzing the geometry of Figure 44-11 in the fashion of Figure 44-10.) For example, if $f = 40$ cm and an object is placed at $s = 30$ cm, we find from Equation 44-2 that $s' = -120$ cm. Moreover, from Equation 44-1 we find the virtual image's size to be $120/30 = 4$ times that of the object.

Thus far we have considered converging lens; such lens are thicker in the center than at the edges when the refractive index of their material exceeds that of the surrounding medium. Now consider the reverse case, that in which a thin lens with spherical surfaces is thinner at its center than at its edges, as shown in Figure 44-12. Such a lens is a *diverging* lens, because it increases the degree of divergence of rays and wave fronts pasing through it. Incident parallel rays diverge after passing through the lens and appear to have originated from a point source at the principal focus on the same side of the lens (Figure 44-12a). Equivalently, incident plane waves emerge

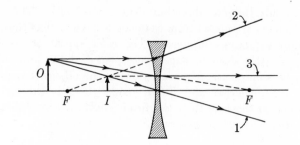

Figure 44-13. Image formation by a diverging lens.

from a diverging lens as diverging spherical wave fronts (Figure 44-12b).
We may again use Equation 44-2 to relate image distance, object distance,
and focal length, provided that we take the focal length of a diverging lens
to be *negative*. The object distance s is, as before, taken as positive. Again
there are two principal foci, one on each side of the lens, and the properties
for focussing paraxial rays are independent of the tilt angle of the lens or
of the face of the lens exposed to the object.

Let us locate an image produced by a diverging lens, using the procedure
in ray construction that we employed earlier. See Figure 44-13. Ray 1
passes undeviated through the lens' center. Ray 2, parallel to the lens axis,
emerges as if originating from the near principal focus F. Ray 3 is "aimed"
to go through the far principal focus and is, therefore, deviated to emerge
parallel to the axis. After refracting through the lens the rays appear to
diverge from image I. The image is reduced, erect,
and virtual. Indeed, a diverging lens *always* forms
a *virtual* image of a real object. That I is virtual
is indicated by the fact that the image distance s',
as computed from Equation 44-2, is negative. For
example, with a diverging lens having $f =
-10$ cm and with an object at the location $s =
15$ cm, we find $s' = -6$ cm.

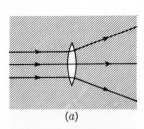

(a)

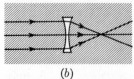

(b)

Figure 44-14. Lenses immersed in an optically
more dense medium: (a)
a diverging lens and (b) a
converging lens.

We have concentrated upon lenses of the usual
variety, ones made of optically dense materials,
such as glass, and intended for use with visible
light. There are, of course, lens devices which are
made of optically light materials. For example,
Figure 44-14 shows converging and diverging
lenses formed by cavities within an optically
dense medium. Here the converging lens has a
pair of concave surfaces, and the diverging lens
has a pair of convex surfaces.

The *term* lens need not be restricted to devices which focus visible light. One may have acoustic lenses or microwave lenses. Indeed, magnetic- and electric-field arrangements which focus a beam of charged particles are referred to respectively as magnetic and electrostatic lenses.

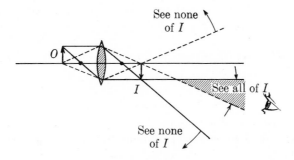

Figure 44-15

Example 1   An object, equal in height to the radius of a thin converging lens, forms a real image, as shown in Figure 44-15. To what regions of space is an eye limited if the eye is to see the entire image?

Two rays are drawn from the upper tip of the object through the upper and lower edges of the lens. Similarly, two rays are drawn from the base of the object through the upper and lower edges of the lens. The eye will receive rays coming from all parts of the object only if it is located within the region shown shaded in Figure 44-15. Outside this region the eye will see only parts of the image, or, if the eye is too far from the lens axis, none of the image.

44-2   Newtonian form of the lens equation   We have taken the object and image distances s and s' to be *measured from the center of the thin lens.* Then the thin-lens equation has the form (the so-called *Gaussian form*) given in Equation 44-2. In the *Newtonian form* of the lens equation, the object and image distances, denoted S and S' respectively, are *measured from the two principal foci*, as shown in Figure 44-16. We wish to find the relation between S, S', and f.

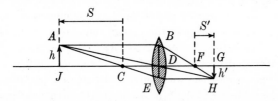

Figure 44-16. Newtonian object distance, S, and image distance, S'.

Triangles AJC and CDE are similar; therefore,

$$AJ/JC = DE/CD$$
$$h/S = h'/f \tag{44-3}$$

Triangles BDF and FGH are also similar; therefore,

$$BD/DF = GH/FG$$
$$h/f = h'/S' \tag{44-4}$$

Eliminating h/h' from Equations 44-3 and 44-4, we have

$$\boxed{SS' = f^2} \tag{44-5}$$

This is the Newtonian form of the thin-lens equation. We can also derive Equation 44-5 from Equation 44-2 simply by replacing s with $(S + f)$ and s' with $(S' + f)$.

As always, one must be careful about the signs given to S and S'. When the object is to the *left* of the *left* focal point, S is *positive*; when the object is to the right of this near focal point of the lens, S is negative. Similarly, S' is *positive* when the image is to the *right* of the *right* focal point, whereas a negative S' implies an image to the left of the far focal point.

The advantage of the Newtonian form over the Gaussian form is that the Newtonian form is algebraically simpler, not only for thin lenses, but also for the more general case of thick lenses or combinations of lenses, as we shall see in Section 44-5.

44-3 Lens aberrations Apart from the fact that an image may be inverted and changed in size, an ideal lens would form an image which is the exact replica of the object. All parts of the image would be in precise focus without distortion, every point in the object appearing as a point in the image; moreover, all colors in the object would be faithfully rendered. But no such ideal lens exists. A variety of aberrations attributable to the lens cause the image to differ from the object, not only in size but also in color, shape, and clarity.

The most fundamental limitation arises from the fact that a lens focusses *waves*. As a consequence of the *diffraction* phenomenon, a point in the object is rendered as a smear in the image, the extent of the smear depending on the wavelength. As we shall see in Section 46-6, the diffraction effects are controlled by the ratio of the wavelength to the outside radius of the lens. The shorter the wavelength, the smaller the diffraction effects. Thus, if one uses short-wavelength ultraviolet light rather than visible light, the diffraction effects are reduced. The limitation arising from diffraction and the wave character of electromagnetic radiation is clearly evident when one recognizes that one cannot "see" any smaller dimension in the object than one wavelength of the waves used to "look" at the object.

Whereas diffraction effects give rise to an inherent lens aberration, the following lens aberrations present in a single lens can be corrected to some degree by using two or more lenses in combination.

Chromatic aberration has its origin in the dispersion phenomenon. The index of refraction for most transparent materials in the visible region of the electromagnetic spectrum depends on the frequency; that is, the

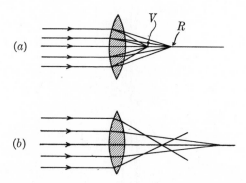

Figure 44-17. (a) Chromatic aberration. (b) Spherical aberration.

refraction angle at an interface differs according to the color of light. Silicate flint glass, for example, has a higher refractive index for violet light (1.64) than for red light (1.61). Thus, if polychromatic light from an object refracts through a converging lens, the violet component will be imaged closer to the lens than the red component, as shown in Figure 44-17a.

Spherical aberration arises from the fact that a spherical lens surface, although easy to grind, is not the ideal shape for focussing all rays originating at the lens axis. As the angle between the rays and the lens axis increases, that is, for rays that are not paraxial, the outer edges of the lens produce a focus at a different point from that formed by the central portion of the lens, as shown in Figure 44-17b. A consequence of spherical aberration is that a point in the object is focussed as a diffused circle in the image.

Still other aberration effects occur when the object does not lie on the lens axis: *coma* is an extension of spherical aberration to objects not on the lens axis, images of point sources appearing comet-shaped (hence, "coma"); *astigmatism* arises because object points in a single transverse plane are imaged in a spherical surface; *distortion* arises from the fact that the magnification depends, to a degree, on the distance of a point in the object from the lens axis.

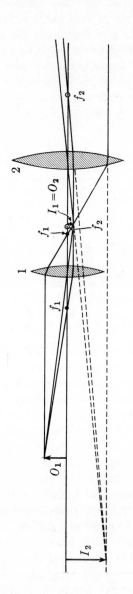

Figure 44-18. Image formation by lens 1 followed by lens 2.

44-4 Lens combinations To trace rays through two or more lenses in sequence one uses the following procedure: treat the image for the first lens as the object for the second lens, treat the image for the second as the object for the third lens, and so forth.

Figure 44-18 shows a combination of two converging lens. Lens 1 forms a real inverted image I_1 of the object O_1. The image I_1 becomes the object O_2 for lens 2. In the particular arrangement shown here, the object O_2 falls just inside the focal point of the second lens. Consequently, the final image I_2 formed by lens 2 is virtual, being to the left of lens 2. Note that the rays chosen to find the image I_1 are *not* continued through the second lens; instead, new rays are chosen, whose deviation through lens 2 are found in the fashion shown in Figure 44-11. Also note that, for the purposes of ray construction, the lenses are assumed to be of infinite transverse size.

The *astronomical telescope* corresponds closely to the lens arrangement in Figure 44-18. The object O_1 is, of course, far from lens 1; its real image I_1 is examined by lens 2. This lens acts as a magnifying glass, giving a greatly magnified image formed at a great distance from the lens. Lens 1 (closer to the object) is known as the *objective lens*; lens 2 (closer to the eye) is known as the *eyepiece*, or *ocular*. In the case of an object O_1 at a great distance from a telescope and of a final image I_2 also at a great distance, it is clear that the total distance between the objective lens and the eyepiece is close to $f_1 + f_2$. This is the minimum length of the telescope.

What matters in any optical instrument used to magnify an object is the size of the image *formed on the retina of the eye*. The image size on the retina is determined, in turn, by the angular spread of the rays entering the eye, as shown in Figure 44-19. Thus, a proper measure of the magnification of an object is the *angular magnification*, or *magnifying power*, which is defined as the angle θ_I, subtended at the eye by the rays coming from the final image, divided by the angle θ_o, subtended at the eye by the object when

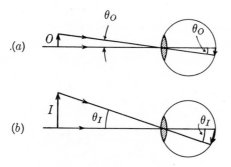

Figure 44-19. Retinal images formed by (a) an object and (b) its image.

viewed directly without the aid of the instrument:

$$\text{Angular magnification} = \theta_I/\theta_o \qquad [44\text{-}6]$$

Equivalently, the magnifying power is the ratio of the size of the retinal image formed by an optical instrument to the retinal image size without the aid of the instrument. That the angular magnification is a more useful criterion than the lateral magnification (Equation 44-1), which depends on the relative image and object sizes, is evident if we note that there is *no* angular magnification, for example, when the image size is doubled and at the same time the image is located at twice the distance of the object from the viewer.

Let us compute the angular magnification of an astronomical telescope. Figure 44-20 shows the rays incident upon a telescope from a very distant object. The angle θ_o subtended by the object at the objective lens is essentially the same as the angle subtended by the object at the unaided eye. The height of the real image of the objective lens (and the object for the eyepiece) is denoted h'. The image is formed at a distance f_o from the objective lens and a distance f_e from the eyepiece, where f_o and f_e are the focal lengths of the objective lens and eyepiece, respectively. From Figure 44-20,

$$\tan \theta_o = h'/f_o \qquad \text{and} \qquad \tan \theta_e = h'/f_e$$

where θ_e is the angle subtended at the eye by the final image. Since the angles θ_o and θ_e are very small,

$$\tan \theta_o \simeq \theta = h'/f_o$$
$$\tan \theta_e \simeq \theta = h'/f_e$$

By definition (Equation 44-6),

$$\text{Angular magnification} = \theta_e/\theta_o = f_o/f_e$$

Thus, the magnifying power of a telescope is simply the ratio of the focal lengths of the objective and the eyepiece. One achieves high magnification by using a long-focal-length objective lens with a short-focal-length eyepiece.

The lens combination shown in Figure 44-21 illustrates the compound

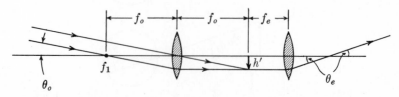

Figure 44-20. Angular magnification of an astronomical telescope.

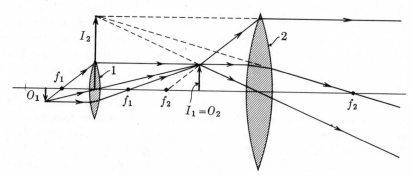

Figure 44-21. A compound microscope.

microscope. Here the object O_1 is placed close to the principal focus f_1 of the objective lens; the image I_1 is enlarged and real. The eyepiece is used to form a still further enlarged but virtual image I_2. Without the aid of an optical instrument, we can see objects most clearly and have retinal images of greatest size by bringing the objects as close to the eye as the eye will permit. Typically, the closest distance is 25 cm from the eye. Therefore, a microscope is most effective if the final image I_2 is located at 25 cm from the eye. The angular magnification of a microscope is θ_I/θ_o, where θ_o is the angle substended by the object held 25 cm from the unaided eye.

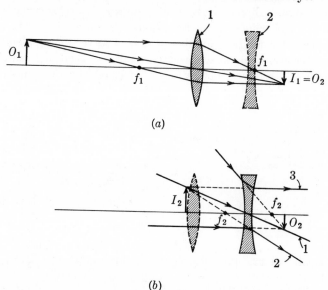

Figure 44-22. A Galilean telescope. Image formation by (a) the objective lens and (b) the eyepiece.

A special situation arises when an image is *not* formed *between* two lenses in combination. Consider Figure 44-22a. If lens 2 were not present, the image I_1 would be formed at the location shown. To locate the final image after rays traverse the second lens, we must regard this image I_1 as a *virtual object* for lens 2. We find the final image I_2 having the virtual object $O_2 = I_1$ in Figure 44-22b. Ray 1 is so "aimed" that it passes through the center of the diverging lens without deviation. Ray 2, initially parallel to the lens axis, is deviated so as to be directed from the near focal point f_2. Ray 3 is aimed to pass through the far focal point and emerges from lens 2 parallel to the axis. Thus, the final image I_2 is greatly enlarged, erect, and virtual. The optical device shown in Figure 44-22, comprised of a converging lens as objective lens and a diverging lens as eyepiece, is known as a *Galilean telescope*, or opera glass.

44-5 Refraction at a spherical surface The most general problem one confronts in lens design is this: given a succession of interfaces of known shape between media of various known indices of refraction, what are the rays, or the paths of light, traced out through such a complex lens? See Figure 44-23. The problem is easy in principle, but may be extremely tedious in solution. The only basic ideas are these: as long as a ray is within a uniform medium of constant refractive index, it is a straight line and when a ray meets an interface between two media, Snell's law gives the change in the ray's direction. Equivalently, one may use Fermat's principle (Section 43-9), of which Snell's law is but one illustration. Thus, one can find the image formed by a number of rays or wave fronts passing through the first interface. This image, whether real or virtual, acts as the object for the second interface. Another image is formed which becomes the object for the next interface, and so on.

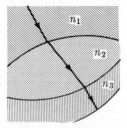

Figure 44-23. Refraction at a succession of interfaces in media of differing indices of refraction.

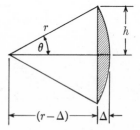

Figure 44-24. The sagitta geometry.

We shall consider the special but important case of refraction from a *spherical* surface by *paraxial* rays; this will lead to the general lens equation, applicable to *all* lenses, thick or thin. Our first task is to prove the basic assumption implicit in our discussion of thin lenses in Section 44-1: when a spherical wave front is incident upon a spherical interface between two refracting media, the refracted wave front is again a *spherical* wave front, but one of different curvature.

As a preliminary we first derive a mathematical approximation which will be useful in what follows. Consider Figure 44-24. We wish to find a

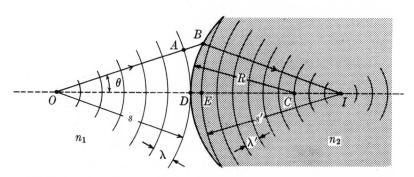

Figure 44-25. Refraction of a spherical wave front by a spherical interface.

relation giving the distance Δ, the so-called sagitta, in terms of the radius r and half-chord h for the approximation in which the angle θ is small, that is, $\Delta \ll r$.

From the Pythagorean theorem, we have

$$r^2 - h^2 = (r - \Delta)^2 = r^2 - 2r\Delta + \Delta^2$$

We may neglect the Δ^2 term, and the above relation simplifies to

$$-h^2 = -2r\Delta$$
$$\Delta = h^2/2r \qquad\qquad [44\text{-}7]$$

Now consider Figure 44-25, which shows spherical wave fronts diverging from a point source, or object O, in medium 1 (with refractive index n_1) to impinge upon a convex spherical interface of radius R with its center at C. The wave fronts in medium 2 (with refractive index n_2) converge into a focus at the point I, which represents the image. Figure 44-25 implies $n_2 > n_1$, or waves traveling at higher speed in medium 1 than in 2. The symbols s and s' denote the radii of the wave fronts touching the interface in the two media; they also denote, as before, the object and image distances, respectively. We again restrict our considerations to paraxial rays, that is, to rays whose angle θ relative to the line joining O to I is so small that we may properly replace cos θ by 1.

According to Fermat's principle, the principle of least time, the actual path followed by a ray between two points corresponds to the least travel time between the two chosen points. Here, however, we have a focussing of wave fronts, and *all* rays from O to I follow paths of least time. Thus, a ray travels the straight-line route from O to I in the same time as does a ray from O to B to I. The second route involves a greater overall distance

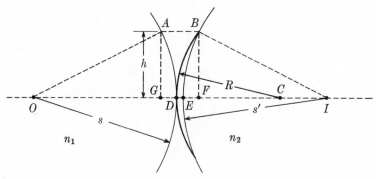

Figure 44-26. The geometry of refraction at a spherical interface for paraxial rays.

than the first, but the travel time is the same, inasmuch as the time over the greater distance OB in the fast medium is exactly compensated for by the time over the lesser distance BI in the slow medium. Now, since $OA = OD$ and $BI = EI$, the time t_{AB} required for a wave front to progress from A to B is the same as the time t_{DE} required for the same wave front to travel from D to E:

$$t_{AB} = t_{DE} \qquad [44\text{-}8]$$

Since the wave speeds in media 1 and 2 are, respectively, c/n_1 and c/n_2, we may write Equation 44-8 as

$$AB/(c/n_1) = DE/(c/n_2)$$
$$n_1(AB) = n_2(DE) \qquad [44\text{-}9]$$

The wave fronts and the spherical interface are shown once again in Figure 44-26. Now, however, the displacement AB is taken as horizontal, rather than oblique; this approximation is permitted, since θ is assumed so small that cos $\theta = 1$. Equation 44-9 can be written

$$n_1(GD + DF) = n_2(DF - EF) \qquad [44\text{-}10]$$

It is clear from the geometry of Figure 44-26 that GD, DF, and EF are the respective sagittas of circles having radii of s, R, and s'. With the use of the sagitta relation, Equation 44-7, Equation 44-10 can be written

$$n_1\left(\frac{h^2}{2s} + \frac{h^2}{2R}\right) = n_2\left(\frac{h^2}{2R} - \frac{h^2}{2s'}\right)$$

Eliminating h^2 and rearranging gives

$$\boxed{\frac{n_1}{s} + \frac{n_2}{s'} = (n_2 - n_1)\frac{1}{R}} \qquad \text{[44-11a]}$$

or, equivalently,

$$\frac{1}{s} + \frac{n_{21}}{s'} = (n_{21} - 1)\frac{1}{R} \qquad \text{[44-11b]}$$

with $n_{21} = n_2/n_1$.

This is the basic lens equation, the general relation describing refraction at a spherical surface. That the refracted wave front is indeed spherical, at least for paraxial rays, follows from the fact that h^2 does *not* appear in Equation 44-11.

Equation 44-11 implies a convention for the signs of the quantities s, s', and R. All three were taken as positive in Figure 44-26, the center C of the spherical interface being located within medium 2. We shall hereinafter always label the medium in which the object is located as medium 1. Then the radius of curvature must be taken as positive if the center lies within medium 2. We can prove this directly by applying the principle of reciprocity. Imagine that the rays in Figures 44-25 and 44-26 are reversed. Then the object becomes the image, s becomes s', s' becomes s, medium 1 becomes 2, and medium 2 becomes 1. Furthermore, we now have $n_1 > n_2$. Now, however, the center C of the interface lies in medium 1, the medium in which the object is located. Since Equation 44-11 must still apply, and since the quantity $(n_2 - n_1)$ is now negative, we must assign a negative sign to the radius of curvature R. Thus, we take R to be positive when its center is in medium 2, and negative when its center is in medium 1.

We now wish to find the locations of the two principal foci, F_1 and F_2, of the interface. First we set $s = \infty$. Then, with an infinitely distant object in medium 1, plane wave fronts impinge upon the interface from the left and come to a focus in medium 2 at F_2 with $s' = f_2$, where f_2 is the focal length *in medium 2*; see Figure 44-27a. From Equation 44-11,

$$\frac{n_2}{f_2} = (n_2 - n_1)\frac{1}{R}$$

$$f_2 = \frac{n_2 R}{(n_2 - n_1)} \qquad \text{[44-12]}$$

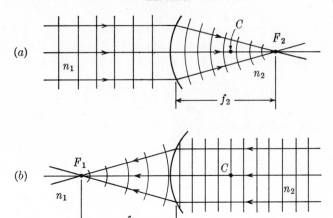

Figure 44-27. The principal focal points in (a) medium 1 and (b) medium 2.

To find the second principal focus we consider the reverse situation, that in which the object is so located within medium 1 that the rays emerging in medium 2 are parallel; then $s = f_1$ with $s' = \infty$, and Equation 44-11 yields

$$\frac{n_1}{f_1} = (n_2 - n_1)\frac{1}{R}$$

$$f_1 = \frac{n_1 R}{(n_2 - n_1)} \qquad\qquad [44\text{-}13]$$

From the reciprocity principle, the second principal focal point F_1 can also be defined as that point at which rays are focussed in medium 1 when they originate as parallel rays from medium 2; see Figure 44-27b.

The focal length f_1 in medium 1 is *different* from the focal length f_2 in medium 2. From Equation 44-12 and 44-13 we see that

$$f_2/f_1 = n_2/n_1 = n_{21} \qquad\qquad [44\text{-}14]$$

the two focal lengths being in the same ratio as their respective refractive indices. The situation here is different from that of a thin lens immersed in a second medium of different refractive index. There the two principal foci were at *equal* distances from the lens (see Figure 44-7); here f_1 and f_2 differ by the factor $n_2/n_1 = n_{21}$, the relative refractive index of the second medium relative to the first.

Note that both f_1 and f_2 depend only on n_1, n_2, and R (the properties of the two media and the curvature of the lens), but *not* on the object and image distances s and s'. Using Equations 44-12 and 44-13, we may write

Equation 44-11 in the form

$$\frac{1}{s} + \frac{n_{21}}{s'} = \frac{1}{f_1} = \frac{n_{21}}{f_2} \qquad [44\text{-}15]$$

We can, of course, compute the image position s', given s, f_1, and f_2, by using Equation 44-15, but we can also locate the image through a simple ray construction, as shown in Figure 44-28. We merely draw two rays: ray 1, which goes from the object, passes through the principal focal point F_1, and emerges parallel to the axis; and ray 2, which is initially parallel to the axis and passes through the second principal focal point, F_2. (We

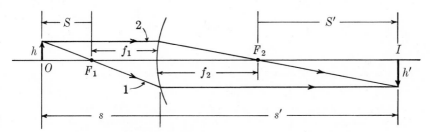

Figure 44-28. Ray construction for locating an image at a spherical interface.

cannot, as in the case of the thin lens, draw a third ray passing undeviated through the center of the interface. Such a ray *is* now deviated!) Of course, we may reverse the directions of the rays and regard s' as representing the object and s the image.

We wish to derive the Newtonian form of Equation 44-15. As before (Section 44-2), the object and image distances, S and S' respectively, are measured from the two principal focal points. That is, $s = S + f_1$ and $s' = S' + f_2$, as shown in Figure 44-28. Denoting the heights of the object and image as h and h', we see from the geometry of Figure 44-28 that

$$h/S = h'/f_1$$
$$h/f_2 = h'/S'$$

Eliminating h and h' from the equations above, we have

$$SS' = f_1 f_2 \qquad [44\text{-}16]$$

This is the generalized Newtonian form of the lens equation. Although we shall not prove it here, it can be shown that Equation 44-16 applies, not only for the refraction at a *single* spherical interface, but also for a combination of *any* number of interfaces.

Consider the situation shown in Figure 44-29, where $n_2 > n_1$, and R is positive. Then f_1 is positive, following Equation 44-13. Now suppose that the object is located closer to the interface than the focal point; that is, $s < f_1$. From Equation 44-15 we see that $s' < 0$. A *negative* image distance corresponds to a *virtual* image, here formed in medium 1, as shown in Figure 44-29.

Now suppose that the interface is flat. We put $R = \infty$. According to Equation 44-13, $f_1 = \infty$, and Equation 44-15 becomes

$$s = -s'/n_{21} \qquad [44\text{-}17]$$

We now imagine an object to be located within the optically more dense medium. We then have $n_1 > n_2$, or $n_{21} < 1$. Equation 44-17 shows that

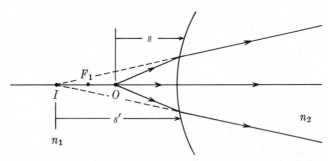

Figure 44-29. Formation of a virtual image at a spherical interface.

the image distance is $s' = -n_{21}s$. The image is virtual and located closer to the surface than s, as shown in Figure 44-30a. For example, if the dense medium is water and the light medium is air, $n_{21} = 1/1.33$. Then an object immersed 4 feet below a water surface will appear, when viewed from air above, to be only $s' = (4 \text{ ft})(1/1.33) = 3$ ft from the surface.

The reverse situation is shown in Figure 44-30b. Here the object is located within the optically light medium, and $n_{21} > 1$. The image is virtual and at greater distance from the surface than the object. This follows from Equation 44-17: $s' = -n_{21}s$. Thus, an object in air at a distance of 3 feet from an air-water interface will appear, when viewed from within the water, to be located $(3 \text{ ft})(1.33) = 4$ ft from the surface. In general, objects within a dense medium appear foreshortened when viewed from a less dense medium, while objects in an optically light medium appear expanded when viewed from a more dense medium.

We use Equation 44-15 to determine the image of an object when the rays enter medium 1 and refract in medium 2. If these rays were now to be incident upon a second interface and refract in a third medium, the final image is found by letting the image formed at the first interface be the object for the second interface. In Equation 44-15 we would replace the subscript 1 by 2, and the subscript 2 by 3, measuring object and image

distances from the second interface. As a simple but important application
of this procedure let us find the equation of a thin lens having a refractive
index n_2 and immersed in a medium of index n_1. The relative refractive
index of the lens to its surroundings is then n_{21}.

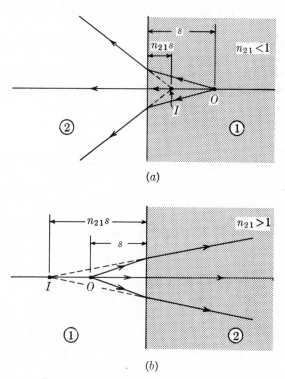

(a)

(b)

Figure 44-30. Refraction at a plane surface: (a) object in optically dense
medium and (b) object in optically light medium.

We label the first interface a with radius R_a and the second interface b
with radius R_b. Then, at the first interface we have, from Equation 44-11,

$$\frac{1}{s_a} + \frac{n_{21}}{s_a'} = (n_{21} - 1)\frac{1}{R_a} \qquad [44\text{-}18]$$

and at the second interface we have

$$\frac{1}{s_b} + \frac{n_{12}}{s_b'} = (n_{12} - 1)\frac{1}{R_b}$$

Multiplying this equation by n_{21} yields

$$\frac{n_{21}}{s_b} + \frac{1}{s_b'} = (1 - n_{21})\frac{1}{R_b} \qquad [44\text{-}19]$$

The image formed by the first interface is the object for the second interface. Since the lens is assumed to have negligible thickness, we put $s_b = -s_a'$. Then adding Equations 44-18 and 44-19 yields

$$\frac{1}{s} + \frac{1}{s'} = (n_{21} - 1)\left(\frac{1}{R_a} - \frac{1}{R_b}\right) \qquad [44\text{-}20]$$

where we have dropped the subscripts a and b, s now denoting the initial object and s' denoting the final image.

We can easily write Equation 44-20 in terms of the focal length f_2 for a thin lens. We recall that $s' = f_2$ when $s = \infty$. Then Equation 44-20 gives

$$\frac{1}{f_2} = (n_{21} - 1)\left(\frac{1}{R_a} - \frac{1}{R_b}\right)$$

Similarly, when $s = f_1$, then $s' = \infty$. Equation 44-20 yields

$$\frac{1}{f_1} = (n_{21} - 1)\left(\frac{1}{R_a} - \frac{1}{R_b}\right)$$

Thus, for a *thin* lens $f_1 = f_2$, and we may define a *single* principal focal length f according to

$$\boxed{\frac{1}{f} = (n_{21} - 1)\left(\frac{1}{R_a} - \frac{1}{R_b}\right)} \qquad [44\text{-}21]$$

This is the *lensmakers' formula*. One may use it to design thin lenses with spherical surfaces. Combining Equations 44-20 and 44-21 gives

[44-2] $1/s + 1/s' = 1/f$

This is just the equation for a thin lens used earlier.

Recall the sign convention which applies to Equation 44-21: n_{21} is the refractive index of the lens material relative to its surroundings; the radii of curvature, R_a and R_b, of the first and second surfaces, respectively, are *positive* if the centers are to the *right* of the lens, and *negative* if the centers are to the *left*. For example, if the lens has two convex surfaces, R_a is positive, R_b is negative, and f is positive (from Equation 44-21), corresponding to a converging lens. On the other hand, if both surfaces are concave, R_a is negative, R_b is positive, and f is negative, as required for a diverging lens. Clearly, if $R_a = R_b$, that is, if the "lens" is equally thick at all points, as in the case of a bent plate of glass, then $f = \infty$, and the "lens" shows no focussing properties (in the first approximation). Examples of converging and diverging lenses are shown in Figure 44-31.

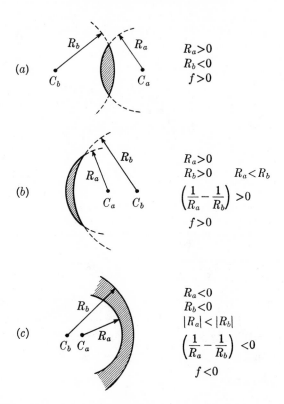

Figure 44-31. Several types of thin lenses. Note the signs of the radii R_a and R_b.

Example 2 A thick glass having a refractive index of 1.50 has concave spherical ends, the left surface being 10 cm in radius and the right surface 5.0 cm in radius. At the lens axis, the thickness of the lens is 2.5 cm. An object is placed 4.0 cm from the left end of the cylinder, as shown in Figure 44-32. Where is the final image formed?

We first deal with the refraction through the left spherical surface (labeled a), taking $s_a = 4.0$ cm, $R_a = -10$ cm, and $n_{21} = 1.50$. Note that one must assign a *minus* sign to the radius since its center lies to the left of the interface. From Equation 44-11,

$$\frac{1}{s_a} + \frac{n_{21}}{s_a{}'} = (n_{21} - 1)\frac{1}{R_a}$$

$$\frac{1}{4} + \frac{1.50}{s_a{}'} = \left(\frac{3}{2} - 1\right)\left(-\frac{1}{10}\right)$$

$$s_a{}' = -5.0 \text{ cm}$$

Thus, the image of the first interface is virtual and is located 5.0 cm to the left of the first interface. This image becomes the object for the second interface (labeled b). For refraction through the second interface, 2.5 cm from the first interface, we have $s_b = 5.0 + 2.5 = 7.5$ cm. The radius of curvature is $R_b = +5.0$ cm, the center now lying to the *right* of the interface. The relative index n_{21} must be taken as $n_{21} = 1/1.50$, since the rays now travel from glass into air. Again using Equation 44-11,

$$\frac{1}{s_b} + \frac{n_{21}}{s_b{}'} = (n_{21} - 1)\frac{1}{R_b}$$

$$\frac{1}{7.5} + \frac{(1/1.50)}{s_b{}'} = \left(\frac{2}{3} - 1\right)\left(\frac{1}{5}\right)$$

$$s_b{}' = -\left(\frac{10}{3}\right) \text{ cm}$$

The final image is virtual and is formed 3.3 cm to the left of the right interface of the lens. It is a simple matter to verify that Equation 44-21, giving the focal length of a *thin* lens in terms of n_{21}, R_a, and R_b, is *not* applicable here.

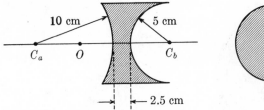

Figure 44-32

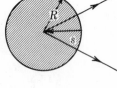

Figure 44-33

Example 3 A glass ball of radius r is immersed in a liquid having a refractive index different from that of the glass ball. Where does a small black spot at the center of the ball appear to be located, when viewed through the surrounding liquid?

Consider the glass and liquid to have respective indices n_1 and n_2. Although the black spot certainly does not act as a light source, we may find its image simply by imagining black and white to be reversed, with a bright source in a black background. The situation is shown in Figure 44-33, where the *object* distance s is chosen as $s = +r$. Note that R is *negative* since the center of the right-hand section of the sphere is to the left of the interface. From Equation 44-11 we have

$$\frac{1}{s} + \frac{n_{21}}{s'} = (n_{21} - 1)\frac{1}{R}$$

which, with $s = +r$, and $R = -r$ reduces to

$$s' = -r$$

The image is virtual and formed exactly at the center of the glass sphere. One sees the black spot *at* the center. Note that we did not require the relative refractive index n_{21}.

We suspect that so simple a result can be arrived at differently. All rays from the center of a sphere intercept the spherical surface along the normals to the surface and are, therefore, undeviated. Consequently, the emerging rays appear to, and *do* in fact, originate from the center.

Example 4 What is the focal length of a concave spherically *reflecting* surface of radius R?

We have not considered spherically reflecting surfaces or spherical mirrors explicitly. We may, however, derive the focussing properties of spherical mirror surfaces quite simply from the relations for spherical *refracting* surfaces. The trick is to assign an appropriate index of refraction to the mirror which will *formally* describe reflection.

First, consider reflection from a flat surface. We know (Section 43-3) that the object and image are at equal distances from the mirror surface. Furthermore, the object and image are located on opposite sides of the reflecting surface, and the image is virtual. We found (Figure 44-30 and Equation 44-17) that, for *refraction* at a flat surface,

$$s = -s'/n_{21}$$

Let us suppose, for definiteness, that our object is located in medium 1; medium 2 then represents the back side of the mirror. Therefore, if an object is at a distance s from the flat surface, its reflection image s' must be at the same distance but on the opposite side of the surface. That is, we represent the virtual image in this case by a *positive* image distance, to denote that it is indeed on the side of the surface opposite to the object. This implies that $s = s'$. Imposing this condition on the equation for refraction above, we have that

$$n_{21} = -1$$

Thus, our relations for refraction also describe reflection, when we replace n_{21} by -1.

We can now find the focal length of a spherical mirror directly. We put $s = \infty$, $s' = f$, and $n_{21} = -1$ in Equation 44-11:

$$\frac{1}{s} + \frac{n_{21}}{s'} = (n_{21} - 1)\frac{1}{R}$$

$$-\frac{1}{f} = -\frac{2}{R}$$

$$f = R/2$$

The focal length of a spherical mirror is *half the radius,* as shown in Figure 44-34.

44-6 Summary The equation for a thin lens is

[44-2] $$1/s + 1/s' = 1/f$$

or, in Newtonian form,

[44-5] $$SS' = f^2$$

The object and image distances, s and s', respectively, are measured relative to the center of the lens. The focal length f is the distance from the lens to

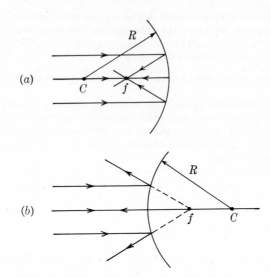

Figure 44-34. The focal length f, for paraxial rays, of a spherical mirror of radius R is $f = \frac{1}{2}R$. (a) Concave mirror; (b) convex mirror.

either of the two principal focal points. When measured relative to the two principal focal points, the object and image distances are, respectively, S and S'.

The sign conventions are as follows:

$$f > 0 \qquad \text{Converging lens}$$
$$f < 0 \qquad \text{Diverging lens}$$
$$s > 0 \qquad \text{Real object}$$
$$s < 0 \qquad \text{Virtual object}$$
$$s' > 0 \qquad \text{Real image}$$
$$s' < 0 \qquad \text{Virtual image}$$

The refraction of paraxial rays at a spherical interface of radius R between a medium of refractive index n_1 and a second medium of refractive index n_2 is governed by

[44-11] $\qquad\qquad n_1/s + n_2/s' = (n_2 - n_1)(1/R)$

where the object is a distance s from the interface in medium 1, and s' is the image distance relative to the interface. The radius R is positive if the center lies within medium 2. The two principal focal points for a spherical interface are *not*, in general, at equal distances from the interface. In Newtonian form the two focal lengths are related to the object and image distances S and S' (measured from the two principal focal points) by

[44-16] $$SS' = f_1 f_2$$

The focal length of a thin lens is given by

[44-21] $$\frac{1}{f} = (n_{21} - 1)\left(\frac{1}{R_a} - \frac{1}{R_b}\right)$$

where n_{21} is the lens' refractive index relative to its surroundings and R_a and R_b are the radii of the two surfaces.

PROBLEMS

44-1 A simple thin converging lens has a focal length of 30 cm. Find the image, both analytically and graphically, and describe its nature (real or virtual) for an object placed at the following distances from the lens: (a) 90 cm, (b) 60 cm, (c) 30 cm, and (d) 15 cm.

44-2 A simple thin diverging lens has a focal length of 30 cm. Find the image, both analytically and graphically, and describe its nature (real or virtual) for an object placed at the following distances from the lens: (a) 90 cm, (b) 60 cm, (c) 30 cm, and (d) 15 cm.

44-3 Show that the minimum distance between an object and its real image formed by a thin converging lens of focal length f is $4f$.

44-4 An object having a height of 1.0 cm is placed 30 cm from a converging thin lens having a focal length of 40 cm. The radius of the lens is 1.0 cm, and the base of the object is placed at the lens axis. Sketch the rays originating from the upper tip and from the base of the object as they pass through the lens, and determine thereby the region of space to which an eye is limited if the eye is to see the entire virtual image formed by the lens.

44-5 ★ A certain point source radiating light isotropically and at a constant rate is located 40 cm along the axis from a converging lens of 20 cm focal length. The lens has an aperture of 2.0 cm radius. (a) What fraction of the light radiated by the source passes through the image? (b) How does the intensity 2.0 cm away from the source compare with the intensity at a point 2.0 cm from the image and 82 cm from the source? (c) Consider a sphere with a radius of 10 cm centered at the location of the image. Is the intensity uniform over the spherical surface? (d) What is the total net radiation into the sphere?

44-6 ★ A point isotropic radiator of light is located at $x = 0$ along the axis of a converging lens having a focal length of 20 cm and located at $x = 40$ cm. The lens' aperture has a radius of 5.0 cm. Plot the intensity of the radiation (in arbitrary units) as a function of x over the range $x = 0$ to $x = 80$ cm.

44-7 Water waves with plane wave fronts are travelling across the surface of a shallow pool. When these surface waves pass through a certain convex-shaped region, the wave fronts are found to converge. Does this region represent a deeper or a more shallow region of water in the otherwise uniform depth? Assume that the wave speed of surface waves varies in this case as the square root of the depth of water.

44-8   An object and its real image are to be separated by 1.00 m. (a) What are the two locations of a thin lens relative to the object position, one of which will produce an image twice the size of the object? (b) What is the focal length of the lens?

44-9   Incident parallel rays make an angle of 5° with the axis of a thin converging lens 20 cm in focal length. Locate the image.

44-10   A certain person can see most clearly objects placed 25 cm from his eyes when he wears converging spectacle lenses having a focal length of 50 cm. Where does he see objects most clearly without his glasses?

44-11   A photographic slide having a width of 35 mm is to be projected onto a screen 4.0 m distant, the width of the projected image being 1.0 m. What must be the focal length of the projection lens?

44-12   An object is placed 40 cm from a lens having a focal length of +20 cm. Where should a plane mirror be placed so that, after the rays refract through the lens, reflect from the mirror, and pass back through the lens, the final image is at the same position as the original object?

44-13   Two identical thin converging lenses, each 40 cm in focal length, are separated by 20 cm. An object is placed 30 cm from the first lens. Where is the final image relative to the position of the object?

44-14   An object 2.0 cm high is placed 20 cm from a converging lens whose focal length is 30 cm and which is followed by a diverging lens having a focal length of −15 cm and separated from the first lens by 10 cm. Find (a) the location relative to the diverging lens and (b) the size of the final image, by both computation and ray construction.

44-15   Show that the equivalent focal length f of a lens combination consisting of two thin lenses in contact is given by $1/f = 1/f_1 + 1/f_2$, where f_1 and f_2 are the focal lengths of the two lenses.

44-16   Through what distance must the lens of a camera having a fixed focal length of 50 mm be displaced, when its focus is changed from that for an infinitely distant object to one 3.0 m away?

44-17   Show that, in general, if a lens, or combination of lenses, forms a virtual image of a real object, then a virtual object at the location of this image will form a real image.

44-18   An astronomical telescope is to be constructed. Its eyepiece is to have a focal length of 1.5 cm. The magnifying power of the telescope is to be 100. (a) What is the required focal length of the objective lens? (b) What will be the overall length of the telescope?

44-19   The *curvature* of a spherical wave front is given by the reciprocal of the wave front's radius of curvature. The curvature C_l of a thin lens is defined as the reciprocal of the radius of the wave fronts emerging from the lens when plane wave fronts (wave fronts of zero curvature) are incident upon the lens. Show that, if the curvatures of the wave fronts leaving the object and converging upon the image are denoted by C_o and C_i respectively, the equation for a thin lens may be written in the form $C_o + C_i = C_l$.

44-20 (a) Will the focal length of a simple converging lens for violet light be greater than or less than the lens' focal length for red light? (b) Which color has the greater focal length for a simple diverging lens?

44-21 Assume that a magnifying glass of focal length f (in centimeters) is placed immediately adjacent to the eye when it is viewing an object located close to the principal focal point. The image formed by the magnifying glass is at a distance of 25 cm from the eye, the so-called *near point* for most distinct vision. Show that the angular magnification of this simple magnifier is given by $25/(f - 1)$.

44-22 A saucer having a concave bottom is filled with water. Will an object on the bottom surface of the saucer be enlarged or reduced in size when viewed from above?

44-23 An object in air is located 20 cm from a concave spherical interface having a radius at 40 cm and lying against glass of refractive index 1.50. (a) Where is the image? Is it real or virtual? (b) Where is the image and what is its nature, if the spherical surface above is convex?

44-24 A spherical goldfish bowl has a radius of 20 cm. A fish within appears to an outside observer to be located 15 cm from the near surface. What is the fish's actual distance from the surface?

44-25 The principal focal lengths f_1 and f_2 for the spherical interface between two media are 30 cm and 40 cm respectively. Determine, both analytically and graphically, the image location of an object in medium 1 whose distance from the interface is (a) 60 cm, (b) 40 cm, and (c) 20 cm.

44-26 A beam of light travels through a glass rod parallel to the rod's axis and emerges out of a convex hemispherical end whose radius is 10 mm. The glass's refractive index is 1.60. At what point outside the rod will the light come to a focus?

44-27 What is the lateral magnification, in terms of s, s', and n_{21}, for refraction from a spherical refracting interface?

44-28 Derive Equation 44-16, the Newtonian form of the equation for refraction at a spherical interface, from Equations 44-11, 44-12, and 44-13.

44-29 A thin planoconvex lens having a focal length of 10 cm is to be made from glass having an index of refraction of 1.58. What is the required radius of curvature of the single spherical surface?

44-30 A thin "lens" of air within water ($n = 1.33$) consists of two convex spherical surfaces, each of 15 cm radius. (a) Is the lens converging or diverging? (b) What is its focal length?

44-31 A certain thin converging lens has a focal length of 20 cm when in air. Its glass has a refractive index of 1.55. What is the lens' focal length when immersed in water ($n = 1.33$)?

44-32 Find the two principal focal points of the thick lens in Example 2.

44-33 A certain convex lens, flat on one side and spherical on the other, has an outside diameter of 5.0 cm and is 4.0 mm thick at its center. Its focal length is found to be 13.5 cm. What is the index of refraction of the material of the lens?

44-34 A nonparabolic reflector shows spherical aberration, in that incident parallel rays are not brought to a focus at a single point. If a concave spherical reflector is used to focus incident parallel rays, will the spherical aberration of rays far from the reflector axis cause these rays to have a larger or smaller focal length than the rays incident close to the reflector axis?

FORTY - FIVE

INTERFERENCE

The phenomenon of interference arises from the superposition of waves from two or more sources. Primary attention will be given here to the simple case of two point sources. We shall investigate the geometrical relations governing the phase difference between the waves from the two sources, and consequently obtain the intensity of the resultant wave. An important example of interference is found in Young's double-slit experiment. Other examples are found with thin films and the Michelson interferometer.

45-1 Superposition and interference for waves in two and three dimensions The rule for finding the resultant wave disturbance produced by two or more waves is the *superposition principle*: to find the net effect of separate waves one merely adds, or superposes, the component disturbances at every instant of time and every point in space. Thus, the resultant pressure difference Δp at a given point in space at a given time is the algebraic sum $\Delta p_1 + \Delta p_2$, where Δp_1 and Δp_2 are the pressure differences at this point and instant arising from the two independent sources. Similarly, the resultant electric field arising from two electromagnetic waves is given by $E = E_1 + E_2$, where the electric fields E_1 and E_2 of the individual waves are now superposed as vectors.† The superposition principle implies, then, that to find the resultant wave disturbance from two sources, we first find the wave disturbance from each source separately and then add these disturbances.

An important consequence of the superposition principle is this: if two waves "collide," both passing through the same region in space at the same time, each wave emerges from the "collision" as if the second wave had not

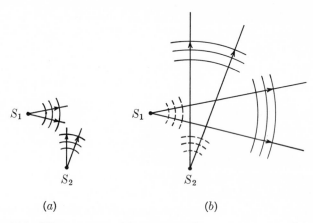

(a)   (b)

Figure 45-1. When superposition occurs, the waves generated by two independent sources in (a) do not interact in (b).

been present at all. The progress of one wave is completely independent of the presence of other waves; see Figure 45-1. Indeed, the validity of the superposition principle is established by the fact that "interfering" waves do not act on one another. For example, what an observer sees in looking at some object emitting or reflecting light is unaffected in shape, color, and brightness by any electromagnetic radiation, light or otherwise, passing through the line connecting the observer with the sighted object. The superposition principle holds (almost) exactly for electromagnetic radiation, however great the intensities of the individual waves.‡ On the other hand,

† We could, of course, equally well choose to find the resultant magnetic field B. It is conventional, however, to give the electric rather than the magnetic field for an electromagnetic wave, primarily because the force of the electric field on a charge in a material is much greater than that of the magnetic field (which is responsible, however, for the radiation force). If the electric field E is known, the magnitude of B is computed from the relation $B = E/c$ (Equation 41-10); the direction of B is found from that of the electric field and of the Poynting vector I through the relation $I = E \times (B/\mu_0)$ (Equation 41-18).

‡ See, however, "The Interaction of Light with Light," *Scientific American*, April, 1964.

the superposition principle holds for elastic waves only when the wave disturbances are so small that the deformations obey Hooke's law precisely. All sound waves of moderate intensity cause pressure changes so small that what one hears from one sound source is not appreciably affected in pitch, quality, and loudness by a second source of sound. Departures from exact superposition are readily seen, however, in interfering surface water waves of large amplitude. In what follows we shall always assume exact superposition.

Whenever two or more waves merge, they are said to interfere. If the resultant wave disturbance from two separate sources at some point is greater than that from either one alone, the waves are said to interfere *constructively*. If, on the other hand, the resultant wave disturbance is less than that of either of the individual disturbances, the waves are said to exhibit *destructive interference*. A point in space at which component waves always show complete destructive interference, with a *zero* resultant wave disturbance at *all* times, is called a *node*.

Hereafter in this chapter we shall be concerned chiefly with the interference from two point sources radiating sinusoidal waves of the same frequency. Although we shall concentrate on the electric field and intensity of radio waves and visible light, it must be understood that the analysis holds equally well for all other types of waves propagating in two and three dimensions. For example, to apply the theory to sound waves we merely replace the electric field by the pressure difference. Indeed, interference effects from two sinusoidal point oscillators are strikingly demonstrated by sound waves and by water surface waves in a ripple tank.

Recall that the time average of the intensity of a sinusoidal electromagnetic wave is given by

$$[41\text{-}17], [41\text{-}30] \qquad\qquad I = \tfrac{1}{2}\epsilon_0 c E_0{}^2 \qquad\qquad [45\text{-}1]$$

where E_0 is now the amplitude of the *resultant* electric field. The intensity is proportional to the *square* of the resultant electric field. Thus, in finding the intensity pattern of two radiators we *first* superpose the individual waves to find E_0 and then square E_0 to find I. We *cannot*, in dealing with two identical sources oscillating continuously, combine the intensities of the two sources; that is, in general I does *not* equal $I_1 + I_2$. In short, one superposes the wave functions, not the intensities.

45-2 Interference from two point sources We first consider the radiation pattern from two identical radio antennas, S_1 and S_2, oscillating at the same frequency f and thereby radiating waves of wavelength $\lambda = c/f$. For example, we might have two electric dipole oscillators (Section 41-5) with their axes at right angles to the plane of the paper, as shown in Figure

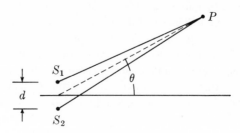

Figure 45-2. Two point sources.

45-2. Then, considering radiation emitted in the plane of the paper, each source separately radiates uniformly in all directions. That is, the intensity of each source is dependent only on the distance from the source, and the electric field is perpendicular to the plane of the paper. We wish to find the resultant intensity I at any point P from the *two* sources as a function of the

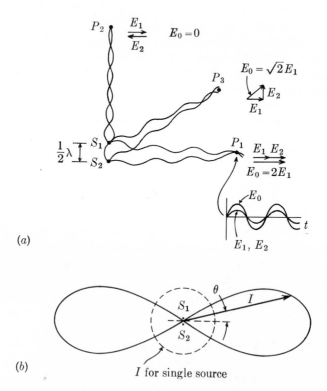

(a)

(b)

I for single source

Figure 45-3. (a) Radiation from two identical point sources oscillating in phase and separated by $\frac{1}{2}\lambda$. (b) The radiation pattern.

angle θ. The point P is a much larger distance from the sources than their separation distance d. Our task is first to find the resultant amplitude E_0 at any point P.

What controls E_0? We can easily see the significant factors by examining two simple examples. Consider point P_1 in Figure 45-3a. Here there are the two sources oscillating *in phase* with one another and separated by one half-wavelength ($d = \lambda/2$). At point P_1 (for $\theta = 0$) the path lengths from S_1 and S_2 are the *same*; consequently, the electric field E_0 at that point is simply the sum of E_1 and E_2, the electric field amplitudes at P_1 arising from the two individual sources. E_1 and E_2 are in phase at P_1, and there is constructive interference at this point. It will be useful to represent the oscillating fields by vectors, in the same fashion that one represents sinusoidally oscillating voltages by rotating vectors for analyzing alternating-current circuits (Section 37-6). We see, then, that at P_1 the electric field is *twice* that arising from one source alone and, since the average intensity is proportional to $E_0{}^2$, the intensity at P_1 is *four* times the intensity we would find if there were a single source.

Now consider point P_2 ($\theta = 90°$) in Figure 45-3a. Here the path lengths differ by $\frac{1}{2}\lambda$, the wave from S_2 traveling $\frac{1}{2}\lambda$ farther than the wave from S_1. Although the sources oscillate in phase, the electric fields from S_1 and S_2 are *out of phase* by 180° at P_2. If P_2 is far from the two sources, the separate electric fields are of nearly the same magnitude, and there is complete destructive interference at this point. At P_2 the intensity is zero.

The situation at point P_3 with $\theta = 30°$ is a little more complicated. The path difference is $d \sin \theta = (\frac{1}{2}\lambda)(\sin 30°) = \frac{1}{4}\lambda$. The electric fields *at point* P_3 are 90° out of phase. We may symbolize this by drawing E_1 and E_2 as vectors 90° out of phase. The resultant amplitude of the electric field is $\sqrt{2}E_1$ and the intensity is proportional to $(\sqrt{2}E_1)^2 = 2E_1{}^2$. Thus, for $\theta = 30°$ the average intensity is twice what it would be from a single radiator.

We could readily compute the intensity at still other points at the same distances from the oscillators, to find I as a function of θ. The results can be plotted on a polar diagram, as shown in the Figure 45-3b. The intensity I is shown as a function of θ. We see that electromagnetic energy is radiated primarily in the directions $\theta = 0°$ and $\theta = 180°$, with none at right angles. The radiation pattern of the two radio antennas is said to consist of two *lobes*. If the two antennas had been exactly at the same place, rather than separated, the radiation pattern would consist of a circle. The interference between the two sources, although it does not change the total energy radiated, redistributes this energy in space.

Suppose, now, that we again have the two sources separated by $\frac{1}{2}\lambda$, but now oscillating out of phase by 180°; see Figure 45-4a. The two sources

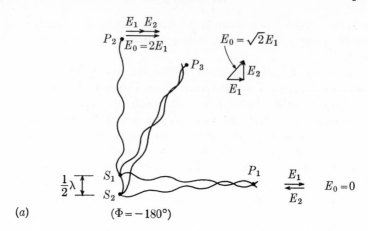

(a)   ($\Phi = -180°$)

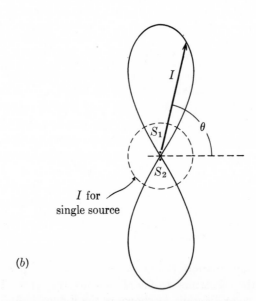

(b)

Figure 45-4. (a) Radiation from two identical point sources oscillating 180° out of phase and separated by $\frac{1}{2}\lambda$; (b) the radiation pattern.

interfere destructively at the point P_1 ($\theta = 0$) because the path length from P_1 to S_1 or to S_2 is the same. On the other hand, at P_2 ($\theta = 90°$) the waves *arrive* in phase and the lag of 180° *in time* of S_2 behind S_1 is compensated for by the $\frac{1}{2}\lambda$ lead *in space* of S_1 over S_2. The intensities at P_1, P_2, and P_3 are now zero, four, and two times, respectively, the intensity from a single source. As Figure 45-4b shows, the radiation pattern is like that of Figure 45-3b, but rotated through 90°. Thus, one may change the direction in which energy is radiated from two antennas simply by changing the relative phases between the oscillators.

In general, the time average of the intensity I is proportional to the resultant electric field amplitude E_0. E_0 depends on the *phase difference* ϕ between the two arriving waves at the *observation point* P. The phase difference ϕ depends, in turn, on (a) the *intrinsic phase difference* Φ between the sources, that is, the difference in phase of the two oscillating point sources, and (b) the *difference in path length* Δr from the two sources to P. We may describe the wave traveling from S_1 by the relation

[39-10]
$$E_1(r_1, t) = E_1 \sin 2\pi \left(\frac{t}{T} - \frac{r_1}{\lambda} \right)$$
[45-2]

where r_1 is the distance from S_1 to P, and E_1 is the electric field amplitude *at the distance r_1*. Similarly, the wave from S_2 is written

$$E_2(r_2, t) = E_2 \sin 2\pi \left(\frac{t}{T} - \frac{r_2}{\lambda} + \Phi \right)$$
[45-3]

where Φ is the *intrinsic phase lead* of S_2 relative to S_1. Oscillator S_2 leads S_1 by the intrinsic phase angle Φ; equivalently, oscillator S_1 lags behind S_2 by the intrinsic phase angle Φ. The amplitudes E_1 and E_2 vary with distance; $E_1 \propto 1/r_1$ and $E_2 \propto 1/r_2$. If $r_1 \simeq r_2$, then $E_1 \simeq E_2$.

Comparing Equations 45-2 and 45-3, we see that the phase difference ϕ is given by

$$\phi = 2\pi \left(\frac{t}{T} - \frac{r_2}{\lambda} + \Phi \right) - 2\pi \left(\frac{t}{T} - \frac{r_1}{\lambda} \right) = \frac{2\pi}{\lambda} (r_1 - r_2) + \Phi$$

$$\boxed{\phi = \left(\frac{2\pi}{\lambda} \Delta r \right) + \Phi}$$
[45-4]

Equation 45-4 shows that, if the two oscillators maintain a constant intrinsic phase difference Φ, the phase difference ϕ at point P and, consequently, the average intensity depends only on the path difference Δr. Thus, if $\Phi = 0$, constructive interference will be found for all points at which Δr is λ or an integral multiple of λ. By the same token, when $\Phi = 0$, nodes corresponding to complete destructive interference will be found at points for which the path difference Δr is $\frac{1}{2}\lambda$ or any odd multiple of it. The reader should confirm the results found earlier in Figures 45-3 and 45-4 by using Equation 45-4.

This is the long and the short of interference. It is simply a matter of geometry, although sometimes a rather difficult geometry, to find the path differences from two or any number of oscillators to the point at which one wishes to find the intensity.

45-3   More on interference from two point sources

Now suppose that the two point sources S_1 and S_2 of Figure 45-2 are separated by an arbitrary distance d and that these sources oscillate *in phase* at the same frequency $f = c/\lambda$. Thus, the intrinsic phase difference Φ between the oscillators is taken to be zero, and Equation 45-4 becomes

$$\phi = \frac{2\pi}{\lambda}\Delta r$$

which we may write as

$$\frac{\text{phase difference (at observation point)}}{2\pi} = \frac{\text{difference in path length}}{\lambda} \qquad [45\text{-}5]$$

We assume the point P to be far from S_1 and S_2 as compared with d, so that the two rays to P make the same angle θ with respect to the perpendicular

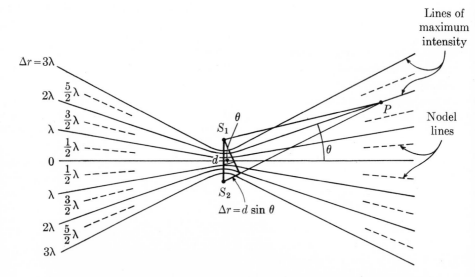

Figure 45-5. Lines of maximum intensity and nodal lines for two point sources oscillating in phase.

bisector of the line joining S_1 and S_2. From the geometry of Figure 45-5 we see that the path difference is

$$\Delta r = d \sin \theta \qquad [45\text{-}6]$$

As Equation 45-5 shows, the phase difference at P will be zero (or an integral multiple of 2π) and there will be constructive interference whenever the path difference is an integral multiple of the wavelength; that is, constructive interference corresponds to $\Delta r = m\lambda$, where $m = 0, 1, 2, \ldots,$. Thus, from Equation 45-6, the directions θ for maximum radiated intensity are given by

Maximum I: $\Delta r = m\lambda = d \sin \theta$,   with $m = 0, 1, 2, \cdots$ [45-7]

On the other hand, when the path difference is an odd multiple of one-half wavelength, we have complete destructive interference, the directions of the nodal points in the intensity being given by

Zero I: $\Delta r = m\left(\dfrac{\lambda}{2}\right) = d \sin \theta$,   with $m = 1, 3, 5, \cdots$ [45-8]

Point P in Figure 45-5 corresponds to a path difference of 2λ, and the locus of points, all with this same path difference, defines a curve of maximum intensity. The curve is, in fact, a hyperbola. This follows from the definition of a hyperbola as the locus of points whose distances from two fixed points (here S_1 and S_2) differ by a constant (here 2λ). The asymptotes of the hyperbola make the angle θ relative to the bisector of the line connecting S_1 and S_2. A series of such hyperbolas gives the locations of maximum intensity. A second set of hyperbolas represents the lines of zero intensity, or *nodal lines*: the path differences for these curves is an odd multiple of $\lambda/2$.

The interference pattern from two sinusoidally oscillating point sources can be demonstrated strikingly with water surface waves generated by two objects oscillating transversely on the water surface. A photograph of such a ripple-tank interference pattern is shown in Figure 45-6.

We wish to derive the general expression giving I as a function of θ. The electric field amplitudes E_1 and E_2 differ in phase by ϕ, as shown in Figure 45-7. Vector E_2 leads E_1 by ϕ.

Figure 45-6. Interference from two point sources in a ripple tank. (From PSSC PHYSICS, D. C. Heath and Company.)

We take the magnitudes of E_1 and E_2 to be the same, $E_1 = E_2$, since both sources are essentially at the same distance from P. Clearly, the sum of the horizontal components of the vectors in Figure 45-7 is given by

$$E_1 + E_2 \cos \phi = E_1(1 + \cos \phi) = 2E_1 \cos^2 (\phi/2)$$

From Figure 45-7, this horizontal component is $E_0 \cos \dfrac{\phi}{2}$. Therefore

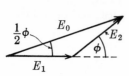

Figure 45-7. Resultant field E_0 from two electric fields, E_1 and E_2, out of phase by ϕ.

$$E_0 \cos (\phi/2) = 2E_1 \cos^2 (\phi/2)$$
$$E_0 = 2E_1 \cos (\phi/2)$$

But,

$$I \propto E_0{}^2$$

Therefore,

$$I \propto \cos^2 (\phi/2)$$

The phase difference ϕ is, from Equations 45-5 and 45-6,

$$\phi = 2\pi d \sin \theta/\lambda$$

Using this result in the relation for I gives

$$I \propto \cos^2 (\pi d \sin \theta/\lambda)$$

Taking the maximum intensity to be I_0 we have

$$\boxed{I = I_0 \cos^2 (\pi d \sin \theta/\lambda)} \qquad [45\text{-}9]$$

The intensity varies with θ according to the square of the cosine, as shown in Figure 45-8. We may confirm Equation 45-7 by noting that the cosine in Equation 45-9 is ± 1 when its argument ($\pi d \sin \theta/\lambda$) is $m\pi$, with $m = 0, 1, 2, \ldots,$. Then, $\pi d \sin \theta/\lambda = m\pi$, or $m\lambda = d \sin \theta$, as in Equation 45-7. Equation 45-8 follows from Equation 45-9 in similar fashion.

The variation in intensity with angle is also portrayed in the polar diagram of Figure 45-9. Since the sources are separated by more than one half-wavelength (actually $d = (7/2)\lambda$ here), the number of lobes in the radiation pattern is increased over the two lobes found in Figure 45-3.

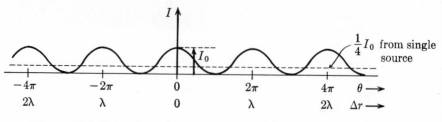

Figure 45-8. Intensity variation with angle for two point sources in phase.

45-4 Reflection and change of phase By an ingenious arrangement known as *Lloyd's mirror* (devised by H. Lloyd, in 1834) one can produce interference effects by using a *single* wave source rather than two sources. (As we shall see, it is essential to have a single source to observe interference effects with visible light.) One places the single source close to a reflecting sheet, or mirror, as in Figure 45-10. Then waves reach point P both through a direct path from S_1 and through a path involving a reflection from the mirror. We may regard the reflected ray as originating from source S_2 located below the mirror surface at the position of S_1's mirror image. We assume that P is far from S_1 and that all radiation striking the mirror is reflected. We might expect, then, that the intensity pattern resulting

Figure 45-9. Intensity pattern from two sources separated by $(7/2)\lambda$.

from interference between the waves from the real source and those from its mirror image (a so-called virtual source) would be just that found earlier for two real sources oscillating in phase. Certainly, the path differences and geometrical relations are unchanged. This is not, however, what is observed. The locations of maximum and minimum intensity are found to be just reversed: nodal lines are found where lines of maximum intensity were found before, and conversely. Apparently, an additional phase change of 180°, not attributable to a path difference, arises here. Indeed, an electromagnetic wave undergoes a *180° shift in phase* whenever it is *reflected from an optically more dense medium or from a conducting surface.*

Recall the results we have found for an elastic wave, such as a transverse wave pulse on a stretched string, reflected from the interface between two media (two strings of different density); see Figure 45-11. A wave reflected

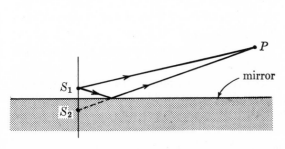

Figure 45-10. Rays from a point source S_1 and its mirror image S_2.

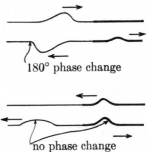

180° phase change

no phase change

Figure 45-11. Phase changes for reflection at a boundary of a transverse wave pulse on a stretched string.

from an interface leading to a medium in which the wave speed is less undergoes a 180° change in phase. There is, however, no phase change when a wave in a "slow" medium is reflected from an interface leading to a "fast" medium. Exactly the same behavior is seen with electromagnetic waves: a change in phase of 180° occurs when the wave impinges upon an interface leading to a more dense medium; otherwise, there is no phase change. This important result can, of course, be deduced from Maxwell's equations. The phase relations for reflection are shown in Figure 45-12. Thus, when visible light traveling in air strikes an optically dense material, such as glass, the reflected waves are reversed in phase; but when visible light impinges upon an interface from glass into air, or into a medium with a smaller index of refraction, there is no phase change. Similarly, a 180°

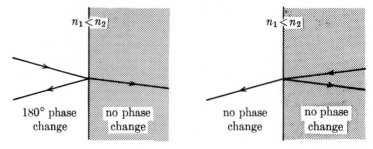

Figure 45-12. Phase changes for an electromagnetic wave at an interface.

phase change appears when an electromagnetic wave is reflected from a conducting surface, as in the case of radio waves incident upon a metal surface or of light upon a mirror. The direct experimental evidence of the phase change comes from interference experiments, such as Lloyd's with a mirror.

45-5 Coherent and incoherent sources We have assumed thus far that the two interfering wave sources generate sinusoidal waves continuously, and that the intrinsic phase difference between the two sources, whether zero or nonzero, is maintained indefinitely. This would surely be the case if two electric dipole oscillators were wired to a single radio oscillator that operated continuously. Any two such sources which maintain a constant phase relation are said to be *coherent* sources, and the waves they generate are said to show *coherence* both in space and in time.

Now suppose that one source oscillates continuously while a second, generating waves of the same frequency and wavelength, is turned on and off *at random*. The separate electric fields E_1 and E_2 from the two sources, and the resultant field, are shown as a function of time in Figure 45-13. Since E_2 is not a *continuous* monochromatic wave, neither is the resultant $(E_1 + E_2)$. The resultant field has the same frequency as the two sources, but both the phase and amplitude of the resultant wave change abruptly and randomly in time. The two sources are said to be *incoherent*. Their interference in time at any point in space leads to an intensity, proportional to $(E_1 + E_2)^2$, which fluctuates erratically in time. This is to be contrasted with the intensity variation in time caused by two coherent sources, as shown in Figure 45-13. Thus, the time average of the resultant intensity over many cycles is proportional to $(E_1 + E_2)^2$ for coherent sources and proportional to $E_1^2 + E_2^2$ for incoherent sources.

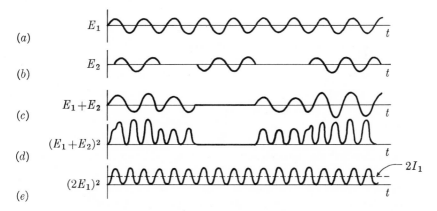

Figure 45-13. Electric field as a function of time for (a) a continuous oscillator, (b) an oscillator turned on and off at random, (c) the resultant wave. Square of the resultant field for (d) two incoherent sources and (e) two coherent sources.

We have seen that the positions of the nodal lines and the lines of maximum intensity depend on the intrinsic phase difference between the oscillators. If the phase of one oscillator is changed by 180°, the nodal lines become lines of maximum intensity, and conversely. That is, a shift in phase causes an angular shift in the radiation pattern. Thus, if two oscillators do not run coherently, because either one oscillator or both oscillators are turned on and off at random, we do not find a fixed interference pattern but, rather, a rapidly fluctuating radiation pattern whose time average, unlike that of Equation 45-9, is independent of the angle θ. Another way of putting it is this: the interference is washed out over a period of time which is long compared with the time during which both oscillators are on.

It is a simple matter to devise a pair of coherent oscillators for sound waves (connect two loudspeakers to a single audio oscillator) or for long-wavelength electromagnetic radiation (connect two radio antennas to a single oscillating electric circuit), but it is *not* possible, without some care, to devise a pair of coherent oscillators for visible light. Visible light is emitted when atoms in certain energy states make transitions discontinuously to lower energy states, the loss of energy by an atom being the energy of the emitted light. A typical atom emitting visible light is "on," that is, radiating, for only 10^{-8} sec. Although very short, this time is long compared with the oscillation period for typical visible-light frequencies, $\sim 10^{-15}$ sec. Most light sources depend upon the heating of the atoms to produce the atomic transitions which raise the atoms to higher energy states, the precondition for radiation. Thus, the excitation of atoms arises from random thermal motion. Consequently, the radiation by a large number of atoms, each over a time of about 10^{-8} sec, is also random. That is to say, the radiation of visible light from thermally excited light sources is *incoherent*. Of course, the radiation from any two emitting atoms *is* coherent over a period of about 10^{-8} sec, but since we register the intensity of visible light in the eye or on photographic film over a time much greater than 10^{-8} sec, the light appears essentially incoherent.

Recently (1960, C. H. Townes, 1915–), coherent sources of visible light have been produced in a device known as a *laser*, the acronym for *l*ight *a*mplification by the *s*timulated *e*mission of *r*adiation. A thoroughgoing explanation of laser operation is possible only through the quantum theory. What follows here are some general features of laser behavior. In a laser the atoms are brought to excited states in preparation for radiation, not by thermal excitation but by *optical pumping*, in which light of higher frequency than that emitted by the atoms is *absorbed* by the active material, which may be, for example, chromium atoms within ruby. The atoms remain in the upper energy states for much longer than 10^{-8} sec. When light of the frequency to be amplified by the laser enters the material, it stimulates the atoms in upper energy states to make transitions to lower energy states, thereby emitting light of the *same* frequency as the "stimulating" radiation.

The waves of light emitted by stimulated atoms must be either in phase or out of phase relative to the waves stimulating the emission. If the emitted waves were out of phase by any amount, the resultant intensity would be reduced, a result which would violate energy conservation. Therefore, light is emitted in synchronism, that is, is in coherence, with the light stimulating the emission. There is light amplification. In practice, the active material which has been optically pumped to the excited states is held between two perfectly parallel reflecting boundaries. Then the emitted light is made to traverse the region between the boundaries repeatedly through multiple reflections. The intensity of the wave grows as the light first present causes atoms to emit light in coherence. The useful light—highly monochromatic, unidirectional, intense, and coherent—leaves the laser by passing through a *partially* reflecting end mirror. The technological applications of lasers are many. They all derive from the fact that with them one can produce electromagnetic radiation in the visible region that has coherence properties heretofore available only in radio waves.

45-6 Young's double-slit experiment Clearly, one *cannot* observe interference effects with visible light simply by using two separate ordinary light sources. Two such sources would be *incoherent*. If one is to see interference effects with visible light, one must, apart from using two laser

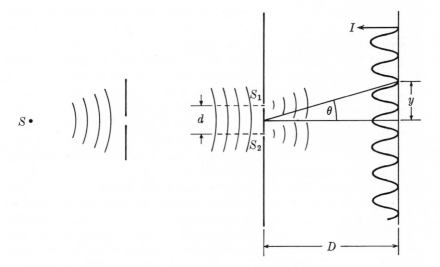

Figure 45-14. Young's double-slit experiment.

beams, divide the waves from a single point source into two beams and then recombine the beams. This is accomplished, in effect, when two slits are illuminated by a single light source in an arrangement like that shown in Figure 45-14.

Here light from a source S passes through a very narrow single slit to fall upon the double slits. As we remarked in Section 43-1, waves do not emerge from a slit whose width is comparable to their wavelength and form a precisely defined geometrical shadow. They are diffracted; that is, the wave fronts spread beyond the geometrical boundaries corresponding to ray optics. We shall consider the details of diffraction in the next chapter. Suffice it to say here that a *single* wave front illuminates both of the double slits; consequently, the slits are, in effect, coherent wave sources, S_1 and S_2, which produce the characteristic interference pattern on the distant screen.

An arrangement like that shown in Figure 45-14 was used by Thomas Young (1773–1829) in 1801 in an experiment of great historical significance. Young's observation of the interference pattern of light demonstrated unambiguously that light does, in fact, consist of waves. It was not known at the time of Young's experiment that light consists of *electromagnetic* waves, but the interference effect, a distinctly wave phenomenon, showed that the particle model for light was simply impotent to account for the experimental results. If light did indeed consist of particles traveling in straight lines, then one surely could *not* find, as Figure 45-14 shows, a *maximum* intensity at the center of the screen ($\theta = 0$), exactly that point in the "shadow" between the two slits where one would expect to have zero intensity. Curiously, Young also devised a ripple-tank experiment (the first) as a model for demonstrating his wave interpretation of the double-slit experiment (actually, he used pinholes, rather than parallel slits, in his first observations).

Figure 45-15. Interference fringes for Young's double-slit experiment. (Courtesy of Klinger Scientific Apparatus Corporation.)

Figure 45-15 is a photograph of a double-slit interference pattern. Note that the intensity of the maxima in pattern is *not* constant, but falls off away from the center of pattern (at $\theta = 0$). There would be essentially uniform intensity maxima if the two slits were of infinitesimal width. With slits of finite width, additional diffraction effects, to be discussed in the next chapter, appear. Of course, since a laser is a coherent light source, one may use a simpler experimental arrangement with it to produce interference effects. One need merely place the double slits in the path of a laser beam (and omit the first single slit).

The alternating regions of brightness and darkness on the screen are known as interference fringes. Clearly, the locations of the bright interference fringes are given by the relation derived earlier,

[45-7] $$m\lambda = d \sin \theta, \quad \text{where} \quad m = 0, 1, 2, \cdots, \quad \text{[45-10]}$$

where d is now the separation distance between the two slits. The angle θ may be measured quite simply by noting that when adjacent interference fringes are very closely spaced (say, a few millimeters apart), as is typically the case when the screen distance from the slits is tens of centimeters, the angle θ is very small, and we may write

$$\sin \theta \simeq \theta \simeq y/D$$

Then Equation 45-10 may be written as

$$m\lambda = yd/D \qquad\qquad [45\text{-}11]$$

All quantities in Equation 45-10, save λ, are directly measurable in an interference experiment, and we compute the wavelength of visible light (a quantity which ranges from 0.0004 to 0.0007 mm), from the geometry of the interference fringes.

Since, for a given m and d, the distance y is proportional to the wavelength, the various colors of the white-light spectrum have different interference patterns. The central interference fringe is white (waves of *any* wavelength

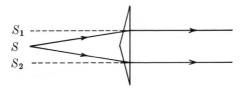

Figure 45-16. The Fresnel biprism.

constructively interfere for $m = 0$); for all other fringes, the locations of the bright regions depend directly on the wavelength, according to Equation 45-11. Thus, for a given fringe (a given m) the long wavelengths (for example, red) will be farther from the center than the shorter wavelengths (violet). Each fringe, except the central one, then consists of a dispersed spectrum of white light.

One can perform a Lloyd's-mirror experiment with visible light, using a single slit and its mirror image as the two coherent light sources. This was, in fact, the first use of this method by Lloyd. Another arrangement avoiding the use of two coherent light sources is the Fresnel biprism, shown in Figure 45-16. Here light from a single source S undergoes different deviations in passing through the two prisms (a biprism) and appears to come from two coherent sources S_1 and S_2.

45-7 Interference in thin films The most familiar examples of interference involve thin films. The variegated colors seen in a thin film of oil on water have their origin in interference between the light waves reflected from the two surfaces of the oil film.

First consider the simple arrangement shown in Figure 45-17. Here a microwave transmitter sends a monochromatic beam of radiation toward two parallel planes, each containing a grid of wires. The two sheets act as partial mirrors, a fraction of the incident waves being reflected backward from each reflector. A receiver at a relatively large distance from the reflectors detects the resultant electric field arising from the interference of waves reflected from mirrors A and B, which are separated by a distance d. The two reflected beams are, of course, coherent, inasmuch as they have their origin in the single wave generator. The reflected waves will interfere constructively if the difference in path length (here approximately $2d$ for nearly normal incidence and reflection) is an integral multiple of the wavelength. That is, a strong signal is registered in the receiver when

$$2d = m\lambda, \qquad \text{where} \quad m = 0, 1, 2, \cdots,$$

The reflected waves here undergo a 180° change in phase, but because this phase change occurs at both reflectors, the relation given is not affected.

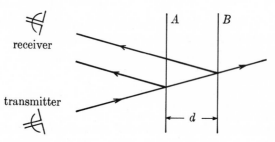

Figure 45-17. Interference from partially reflected radio waves at interfaces A and B.

The device shown in Figure 45-17 is a simple form of *interferometer*. One can use such an instrument to measure wavelengths through interference effects; conversely, knowing the wavelength, one can measure the displacement of one of the mirrors. Suppose, for example, that the mirrors A and B are separated by such a distance as to give constructive interference. Then, if mirror B is displaced by $\frac{1}{4}\lambda$ to the left or right, the overall path length of the ray reflected from B is increased by $\frac{1}{2}\lambda$, and its interference with the wave from A at the receiver is now destructive. We shall later discuss one form of interferometer with which it is possible to measure displacements to a fraction of the wavelength of visible light, that is, to a few thousands of Ångstroms.

Now consider a situation involving visible light, as shown in Figure 45-18. Here we have light rays incident nearly along the normal to two parallel interfaces which separate media with refractive indices n_1, n_2, and n_3. In determining whether the reflected rays interfere constructively or destructively we must take into account the following facts: (1) a reflected wave undergoes a 180° phase change relative to the incident (and transmitted) waves, if the wave is incident from a medium of lower refractive index into a second medium of higher refractive index (Section 45-4); (2) the wavelength λ_m within any medium of refractive index n is

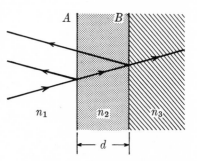

[43-9] $\lambda_m = \lambda/n$ [45-12]

where λ is the wavelength in free space.

The shrinking of wavelengths in an optically dense medium gives rise to the idea of *optical path length*, which is defined as the geometrical path length

Figure 45-18. Interference arising from reflections from two interfaces.

multiplied by the refractive index of the medium. For example, the wavelength of red light in vacuum is 6000 Å, whereas the wavelength of the same radiation in glass, with $n = 1.50$, is $(6000 \text{ Å})/1.5 = 4000$ Å. A geometrical path length of 6.0 mm in vacuum contains 10,000 wavelengths of red light, whereas these same 10,000 wavelengths will extend over only 4.0 mm in glass. Thus, the geometrical path *in glass* is 4.0 mm; the equivalent optical path is $(4.0 \text{ mm})(1.5) = 6.0$ mm, since this is the geometrical path length in vacuum containing the same number of wavelengths. Clearly, then, in computing phase differences one can take into account the change in wavelength in a refracting medium by replacing the geometrical path length by the optical path length.

Suppose, for example, that we have a thin film of oil on water, with $n_1 = 1.00$, $n_2 = 1.46$, and $n_3 = 1.33$, illuminated at normal incidence with monochromatic light of wavelength λ (in vacuum). Since $n_1 < n_2$, but $n_2 > n_3$, a 180° phase change occurs at the reflections from surface A but not from surface B. Then the condition for maximum reflected intensity is

$$2d = (m + \tfrac{1}{2})\lambda_{m_2}, \quad \text{where} \quad m = 0, 1, 2, \cdots,$$

or, equivalently,

$$2d = (m + \tfrac{1}{2})\lambda_{m1}/n_{21}$$

The light shining on an oil film reaches the eye from various sources. Therefore, the path differences vary according to the angle of incidence on the film. In addition, the film may not be of constant thickness. Finally, the various colors have different wavelengths, so that if there is constructive interference for one wavelength, there may be destructive interference for another. Consequently, one sees a variety of colors in the film.

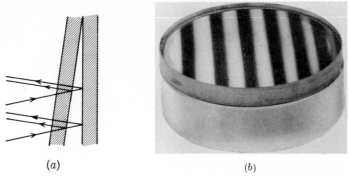

(a)   (b)

Figure 45-19. (a) Interference from an air wedge. (b) The observed fringes (Courtesy of Bausch and Lomb, Inc., Rochester, New York).

A simpler situation obtains when there are two perfectly flat plates of glass slightly inclined to produce a wedge-shaped film of air between them, as in Figure 45-19a. Because the film changes thickness uniformly, one sees, in viewing the nearly parallel plates, a succession of parallel interference fringes, as shown in Figure 45-19b. Note that in this case $n_1 > n_2$ and $n_2 < n_3$; consequently, a phase reversal occurs at the far reflection but not at the near. Then the condition for maximum intensity becomes $2d = (m + \frac{1}{2})\lambda$, where d is the thickness of the film, λ is the wavelength in air, and the $\frac{1}{2}$ appears with the integer m to account for the phase change in one of the two reflections. The arrangement of Figure 45-19 provides a direct way of testing a surface for optical flatness (flatness to within a fraction of the wavelength of light). A departure from a truly plane surface is manifest in the

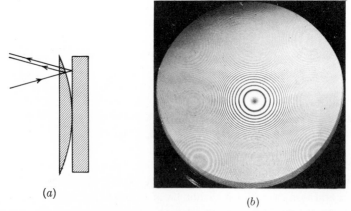

(a)
                                            (b)

Figure 45-20. (a) Interference leading to Newton's rings. (b) The observed rings (Courtesy of Bausch and Lomb, Inc., Rochester, New York).

interference pattern through nonparallel or unequally spaced interference fringes.

A modification of the arrangement with two flat plates is shown in Figure 45-20a. Here a planoconvex lens (with a large radius of curvature for the spherical surface) is in contact with a flat plate of glass. The air wedge has cylindrical symmetry and is not uniform in thickness. Consequently, the interference fringes appear as alternating bright and dark circles, as shown in Figure 45-20b, the outer circles being crowded together. This phenomenon is known as *Newton's rings*. Discovered by Robert Hooke (1635–1703), the rings were studied by Isaac Newton, who attempted (unsuccessfully) to give an explanation of this effect on the basis of a *particle* model of light! Of course, this interference effect, as well as all other interference phenomena, can be comprehended only on the basis of the wave theory. Note particularly, that the central region is *dark*, not bright. At the point of contact there is *zero* path difference between the rays reflected from the two adjoining interfaces, but the reflected rays are out of phase, because one interface is between glass and air whereas the second interface is between air and glass. Just as one can use interference fringes to test a surface for optical flatness, one can use Newton's rings to test a curved surface for sphericity.

45-8 The Michelson interferometer This remarkable optical instrument was invented by A. A. Michelson (1852–1931, the first American Nobel laureate in physics) as the basis of the renowned Michelson-Morley experiment, through which the constancy of the speed of light, irrespective of the motion of a light source or of the observer, was established. The experiment gave the first experimental basis for the theory of special relativity, in showing that electromagnetic waves do not travel in a unique reference frame, or "ether."

The essential parts of the interferometer are shown in Figure 45-21. An incident beam of light is split by a partially silvered mirror M into two beams, which travel separate perpendicular paths to mirrors M_1 and M_2 and are then recombined to interfere as they enter the observer's eye. A plate of glass, equal in thickness to partially silvered mirror M and also inclined at 45° relative to the ray directions, is placed as shown in the figure, to insure that the optical paths up-down and right-left are at least approximately equal.

If the mirrors M_1 and M_2 are exactly perpendicular to the rays incident at their centers, the interference pattern seen by the eye is like that in Figure 45-22, a series of circular interference fringes, reminiscent of Newton's rings. This pattern arises from the fact that the noncentral rays on the mirrors travel slightly different path lengths from those traveled by rays striking the mirrors at their centers.

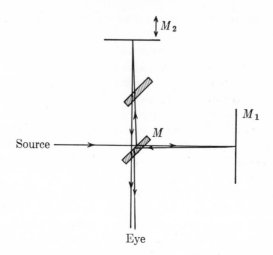

Figure 45-21. The elements of a Michelson interferometer.

Suppose that a dark circle first appears in the interference pattern. Then, the central rays taking the two routes have interfered destructively. Now imagine the mirror M_2 to be displaced $\frac{1}{4}\lambda$. The path length of the up-down ray has thereby been changed by $\frac{1}{2}\lambda$, and the combining central rays reaching the eye now interfere constructively. Consequently, the central spot has been changed from dark to bright (and white and black have been interchanged in all the surrounding interference fringes). A further displacement of $\frac{1}{4}\lambda$ restores the dark central spot. As the mirror M_2 is moved, one sees a succession of interference rings collapsing into the center of the pattern, every alternation of black and white corresponding to a mirror displacement of $\frac{1}{4}\lambda$. Thus, one may measure the wavelength of light by counting the total number of fringe shifts for a known displacement of the mirror. Conversely, knowing the wavelength, one measures displacements of the mirror to within a fraction of the wavelength of light.

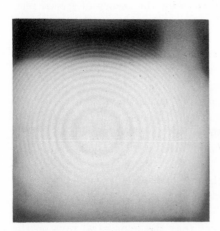

Figure 45-22. Interference pattern seen in a Michelson interferometer.

The Michelson interferometer was earlier used to count the number of wavelengths of light within the distance between the two scratches on a platinum bar marking the standard meter. Since the meter is now defined as 1,650,763.73 wavelengths of krypton-86 light, one may reverse the procedure, measuring a distance in terms of wavelengths of light.

A Michelson-type interferometer may be constructed to operate with electromagnetic radiation of much larger wavelength, such as microwaves of a few centimeters. A simple form of microwave interferometer is shown in Figure 45-23. In refined versions one can measure microwave wavelengths with remarkably high precision. (The macroscopic displacement of one of

Figure 45-23. A simple form of Michelson microwave interferometer.

the mirrors may be measured with an *optical* Michelson interferometer and krypton-86 light.) Then, if the frequency of the microwave radiation also is known with high accuracy (for example, by means of an atomic clock), one can compute the speed of light with high precision through the relation $c = f\lambda$. The most precise measurements of c utilize this procedure.

Since an optical Michelson interferometer is easily capable of detecting a difference in overall path length over the two routes as small as one optical wavelength, it measures indirectly a very small difference in the travel times for the two routes. For example, with $\lambda = 5000$ Å, a mirror displacement of $\frac{1}{2}\lambda$ corresponds to a difference in round-trip travel times of only

$$(\tfrac{1}{2} \times 5000 \text{ Å})/(3.0 \times 10^8 \text{ m/sec}) \simeq 8 \times 10^{-16} \text{ sec}$$

The possibility of measuring such very small differences in travel time by light is the basis of the use of the Michelson interferometer in the Michelson-Morley experiment.

45-9 Summary To find the resultant intensity from two of more wave sources we apply the superposition principle, adding the separate wave functions at any instant of time and any point in space to find the resultant wave function whose square is proportional to the intensity.

For two coherent sources radiating waves of the same wavelength λ, the resultant amplitude is determined by the phase difference ϕ at any observation point,

[45-4] $$\phi = \left(\frac{2\pi}{\lambda}\right) \Delta r + \Phi$$

where Δr is the path difference and Φ is the intrinsic phase difference between the two sources. If the two sources oscillate in phase and are separated by a distance d, the intensity I at a distant point is maximum when

[45-7] Maximum I: $\quad \Delta r = m\lambda = d \sin \theta, \quad$ with $m = 0, 1, 2, \cdots$,

[45-9] $$I = I_0 \cos^2 (\pi d \sin \theta / \lambda)$$

where θ is the angle measured from the perpendicular bisector of the line joining the sources. In Young's double-slit experiment the point sources are replaced by two parallel slits illuminated through a single slit.

Electromagnetic waves undergo a 180° phase shift when reflected from an optically light to an optically dense medium. Similarly, a 180° phase shift occurs in reflection from a conducting surface.

Interference effects are seen when light is reflected from (or transmitted through) two closely spaced interfaces. The Michelson interferometer is a device for measuring wavelengths or distances with high precision.

PROBLEMS

45-1 An oscillator S_1 generating waves of wavelength λ produces a constant intensity of 1.0 mw/m² in all horizontal directions at a distance of 100 m ($\gg \lambda$) from the oscillator. A second, identical, oscillator S_2 is placed a distance d north of S_1. What are the intensities at a distance of 100 m in the directions north, south, east, and west of the two oscillators when (a) $d = \frac{1}{2}\lambda$ and S_1 and S_2 oscillate in phase, (b) $d = \frac{1}{2}\lambda$ and S_1 and S_2 oscillate 180° out of phase, and (c) $d = \frac{1}{4}\lambda$ and S_1 lags S_2 in phase by 90°?

45-2   Two separated isotropic oscillators generate waves of slightly different wavelengths. Discuss qualitatively how the radiated intensity varies with angle and with time.

45-3   Two identical point sources oscillate in phase. Locate the points of minimum oscillation along the line joining the two sources when (a) the sources are separated by a distance of 5 wavelengths and (b) the sources are separated by a distance of $5\frac{1}{2}$ wavelengths.

45-4   Two loudspeakers, oscillating in phase and each generating sound waves 3.0 feet in wavelength, are separated by 8.0 feet. A microphone is placed along the line in front of one loudspeaker and perpendicular to the line joining the two loudspeakers. Find the positions of the microphone, relative to the nearer loudspeaker, for the first three minima in the sound intensity.

45-5   Two microwave generators separated by 12.0 cm oscillate in phase at the frequency of 10 kMcycles/sec. What is the angular separation between the lobes in their radiation pattern?

45-6   An oscillator generates waves of 4.0 m. A second oscillator, 10.0 m north of the first oscillator, oscillates at the same frequency but 180° out of phase relative to the first oscillator. Find the locations, measured east of the first oscillator, of the zeroes in the resultant intensity.

45-7   Two identical point sources generate circular water waves of wavelength λ, each generator emitting an average power P. The generators are $\frac{3}{2}$ wavelengths apart. Find the average resultant intensity I at the points A, B, and C in Figure 45-24 for the following situations (assume $R \gg \frac{3}{2}\lambda$): (a) only one generator operating, (b) both generators on and oscillating in phase, (c) both generators on and oscillating 180° out of phase, and (d) both generators on and operating in random phase.

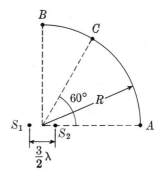

Figure 45-24

45-8   The radiation pattern of two identical isotropic radio oscillators consists of six equally spaced lobes. What is the separation distance between the oscillators if the oscillators are radiating at a frequency of 10 Mcycles/sec?

45-9   Show that the angle θ between a radiation lobe of two oscillators and the line joining the oscillators is related to the intrinsic phase difference Φ, the wavelength λ, and the distance between the oscillators d by $\cos \theta = (m - \Phi/2\pi)(\lambda/d)$.

45-10   Two oscillators are similar to those in Figure 45-3, except the angle between the lobes and the line joining the oscillators is 30°. Find the intrinsic phase difference between the two oscillators.

45-11 Assume two oscillators are similar to those in Figure 45-3 except that the sources are 45° out of phase. What is the angle between the lobes and the axis?

45-12 A point generator of waves on a water surface is 4.0 inches from a plane reflecting boundary. The water waves have a wavelength of 2.0 inch. At what angles, measured relative to the normal to the boundary, will the intensity be zero at great distances from the generator?

45-13 A microwave oscillator generating 1.4 cm microwaves is placed 5.0 cm from a large conducting sheet. A microwave receiver is a distance of 30.0 cm (measured along the sheet) from the oscillator. What is the minimum (nonzero) distance of the receiver from the sheet that will give zero received intensity?

45-14 The radar antenna on a boat transmits and receives waves of 10 cm wavelength. The antenna is 10 m from the water surface. At what minimum height (non-zero) above the water surface must an airplane be located, when it is 4.0 km from the boat, to elude detection by the radar set?

45-15 The phenomenon of "fading" in radio reception arises in large measure from the interference between two waves from the transmitter to the receiver, one following a direct route and another involving reflection from a conducting layer of charged particles (the ionosphere), lying above the Earth. Suppose that a transmitter and receiver are separated by 10 km. What is the minimum height of an ionospheric layer which will produce a minimum in the received signal for radio waves of 600 kcycles/sec?

45-16 Because laser beams are coherent, one can modulate them with a signal in the fashion that a radio beam is modulated with an audio signal. Taking the bandwidth required for intelligent speech to be 2 kcycles/sec, how many nonoverlapping voice bands can be accommodated in the green region of the visible spectrum (from 5000 to 5700 Å)?

45-17 In a Young double-slit experiment light of 5000 Å wavelength illuminates two slits separated by 0.40 mm. The interference pattern is observed on a screen 0.60 m from the slits. What is the separation between adjacent fringes in the interference pattern?

45-18 Two identical parallel slits, illuminated by light of 6000 Å wavelength, produce an interference pattern on a screen 0.80 m from them. The pattern is adjacent fringes separated by 0.60 mm. What is the separation distance between the two slits?

45-19 A thin wedge of air is formed by two glass plates in contact along one edge and separated by a sheet of paper at the other. The distance between the two ends of the plates is 6.0 cm. One sees 30 interference fringes between these ends when the plates are illuminated from above with light of 6000 Å wavelength. What is the thickness of the sheet of paper?

45-20   *   A planoconvex lens touches a plane plate of glass, and one sees Newton's rings with a dark central spot, when viewing from above. Show that the radii of the dark interference fringes are given approximately by $\sqrt{m\lambda R}$, where λ is the wavelength, R is the radius of curvature of the spherical interface, and $m = 0, 1, 2, \ldots, .$ (*Hint:* use the sagitta relation, Equation 44-7).

45-21   Reflection from a camera lens may be appreciably reduced if the lens is coated with a thin film of transparent material. Assuming that the film thickness is so chosen as to prevent the reflection of yellow light of 5800 Å wavelength (at the center of the visible spectrum), what is the minimum thickness, if the refractive index of the coating is 1.30 and that of the lens glass is 1.60? (Such a coated lens appears purple, a mixture of red and violet light, because light from the extremes of the visible spectrum, having wavelengths widely different from those of light at the center of the spectrum, is not discriminated against by such a coating.)

45-22   A thin film of transparent material having a refractive index of 1.50 is placed into one of the beams of a Michelson interferometer (Figure 45-21). When light of wavelength 5000 Å is used, it is observed that the insertion of the film causes a displacement of 30 fringes. What is the film thickness?

FORTY - SIX

DIFFRACTION

The term *diffraction* is used to describe the distinctive wave phenomena resulting from the interference of *many* (even an infinite number of) wave point sources oscillating coherently. Thus, diffraction is nothing more than "interference" extended from two (or a small number of) wave sources to the more complicated situation in which one must superpose the waves from very many sources. The physics is the same; the geometry is more complicated.

In this chapter we first consider the intensity pattern radiated by a large number of coherent point oscillators equally spaced and arranged in a row of finite length. By taking the number of such oscillators to be infinite we find the diffraction pattern for waves through a single narrow slit. We consider briefly other diffraction effects: the diffraction through an aperture, around an opaque disc, and at a straight edge. We shall see that the edges of a shadow are never perfectly sharp, but rather consist of alternating regions of light and darkness. We are thereby led to the fundamental limitation imposed by the wave nature of light, or any other form of electromagnetic radiation, on the resolving power of an optical instrument. Finally, we describe the diffraction grating, a high-resolution instrument for analyzing a spectrum of radiation.

46-1   Radiation from a row of point sources   Consider the situation shown in Figure 46-1, in which a large number (here, twelve) of identical point oscillators are arranged in a row of total width w, each source being separated from neighboring sources by the distance d. One might, for example, have twelve equally spaced electric dipole radio antennas. We

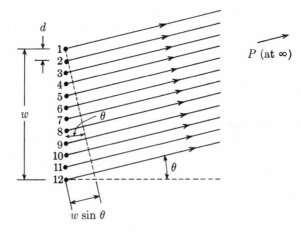

Figure 46-1. A row of equally spaced point oscillators ($d \ll \lambda$).

suppose that all point sources oscillate at the same frequency and in phase; there is *no intrinsic phase difference* among them. The sources generate waves of length λ, this wavelength being *large* compared with the distance d.

We wish to find the relative intensity, observed at some very distant point P, as a function of the angle θ between the normal to the line of oscillators and the line joining any of the oscillators to the point P; that is, we wish to find the radiation pattern of this array of equally spaced oscillators. Since there is no intrinsic phase difference between any two of the oscillators, the phase difference ϕ at a distant point arises solely from the difference Δr in path length, where

[45-5]
$$\phi = \frac{2\pi\,\Delta r}{\lambda}$$
[46-1]

Clearly, when $\theta = 0$, all rays drawn horizontally to an infinitely distant point have the same length, and the sources interfere constructively. Thus, the electric field at the angle $\theta = 0$ is N (here, 12) times the electric field produced by any one single oscillator. Now let us find the angles for which the intensity is zero. Our procedure will be as follows. We shall choose pairs of oscillators such that the resultant field at P from any pair is zero. Thus, we must so choose the oscillators and the angle θ such that the difference in path length between each pair is $\frac{1}{2}\lambda$, or any other odd multiple of $\frac{1}{2}\lambda$; then the pair of oscillators will interfere destructively. Suppose, then, that the angle θ is such that the difference in path length between oscillator 1 and oscillator 7 is $\frac{1}{2}\lambda$. At a distant point, the resultant electric field from this pair is zero. But, by the geometry of Figure 46-1, we see that oscillator 2 and oscillator 8 also differ in path length by $\frac{1}{2}\lambda$, and annul one another. Indeed, we can match up all of the oscillators in pairs—1 and 7, 2 and 8, 3 and 9, etc.—so that the resultant electric field at point P from *all* oscillators is zero. Clearly, then, the path difference $\Delta r = w \sin \theta$ between oscillator 1 and oscillator 12, those at the extreme ends of the array, must be exactly one wavelength. Thus,

$$\text{First intensity zero:} \qquad w \sin \theta = \lambda$$

We may write this alternatively as

$$(N - 1)d \sin \theta = \lambda$$

where N represents the total number of oscillators and $N - 1$ is the number of separation distances, each equal to d.

We find the second intensity zero in similar fashion. Now we divide up the array into *four* zones, or groups of oscillators, rather than the two zones used earlier: oscillators 1 through 3, 4 through 6, 7 through 9, and 10 through 12. The angle θ must now be larger, so large, in fact, that the path difference between oscillator 1 and oscillator 4 is $\frac{1}{2}\lambda$. These two sources interfere destructively at an infinite distance. In like fashion we match up oscillators 2 and 5, 3 and 6, etc., so that again the resultant field of the array is zero. The path difference $w \sin \theta$ between the sources at the extremes of the array is now 2λ, and we have

$$\text{Second intensity zero:} \qquad w \sin \theta = 2\lambda$$

It is then obvious that the angles for *zero* intensity are given, in general, by

$$\boxed{w \sin \theta = n\lambda} \qquad\qquad [46\text{-}2]$$

where $n = 1, 2, 3, \ldots$, (but *not* zero) and the number of sources N is large.

Figure 46-2 shows the radiated intensity I as a function of θ (we shall shortly derive the relation for this curve). This *diffraction pattern* consists of an intense maximum at $\theta = 0$, which is twice the width of the relatively weaker secondary maxima, arranged symmetrically to the sides. The zeroes are given by Equation 46-2. The same information is portrayed in a different

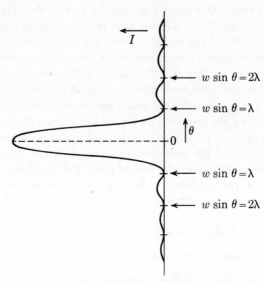

Figure 46-2. Intensity as a function of angle θ.

graphical form in Figure 46-3, which shows the radiation pattern of the array of oscillators; it consists of two strong narrow central lobes, into which most of the radiated energy is directed, together with small side lobes. Thus, an array of equally spaced antennas, with $d < \lambda$, will radiate strongly only in the directions perpendicular to the line of antennas. This pattern, a consequence of the mutual interference of *many* separate wave sources oscillating coherently in phase, is to be contrasted with the radiation pattern with many equal lobes (Figure 45-9) found earlier for only two oscillators.

An array of small antennas, arranged to form one large antenna, as in Figure 46-1, is, in fact, one simple arrangement that insures that the energy is radiated almost entirely in one direction. (One may avoid wasting the half of the energy radiated in the unwanted direction by placing a mirror or other reflector an appropriate distance behind the array.)

We have assumed all of the separate oscillators to have zero relative intrinsic phase difference. Suppose, now, that there is a constant relative

Figure 46-3. Radiation pattern for a row of equally spaced point oscillators.

intrinsic phase difference between each adjoining pair of oscillators, oscillator 2 leading oscillator 1 by Φ, oscillator 3 leading oscillator 1 by 2Φ, etc. Then the entire radiation pattern is rotated through an angle so that the maximum no longer comes at $\theta = 0$. It is not difficult to show that the angle θ for the central peak is given by $\sin \theta = \Phi\lambda(N - 1)/2\pi w$. Thus, if one had all the small antennas in an array fixed to the ground at some location, the direction of the narrow radiated beam could be shifted from $\theta = 0$, with all oscillators in phase, to another angle, merely by an adjustment of the constant phase difference between adjoining oscillators, without an actual relocation of the positions of the oscillators.

Such an array can be used not only as an antenna which transmits radiation in a narrow beam of variable angle, but also as a receiving antenna, sensitive to incoming radiation only over a rather restricted angular width. This follows from the principle of reciprocity (Section 42-6), according to which one may reverse ray directions without changing the physical situation. Under ray (or time) reversal, signals from distant sources impinge

Figure 46-4. A radio telescope consisting of 32 equally spaced parabolic antennas. This so-called multiple-wave interferometer behaves effectively as a diffraction grating (Section 46-7). (Courtesy of Professor W. N. Christiansen, C.S.I.R.O., University of Sydney, Australia.)

upon the antenna array and induce currents in each component antenna. Therefore, if one combines the signals from the separate antennas suitably, one may "aim" the receiving antenna to detect signals coming from specific directions. For example, when the detecting instruments respond only to the separate signals combined in phase, the antenna is sensitive only to signals from the direction $\theta = 0$, whereas a readjustment of the phase differences among the separate antenna elements makes the array sensitive to signals from other directions. This is precisely the procedure used in certain antennas, or telescopes, used in radio astronomy. The array of antenna elements is fixed on the ground, and one tunes in the radio signals from distant stars in various directions by electronically combining the signals from the separate elements. Figure 46-4 shows such a radio telescope.

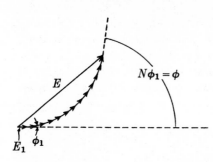

Figure 46-5. Electric field vectors arranged according to their relative differences in phase.

46-2 Intensity as function of θ

To find the angular dependence of the radiation from many oscillators (Figure 46-1) we must first find the resultant electric field E at a distant point arising from all oscillating sources. Then, $I \propto E^2$. We can compute the resultant field E most simply by using the vector representation of simple harmonic oscillators, described in Sections 37-2 and 45-2 and shown for two sources in Figure 45-7.

Figure 46-5 shows a number of vectors of equal length E_1 arranged with a constant phase difference ϕ_1 between adjoining vectors. The magnitude and orientation of the electric field vectors represent the contributions from the separate oscillators in Figure 46-1. The constant phase difference ϕ_1 arises from the constant path difference between any two adjoining oscillators. The cumulative phase difference from all N oscillators is given by

$$\phi = N\phi_1 = N\left(\frac{2\pi \, \Delta r}{\lambda}\right) = \frac{2\pi w \sin \theta}{\lambda} \qquad [46\text{-}3]$$

Clearly, the angle ϕ for phase difference increases as the space angle θ increases.

We wish to find the magnitude of the vector E, representing the amplitude of the resultant electric field at a distant point. Before computing E explicitly, let us see qualitatively how the separate vectors are arranged at the maxima and minima of the intensity pattern shown in Figure 46-2. We shall thereby deduce the general features of the I versus θ curve.

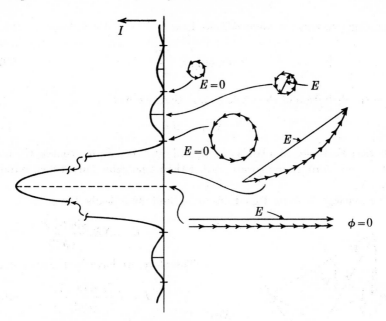

Figure 46-6. Arrangement of electric field vectors for various locations in the intensity pattern.

At the central peak, $\theta = 0$; therefore, $\Delta r = 0$, and $\phi = 0$. Here the little vectors are all aligned parallel, and one has the maximum possible E, namely $E = NE_1$; see Figure 46-6. As θ increases, ϕ increases; that is, the electric fields become progressively out of phase. Then the vertices of the vectors lie on a circular arc. The magnitude of E is now less than NE_1. Suppose that the total phase difference ϕ is 2π. The vectors now complete one circle; E is zero, as is also the intensity. Equation 46-3 shows that, when $\phi = 2\pi$, then $w \sin \theta = \lambda$, in accord with our earlier finding. Note also that when $\phi = 2\pi$ the vectors for oscillators 1 and 7, 2 and 8, etc., are antiparallel, corresponding to a 180° phase difference, or a $\frac{1}{2}\lambda$ path difference, for each pair.

The maximum in the first secondary peak occurs very nearly at that angle θ for which the little vectors make one and a half turns. The magnitude of the resultant E is now much less NE_1, so that the intensity, $I \propto E^2$, at the secondary peak is much less than that of the central maximum. The second zero of intensity is found at that space angle θ and phase angle ϕ for which the little electric field vectors complete two circles.

We can compute the magnitude of E in general by reference to Figure 46-7. The radius of the circle is R, the angle subtended by the chord of length E is ϕ, and the length of the corresponding circular arc is NE_1. In the triangle having the angle $\phi/2$, we have

$$\sin\left(\tfrac{1}{2}\phi\right) = \frac{\tfrac{1}{2}E}{R} \qquad [46\text{-}4]$$

From the definition of the angle ϕ in radians we have

$$NE_1 = R\phi \qquad [46\text{-}5]$$

Note that Equation 46-5 holds exactly only if N is *infinite*; that is, the little vectors truly form a circular arc, rather than a polygon, only if their number is infinite.

Eliminating R from Equations 46-4 and 46-5 leads to

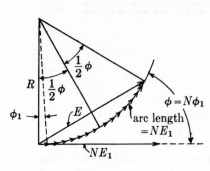

Figure 46-7

$$E = NE_1 \frac{\sin(\phi/2)}{(\phi/2)}$$

Therefore, we have for the intensity

$$I = I_0\left[\frac{\sin(\phi/2)}{(\phi/2)}\right]^2 \qquad [46\text{-}6]$$

where I_0 is the radiated intensity with $\phi = 0$ (at $\theta = 0$). We relate the phase angle ϕ to the space angle θ through Equation 46-3:

$$[46\text{-}3] \qquad \phi = 2\pi w \sin\theta/\lambda$$

The diffraction pattern shown in Figure 46-2 is a plot of Equation 46-6. It is readily verified from this equation that $I = 0$ for $w \sin\theta = n\lambda$, where $n = 1, 2, 3, \dots$, in agreement with Equation 46-2. One can also verify with Equation 46-6 that the intensities of the secondary peaks relative to that of the central peak (as 1.00) are 0.045, 0.016, 0.008, ..., . The central peak is much more intense than the secondary peaks; in fact, one half of the radiated energy falls within the middle half of the central peak.

We must emphasize that Equation 46-6 holds exactly, only if the number of sources is infinite and the separation distance d is less than one wavelength. We shall relax these restrictions in treating the diffraction grating in Section 46-7.

46-3 Diffraction at a single slit Given a monochromatic light source illuminating a single narrow slit at a great distance from the source, what is the intensity pattern of the light falling on a distant screen? We have already solved this problem! We merely recognize that when a plane wave front of light impinges upon an opening in an otherwise opaque plane, we

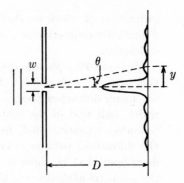

Figure 46-8. Diffraction from a single slit.

may, through the Huygens construction, imagine each point on the wave front as a new point source of radiation. These coherent point sources, separated by infinitesimal distances on the wave front, all oscillate in the same phase. Thus, we have an infinite array of point sources spread over the finite width of the slit, and the intensity pattern radiated from the plane of slit must be precisely what we have already derived.

The arrangement for single-slit diffraction is shown in Figure 46-8. The angle θ is, for small displacements y, given by $\sin \theta \simeq \theta \simeq y/D$. The light source S is at so great a distance from the slit that the spherical or cylindrical wave fronts impinging on the slit are effectively plane waves; moreover, the observation screen, at a distance D from the slit of width w, is far from the slit.

Under these conditions one observes *Fraunhofer diffraction*. Fraunhofer diffraction applies when the source and screen are *infinitely* distant from the slit or, equivalently, when the wave front at the slit is *plane*. These conditions can be met, even when the source and screen are physically close to the slit, by placing the light source at the near principal focus of a converging lens. Then the spherical or cylindrical wave fronts diverging from the source become *plane* wave fronts upon emerging from the lens and striking the slit. Similarly, one may place the observation screen at the far principal focal plane of a second converging lens; then parallel rays leaving the slit are brought to a focus in the focal plane of the screen; see Figure 46-9. The general case of diffraction, with no restrictions on distances or wave fronts, is known as *Fresnel*

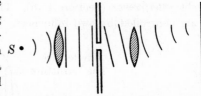

Figure 46-9. Conditions for Fraunhofer diffraction, achieved with source and screen at *finite* distances from the slit by use of converging lenses.

Figure 46-10. A single-slit diffraction pattern.

diffraction, of which we shall have later examples. Fraunhofer diffraction is a special case of Fresnel diffraction.

Figure 46-10, a photograph of a single-slit diffraction pattern, corresponds to Figure 46-2. The weak secondary diffraction fringes have the same angular width, half that of the central fringe. Note that, following Equation 46-2, for a given wavelength the diffraction pattern *expands* as the slit width decreases; that is, light is diffracted far beyond the geometrical shadows of the slit edges, when the slit width becomes comparable to the wavelength. Indeed, the diffraction pattern bears no resemblance to the constant intensity pattern with sharp edges that appears when light passes through a wide slit. We shall see in Section 46-5 under what circumstances the diffraction pattern approximates this familiar case.

46-4   Diffraction at a double slit   Suppose now that we have *two* parallel slits, each of width w, their centers being separated by a distance d. The two slits are illuminated by a monochromatic plane wave. If we cover one slit and leave the second slit exposed, the diffraction pattern is, of course, that of a single slit, as shown in Figure 46-10; if we cover the second slit and expose the first, we see the *same* diffraction pattern on the screen (shifted by the distance d). When both slits are exposed to a beam of light with plane wave fronts, the pattern observed at a distant screen is as shown in Figure 46-11. We see a diffraction pattern just as before, but now there are additional rapid variations in the intensity arising from double-slit *interference* (Section 45-6). The intensity variations in Figure 46-11 are controlled by two influences. The first is the *interference* between the

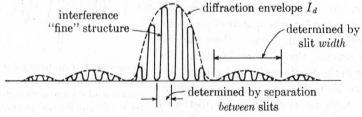

Figure 46-11. Intensity variation for a double slit.

two slits, which is responsible for the narrow interference fringes, all of equal width determined by the *slit separation distance d* according to

[45-7] $\qquad m\lambda = d \sin \theta,$ where $m = 0, 1, 2, \cdots,$

The *interference* intensity variations, I_i, are given by

[45-9] $\qquad I_i = I_0 \cos^2 (\pi d \sin \theta / \lambda)$

The second is the *diffraction* from each of the two slits, which is responsible for the slow variations in the intensity of the interference fringes, the diffraction pattern being determined by the *slit width w* according to

[46-2] $\qquad n\lambda = w \sin \theta,$ where $n = 1, 2, 3, \cdots,$

The *diffraction* intensity, I_d, variations are given by

[46-6] $$I_d = I_0 \left[\frac{\sin (\phi/2)}{(\phi/2)} \right]^2$$

where $\phi = 2\pi w \sin \theta / \lambda$, from Equation 46-3. The observed intensity I from the double slit is then given by

$$I = I_i I_d$$

as shown in Figure 46-11. One may describe this curve by saying that the interference pattern is "modulated" by the diffraction pattern, in the sense that the envelope of the curve is controlled by I_d (Figure 46-2) while the "fine structure" is controlled by I_i (Figure 45-8). Note that $d > w > \lambda$.

It is now clear why the interference fringes observed in Young's double-slit experiment (shown in Figure 45-15) decrease in intensity as one leaves the central region at $\theta = 0$; the diffraction from slits of *finite*, rather than infinitesimal, widths is responsible.

Example 1 The central dark fringes in the diffraction pattern from a single slit are separated by 1.0 mm when the slit is illuminated with light of 6000 Å wavelength and the screen is placed 1.0 m from the slit. What is the slit width?
From Equation 46-2,

$$w \sin \theta \simeq w(y/D) = n\lambda$$

where D is the slit-screen distance and y is the distance from the central maximum in the diffraction pattern to a zero. Here $2y = 1.0$ mm, with $n = 1$. Thus,

$$w = n\lambda D/y = \frac{(1)(6.0 \times 10^{-7} \text{ m}) (1.0 \text{ m})}{\frac{1}{2}(1.0 \times 10^{-3} \text{ m})} = 1.2 \times 10^{-3} \text{ m} = 1.2 \text{ mm}$$

46-5 Examples of Fresnel diffraction Unless the conditions for Fraunhofer diffraction are met (infinitely distant sources, observation at an infinite distance from the diffracting object), the computations of the resultant electric field and the intensity from many sources are mathematically complicated. Whenever the source or observer or both are *finite* distances from the diffracting object, we have the conditions for so-called *Fresnel diffraction* (after A. J. Fresnel, 1788–1827). Here we illustrate, for the most part qualitatively, some important examples of Fresnel diffraction, in which the restrictions of Fraunhofer diffraction are not imposed.

First consider Figure 46-12, which shows a single slit illuminated by plane wave fronts. Here we wish to investigate the intensity at a central point P relatively *close* to the diffracting slit. We imagine the Huygens oscillators, which are distributed continuously over the wave front, to be divided into

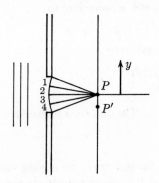

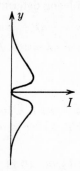

Figure 46-12. An example of Fresnel diffraction. The four zones are chosen such that the intensity at P is zero.

Figure 46-13. Intensity variation corresponding to the Fresnel diffraction shown in Figure 46-12.

four groups, or *Fresnel zones*, zones 1, 2, 3, and 4, all of equal area. The rays from the plane of the slit to P have different path lengths. Indeed, point P is so chosen that the path difference between a source at the top of zone 1 and a source at the top of zone 2 is exactly $\frac{1}{2}\lambda$. These two sources destructively interfere. We can then also match off all other oscillators in zones 1 and 2 in pairs, such that the path difference for each pair is $\frac{1}{2}\lambda$. Consequently, the resultant intensity at P from zones 1 and 2 is zero. By symmetry, zones 3 and 4 also give zero intensity. When a location such as P' is *off* the axis of the slit, there is not complete annulment. The intensity pattern is as shown in Figure 46-13: there is a *black* line precisely in the middle.†

What an extraordinary result! The diffraction pattern of a single slit, observed at the proper close distance to the slit, has *darkness* at precisely those points where one would, on the basis of naïve intuition, the simple

† Of course, the pattern will depend upon the distance between P and the slit. The pattern of Figure 46-13 is that for the case of maximum separation distance. There are still other distances of the observation plane from the slit for which the intensity is a minimum at the center.

(but incorrect) considerations of ray optics, and a particle model of light, expect to see the brightest light.

A similar result is found when one examines the light passing through a circular aperture. On a screen placed *far* from the hole, one sees a (Fraunhofer) diffraction pattern consisting of a *bright* central spot (known as Airy's disc) surrounded by diffraction rings, as shown in Figure 46-14; but on a

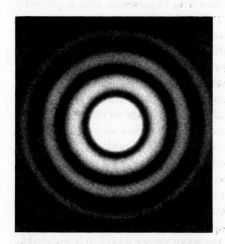

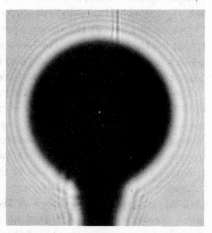

Figure 46-14. Fraunhofer diffraction pattern through a circular aperture. (From *Atlas of Optical Phenomena*, M. Cagnet, M. Francon, J. C. Thierr, Springer-Verlag, 1962. Courtesy of Springer-Verlag, Heidelberg.)

Figure 46-15. Diffraction around an opaque sphere. The Arago spot is at the center.

screen at certain *close* positions, one sees a (Fresnel) diffraction pattern with a *black* spot at its center. The diffraction pattern of Figure 46-14 is similar to that of a single slit, as shown in Figure 46-10, but it has circular rather than straight diffraction fringes. It can be shown that the first circle of zero intensity is given by

$$\sin \theta = 1.22(\lambda/d) \qquad [46\text{-}7]$$

where d is the hole diameter. The center of the pattern corresponds to $\theta = 0$. On the other hand, as Equation 46-2 shows, the first intensity zero for a single slit is given by

$$\sin \theta = (\lambda/w)$$

The factor 1.22 in Equation 46-7 is, of course, a consequence of the different geometry.

We have seen that a hole in an opaque plane can produce a diffraction pattern with a black spot at its center. What do we see in the reverse situation, an opaque circle, or disc, placed in the beam from a point source? The observed diffraction pattern, mostly dark in the shadow region, has a small *bright* spot at its center! It is as if a hole had been drilled through the disc's center; see Figure 46-15. Such are the remarkable possibilities of wave behavior. The bright spot is sometimes called the *Arago spot* (after D. J. Arago, 1788–1827). The same behavior is, of course, expected for an opaque sphere. Indeed, it has been shown in experiment that a perfectly spherical steel ball actually will act as a "lens," in the sense that an extended object on one side of the sphere appears as an image (a collection of bright spots) on the other side. The same effect is found on a much larger scale, when a radio transmitter produces an exceptionally strong signal at a receiver placed at a point on Earth diametrically opposite to the transmitter.

The bright spot in Figure 46-15, completely inexplicable in terms of ray optics, played, understandably, a significant role in the development of the wave theory of light. Curiously, many physicists were unconvinced when Young first demonstrated interference effects with his double-slit experiment, believing that, somehow, a particle model could account for the interference fringes. They remained dubious of the wave theory even when other interference and diffraction effects were observed. S. D. Poisson (1781–1840) showed, using the wave theory of Huygens and Fresnel, that a bright spot was expected to be seen behind an opaque object, and he concluded that this effect was so patently absurd that the wave theory was clearly untenable. When D. F. Arago (1786–1853) and Fresnel showed that the bright spot was indeed there, there was no alternative to considering light as a strictly wave phenomenon—no alternative, that is, until the advent of the quantum theory in 1905, when Einstein proposed the *photon* as a "particle" of light (but *not* is the earlier naïve sense), and the wave-particle issue was raised anew.

Diffraction was first observed in 1655 by F. M. Grimaldi (1618–1663), when he noticed that the shadow of a sharp straight edge is *not* perfectly sharp, as predicted by ray optics, but shows characteristic diffraction variations in the intensity near the edge. When a plane wave is incident upon an opaque straight edge, the intensity variations along a near-by screen are as shown in Figure 46-16a and b. The intensity decreases gradually to zero *beyond* the geometrical edge of the shadow, shows variations near the edge, but becomes constant for points far from the edge.

Although the detailed derivation for the intensity is complicated, we can easily show that the intensity on the screen is, in fact, constant far from the edge. Consider the contributions from the Huygens wavelets in the incident plane wave front at the point P. For convenience, the wave front is imagined divided into a number of zones (marked 1, 1', 2, 2', etc.) in such a way that

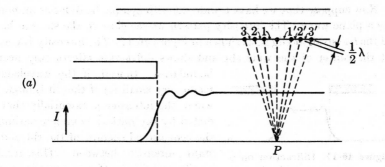

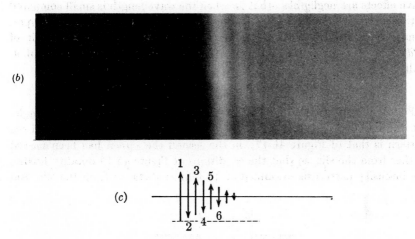

Figure 46-16. (a) Diffraction at an opaque straight edge. (b) Diffraction pattern at an opaque straight edge. (c) Electric field vectors for point P of part (a).

the path difference between adjoining zones is $\frac{1}{2}\lambda$. Then the electric field at P produced by zones 1 and 1' is nearly annuled by the electric field from zones 2 and 2'. We say *nearly* annuled, because the electric field from 2 and 2' is slightly less than that from 1 and 1', as indicated by the vectors in Figure 46-16c. Continuing to add the contributions to the resultant E from more distant zones, we find that the electric fields alternate in phase (vectors alternately up and down) and become progressively of smaller amplitude; see Figure 46-16c. Therefore, the resultant field at *any* point P relatively far from the edge is the same. This does not apply, however, when the observation point is brought close to the edge; then we do not have symmetrically located Fresnel zones on the wave front.

Now suppose that we have a wide slit with opaque boundaries illuminated by a plane wave. The intensity pattern we see close to the slit will be that of the *two* straight edges, as shown in Figure 46-17. The intensity is constant at the center of the wide slit and shows diffraction effects only near the boundaries. Indeed, if the wavelength is made very small (or if the slit is made very wide), the intensity is essentially that predicted by ray optics: complete darkness in the geometrical shadow of the slit and constant intensity between. This result is hardly surprising. If ray optics successfully accounts for light's properties when the wave effects are negligible—that is, when the wave length is small compared with the dimensions of any apertures or objects—then the more comprehensive wave theory *must* yield the results of ray optics in the limit of $(\lambda/d) \to 0$, where d is a characteristic length. Thus, we may write symbolically

Figure 46-17. Diffraction on a screen close to a single slit.

$$\text{Limit}_{(\lambda/d \to 0)} \text{ (wave optics)} = \text{ray optics}$$

Figure 46-18 illustrates the transition from ray to wave optics for single-slit diffraction. In the first figure the screen is very close to the slit and the pattern is that of Figure 46-17; in the second the screen has been moved farther from the slit, so that the conditions of Figure 46-13 obtain; finally, the intensity pattern is examined at an infinite distance from the slit, and

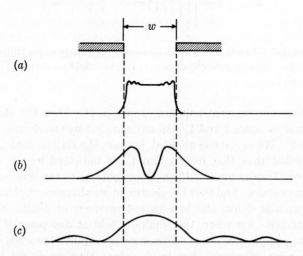

Figure 46-18. Diffraction from a single slit: (a) screen close to slit, (b) screen farther from slit, (c) screen very far from slit.

there is the characteristic single-slit diffraction pattern of Figure 46-2. Note that the "shape" of the slit is clearly seen in the first figure, vaguely discernible in the next, but completely masked in the last. We could see the transition from wave optics to ray optics in a different way. Suppose that the screen is sufficiently far from the slit to produce the diffraction pattern of Figure 46-18c. If the wavelength is decreased, the pattern of Figure 46-18b appears on the screen (the pattern of Figure 46-18c now appears only if the screen is removed still farther from the screen). Finally, if the wavelength is made still shorter, the observed pattern is that of Figure 46-18a, the pattern expected on the basis of ray optics.

46-6 Diffraction and resolution We have seen that the image of a distant *point* source of light, viewed through a circular hole in an opaque screen, is *not* a point. As Figure 46-14 shows, the image is a somewhat fuzzy bright disc surrounded by rather weaker circular diffraction fringes. The angular separation θ between the center of the bright spot and the first zero in the diffraction is shown in Figure 46-19 and is given by

[46-7] $\sin \theta \simeq \theta = 1.22(\lambda/d)$

where d is the hole diameter. Since the angle θ is proportional to the ratio λ/d, θ decreases as λ decreases or as d increases. The *finite* diameter of the central bright spot arises from the fact that no circular aperture is infinitely large. The complicated diffraction image is always present, although it is discerned only if the image of a distant point source, always a fuzzy one with diffraction rings, is examined with care.

We have spoken of the diffraction image produced by a circular hole in an opaque screen; exactly the same kind of diffraction effect occurs whenever the wave fronts from a point source are limited in some way. For example, the image of a point source through a circular lens of outer diameter d is like that of Figure 46-14, even when all other lens aberrations are absent, and the image formed by a perfectly parabolic mirror is again one showing diffraction effects, which arise from the finite outer diameter of the mirror.

Now, the inexact, nonpoint character of the image from a point object is not in itself a serious difficulty if one looks at a *single* point object. Complications arise when there are *two* point objects and their corresponding two images. If the two images, each a blur, are too close together, they cannot be distinguished from a single image. Thus, there is a fundamental

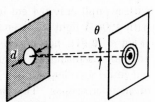

Figure 46-19. Diffraction through a circular aperture; angle θ gives the angular radius of the first dark fringe.

limitation, having its origin in diffraction and in the wave character of light, in the resolution of *two* point objects. Of course, any extended object is merely a collection of point objects.

Suppose, for example, that two stars show an angular separation ϕ when viewed directly, the waves passing through no aperture of any sort.† When an aperture is interposed, such as the objective lens of an astronomical telescope, one sees two discs each of "radius" θ, given in Equation 46-7, separated by ϕ, as shown in Figure 46-20a. The question is, then, what is the minimum ϕ that will permit two definite images to be resolved? Figures 46-20b and c show two diffraction images from two point sources. The images have an angular separation ϕ just equal to the angular radius θ of either image separately. The center of one image falls exactly at the first zero in the intensity of the second image. One can just barely tell that there are, in fact, *two* images. This situation, in which two separate images have the minimum angular separation for resolution, corresponds to *Rayleigh's criterion* for resolution, the minimum angle ϕ for resolution being

$$\phi_{min} = \theta = 1.22(\lambda/d) \qquad [46\text{-}8]$$

from Equation 46-7.

All optical devices—mirrors, lens, apertures, and the eye itself—are ultimately limited in their resolving power by diffraction effects. The images are intrinsically fuzzy and their resolution can be improved only by using waves of shorter length or apertures of larger size. Thus, the motivation for constructing telescopes, whether for visible or radio electromagnetic radiation, with large-diameter lenses or mirrors is not only to capture more radiation and increase thereby the intensity of the image, but also to improve the resolution of the images; that is, big telescopes produce bright and sharp images. For example, the Mt. Palomar telescope, a reflecting telescope with a parabolic mirror whose outer diameter is 200 inches, when used with short-wavelength light, of 4000 Å, can resolve point objects with an angular separation of only 0.02 seconds of arc. On the other hand, the human eye with a pupil only 0.4 cm in diameter has a resolution of 25 seconds of arc with 4000 Å light. The enormous radio telescope at Jodrell Bank, England (Figure 46-21), has a reflecting "mirror" of a 250-foot diameter, but its angular resolution for 21 cm microwaves is 700 seconds of arc. The small but finite wavelengths of visible light impose a limit on the resolving power of all microscopes. This precludes "seeing" any object comparable in size to several thousand angstroms. The electron microscope, in which light beams are replaced by electron beams and refracting lenses by focussing magnets, has a high resolving power because electrons, regarded as waves

† Strictly, one always views through an aperture, if only that of the eye's pupil.

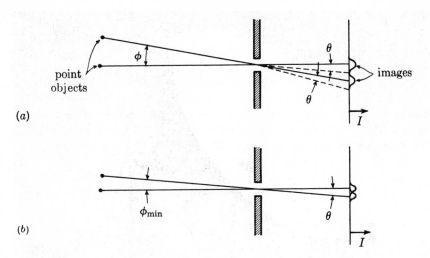

(a)

(b)

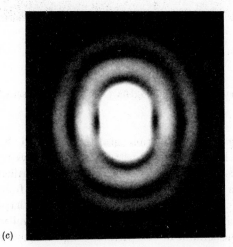

(c)

Figure 46-20. (a) Two point objects of angular separation ϕ clearly resolved as two distinct images, each of angular radius θ. (b) The limit of resolution, $\phi_{min} = \theta$. (c) Intensity pattern corresponding to part (b). (From *Atlas of Optical Phenomena*, M. Cagnet, M. Francon, J. C. Thier, Springer-Verlag, 1962. Courtesy of Springer-Verlag, Heidelberg.)

Figure 46-21. Radio telescope at Jodrell Bank, England. The diameter of the parabolic "mirror" is 250 feet. (Courtesy Central Office of Information, London.)

in the quantum theory, have very short wavelengths (1 Å for electrons of 150 ev).

46-7 The diffraction grating The diffraction grating, invented by J. Fraunhofer (1787–1826), is a high-resolution instrument for analyzing polychromatic radiation into its component wavelengths. A so-called transmission grating consists of a series of N parallel slits separated from one another by a distance d. For example, closely spaced lines (perhaps 10,000 slits in 1 cm) may be scratched onto a plate of glass. (A more familiar example of a diffraction grating, one suitable for use with very-high-frequency sound waves, is a Venetian blind.)

A diffraction grating is illustrated in Figure 46-22. This arrangement is, in fact, just like the array of equally spaced sources shown in Figure 46-1. Here we assume, however, that, unlike the similar case of diffraction from a large number of closely spaced sources, the *separation distance d between each of the N adjoining slits is greater than one wavelength*.

The grating is illuminated with monochromatic plane waves from the left, and we wish to find the intensity pattern on a very distant screen;

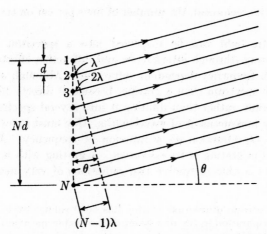

Figure 46-22. Arrangement of sources in a diffraction grating ($d > \lambda$).

that is, we wish to find I as a function of the angle θ. Suppose that the path difference between slits 1 and 2 is one wavelength. The waves from these two slits constructively interfere. This is exactly the condition we found earlier (Section 45-6) with the first noncentral interference maximum in the Young double-slit experiment. The path difference $d \sin \theta$ is, then, one wavelength between *any* two adjoining slits, and *all* slits send waves that add constructively in the direction θ given by $d \sin \theta = \lambda$. The intensity of this peak is far stronger than that in the double-slit experiment, since the number of slits is now N, not 2.

There are, of course, still other interference peaks. *All* slits will interfere constructively at a distant point when the path difference, $d \sin \theta$, between adjacent slits is an integral multiple m of the wavelength. Thus, strong interference peaks occur when

$$m\lambda = d \sin \theta \qquad \text{[46-9]}$$

where $m = 0, 1, 2, \ldots,$. The integer m denotes the *order* of the interference peak.

Note that the angle θ depends on the wavelength. If the incoming radiation consists of many wavelengths, each component wavelength will be deviated differently. Thus, the red end of the visible spectrum will be deviated more than the violet end, and one will see a spectrum on a distant screen. Of course, when $m = 0$, then $\theta = 0$ for all wavelengths; the *zero-order* "spectrum" consists of white light. But the first-order spectrum ($m = 1$), second-order spectrum ($m = 2$), etc., show the light increasingly dispersed. One can measure the wavelength readily if one knows the slit separation (or its reciprocal, the number of lines per cm on the grating) and measures θ.

Polychromatic light can be dispersed into a spectrum both with a diffraction grating (through interference and diffraction effects) and with a prism (through frequency-dependent refraction). Although a prism forms a more intense spectrum than a grating, because it directs *all* the incident into *one* spectrum, rather than diluting it into several spectra, it does not permit an easy measurement of wavelengths. One must know precisely the prism's index of refraction as a function of frequency. Another great advantage of the grating is its *resolution*. A grating with a large enough number of slits is able to resolve two radiations of very nearly the same wavelength.

Example 2 A certain diffraction grating has 5000 rulings over 1.0 cm. What is the angular separation in the first order of the visible spectrum (from 4000 to 7000 Å wavelength)?

The grating spacing d is $(1/5000)$ cm. From Equation 46-9,

$$\theta = \sin^{-1}(m\lambda/d)$$

For $\lambda = 4000$ Å,

$$\theta = \sin^{-1}(4.0 \times 10^{-7} \,\text{m})(5.0 \times 10^{5} \,\text{m}^{-1}) = 11.5°$$

Similarly, for $\lambda = 7000$ Å, we find $\theta = 20.5°$. The entire visible spectrum is found in the 9° between the violet and red limits.

We can see from a simple consideration that the interference peaks given by Equation 46-9 have a very narrow angular width. First note that the angle θ in Figure 46-22 is initially set so that *all* path differences between adjoining slits is λ. This implies that the path difference between the first slit and the Nth slit is $(N - 1)\lambda$ (if there are N slits, there are $N - 1$ spaces between slits). Now suppose that the angle θ is made just slightly larger, so that the path difference between the first and Nth slit is $N\lambda$, rather than $(N - 1)\lambda$. The change in angle is very small indeed if N is very large (perhaps 20,000 for a typical grating for light), and the slit separation is larger than λ. What is the intensity from all N slits at this new angle?

We have already dealt with a situation of this sort in describing the diffraction from an array of oscillators (Section 46-1). Let the slits be considered as of two groups, a top half and a bottom half. At the new angle the ray from the uppermost slit in the top half will have a path difference of $\frac{1}{2}\lambda$ relative to the uppermost slit of the lower half. These two rays will interfere destructively. So will every pair of corresponding top-half and bottom-half slits. The interference peak falls to zero intensity for a very small change in angle. Because of these *diffraction* effects (hence, *diffraction* grating), the interference peaks are accompanied by diffraction fringes. When the number of slits is large, the width of the interference peaks is very small, and each wavelength in a spectrum has a narrow peak falling at a different θ.

Figure 46-23 shows the intensity pattern from a diffraction grating with only a few slits. This pattern looks like the diffraction pattern of a single slit (Figure 46-2) repeated several times—and that is in effect what it is. The reason we see several diffraction patterns, not one, is that the distance between adjacent sources is now *greater* than λ, rather than infinitesimally small. Said differently, the sources were earlier taken to be so close that only the zeroth-order interference peak could be seen; the interference peaks for $m = 1, 2, \ldots$, then came, so to speak, at $\theta > 90°$.

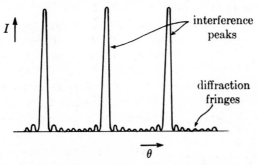

Figure 46-23. Intensity variation for a diffraction grating.

We have seen that the strong interference peaks in the pattern of a diffraction grating with many slits are very narrow. That is, a diffraction grating has a very large resolving power, since it is able to delineate between wavelengths that are very nearly equal. It is useful to have a quantitative measure of the resolving power, R. Following the criterion for resolution used for superposed diffraction images, we take two wavelengths differing by $\Delta\lambda$ and having an average wavelength λ to be resolved—that is, distinguishable as two distinct lines—when the interference intensity peak of one line falls at the nearest zero of the second line. The resolving power is defined as

$$R = \lambda/\Delta\lambda \qquad [46\text{-}10]$$

We wish to find R as a function of the number of slits N and the order m. We have seen that the intensity of an interference peak drops to zero when the path difference between the first and the Nth slit goes from $(N - 1)\lambda$ to $N\lambda$. Now, this applies to the *first* order, $m = 1$. More generally, for the mth order the path difference would go from $(N - 1)m\lambda$ to $[(N - 1)m + 1]\lambda$ but, since the intensity peak for $\lambda - \Delta\lambda$ is at the *same* angular position as the intensity zero for λ, we have that

$$(N - 1)m\lambda = [(N - 1)m + 1](\lambda - \Delta\lambda)$$

$$\frac{\lambda}{\Delta\lambda} \simeq Nm$$

$$\boxed{R = Nm} \qquad [46\text{-}11]$$

The resolving power is proportional to the total number of slits and the order of the spectrum but, curiously, does *not* depend on the slit separation d. For example, in the case of a high-quality grating with 100,000 lines operating in the second order, $R = 2.00 \times 10^5$. With such a grating one could resolve and measure the wavelengths of light centered at 5000 Å to within two parts in 10^5, or with an uncertainty in wavelength of only $\Delta\lambda = \lambda/R = (5000 \text{ Å})/(2 \times 10^5) = 0.025$ Å.

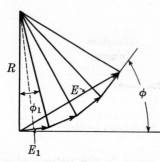

It is not difficult to derive, by means of our earlier results for single-slit diffraction (Section 46-2), an explicit expression giving the intensity I as a function of θ for a diffraction grating, as shown in Figure 46-23. The only change is this: we take the separation distance between adjacent sources to be *finite* and greater than λ, and the number of sources to be *finite* although very large. Then, the little electric field vectors in Figure 46-7 cannot properly be regarded as lying perfectly on a circular arc, and Equation 46-5, which implies that they do, is no longer applicable. We replace Equation 46-5, by using Figure 46-24, with

Figure 46-24. Electric field vectors for the slits of a diffraction grating.

$$\sin(\tfrac{1}{2}\phi_1) = \frac{\tfrac{1}{2}E_1}{R} \qquad [46\text{-}12]$$

where ϕ_1 is the phase difference between waves from any two adjacent slits. Therefore, as in Equation 46-3,

$$\phi_1 = \frac{2\pi d \sin\theta}{\lambda} \qquad [46\text{-}13]$$

The *total* phase difference ϕ of Equation 46-5 is now N times that for each slit, or

$$\phi = N\phi_1 \qquad [46\text{-}14]$$

and Equation 46-4 now becomes

$$\sin \left(\tfrac{1}{2} N \phi_1\right) = \frac{\tfrac{1}{2}E}{R} \qquad [46\text{-}15]$$

Eliminating R between Equations 46-12 and 46-15, we have for the resultant field

$$E = NE_1 \frac{\sin (N\phi_1/2)}{\sin (\phi_1/2)}$$

and, for the intensity,

$$I = I_0 \left[\frac{\sin (N\phi_1/2)}{\sin (\phi_1/2)}\right]^2 \qquad [46\text{-}16]$$

This is the function plotted in Figure 46-23. The numerator of Equation 46-16 controls the angular positions of the closely spaced diffraction fringes; the denominator (now with the sine of $\phi_1/2$, rather than $\phi_1/2$, as in Equation 46-6) controls the angular positions of the widely separated interference peaks. The reader should verify with Equations 46-16 and 46-13 that the interference peaks *are* given by Equation 46-9, as derived earlier.

46-8 Summary Diffraction is interference from a large number of sources. The zeroes in the radiated intensity of a row of many sources, which are oscillating coherently in phase and separated by equal distances much less than a wavelength λ, are given by

[46-2] $w \sin \theta = n\lambda$

where w is the width of the row and $n = 1, 2, 3, \ldots ,$. This relation then gives as well the zeroes in the intensity pattern for diffraction from a single slit under the conditions that the source and observation point are far from the slit (Fraunhofer diffraction).

Diffraction effects due to any aperture limit the resolution of two point objects, the limit of resolution being reached when the angular separation between the point objects is equal to the angular radius of the central dark diffraction fringe of either source.

The strong and sharply resolved interference peaks of a diffraction grating occur when

[46-9] $m\lambda = d \sin \theta$

where d is the distance between adjacent slits and $m = 0, 1, 2, \ldots ,$. The resolving power of a diffraction grating is given by

[46-10], [46-11] $R = \lambda/\Delta\lambda = Nm$

where N is the total number of lines in the grating.

PROBLEMS

46-1   Six identical oscillators, each generating waves of 10.0 cm, are aligned
along a north-south line with a constant spacing of 1.0 cm between
adjacent oscillators. Sketch the radiation pattern as observed at
great distances from the oscillators.

46-2   Ten identical radio oscillators generate waves 10 m in wavelength.
The oscillators are aligned along a north-south line, the separation
distance between adjacent oscillators being 2.0 cm. Find the intensity
as a function of angle θ, measured from the east-west line.

46-3 ★ (a) Show that the radiated intensity I given by Equation 46-6 has the
maximum value I_0 at $\theta = 0$. (b) Verify that the intensities of the
first two secondary peaks of Equation 46-6 are $0.045I_0$ and $0.016I_0$,
respectively, and show that these peaks do *not* occur exactly midway
between bands of zero intensity.

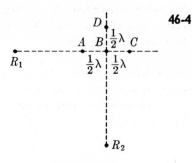

Figure 46-25

46-4   Four identical monochromatic wave
sources, located as shown in Figure
46-25, produce waves of the same wavelength λ. Two receivers, R_1 and R_2,
are great (but equal) distances from
the sources. (a) Which receiver picks
up the greater signal? (b) Which receiver picks up the greater signal if
source B is turned off? (c) If source
D is turned off? (d) Which receiver
can tell which source, B or D, has been
turned off?

46-5   The diffraction pattern on a screen 0.75 m from a single slit shows the
central maximum bounded by dark fringes separated by 2.0 mm. The
wavelength of the light is 6000 Å. What is the slit width?

46-6   Plane waves of sound having a frequency of 375 $\sec^{-1}$ are incident
upon a very tall window 8.0 feet wide, leading into a very large room.
It is found that the intensity of the sound falls continuously to zero at
an angle of 30° relative to the normal to the window surface. What is
the speed of the sound waves?

46-7   A single-slit diffraction pattern is seen on a screen. What changes will
occur in the pattern if the entire apparatus, from light source to screen,
is immersed in a medium of refractive index n?

46-8   Two slits, each of width w, have their centers separated by $4w$. Sketch
the interference-diffraction pattern, giving the intensity as a function
of angle.

46-9   Plane monochromatic waves impinge upon a double slit, the distance
between slits being 10 times the wavelength of the waves. The width

of the slit openings is much less than the wavelength. Interference effects are observed on a screen whose distance from the slits is much greater than the wavelength. (a) At what angle does the first dark band fall? (b) At what angle would the first dark band fall, if a third slit were located midway between the first two? (c) At what angle would the first minimum fall, if an infinite number of slits were placed between the first two (single-slit diffraction)?

46-10 A slit having a width of 0.20 mm is illuminated with light of 5000 Å wavelength from a very distant source. At what maximum distance from the slit must a screen be placed to show a zero in the intensity at the axis of the slit, as in Figure 46-13?

46-11 Light of wavelength 6000 Å from a very distant source falls upon a first screen with a slit of 0.20 mm width. One meter behind the first screen is a second screen with two very narrow slits separated by 6.0 mm. These two slits are centered relative to the single slit in the first screen. Finally, there is a third screen 1.0 m behind the second screen. (a) Sketch the intensity of light as a function of position on the second screen with attention to the locations of the minimum and maxima in the pattern. (b) Sketch the intensity as a function of position on the third screen.

46-12 Light from two identical line sources passes through a single slit of width w and thence to a distant screen. The sources are a distance D from the slit, and produce light of wavelength λ. What is the minimum separation distance between the line sources that will permit them to be resolved from the resultant diffraction pattern on the screen into two distinct sources?

46-13 What is the closest two point objects can be together to be resolvable by the eye (diameter of pupil, 4.0 mm) when the objects are 25 cm from the eye. Assume the wavelength of light to be 5000 Å.

46-14 The Mount Palomar telescope has a mirror 200 inches in diameter. What is the diameter of a reflecting mirror for a radio telescope operating with 21 cm wavelengths which will have the same resolving power as the Palomar telescope?

46-15 A radar set with a "dish" (parabolic reflector) of 1.0 m radius is fed by microwaves of 10 cm wavelength. What is the resolving power of this antenna?

46-16 * A magnifying glass of focal length 5 cm and diameter 1.0 cm is used to aid the eye (diameter of pupil, 4 mm) in looking at two point objects close together. How close can the two objects be so that they will be resolvable as two distinct objects? Assume the wavelength of light to be 5000 Å and the near point for the eye to be 25 cm.

46-17 A diffraction grating consists of 1000 lines, adjacent lines being separated by 20,000 Å. What is the number of secondary maxima occurring between the principal maxima in the diffraction pattern?

46-18 A venetian blind having a "grating spacing" of 1.75 inch is to be used as a diffraction grating for sound waves of 0.50 inch. At what angles relative to the normal to the "grating" will one find the intensity maximum in the first-order spectrum?

46-19 (a) For what spacing of lines in a diffraction grating will there be a maximum angular spread of the first-order in visible spectrum (4000 to 7000 Å)? (b) Calculate the angular spread of the visible spectrum of part (a).

46-20 A diffraction grating is to be so constructed that it will resolve lines separated in wavelength by 0.5 Å in the first-order visible spectrum (say, 4000 to 7000 Å). What is the number of grating lines?

46-21 The two closely spaced yellow lines in the spectrum of sodium (the sodium D lines) have wavelengths of 5890 Å and 5896 Å. What is the minimum number of lines in a diffraction grating having a grating spacing of 20,000 Å, that will permit the two lines to be resolved in the first-order spectrum?

46-22 Show that the intensity maxima for a diffraction grating having N lines are proportional to N^2.

46-23 Six identical oscillators, each generating waves of 10.0 cm wavelength, are aligned along a north-south line with a constant spacing of 1.0 m between adjacent oscillators. (a) In what directions is the intensity a maximum? (b) At what angle closest to the east-west line is the intensity first equal to zero? (c) Now suppose that six additional oscillators are added to those above, giving twelve oscillators along a line; what are the directions of the intensity maxima? (d) At what angle is the intensity first equal to zero?

46-24 N sources radiating waves of wavelength λ are arranged in a row. The sources are separated by equal distances, and the total distance from the first to the last is w. There is a constant relative intrinsic phase difference between each adjoining pair of oscillators, the second oscillator leading the first by Φ, the third leading the second by Φ, etc. Show that the angle θ relative to the line perpendicular to the row of oscillators at which the peak in the principal radiation lobe is found is given by $\sin \theta = \Phi \lambda (N - 1)/2\pi w$.

FORTY-SEVEN

POLARIZATION

All types of waves show interference and diffraction effects, but only *transverse* waves, those in which the propagated disturbance is a *vector* quantity, show the phenomenon of *polarization*. We have already discussed (Section 39-11) the polarization properties of transverse waves on a string. In this chapter we are concerned with the polarization properties of electromagnetic waves. We first consider the superposition of simple harmonic motions giving rise to linear, circular, and elliptical polarization. Then we treat polarization properties of the radiation from an electric dipole oscillator. Next we turn to the meaning of polarization of visible light and the means by which polarized light is achieved: polaroid sheets, scattering, reflection, and refraction. We derive the relation giving the angular momentum carried by circularly polarized electromagnetic waves. Finally, we treat briefly certain aspects of optical anisotropy.

47-1 Superposition of simple harmonic motions Figure 47-1 shows several situations in which two simple harmonic motions at the same frequency and at right angles to one another, but having varying relative

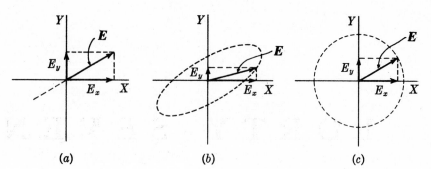

(a)   (b)   (c)

Figure 47-1. Simple harmonic motions of the same frequency at right angles, with (a) no phase difference, (b) a phase difference, and (c) a 90° phase difference.

phases, are superposed. The oscillation along the X-axis is represented by E_x; that along Y, by E_y. The resultant of E_x and E_y is E. These oscillations may be identified with the electric field of electromagnetic waves propagating at right angles to the plane of the paper.†

In Figure 47-1a the two oscillations are *in phase*, and their resultant is also simple harmonic motion along a single line. The corresponding wave is said to be *linearly* polarized, the plane of polarization being that containing the resultant electric field vectors and the direction of wave propagation. The angle of the resultant field relative to the X-axis depends on the relative amplitudes of E_x and E_y. By the same token, a single linearly polarized wave along some oblique direction relative to the X-axis is equivalent to two linearly polarized waves in phase along X and Y.

In Figure 47-1b the two component oscillations are *not* in phase, and the tip of the resultant electric field vector E traces out an ellipse in the plane transverse to the direction of wave propagation. The orientation of the ellipse's major axis depends on the phase difference between the two oscillations. For example, if the phase difference is 45°, the major axis of the ellipse makes an angle of 45° relative to the X-axis. A resultant wave produced by two linearly polarized waves at right angles to one another, but differing in phase, is said to be *elliptically polarized*.

Now suppose that the two component oscillators are 90° out of phase and of equal amplitude, as in Figure 47-1c. The resultant E is now of constant magnitude, and it rotates at the frequency of the component waves, the tip of the E vector tracing out a circle. This is a *circularly* polarized wave. The

---

† The magnetic field B is, of course, always at right angles to the electric field E, the directions of E, B, and I, the vector intensity of the electromagnetic wave, being related by the Poynting formula, $I = E \times B/\mu_0$, Equation 41-18.

sense of rotation depends on the relative phases of E_x and E_y. If E_y lags behind E_x by 90°, the vector E rotates in the counterclockwise sense, and the corresponding wave emerging out of the paper is said to be *right* circularly polarized. On the other hand, if E_x lags behind E_y by 90°, the rotation sense of E is clockwise, and the wave is *left* circularly polarized.

The three cases shown in Figure 47-1 and all others are illustrated by the motion of a pendulum bob in the horizontal plane. As a simple pendulum, the bob moves in simple harmonic motion along a single line; as a conical pendulum, it moves in a horizontal circle; the most general motion is in the path of an ellipse. Less mechanically, these oscillation patterns are seen on an oscilloscope screen by applying sinu-soidal variations to the horizontal and ver-tical deflecting plates.

47-2 Polarization properties of waves from an electric dipole oscillator

Recall some results given in Section 41-4 concerning the electromagnetic waves radi-ated by an electric dipole oscillator. The waves are generated by electric charges of opposite sign oscillating sinusoidally along a line, the dipole axis. At large distances from the dipole, the wave fronts are spheres. Moreover, the radiated waves are *linearly polarized*, the electric field lying in the plane containing the electric dipole and the direc-tion of wave propagation. The magnitude

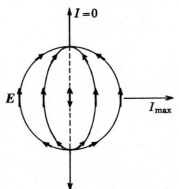

Figure 47-2. Radiated electric field for an electric dipole oscillator.

of the electric field is *not* the same in all directions; E is maximum in the plane perpendicular to the dipole axis and zero along the dipole axis, as shown in Figure 47-2. Thus, since the radiation intensity varies as E^2, no energy is radiated along the direction of the line in which the electric charges accelerate.

Figure 47-3a shows an electric dipole oscillator transmitting waves to a near-by electric dipole receiver. The orientations of the two dipole antennas must be proper if the maximum energy is to be transferred from transmitter to receiver. If the receiving dipole is parallel to the electric field of the arriving waves this electric field will drive charges along the axis of the dipole and therby produce a large signal at the receiver. If the receiving antenna were turned through 90°, as in Figure 47-3b, the linear polarization of the transmitted waves would preclude their being received.

Now suppose that we place a screen consisting of a series of parallel wires or rods between the transmitter and receiver, the conducting wires first

Figure 47-3. (a) A dipole transmitter radiates to a dipole receiver.
(b) No signal is received when the axes of the two dipoles make an angle
of 90°.

being orientated parallel to the direction of polarization of the electromagnetic waves, as shown in Figure 47-4a. The electric field, since it
oscillates along the long direction of the wires, causes the charges within
the wires to oscillate. Therefore, the incident wave is strongly absorbed by
the wire grid. This is confirmed by the extremely reduced signal at the
receiver. On the other hand, if the wire grid is rotated through 90°, so that
the electric field is perpendicular to the direction of "easy absorption" by
the wires, the electromagnetic waves pass through the grid with essentially
no absorption, as indicated by the strong signal appearing at the receiver.

These fundamental effects, which have their exact counterpart in the
polarization properties of ordinary light waves, can be readily demonstrated
by a microwave transmitter generating waves of several centimeters'
wavelength.

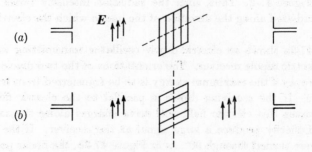

Figure 47-4. (a) No signal reaches the receiver when the wires in the
grid are parallel to the polarization direction of the radiation. (b) When
the wires are turned 90°, the signal reaches the receiver.

47-3 Polarization of visible light When an electric dipole radio oscillator is driven continuously at a constant frequency, the emitted waves are coherent and linearly polarized. This is not the case for visible light. Except for the rather special case of lasers (Section 45-5), visible light from ordinary sources arises from the random radiation from individual atoms, each atom radiating for a time of approximately 10^{-8} sec. Not only is the emitted light incoherent in the sense that the phases of successive individual light trains are not the same; the polarization direction of the light from individual atoms also varies over all possible orientations, the electric field in the plane transverse to the direction of propagation assuming all possible directions. Thus, if one were actually able to measure the polarization of light from a source containing very many radiating atoms, one would first find one direction of polarization for the light from one atom, then another polarization direction for the light from the next atom, and so on. The individual wave trains arrive, however, at such very small time intervals (much less than 10^{-8} sec), that it is impracticable to specify the polarization direction of the light at each instant. In this case, in which the polarization direction changes so randomly and rapidly that one cannot follow it in time, the light is said to be *unpolarized*.

One way of representing unpolarized light is shown in Figure 47-5. Here the various electric field vectors, viewed from along the direction of propagation of the separate wave trains, are shown as randomly oriented. Each electric field oscillation may be replaced by its rectangular components.

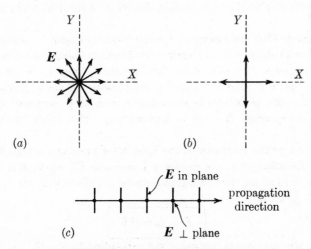

Figure 47-5. (a) Representation of the electric fields for an unpolarized wave. (b) Equivalent fields (of random phase) for an unpolarized wave. (c) A representation of an unpolarized wave.

Therefore, the unpolarized light is equivalent to two mutually perpendicular and linearly polarized electric field oscillations of equal magnitude, which we have taken for convenience as horizontal and vertical. It must be emphasized, however, that the X- and Y-components are *not* continuous and coherent. Since the separate wave trains in an unpolarized light beam are random in phase as well as in polarization direction, the two rectangular components fluctuate randomly in phase. We shall represent unpolarized light as in Figure 47-5c: where mutually perpendicular lines transverse to the propagation direction represent the two equivalent linearly polarized waves of random phase.

The simplest way to produce linearly polarized visible light is to pass the unpolarized light beam through a sheet of the commercial material Polaroid. This material consists of needlelike molecules of herapathite aligned mostly along one direction. The alignment is achieved by stretching the flexible transparent sheet as the material solidifies. A sheet of Polaroid is similar, then, in its polarization properties for visible light, to the grid of parallel wires for microwaves: when the electric field is parallel to the long axis of the molecules, the wave is absorbed, and when the electric field is perpendicular to the long axis, the wave is (mostly) transmitted.

It is useful to designate the direction of easy transmission within the Polaroid sheet as the *polarization direction*. Then, if an unpolarized beam is incident upon one Polaroid sheet, only the electric field oscillations parallel to the polarization directions are transmitted. We take the two equivalent polarization directions in the unpolarized beam as lying parallel and perpendicular to the polarization direction of the Polaroid; see Figure 47-6.

Now suppose that the emerging linearly polarized light is incident upon a second Polaroid sheet, whose polarization direction makes an angle θ relative to the polarization direction of the light incident upon it. We may resolve the electric field E into rectangular components, $E \cos \theta$ parallel to the second Polaroid's polarization direction and $E \sin \theta$ perpendicular to it. Only the component $E \cos \theta$ is transmitted; the other component is absorbed.

What, then, is the intensity of the light after passing through the second Polaroid? Recalling that the intensity I varies as E^2, where E is the resultant electric field of an electromagnetic wave, it follows that the transmitted intensity is given by

$$I = I_0 \cos^2 \theta \qquad [47\text{-}1]$$

where I_0 is the maximum intensity, corresponding to $\theta = 0$.

When $\theta = 90°$, that is, when the polarization directions of the two Polaroid sheets are at right angles, the transmitted intensity is zero. Said

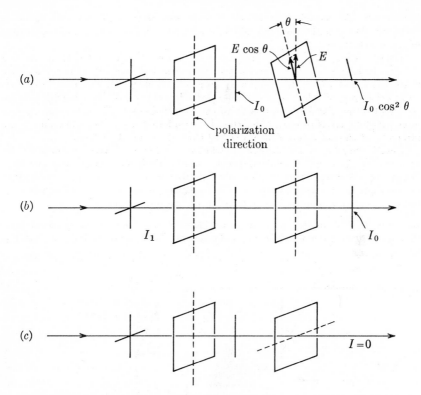

Figure 47-6. Polaroid sheets whose polarization directions differ by (a) θ, (b) $0°$, and (c) $90°$.

differently, there is *extinction* for the *polarizer* and *analyzer* at right angles. Equation 47-1, which governs the intensity through *any* two devices (not merely Polaroid sheets) that transmit only one polarization direction, is known as *Malus' law*, after its discoverer, E. L. Malus (1775–1812) who first found this effect in 1809.

We have spoken of the polarization direction of a Polaroid sheet. This direction cannot be established, however, unless there is an independent means of determining the polarization direction of a wave. That is, experiments with two Polaroid sheets give the relative polarization directions of two sheets as differing by 90° when no light is transmitted through them, but such experiments alone do not give the polarization direction of any one sheet. Polaroid is one example of materials exhibiting *dichroism*, the attenuation of one polarization component and the transmission of the mutually perpendicular component. A naturally occurring crystal showing this effect is tourmaline.

Example 1 An unpolarized beam of light passes through a *single* sheet of Polaroid. What is the intensity of the transmitted beam as compared with that of the incident beam?

If there is no preferred polarization direction in the incident light, that is, if the incident light is truly unpolarized, then the two equivalent perpendicular oscillations into which the beam may be resolved, shown in Figure 47-5b, must be of equal magnitude. We may choose the orientation of one oscillation to be parallel to the polarization direction of the Polaroid sheet. Then this component is completely transmitted; the other is completely absorbed. Therefore, the intensity of the transmitted beam is *half* that of the incident beam.

Now, if there were no absorption whatsoever for oscillations parallel to the polarization direction of a Polaroid sheet, adding a second Polaroid sheet with its polarization direction parallel to that of the first sheet would produce *no* further attenuation in the light intensity. This ideal behavior is not found, however, because partial absorption occurs even in the preferred orientation.

Example 2 An unpolarized light beam falls on two Polaroid sheets so oriented that no light is transmitted through the second sheet. A third Polaroid sheet is

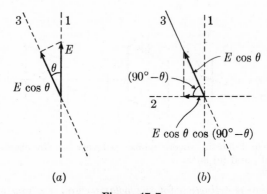

(a) (b)

Figure 47-7

then introduced between the first two sheets. How does the intensity of transmitted light vary with the orientation of the third sheet? (The intensity is *not* zero for all orientations!)

The polarization directions of sheets 1 and 2 are mutually perpendicular. We take the angle between the polarization directions of sheets 1 and 3 to be θ. Then, as Figure 47-7a shows, if E is the magnitude of the electric field transmitted through the first sheet, the component emerging through the third sheet (the one placed *between* the first and second sheets) is $E \cos \theta$. From Figure 47-7b we see that the component emerging through the last sheet has the magnitude $E \cos \theta \cos (90° - \theta) = E \cos \theta \sin \theta$. Thus, the intensity varies according to

$$I = I_0 \cos^2 \theta \sin^2 \theta = \tfrac{1}{4} I \sin^2 2\theta$$

where I_0 is the intensity transmitted through the first sheet. Note that there are *four* positions at which the intensity is maximum: 45°, 135°, 225°, and 315°. Note also that interchanging the sheets, say 1 and 3, changes the dependence of I on θ.

47-4 Polarization in scattering Suppose that a linearly polarized electromagnetic wave is incident upon an object much smaller than the wavelength of light. For example, consider a molecule whose size is of the order of 10 to 100 Å. The electric field of the incident wave acts on the charges within the molecule and causes the electrons to oscillate along the polarization direction. But such charges oscillating along a single line constitute an electric dipole oscillator, and the molecule acts as a dipole oscillator and radiates accordingly. Thus, the molecule absorbs radiation from an incident wave and reradiates this energy in various directions. The incident wave is said to be *scattered* by the molecule.

Let us examine the polarization properties of the scattered radiation. Figure 47-8a shows a linearly polarized wave incident upon a scattering center. Recalling the polarization and intensity properties of the radiation emitted by an oscillating electric dipole (Figure 47-2), we see that, if the incident wave is linearly polarized in the plane of the paper and the axis of the induced dipole oscillator is therefore parallel to the direction of the electric field of the incident wave, there is *no* radiation scattered outward along the dipole axis, that is, scattered through 90° in the plane of the paper. The scattered radiation is also linearly polarized in the plane determined by the dipole and the propagation direction of the scattered wave. The intensity is a maximum in the plane perpendicular to the oscillating dipole, but falls to zero as the scattering direction approaches 90°.

Figure 47-8b shows the more general case, in which unpolarized light is incident upon a scattering center. The dipole oscillates both in and perpendicular to the plane of the paper. Now, of course, there is radiation scattered in *all* directions, but the radiation scattered through 90° is completely linearly polarized, and partially polarized in all directions except that along which the incident wave travels. This is shown also in Figure 47-8c.

The electrons in a typical atom or molecule have natural oscillation frequencies corresponding to ultraviolet light. Thus, when visible light impinges on a scattering center, it drives the electrons into oscillation at a frequency which is lower than the natural, or resonant, oscillation frequency. Of course, blue or violet light comes closer to the natural frequency than does red light, and it is to be expected that, other things being equal, blue light is scattered more effectively than red light. Detailed analysis shows that the scattered intensity varies as the fourth power of the frequency. Since the ends of the visible spectrum differ in frequency by a factor of approximately 2, the intensity of the scattered violet light is roughly 2^4, or 16, times that of red light.

Those aspects of the scattering of visible light which depend on the frequency and state of polarization are illustrated by the scattering of the

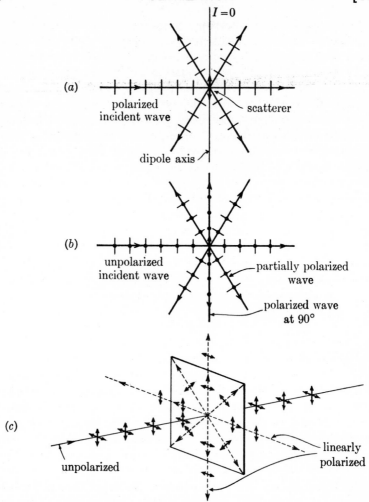

Figure 47-8. (a) Scattering of a linearly polarized wave by an induced electric dipole oscillator. (b), (c) Scattering of an unpolarized wave.

Sun's visible radiation by particles and molecules in the Earth's atmosphere. The sky appears blue overhead, because blue is scattered to a greater degree by air molecules and dust particles than is red light (the same effect is seen in the bluish cast of a smoke-filled room). On the other hand, viewing the Sun directly, particularly through a thick dust-filled atmosphere at sunset, shows predominantly colors other than blue, inasmuch as the blue light has been scattered from the forward direction. As one would expect, the scattered blue light in the sky is at least partially polarized. This polarization effect can easily be confirmed by using Polaroid sheets. Indeed, one may use the polarization properties of scattered light to navigate by, particularly near the Earth's poles, where compasses are unusable. Precisely the same navigation scheme is used by bees; each of the many eyes on a bee's head can detect the state of polarization of the light scattered from the Sun.

Polarization effects also enter in the *double* scattering of electromagnetic waves. Suppose that unpolarized light is incident upon a first scatterer, and the radiation scattered 90° then excites a second scatterer. We are interested in the intensity of the doubly scattered light. As Figure 47-9 shows, the intensity of waves scattered by the second scattering center is zero along a direction perpendicular to the plane containing the incident beam and the two scattering centers. This effect can be demonstrated with

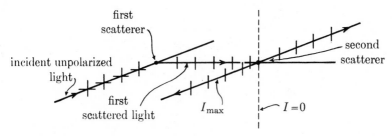

Figure 47-9. Polarization characteristics of double scattering.

visible light and also with x-rays. In fact, such intensity variations, which have their origin in the polarization properties of the scattered radiation, were first observed by C. G. Barkla (1877–1944) in 1906, who established thereby that x-rays consist of transverse waves.

47-5 Polarization by reflection and refraction   When light strikes an interface leading to an optically dense material, the electric field of the incident electromagnetic wave sets the electric charges within the material in motion. These oscillating charges then scatter the radiation. Indeed, the refracted beam within the material is the resultant wave produced by many atomic scatterers; similarly, the reflected beam is produced by atomic radiators *within* the material, not merely those at the surface. Thus, reflection, as well as refraction, has its origin in scattering. Since scattered radiation may be polarized, we would expect to find polarization effects associated with reflection and refraction.

Let us consider a linearly polarized beam incident upon an interface, as in Figure 47-10a. The plane of polarization contains the normal to the surface. We suppose the direction of the incident ray is such that the angle between the refracted and reflected rays is 90° (we shall prove that there is,

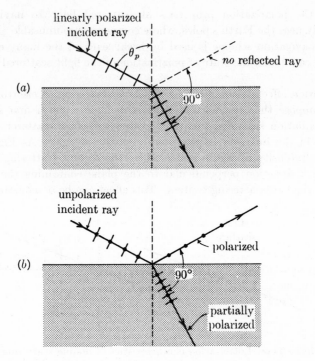

Figure 47-10. (a) Linearly polarized light incident upon a refracting medium at the polarizing angle θ_p. (b) Unpolarized light incident at the polarizing angle.

in fact, *no* reflected wave). Since the refracted ray is bent relative to the incident ray, so too are the lines representing the directions of the electric field oscillations. (Fundamentally, it goes the other way: the beam within the material is indeed refracted, because the directions of the resultant oscillating fields are reoriented by virtue of the atomic scattering.) Any reflected wave is created by the atomic scatterers within the material. The axes of the atomic electric dipoles here point in the direction of the reflected ray. Therefore, there can be no radiation produced in this direction. There is, in fact, *no reflected ray*!

Now let us consider Figure 47-10b, in which an *unpolarized* wave is incident upon a surface at the so-called *polarizing angle*, that angle of incidence for which the refracted and reflected rays make an angle of 90°. There *is* a reflected ray. It is completely polarized, and its direction of polarization is in the plane of the interface. Moreover, the refracted ray is *partially* polarized. This arises because some of the incident beam has been removed as a completely polarized reflected ray; what remains in the refracted ray must predominate in polarization in the plane containing the incident and refracted rays.

Let us find the polarizing angle θ_p for rays incident from medium 1 into medium 2. From Snell's law,

[43-2] $n_1 \sin \theta_1 = n_2 \sin \theta_2$

For complete polarization of the reflected ray,

$$\theta_1 = \theta_p \quad \text{with} \quad \theta_1 + \theta_2 = 90°$$
$$n_1 \sin \theta_p = n_2 \sin (90° - \theta_p) = n_2 \cos \theta_p$$

Therefore,

$$\tan \theta_p = n_2/n_1 = n_{21} \qquad \text{[47-2]}$$

For example, when light is incident from air upon water ($n = 1.33$) at an angle of $\theta_p = \tan^{-1}(1.33) = 53°$, the reflected ray is completely polarized. Equation 47-2 is referred to as *Brewster's law*, after D. Brewster (1781–1868), who discovered this relation by experiment in 1812.

Although the reflected beam is completely polarized only at the polarizing angle, it is partially polarized at any angle of incidence different from 0°.

47-6 The angular momentum of light An electromagnetic wave is said to be circularly polarized when the resultant electric field in any plane transverse to the direction of wave propagation is constant in magnitude and changes direction at a uniform rate. That is to say, the tip of the resultant electric field vector traces out a circle in a fixed transverse plane, as shown in Figure 47-1c. The electric field of a circularly polarized electromagnetic wave at one instant is shown in Figure 47-11. The tips of the electric field vectors lie on a helix whose symmetry axis is the direction of wave propagation.

It is easy to generate circularly polarized radio waves. One simply superposes the radiation from two electric dipole antennas, whose dipole

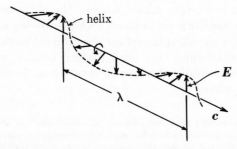

Figure 47-11. The electric field vectors for a circularly polarized electromagnetic wave.

axes are oriented at right angles to one another and which oscillate at the same frequency and generate waves of the same intensity but *90° out of phase* (see Section 47-1). The matter of generating circularly polarized visible light requires special techniques, to be described in the next section.

Just as one associates angular momentum with a circularly polarized transverse wave propagated along a stretched string (Section 39-11), one attributes angular momentum to a circularly polarized electromagnetic wave. First recall that a linearly polarized wave causes electrons within a material upon which it impinges to oscillate along the direction of the electric field. Although the frequency of the electron's motion is the same as that of the driving electromagnetic wave, the electrons, bound to their parent atoms, do *not* oscillate in phase with the exciting electric field. The phase lag causes the electrons to absorb energy (and linear momentum)

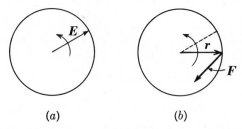

(a)   (b)

Figure 47-12. (a) Rotating electric field of a circularly polarized wave. (b) Force acting on an electron in an absorber.

from the incident wave. A circularly polarized wave is equivalent to two linearly polarized waves at right angles but 90° out of phase. Thus, when a circularly polarized wave impinges on an absorber, the electrons are set in oscillation simultaneously in two mutually perpendicular directions but 90° out of phase. Said differently, the resultant electric field causes the electrons to move in a circle. Again, because the electrons are bound, the electrons' circular motion is *not* in phase with the driving electric field; see Figure 47-12. Since the electrons are set in rotational motion, they and the absorbing material in which they are imbedded acquire, not only energy, but also angular momentum, this angular momentum having been removed from the incident wave.†

† The rotating electric field acts not only on the electrons but also on the positive charges. Since the charges are opposite in sign, the forces are opposite in direction, but not colinear. The line representing the direction of the electric field at one instant is *not* parallel to the line joining the opposite charges, because of the phase lag. Consequently, the force pair produces a torque couple on the charges within the material.

The power P produced by a torque τ rotating an object at angular speed ω is given by

[14-12] $P = \tau\omega$

and, the energy dE transferred in time dt is

$$dE = P\,dt = \tau\omega\,dt \qquad [47\text{-}3]$$

By Newton's second law for rotational motion, the torque is the time rate of the angular momentum L:

[15-11] $\tau = \dfrac{dL}{dt}$ [47-4]

Substituting Equation 47-4 into Equation 47-3 gives

$$dE = (dL/dt)\omega\,dt = \omega\,dL$$

$$\boxed{L = \frac{E}{\omega}} \qquad [47\text{-}5]$$

The angular momentum L of a circularly polarized electromagnetic wave is equal in magnitude to the energy E carried by the wave, divided by the wave's angular frequency ω. Unlike the linear momentum E/c of an electromagnetic wave (Equation 41-25), which is frequency-independent, the angular momentum varies inversely with frequency. Thus, a beam of visible light carries less angular momentum than a radio beam of the same energy.

What is the direction of the angular momentum? A circularly polarized wave in which the electric field rotates in the counterclockwise sense, when viewed from the direction in which the wave is headed, is said to be *right* circularly polarized (one may use the right-hand rule to relate the propagation direction to the rotational sense of the electric field). The reverse rotational sense corresponds to left circularly polarized light. The sense in which the electric field rotates is the same as the sense in which the (positive) charged particles in the absorbing material rotate. Therefore, one may use the right-hand rule to relate the direction of a wave's angular momentum to the direction of wave propagation. For right circularly polarized waves, the angular momentum is in the *same* direction as that of wave propagation; that is, the linear momentum and angular momentum of the wave are parallel. Conversely, the angular momentum is in the opposite direction to that of the linear momentum for a left circularly polarized light.† See Figure 47-13.

† Unhappily, there is no single convention for relating the relative directions of angular momentum and linear momentum of visible light with the terms "right" and "left." Since some authors use the opposite convention, one must be careful. The convention used here corresponds to that in universal use in discussions of the linear and angular momenta of elementary particles.

If light carries angular momentum, it is implied that a circularly polarized beam, when absorbed, imparts a twist to the absorbing material. Similarly, when a circularly polarized wave is reflected, angular momentum (twice as much) is transferred to the reflector. This follows from the fact that the direction of wave propagation, and hence also of the wave's angular momentum vector, is reversed. The angular momentum of light was first observed directly by R. A. Beth (1906–   ) in 1936, when circularly polarized light was seen to impart a torque to an absorber in a sensitively mounted torsion pendulum.

The angular momentum carried by an electromagnetic wave must be described as *spin angular momentum* rather than orbital angular momentum.

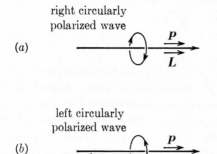

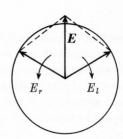

Figure 47-13. Relative directions of the linear momentum p and angular momentum L for a (a) right and (b) left circularly polarized electromagnetic wave.

Figure 47-14. Right (E_r) and left (E_l) circularly polarized waves when superposed are equivalent to a linearly polarized wave.

Recall that the Earth has orbital angular momentum by virtue of its orbit about the Sun; the magnitude and direction of this orbital angular momentum depends, however, on the choice of the axis relative to which it is measured (the orbital angular momentum is constant only when measured relative to a point at the force center, that is, at the Sun). On the other hand, the spin angular momentum of the Earth about its axis is the *same* whatever the location of the point relative to which it is measured. Therefore, it is appropriate to term the spin angular momentum of a body as *intrinsic* angular momentum, since its magnitude and direction are independent of the choice of axis. In this sense the angular momentum of a circularly polarized electromagnetic wave is *intrinsic*, or *spin*, angular momentum: its magnitude and direction are independent of the choice of axis.

Just as one may regard a circularly polarized wave as consisting of the superposition of two linearly polarized waves at right angles and $90°$ out of phase, one may regard any linearly polarized wave as being the superposition of two circularly polarized waves of opposite sense. See Figure 47-14, which shows the resultant field E contributed by the vector E_r (right) rotating in the counterclockwise sense and the vector E_l (left) rotating in the clockwise sense. Heretofore we have found that any wave, polarized or unpolarized, may be regarded as the superposition of linearly polarized waves. Now we find that any wave may be regarded as the superposition of right- and left-circularly polarized waves. There is a fundamental reason for preferring the latter description. From the point of view of the quantum theory of light, in which electromagnetic radiation is thought to consist of particle-like "photons," one must attribute an intrinsic angular momentum, or spin, to each photon. Thus, the polarization properties of any radiation must be regarded as arising from a number of superposed circularly polarized photons.

Example 3   A right circularly polarized radio beam of 1.0 Mw and 100 kcycles/sec is turned on for 1.0 sec. What is the angular momentum of this beam?
From Equation 47-5,

$$L = E/\omega = E/2\pi f = Pt/2\pi f$$
$$= \frac{(1.0 \times 10^6 \text{ w})(1.0 \text{ sec})}{2\pi(1.0 \times 10^5 \text{ sec}^{-1})} = 1.6 \text{ joule-sec} = 1.6 \text{ kg-m}^2/\text{sec}$$

If this rather sizeable angular momentum were to be absorbed completely in a ring of 10 cm radius and 10 gm mass initially at rest, the ring would be set into rotation at a speed of over 2500 rotations/sec! On the other hand, for visible radiation, with frequencies larger by a factor of 10^{10}, the angular momentum of circularly polarized light, even of large intensity, would be much smaller.

47-7   Optical anisotropy   Many crystalline solids are optically aniso-tropic; that is, they do not have the same optical properties in all directions. The optical anisotropy is closely related to the mechanical and electrical anisotropy of the crystal. For example, a crystal of calcite is composed of molecules of $CaCO_3$ arranged in such a three-dimensional geometric pattern that, when an electron is displaced from its equilibrium position in one direction and released, it oscillates at a characteristic frequency which is different from the oscillation frequency arising when the electron is displaced in some other direction and released.

Consider Figure 47-15a, which shows an electron displaced in the XY-plane from its equilibrium position. The characteristic oscillation frequency $f_\perp$ of such an electron lies in the ultraviolet region of the electromagnetic spectrum. Now, if the electron is displaced along the Z-axis, as in Figure 47-15b, its characteristic frequency $f_\parallel$ is different. Indeed, the Z-axis here was chosen to lie along a particular direction within the anisotropic crystal,

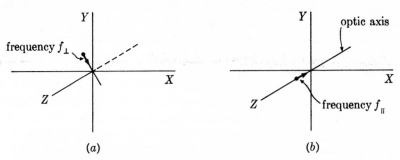

Figure 47-15. (a) Any electron displaced in the YZ-plane oscillates at the natural frequency $f_\perp$. (b) The natural oscillation frequency $f_\parallel$ of an electron displaced along the Z-axis (the optic axis) is different.

called the *optic axis*. The frequency $f_\parallel$ along this axis is different from the frequency $f_\perp$ of oscillation along *any* direction at right angles to the optic axis. We recall (Section 43-7) that the propagation of light within a transparent medium involves the excitation of electrons by the electric field of the electromagnetic wave, the speed of propagation depending upon the degree to which the frequency of the driving electric field differs from the natural frequency of the electrons' oscillation. Thus, anisotropy in the resonant frequency of oscillation will be manifest in anisotropy in the speed of propagation of light; that is, light causing oscillations at the frequency $f_\perp$ will travel at the speed $c/n_\perp$, while light causing oscillations at the frequency $f_\parallel$ will travel through the medium at the speed $c/n_\parallel$, where $n_\parallel$ and $n_\perp$ are the refractive indices for propagation respectively parallel to and perpendicular to the optic axis. For example, in calcite $n_\perp = 1.658$ and

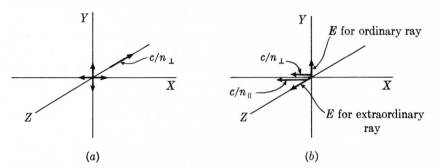

Figure 47-16. (a) A single unpolarized wave travels along the optic axis at the speed $c/n_\perp$. (b) For propagation at right angles to the optic axis there are *two* waves: an ordinary wave, polarized along Y and traveling at the speed $c/n_\perp$, and an extraordinary wave, polarized along Z and traveling at the speed $c/n_\parallel$.

$n_\parallel = 1.486$ for light of 5890 Å wavelength (yellow sodium light). In other anisotropic materials, such as quartz, $n_\parallel$ exceeds $n_\perp$.

Now consider unpolarized light traveling through an anisotropic crystal parallel to the optic axis, as in Figure 47-16a. We can represent the unpolarized light by electric fields along X and Y. These driving fields will cause oscillations at the frequency $f_\perp$, for *any* direction of the electric field in the XY-plane, and all components of the *unpolarized* light will travel along the optic axis at the same speed $c/n_\perp$. This is *not* the case for other propagation directions. Consider, for example, unpolarized light incident perpendicular to the optic axis, as in Figure 47-16b. The light is incident along the X-axis, and the associated electric fields cause oscillations along the Y- and Z-axes. Oscillations along the Y-axis are at the frequency $f_\perp$, and these oscillations correspond to a wave traveling along X at the speed $c/n_\perp$. Oscillations along the Z-axis, on the other hand, are at the frequency $f_\parallel$, and the corresponding wave again travels along X, but at a *different* speed, $c/n_\parallel$. Moreover, the polarization properties of the two waves are different. The wave traveling at the speed $c/n_\perp$ (the so-called ordinary ray) is linearly polarized in the Y-direction, whereas the wave traveling at the speed $c/n_\parallel$ (the extraordinary ray) is linearly polarized along the Z-direction. In short, when light is incident perpendicular to the optic axis, there exist *two* waves traveling through the material; the waves differ in refractive index and also in polarization.

Using an optically anisotropic, or doubly refracting, crystal, we have the condition for producing circularly polarized light. Two linearly polarized waves, whose polarization axes are at right angles, travel through the material at right angles to the optic axis. Thus, if the oscillations along Y and Z are initially in phase at the front surface where the light enters the material, these oscillations will become progressively out of phase as the light advances through the material, since the two waves travel at different speeds. At some particular thickness of material we will (first) have the oscillations of the slow and fast waves out of phase by 90°. At this plane, then, the resultant wave disturbance consists of two mutually perpendicular and linearly polarized oscillations of equal amplitude and 90° out of phase. But this corresponds to a circularly polarized wave! An anisotropic crystal of such thickness that the two emerging waves differ in phase by one quarter-wave, or 90°, is called a *quarter-wave plate*. The optic axis lies in the plane of the parallel surfaces. (In a typical material the minimum thickness of a quarter-wave plate for visible light is a small fraction of a millimeter.)

Because light shows dispersion, both the indices of refraction of an anisotropic crystal depend on the wavelength. Thus, a thin slab which is a quarter-wave plate for one frequency will not be a quarter-wave plate for a different frequency. Consider the following arrangement. Two Polaroid sheets are first arranged with their polarization axes at 90°. When unpolarized light is incident upon the first Polaroid, no light emerges from the second Polaroid. Now suppose that a quarter-wave plate is introduced between the two Polaroids; see Figure 47-17. The quarter-wave plate rotates the polarization direction through 90°. Thus, the linearly polarized light emerging from the first Polaroid is turned, in polarization direction, by just the right amount to allow it to pass through the second Polaroid. Strictly, only that wavelength for which the plate is truly a quarter-wave plate will be so passed. Other wavelengths will be at least partially absorbed.

Materials which are ordinarily optically isotropic can be rendered anisotropic. For example, a plastic, when subjected to a stress, becomes anisotropic. Indeed, ordinary thin sheets of cellophane are optically anisotropic

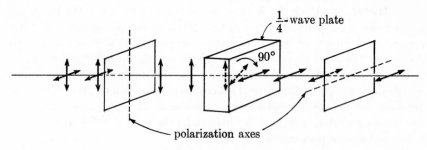

Figure 47-17. Unpolarized light is incident upon the first sheet. The emerging linearly polarized light is turned, in polarization direction, through 90° in traversing the quarter-wave plate, to be transmitted through the second polarizing sheet.

by virtue of stresses along the sheets produced in manufacture. Certain liquids with molecules having permanent electric dipole moment (polar liquids) are rendered anisotropic when an electric field is applied to them. The dipoles line up along the direction of the applied field, which becomes the direction of the optic axis. The phenomenon is called the Kerr effect. An important application of this effect is the production of electric switches for light. Thus, one can make a liquid, in effect, a quarter-wave plate by switching on an external field; the liquid, placed between crossed Polaroid sheets, will then transmit light; see Figure 47-18.

The optical anisotropy of materials leads to the phenomenon of *double refraction*, or *birefringence*. Heretofore we considered propagation of waves either parallel or perpendicular to the optic axis. For other directions of wave travel there are not only two wave speeds and two polarizations, but also two different directions. The so-called *ordinary ray* has a refractive index n; it travels at a single speed in *all* directions, obeying Snell's law.

The so-called *extraordinary ray*, involving both $n_\perp$ and $n_\parallel$, has different speeds in different directions (depending on the angle between the direction of wave propagation and that of the optic axis) and—extraordinarily—it does *not* follow Snell's law. Because the ordinary and extraordinary rays have, in general, different propagation directions, an anisotropic, or doubly refracting, transparent crystal produces *two* images, as shown in Figure 43-20.

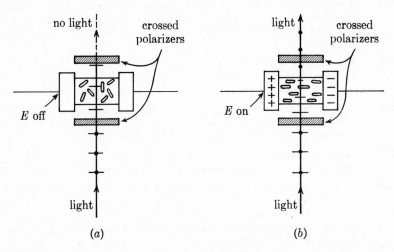

Figure 47-18. Schematic arrangement for a Kerr cell: (a) no light transmission with the electric field off; (b) transmission with the electric field applied and the polarization direction turned through 90°.

Example 4   A quarter-wave plate is to be constructed from calcite, for which $n_\perp = 1.658$ and $n_\parallel = 1.486$ with $\lambda = 5890$ Å. What is the required thickness for this wavelength?

The *optical* path length of the ordinary ray traveling through a plate of thickness t is $n_\perp t$. Similarly, the optical path length of the extraordinary ray is $n_\parallel t$. Since the two rays must emerge from the plate with a 90° phase difference, the optical paths must differ by $\tfrac{1}{4}\lambda$:

$$\tfrac{1}{4}\lambda = t(n_\perp - n_\parallel)$$

$$t = \frac{\lambda}{4(n_\perp - n_\parallel)} = \frac{5890\ \text{Å}}{4(1.658 - 1.486)} = 0.00086\ \text{mm}$$

PROBLEMS

47-1   The simple harmonic oscillations along the Y-axis lag behind the simple harmonic oscillations of the same frequency along the X-axis by 45°. What is the orientation of the major axis of the ellipse produced by the superposition of the two oscillations?

47-2 What must be the angle between the polarization axes of two ideal polarizing sheets, if the transmitted light intensity is to be 37.5 per cent of the intensity incident on the first sheet?

47-3 Some sun glasses are made of Polaroid. The polarizing sheets serve the purpose of minimizing the intensity of light reflected from surfaces in a horizontal plane. Should the polarization axis of the Polaroid be horizontal or vertical?

47-4 The Sun is in the East. A man looks into the overhead sky through a polarizing sheet. For what orientation of the polarization axis of the sheet, east-west or north-south, will the intensity of the light be a minimum?

47-5 Unpolarized light travels upward and is scattered. Some of this scattered light travels north and is then scattered a second time. In what direction will the intensity of the doubly scattered light be zero?

47-6 It is found that when unpolarized light is incident from air upon the surface of a liquid at an angle of 50°, the reflected light is linearly polarized. What is the refractive index of the liquid?

47-7 Light is incident from water ($n = 1.33$) onto glass ($n = 1.50$). At what angle of incidence will the reflected light be linearly polarized?

47-8 A 10 w source of circularly polarized light of 6000 Å wavelength is turned on for 5.0 sec. What are (a) the linear momentum of the beam and (b) the angular momentum of the beam? If this beam is completely absorbed what are (c) the radiation force and (d) the radiation torque, on the absorber?

47-9 Show that the ratio of the radiation torque to the radiation force for a circularly polarized electromagnetic wave of wavelength λ is $\lambda/2\pi$.

47-10 Circularly polarized light passes through an ideal polarizing sheet. What fraction of the incident intensity is absorbed in the sheet?

47-11 A small disk having a moment of inertia of 2.0×10^{-11} kg-m² absorbs all of the circularly polarized light of 6000 Å wavelength coming from a 50 w monochromatic light source. For what period of time must the light shine on the absorbing disk, if it is to be set in motion from rest to an angular speed of one rotation per minute?

47-12 A radar antenna transmits pulses of circularly polarized microwaves 3.0 cm in wavelength. Each pulse has a "width" of 2.0 μsec and power of 4.0 Mw. What is the recoil torque on the antenna while the transmitter is on?

47-13 What is the resultant polarization of a beam, arising from the superposition of a right circularly polarized wave and a left circularly polarized wave of unequal amplitudes?

47-14 From the point of view of the quantum theory, electromagnetic radiation consists of particle-like photons, each photon, whatever its frequency, being circularly polarized and carrying the *same* spin angular momentum. How does the energy of a photon depend on frequency?

47-15   The indices of refraction for the propagation of light of 5890 Å wave-length through quartz are 1.553 and 1.544, respectively. What is the minimum thickness of a quartz quarter-wave plate for this wavelength?

47-16   In Beth's experiment for measuring the angular momentum of light, circularly polarized light fell on a quarter-wave plate backed by a reflecting surface. Why is this a favorable arrangement for observing the angular momentum of light?

47-17   Circularly polarized light strikes a quarter-wave plate coated on the far side with a perfectly reflecting material. (a) What fraction of incident radiation is reflected from the plate? (b) What is the torque exerted on the plate by a beam of power P and angular frequency ω?

a p p e n d i x I

FUNDAMENTAL CONSTANTS

The values listed below for electric, magnetic, and atomic constants are those recommended by the Committee on Fundamental Constants of the National Academy of Sciences—National Research Council (see *Physics Today* 17, p. 48, February, 1964). The last significant figure may in some instances be indefinite.

Name of quantity	Common symbol	Value
Coulomb force constant	$k = 1/4\pi\epsilon_0$	8.9878×10^9 nt-m^2/coul^2
Permittivity of free space	ϵ_0	8.85415×10^{-12} coul^2/nt-m^2
Permeability of free space	μ_0	$4\pi \times 10^{-7}$ weber/amp-m
Speed of light (in vacuum)	c	2.997925×10^8 m/sec^2
Electron charge	e	1.6021×10^{-19} coul
Electron charge-to-mass ratio	e/m_e	1.7588×10^{11} coul/kg
Electron mass	m_e	9.1091×10^{-31} kg
Proton mass	m_p	1.67252×10^{-27} kg
Acceleration due to gravity (standard value)	g	9.80665 m/sec^2
Universal gravitational constant	G	6.670×10^{-11} nt-m^2/kg^2
Faraday constant	F	9.6487×10^4 coul/gm-mole
Avogadro's number	N_0	6.0225×10^{23} /gm-mole
Boltzmann's constant	k	1.3805×10^{-23} joule/K°
Universal gas constant	R	8.314 joule/gm-mole K°
Earth-sun mean distance (1 astronomical unit)	1 AU	1.49×10^{11} m $= 92.9 \times 10^6$ mi
Standard atmospheric pressure	1 atm	1.013×10^5 nt/m^2 $= 76$ cm Hg
Absolute zero of temperature		$-273.15°$ C

a p p e n d i x   II

CONVERSION FACTORS

See Appendix III for electric and magnetic conversion factors.

Length

	M	CM	KM
1 meter	1	10^2	10^{-3}
1 centimeter	10^{-2}	1	10^{-5}
1 kilometer	10^3	10^5	1
1 inch	2.540×10^{-2}	2.540	2.540×10^{-5}
1 foot	0.3048	30.48	3.048×10^{-4}
1 mile	1609	1.609×10^5	1.609

	IN.	FT	MI
1 meter	39.37	3.281	6.214×10^{-4}
1 centimeter	0.3937	3.281×10^{-2}	6.214×10^{-6}
1 kilometer	3.937×10^4	3.281×10^3	0.6214
1 inch	1	8.333×10^{-2}	1.578×10^{-5}
1 foot	12	1	1.894×10^{-4}
1 mile	6.336×10^4	5280	1

1 foot $= \frac{1200}{3937}$ m
1 mile $= 10^{-3}$ in.
1 light-year $= 9.4600 \times 10^{12}$ km
1 parsec $= 3.084 \times 10^{13}$ km
1 astronomical unit (mean Earth–Sun distance) $= 1$ AU $= 1.49 \times 10^{11}$ m
1 micron $= 1 \, \mu = 10^{-6}$ m
1 millimicron $= 1 \, m\mu = 10^{-9}$ m
1 Ångstrom $= 1 \, Å = 10^{-10}$ m
1 X-unit $= 1 \, XU = 10^{-13}$ m

Plane Angle

$1 \text{ rev} = 2\pi \text{ radian} = 360°$

Mass

	KG	GM	SLUG	AMU
1 kilogram	1	10^3	6.852×10^{-2}	6.024×10^{26}
1 gram	10^{-3}	1	6.852×10^{-5}	6.024×10^{23}
1 slug	14.59	1.459×10^4	1	8.789×10^{27}
1 atomic mass unit	1.660×10^{-27}	1.660×10^{-24}	1.137×10^{-28}	1

Time

	SEC	MIN	HR	DAY	YR
1 second	1	1.667×10^{-2}	2.778×10^{-4}	1.157×10^{-5}	3.169×10^{-8}
1 minute	60	1	1.667×10^{-2}	6.994×10^{-4}	1.901×10^{-6}
1 hour	3600	60	1	4.167×10^{-2}	1.141×10^{-4}
1 day	8.640×10^4	1440	24	1	2.738×10^{-3}
1 year	3.156×10^7	5.259×10^5	8.766×10^3	365.2	1

Speed

	M/SEC	CM/SEC	FT/SEC	MI/HR
1 meter/second	1	10^2	3.281	2.237
1 centimeter/second	10^{-2}	1	3.281×10^{-2}	2.237×10^{-2}
1 foot/second	0.3048	30.48	1	0.6818
1 mile/hour	0.4470	44.70	1.467	1

$1 \text{ mi/min} = 60 \text{ mi/hr} = 88 \text{ ft/sec}$

Force

	NT	DYNE	LB
1 newton	1	10^5	0.2248
1 dyne	10^{-5}	1	2.248×10^{-6}
1 pound	4.448	4.448×10^5	1

Work, Energy, Heat

	JOULE	ERG	FT-LB
1 joule	1	10^7	0.7376
1 erg	10^{-7}	1	7.376×10^{-8}
1 ft-lb	1.356	1.356×10^7	1
1 ev	1.602×10^{-19}	1.602×10^{-12}	1.182×10^{-19}
1 gm-cal	4.186	4.186×10^7	3.087
1 BTU	1.055×10^3	1.055×10^{10}	7.779×10^2
1 kw-hr	3.600×10^6	3.600×10^{13}	2.655×10^6

	EV	CAL	BTU	KW-HR
1 joule	6.242×10^{18}	0.2389	9.481×10^{-4}	2.778×10^{-7}
1 erg	6.242×10^{11}	2.389×10^{-8}	9.481×10^{-11}	2.778×10^{-14}
1 ft-lb	8.464×10^{18}	0.3239	1.285×10^{-3}	3.766×10^{-7}
1 ev	1	3.827×10^{-20}	1.519×10^{-22}	4.450×10^{-26}
1 gm-cal	2.613×10^{19}	1	3.968×10^{-3}	1.163×10^{-6}
1 BTU	6.585×10^{21}	2.520×10^2	1	2.930×10^{-4}
1 kw-hr	2.247×10^{25}	8.601×10^5	3.413×10^2	1

Pressure

	NT/M^2	DYNE/CM^2	ATM
1 newton/meter^2	1	10	9.869×10^{-6}
1 dyne/centimeter^2	10^{-1}	1	9.869×10^{-7}
1 atmosphere	1.013×10^5	1.013×10^6	1
1 centimeter mercury†	1.333×10^3	1.333×10^4	1.316×10^{-2}
1 pound/inch^2	6.895×10^3	6.895×10^4	6.805×10^{-2}
1 pound/foot^2	47.88	4.788×10^2	4.725×10^{-4}

	CM HG	LB/IN.^{2}	LB/FT^2
1 newton/meter^2	7.501×10^{-4}	1.450×10^{-4}	2.089×10^{-2}
1 dyne/centimeter^2	7.501×10^{-5}	1.450×10^{-5}	2.089×10^{-3}
1 atmosphere	76	14.70	2.116×10^3
1 centimeter mercury†	1	0.1943	27.85
1 pound/inch^2	5.171	1	144
1 pound/foot^2	3.591×10^{-2}	6.944×10^{-3}	1

† At 0° C and at a location where the acceleration due to gravity has its "standard" value, 9.80665 m/sec^2.

Power

1 horsepower = 550 ft-lb/sec = 0.7457 kilowatt

appendix III

ELECTRIC AND MAGNETIC UNITS

AND CONVERSION FACTORS

In addition to the mksa, or Giorgi, system of electromagnetic units, the Gaussian system of electric and magnetic units is commonly used in scientific work. In the Gaussian system all mechanical units are those of the cgs absolute system, for example, length in cm, force in dyne, work in erg. The Gaussian system is subdivided into the electrostatic system of units (esu) for strictly electric effects and the electromagnetic system of units (emu) for strictly magnetic effects.

The basic relation defining the unit of electric charge in the esu system is Coulomb's law, which is now written in the form:

$$F = q_1 q_2/r^2 \tag{III-1}$$

where q_1 and q_2 are in esu (or statcoulomb), r is in cm, and F is in dyne. Thus, by definition, each of two equal point charges has a charge of 1 esu if they exert an electric force of 1 dyne on one another when separated by a distance of 1 cm. To express electric relations of the mksa system in a form appropriate for esu units, one replaces the constant $k = 1/4\pi\epsilon_0$ by 1. Derived units involve the prefix "stat" followed typically by the mksa unit name. Thus, current is expressed in statamp, where 1 statamp = 1 statcoulomb/sec; potential difference in statvolt, where 1 statvolt = 1 erg/statcoulomb, etc. Sometimes, however, electric units in the esu system are given simply as esu; thus, 1 esu of charge per second is said to constitute an electric current of 1 esu.

The unit for charge in the emu system is called the abcoulomb, and it is related to the unit for electric current, the abampere, by 1 abampere = 1 abcoulomb/sec, where, by definition, the force per unit length between two infinite parallel straight conductors separated by a distance d is given by

$$F = 2I^2/d \tag{III-2}$$

with I in abampere, F in dyne/cm, and d in cm. Thus, by definition, the equal currents in two parallel straight conductors separated by 1 cm are each 1 abampere when the magnetic force between them is exactly 2 dyne/cm. Other derived emu units typically take the prefix "ab" followed by the mksa unit name; for example, 1 abvolt = 1 erg/abcoul. Again, however, the units of quantities in the emu system may be given simply as emu; thus, 1 erg per emu charge corresponds to the potential difference which may be expressed merely as 1 emu, as well as 1 abvolt.

The magnitudes and units of electric charge in the esu and emu systems differ. In fact, their numerical ratio is approximately

$$1 \text{ abcoulomb}/1 \text{ statcoulomb} = 3 \times 10^{10}$$

We recognize this numerical factor to be the speed of light in vacuum expressed in cgs units, $c = 3 \times 10^{10}$ cm/sec. Relations involving both electric and magnetic quantities, such as Maxwell's equations, therefore may have the speed of light c appearing explicitly in them.

Because Equations III–1 and III–2, which define the charge units for the esu and emu systems, differ from the corresponding equations in the mksa system (Equations 25–7 and 33–21, respectively), other equations in electromagnetism may also differ in form. Listed below are some basic relations in the forms appropriate for the mksa and Gaussian systems. Following this is given a table of conversion factors. Wherever the factor 3 (or its square, 9) appears in conversion factors this number is to be taken as the numerical factor 2.997925 appearing in the speed of light when expressed in metric units, $c = 2.997925 \times 10^8$ m/sec.

RELATION	MKSA FORM	GAUSSIAN FORM
Coulomb's law (25–7)	$F = \dfrac{1}{4\pi\epsilon_0}\dfrac{q_1 q_2}{r^2}$	$F = \dfrac{q_1 q_2}{r^2}$
Biot-Savart relation (33–4)	$d\boldsymbol{B} = \dfrac{\mu_0}{4\pi}\dfrac{i\, d\boldsymbol{l} \times \boldsymbol{r}}{r^3}$	$d\boldsymbol{B} = \dfrac{i\, d\boldsymbol{l} \times \boldsymbol{r}}{r^3}$
Lorentz force (32–8)	$\boldsymbol{F} = q(\boldsymbol{E} + \boldsymbol{v} \times \boldsymbol{B})$	$\boldsymbol{F} = q\left(\boldsymbol{E} + \dfrac{1}{c}\boldsymbol{v} \times \boldsymbol{B}\right)$
Gauss's law (27–3)	$\oint \boldsymbol{E}\cdot d\boldsymbol{S} = q/\epsilon_0$	$\oint \boldsymbol{E}\cdot d\boldsymbol{S} = 4\pi q$
Faraday's law (34–9)	$\oint \boldsymbol{E}\cdot d\boldsymbol{l} = -\dfrac{d\phi_B}{dt}$	$\oint \boldsymbol{E}\cdot d\boldsymbol{l} = -\dfrac{1}{c}\dfrac{d\phi_B}{dt}$
Ampère's law (38–6)	$\oint \boldsymbol{B}\cdot d\boldsymbol{l} = \mu_0 i + \epsilon_0\mu_0\dfrac{d\phi_E}{dt}$	$\oint \boldsymbol{H}\cdot d\boldsymbol{l} = \dfrac{4\pi i}{c} + \dfrac{1}{c}\dfrac{d\phi_E}{dt}$
The field vectors (36–5) (36–18)	$\boldsymbol{D} = \epsilon_0 \boldsymbol{E} + \boldsymbol{P}$ $\boldsymbol{B} = \mu_0(\boldsymbol{H} + \boldsymbol{M})$	$\boldsymbol{D} = \boldsymbol{E} + 4\pi\boldsymbol{P}$ $\boldsymbol{B} = \boldsymbol{H} + 4\pi\boldsymbol{M}$

QUANTITY	MKSA UNIT	ESU UNIT	EMU UNIT
Electric charge	1 coul =	3×10^9 statcoul =	$\frac{1}{10}$ abcoul
Electric field (E)	1 volt/m =	$\frac{1}{3} \times 10^{-4}$ statvolt/cm =	10^6 abvolt/cm
Electric potential	1 volt =	$\frac{1}{300}$ statvolt =	10^8 abvolt
Capacitance	1 farad =	9×10^{11} statfarad =	10^{-9} abfarad
Current	1 amp =	3×10^9 statamp =	$\frac{1}{10}$ abamp
Magnetic flux	1 weber =	$\frac{1}{300}$ erg/statamp =	10^8 maxwell
Magnetic induction (B)	1 weber/m^2 =	$\frac{1}{3} \times 10^{-6}$ dyne/statamp-cm =	10^4 gauss
Magnetic field intensity (H)	1 amp-turn/m =	$3(4\pi) \times 10^7$ esu =	$4\pi \times 10^{-3}$ oersted
Resistance	1 ohm =	$\frac{4\pi}{9} \times 10^{-12}$ statohm =	10^9 abohm

appendix IV

MATHEMATICAL RELATIONS

Series Expansions

$$(a + b)^n = a^n + \frac{n}{1!} a^{n-1} b + \frac{n(n-1)}{2!} a^{n-2} b^2 + \cdots$$

$$\lim_{n \to \infty} \left(1 + \frac{x}{n}\right)^n \equiv e^x = 1 + x + \frac{x^2}{2!} + \frac{x^3}{3!} + \cdots$$

$$\sin x = x - \frac{x^3}{3!} + \frac{x^5}{5!} - \cdots$$

$$\cos x = 1 - \frac{x^2}{2!} + \frac{x^4}{4!} - \cdots$$

$$\tan x = x + \frac{x^3}{3} + \frac{2x^5}{15} + \cdots \qquad \left(\text{for } -\frac{\pi}{2} < x < \frac{\pi}{2}\right)$$

Trigonometric Identities

$$\sin^2 a + \cos^2 a = 1$$

$$\sin (a \pm b) = \sin a \cos b \pm \cos a \sin b$$

$$\cos (a \pm b) = \cos a \cos b \mp \sin a \sin b$$

Numerical Constants

$$\pi = 3.14159$$

$$e = 2.71828$$

$$\sqrt{2} = 1.414$$

$$\sqrt{3} = 1.732$$

Numerical Constants (*cont.*)

$$1 \text{ radian} = 57.3°$$

$$\sin 30° = \cos 60° = \frac{1}{2} = 0.500$$

$$\cos 30° = \sin 60° = \frac{\sqrt{3}}{2} = 0.866$$

$$\sin 45° = \cos 45° = \frac{\sqrt{2}}{2} = 0.707$$

For small θ (in radians), $\sin \theta \simeq \theta$, $\tan \theta \simeq \theta$.

appendix V

CHRONOLOGY OF IMPORTANT ADVANCES IN CLASSICAL ELECTROMAGNETISM AND WAVE MOTION

Listed below are the dates of first publication or announcement of important advances in classical electromagnetism, light, and wave motion, together with the scientist responsible. This brief chronology does not list significant advances in mathematics or in the philosophy of science, nor does it list contributions of the scientists to other branches of physics (see Appendix IV, Volume I).

The following books give excerpts (in English) from original papers:

Magie, W. F., *A Source Book of Physics*, New York: McGraw-Hill Book Company, Inc., 1935.

M. H. Shamos, *Great Experiments in Physics*, New York: Holt, Rinehart and Winston, Inc., 1960.

Elementary physics textbooks giving more emphasis to the history of classical physics are:

Taylor, L. M., *Physics, the Pioneer Science*, New York: Dover Publications, 1959.

Holton, G. J., and D. H. D. Roller, *Foundations of Modern Physical Science*, Reading, Mass.: Addison-Wesley Publishing Company, 1958.

Rogers, E. M., *Physics for the Inquiring Mind*, Princeton, N.J.: Princeton University Press, 1960.

Publication date	*Scientist or Group*	*Discovery or Accomplishment*
ca. 500 B.C.	Thales (ca. 636–ca. 546 B.C.)	Electrostatic attraction
ca. A.D. 140	Ptolemy, Claudius (ca. A.D. 140)	Approximate form of Snell's law

Publication date	Scientist or Group	Discovery or Accomplishment
A.D. 1600	Gilbert, William (1544–1603)	Properties of magnets
1621	Snell, Willebrod (1591–1626)	Refraction law for light
1637	Descartes, René (1596–1650)	Particle theory of light refraction
1650	de Fermat, Pierre (1608–1665)	Principle of least time for light propagation
1665	Grimaldi, Francesco M. (1618–1663)	Diffraction of light discovery
1665	Hooke, Robert (1635–1703)	Wave theory of light
1669	Bartholinus, Erasmus (1625–1692)	Double refraction
1672	Newton, Sir Isaac (1642–1727)	Dispersion of white light into spectrum, Newton's rings, particle theory of light
1676	Roemer, Ole (1644–1710)	First measured speed of light
1678	Huygens, Christian (1629–1695)	Wave theory of light
1729	Bradley, James (1692–1762)	Speed of light by stellar aberration
1731	Gray, Stephen (1696–1736)	Electric conductors and non-conductors
1734	Dufay, Charles (1698–1739)	Observed two kinds of electricity
1746	Nollet, Jean A. (1700–1770)	Leyden jar (a rudimentary capacitor)
1747	Franklin, Benjamin (1706–1790)	Static electricity, the "one-fluid" theory
1785	de Coulomb, Charles-Augustin (1736–1806)	Electric force law
1791	Galvani, Luigi (1737–1798)	Electric current and its effect on frogs' legs
1800	Volta, Alessandro (1745–1827)	Voltaic cell
1803	Young, Thomas (1773–1829)	Interference of light
1809	Malus, Étienne L. (1775–1812)	Polarization of light in reflection
1814	Fresnel, Augustin J. (1788–1827)	Diffraction theory
1815	Brewster, Sir David (1781–1868)	Polarization of light and reflected intensity
1819	Arago, Dominique-François J. (1786–1853)	Diffraction and polarization of light waves, magnetization by electric currents

Publication date	Scientist or Group	Discovery or Accomplishment
A.D. 1820	Biot, Jean Baptiste (1774–1862) and Savart, Félix (1791–1841)	Magnetic field around a long straight current-carrying conductor
1820	Oersted, Hans Christian (1777–1851)	Magnetic field associated with electric current
1820	Ampère, André-Marie (1775–1836)	Magnetic force between current-carrying conductors
1821	von Fraunhofer, Joseph (1787–1826)	Diffraction grating
1826	Ohm, George S. (1789–1854)	Law for electrical resistance
1828	Green, George (1793–1841)	Concept of potential, theory of wave propagation in elastic media
1831	Faraday, Michael (1791–1867)	Electromagnetic induction, electrolysis, ice-pail experiment, concept of field lines, diamagnetism
1832	Henry, Joseph (1797–1878)	Electromagnetic induction
1834	Lenz, Heinrich F. E. (1804–1865)	Lenz's law for the sense of induced currents
1837	Wheatstone, Sir Charles (1802–1875)	Electric circuits, telegraphy, color and vision
1841	Gauss, Karl F. (1777–1855)	Measurement of electric and magnetic quantities in absolute units
1841	Joule, James P. (1818–1889)	Thermal energy dissipation in electric conductors
1842	Doppler, Christian J. (1803–1853)	Wave frequencies with source or observer in motion
1849	Fizeau, Armand H. L. (1819–1896)	Speed of light measurement
1850	Foucault, Jean B. L. (1819–1868)	Speed of light measurement
1859	Kirchhoff, Gustav R. (1824–1887)	Spectroscope studies, electric circuits
1864	Maxwell, James Clerk (1831–1879)	Unified electromagnetic theory, electromagnetic waves
1878	Rowland, Henry A. (1848–1901)	Magnetic field produced by charges in motion
1879	Hall, Edwin H. (1855–1938)	The Hall effect
1880	Lorentz, Hendrik A. (1853–1928)	Electromagnetic theory
1881	Michelson, Albert A. (1852–1931)	Interferometer, speed of light measurements

Publication date	Scientist or Group	Discovery or Accomplishment
A.D. 1884	Poynting, John H. (1852–1914)	Electromagnetic energy flow
1887	Hertz, Heinrich R. (1857–1894)	Measured properties of electromagnetic waves
1897	Thomson, Sir Joseph J. (1856–1940)	Electron discoverer, e/m measurement
1901	Lebedev, Pëtr N. (1866–1912)	Pressure of light detected
1906	Barkla, Charles G. (1877–1944)	X-rays as transverse waves through double scattering experiment
1909	Millikan, Robert A. (1868–1953)	Electronic charge measurement in oil-drop experiment
1911	Kamerlingh-Onnes, Heike (1853–1926)	Superconductivity
1911	Rutherford, Sir Ernest (1871–1937)	Coulomb scattering of charged particles by atomic nuclei
1931	Van de Graaff, Robert J. (1901–)	Electrostatic particle accelerator
1932	Lawrence, Ernest O. (1901–1958) and Livingston, M. S. (1905–)	Cyclotron particle accelerator
1934	Cerenkov, Pavel A. (1904–)	Electromagnetic radiation from charged particles moving through dielectrics
1935	Beth, Richard A. (1906–)	Angular momentum of circularly polarized light measurement
1941	Kerst, Donald W. (1911–)	Betatron electron accelerator
1960	Townes, Charles H. (1915–)	Laser concept

a p p e n d i x V I

NATURAL TRIGONOMETRIC FUNCTIONS

ANGLE		SINE	COSINE	TANGENT	ANGLE		SINE	COSINE	TANGENT
DEGREES	RADIANS				DEGREES	RADIANS			
0°	0.000	0.000	1.000	0.000					
1°	0.018	0.018	1.000	0.018					
2°	0.035	0.035	0.999	0.035	46°	0.803	0.719	0.695	1.036
3°	0.052	0.052	0.999	0.052	47°	0.820	0.731	0.682	1.072
4°	0.070	0.070	0.998	0.070	48°	0.838	0.743	0.669	1.111
5°	0.087	0.087	0.996	0.087	49°	0.855	0.755	0.656	1.150
					50°	0.873	0.766	0.643	1.192
6°	0.105	0.105	0.995	0.105					
7°	0.122	0.122	0.993	0.123	51°	0.890	0.777	0.629	1.235
8°	0.140	0.139	0.990	0.141	52°	0.908	0.788	0.616	1.280
9°	0.157	0.156	0.988	0.158	53°	0.925	0.799	0.602	1.327
10°	0.175	0.174	0.985	0.176	54°	0.942	0.809	0.588	1.376
					55°	0.960	0.819	0.574	1.428
11°	0.192	0.191	0.982	0.194					
12°	0.209	0.208	0.978	0.213	56°	0.977	0.829	0.559	1.483
13°	0.227	0.225	0.974	0.231	57°	0.995	0.839	0.545	1.540
14°	0.244	0.242	0.970	0.249	58°	1.012	0.848	0.530	1.600
15°	0.262	0.259	0.966	0.268	59°	1.030	0.857	0.515	1.664
					60°	1.047	0.866	0.500	1.732
16°	0.279	0.276	0.961	0.287					
17°	0.297	0.292	0.956	0.306	61°	1.065	0.875	0.485	1.804
18°	0.314	0.309	0.951	0.325	62°	1.082	0.883	0.470	1.881
19°	0.332	0.326	0.946	0.344	63°	1.100	0.891	0.454	1.963
20°	0.349	0.342	0.940	0.364	64°	1.117	0.899	0.438	2.050
					65°	1.134	0.906	0.423	2.145
21°	0.367	0.358	0.934	0.384					
22°	0.384	0.375	0.927	0.404	66°	1.152	0.914	0.407	2.246
23°	0.401	0.391	0.921	0.425	67°	1.169	0.921	0.391	2.356
24°	0.419	0.407	0.914	0.445	68°	1.187	0.927	0.375	2.475
25°	0.436	0.423	0.906	0.466	69°	1.204	0.934	0.358	2.605
					70°	1.222	0.940	0.342	2.747
26°	0.454	0.438	0.899	0.488					
27°	0.471	0.454	0.891	0.510	71°	1.239	0.946	0.326	2.904
28°	0.489	0.470	0.883	0.532	72°	1.257	0.951	0.309	3.078
29°	0.506	0.485	0.875	0.554	73°	1.274	0.956	0.292	3.271
30°	0.524	0.500	0.866	0.577	74°	1.292	0.961	0.276	3.487
					75°	1.309	0.966	0.259	3.732
31°	0.541	0.515	0.857	0.601					
32°	0.559	0.530	0.848	0.625	76°	1.327	0.970	0.242	4.011
33°	0.576	0.545	0.839	0.649	77°	1.344	0.974	0.225	4.331
34°	0.593	0.559	0.829	0.675	78°	1.361	0.978	0.208	4.705
35°	0.611	0.574	0.819	0.700	79°	1.379	0.982	0.191	5.145
					80°	1.396	0.985	0.174	5.671
36°	0.628	0.588	0.809	0.727					
37°	0.646	0.602	0.799	0.754	81°	1.414	0.988	0.156	6.314
38°	0.663	0.616	0.788	0.781	82°	1.431	0.990	0.139	7.115
39°	0.681	0.629	0.777	0.810	83°	1.449	0.993	0.122	8.144
40°	0.698	0.643	0.766	0.839	84°	1.466	0.995	0.105	9.514
					85°	1.484	0.996	0.087	11.43
41°	0.716	0.656	0.755	0.869					
42°	0.733	0.669	0.743	0.900	86°	1.501	0.998	0.070	14.30
43°	0.751	0.682	0.731	0.933	87°	1.518	0.999	0.052	19.08
44°	0.768	0.695	0.719	0.966	88°	1.536	0.999	0.035	28.64
45°	0.785	0.707	0.707	1.000	89°	1.553	1.000	0.018	57.29
					90°	1.571	1.000	0.000	∞

appendix VII

THE GREEK ALPHABET

Alpha	α	A
Beta	β	B
Gamma	γ	Γ
Delta	δ	Δ
Epsilon	ϵ	E
Zeta	ζ	Z
Eta	η	H
Theta	θ, ϑ	Θ
Iota	ι	I
Kappa	κ	K
Lambda	λ	Λ
Mu	μ	M
Nu	ν	N
Xi	ξ	Ξ
Omicron	o	O
Pi	π	Π
Rho	ρ	P
Sigma	σ, s	Σ
Tau	τ	T
Upsilon	υ	Υ
Phi	ϕ, φ	Φ
Chi	χ	X
Psi	ψ	Ψ
Omega	ω	Ω

ANSWERS

to odd-numbered numerical problems

CHAPTER 25

25–1 $1.91 \, kq^2/L^2$

25–3 4.0×10^{-7} coul

25–5   21 cm from the 0.30 μcoul charge, 15 cm from the −0.15 μcoul charge.

25–9   Perpendicular to line of charge

25–11 $2q(2k/md)^{1/2}/\pi d$ cps, where d is distance between fixed charges

25–15   due to polarization effects

25–17 3.6×10^{16} rad/sec

25–19   heavy nuclei

25–23   due to the weakness of the gravitational force compared with the electrical force

25–25 1.1×10^6 m/sec

25–27   Stars do not attract or repel one another by electric force

25–29   3.0 gm

25–31   (a) 33°;   (b) 143°

25–33   45° with respect to incident proton

CHAPTER 26

26–1 2.0×10^4 nt/coul west

26–3 $1.3 \times 10^{13}Q$ nt/coul nearly parallel to positive X-axis

26–7   (d) $0.35d$

26–9   (a) 34 nt/coul east;   (b) 63,000 nt/coul east

26–11 6.7×10^5 volts/m

26–13   (a) 5.1×10^{11} nt/coul;   (b) 4.5 coul/m²

26–15   (a) as r^{-2};   (b) as r^{-3}

26–19 1.1×10^{-10} coul/m

26–21 1.1×10^{-8} coul/m²

26–23   Induced charges on conductor, but not on dielectric

26–25   (a) 1.6×10^{-10} nt-sec/m;   (b) 0.60 mm/sec downward;   (c) 4.9 mm/sec upward

26–27   (a) 6.0×10^{-9} coul-m;   (b) 8.0×10^{-5} joule

26–31   (a) center of mass moves along parabolic path, rod oscillates about center of mass in simple harmonic motion;   (b) $\pi v \sqrt{md}/10qE$;   (c) velocity component parallel to $E = \pi\sqrt{qEd/90m}$, velocity component perpendicular to $E = v$, angular velocity $= \sqrt{5qE/2md}$

CHAPTER 27

27–1   1.0 nt-m²/coul

27–3   (a) $Q/6\epsilon_0$;   (b) not at all;   (c) different faces would have different fluxes

27–7   Zero

27–9 $\dfrac{1}{2\pi} \sqrt{kqQ/mR^3}$

27–11   (a) Zero; nt/coul;   (b) 3.2×10^6 nt/coul outward;   (c) -4.5×10^5 nt/coul inward

27–13   As $1/r$

27–17   (a) zero

27–19   (a) periodic motion with constant velocity while inside shell; (b) 11×10^{-9} sec $<$ period $< 16 \times 10^{-9}$ sec

CHAPTER 28

28–1 4.6×10^{-19} joule

28–3 1.2×10^{-18} joule

28–5 4.2×10^7 m/sec

28–7   (a) zero; (b) zero

28–9 $\sqrt{2.6kq^2/mL^3}$ rad/sec

28–13   (a) -40 joule;   (b) -40 joule;   (c) $+180$ joule;   (d) $+140$ joule; (e) -360 joule

28–15 4.6×10^6 m/sec

28–17   0.11 volt

28–19   1.0 cm

28–25   (a) $15ke^2/4R$; (b) $2ke^2/R$

28–29   0.062

CHAPTER 29

29–1 1.6×10^{-9} farad

29–7 5.0×10^{-10} farad

29–9   16

29–11   (a) two in series connected to three in parallel; (b) ten in series (c) five in series

29–13   (a) 1.4×10^{-6} farad; (b) 2.3×10^{-6} farad

29–17   (a) 8.8×10^{-9} farad; (b) 240 volt

29–19 $2\epsilon_0 A\kappa/d(\kappa + 1)$

29–23 1.0×10^8

29–25 1.5×10^{-2} joule

29–29 1.8×10^3 joule/m³

CHAPTER 30

30–1 2.4×10^{-6} amp

30–3 2.2×10^4 amp/m²

30–5   0.71 amp

30–7   50 watt

30–9   14 hours

30–11   (a) 0.80 amp; (b) 80 watt; (c) 0.80 amp; (d) 160 watt

30–13   5.9 m

30–15   (a) 3.9×10^7 amp/m²; (b) 0.58 volt; (c) 4.2×10^{-3} m/sec

30–17 4.0×10^7 volt

30–19 $(r_2 - r_1)/4\pi\sigma r_1 r_2$

30–23 2.2×10^7 ohm

CHAPTER 31

31–1   12 volt

31–3   2.0

31–5   130 volt
31–7   (a) 2.0 volt;   (b) 0.50 amp;   (c) 16 watt
31–9   0.83 ohm
31–11 Nine resistors.   Three groups in series, each group having three resistors in parallel
31–13 1.3 amp, 0.71 amp, −2.0 amp
31–17 (a) 0.22 ohm;   (b) 0.020 ohm
31–19 (a) zero;   (b) 9000 ohm;   (c) 90,000 ohm
31–21 (a) $[(R_2R_x − R_1R_s)(i_1 + i_2)]/$
$[R_G(R_1 + R_2 + R_s + R_x) + (R_1 + R_x)(R_2 + R_s)]$

31–23 (a) 5.0 amp;   (b) 250 volt;   (c) 1250 amp (off scale);   (d) 250 volt;
(e) ammeter

CHAPTER 32
32–1 $2\pi m/qB$
32–3 1.2×10^7 nt/coul
32–5   (a) electron;   (b) 1.8×10^7 m/sec; 88 kev
32–7 2.3×10^{-5} weber
32–9   45°
32–11 $2V/B^2R^2$
32–15 (a) 1.7 cm;   (b) 1.7 cm
32–17 ∼3
32–19 (a) west;   (b) 0.80 nt
32–21 $mg(\tan \theta)/BL$
32–23 4.7×10^{-5} m-nt
32–25 4.0×10^3 amp-m²
32–27 Counterclockwise

CHAPTER 33
33–1 2.0×10^{-10} w/m²
33–5   3.3 cm
33–7   5.6 amp
33–9   9.6 nt-m
33–11 $\sqrt{2}\ \mu_0I/\pi L$
33–13 $(\mu_0IL/2\pi) \ln (1 + L/R)$
33–15 (a) tends to align plane of loop perpendicular to paper and then attracted toward wire;   (b) loop remains motionless
33–19 (a) 2.0×10^{-2} w/m²;   (b) 1.0×10^{-2} w/m²;   (c) 1.0×10^{-2} w/m²
33–21 Current density varies as $1/r$

CHAPTER 34
34–1 9.0×10^{-2} volt
34–5 3.0×10^{-5} volt, counterclockwise as seen by man
34–7   Counterclockwise (looking down)
34–9 2.5×10^{-3} volt
34–11 2.0×10^{-5} volt
34–13 0.28 weber/m²-sec
34–15 (a) 1.6 volt;   (b) moving end
34–17 $Rmg \sin \theta/B^2l^2 \cos^2 \theta$
34–21 (a) 1.0×10^{-3} volt/m;   (b) 1.6×10^{-3} volt/m;   (c) 0.80×10^{-3} volt/m
34–23 $(6.0 \times 10^{-3}$ volt/m$) \cos 2\pi t$
34–27 (a) 2.5×10^4;   (b) 1.6×10^5 m;   (c) 32 volt/m;   (d) 64 weber/m²-sec

CHAPTER 35
35–1 (a) 6.3×10^{-5} weber/m²; (b) 2.0×10^{-8} weber; (c) 4.0×10^{-8} volt
35–3 (a) 2 henry; (b) 5 ohm
35–9 (a) 30 mh; (b) 10 ohm
35–11 (a) $\mathcal{E}/R_1$, 0, $\mathcal{E}/R_1$; (b) $\mathcal{E}/R_1$, 0, $\mathcal{E}/R_1$
35–13 (a) 0.25 volt; (b) 0.10 joule
35–15 (a) 7.7×10^{-4} sec; (b) 10×10^{-4} sec
35–17 $\mu_0 N^2 i^2 / 8 r^2$

CHAPTER 37
37–1 1.8 μf
37–3 2

37–5 (a) $L \dfrac{d^2q}{dt^2} + R \dfrac{dq}{dt} + q/C = 0$

37–7 (a) 1.7×10^{-2} henry; (b) 28 ohm
37–9 Decrease the frequency
37–11 (a) inductive; (b) 9.1 millihenry
37–13 Increase

CHAPTER 39
39–1 0.62 kg/m
39–5 (a) 7.0 m/sec; (b) 9.9 m/sec
39–13 (a) 64 cm/sec; (b) 3.0 cm; (c) 3.2 cycles/sec; (d) 20 cm; (e) to the right; (f) $y = (3.0 \text{ cm}) \cos (0.31x - 20t)$
39–17 (a) 57 watt; (b) 5700 watt
39–19 (a) $2.0\sqrt{\rho_1/\rho_2}$ cm; (b) 100 cycles/sec; (c) $(2.00 \text{ mm}) \sqrt{4 - \sqrt{\rho_2/\rho_1}}$
39–21 1.4 Å
39–23 1.0×10^3 cycles/sec
39–27 2.1 m
39–29 2
39–33 (b) $(2n + 1)c/4L$
39–35 1.1
39–43 (a) standing linearly polarized wave; (b) standing circularly polarized wave

CHAPTER 40
40–1 (a) 1.3×10^3 m/sec; (b) 4.3×10^{10} nt/m²; (c) 0.33
40–5 2.1×10^9 nt/m²
40–7 0.071 sec
40–9 $\sqrt{F_t/YA}$
40–11 (a) 2.0 m; (b) 2.0×10^{11} nt/m²
40–15 30° C
40–17 (a) no; (b) no
40–19 1.7×10^{-3} C°
40–21 (a) 2.0 nt/m²; (b) 32 cycles/sec; (c) 1.0 m; (d) 32 m/sec
40–23 (a) 3.6×10^{-3} m; (b) 0.35 watt; (c) 1.1×10^3 watt/m²
40–25 5.4×10^{-4} m
40–27 0.41 m

40–29   2.9
40–31   (a) 60 db;   (b) 120 db

CHAPTER 41
41–1   (a) along negative X-axis;   (b) 3.3×10^{-7} weber/m²
41–3 N/v
41–9 7.3×10^4 watt
41–11 1.6×10^{-4} m
41–13 PL/c
41–15   (a) $1.4\ P/c$;   (b) perpendicular to surface
41–17   (a) 3.0 m;   (b) 6.0×10^6
41–19 9.5×10^{24} m
41–21 7.6×10^{-6} sec
41–23 5.8×10^{-5} sec
41–25   0.17

CHAPTER 42
42–1 1.3×10^{-9} watt
42–3 3.9×10^{26} watt
42–5 1.3×10^6 m²
42–7 1.5×10^{14} watt
42–9 2.0×10^{-9} joule
42–11 2.7×10^3 cycles/sec
42–13   (a) 88 ft/sec;   (b) 1.0×10^3 cycles/sec
42–15   (a) f_0;   (b) $f_0(1 - v/c)/(1 + v/c)$;   (c) $f_0/(1 + v/c)$;   (d) $f_0/(1 + v/c)$
42–17   10 Mc/sec less 1.8 c/sec
42–19   (a) 10,000 cycles/sec;   (b) 10,000 cycles/sec
42–23   15 sec
42–25   3600 Å
42–29 2.8×10^8 m/sec

CHAPTER 43
43–9 8.8×10^{-4} m
43–11   (a) 1.8 percent;   (b) 7.8 percent
43–13   16 feet
43–17   0.75 mm
43–25   (a) 63°;   (b) glass

CHAPTER 44
44–1   (a) real image 45 cm on opposite side;   (b) real image 60 cm on opposite
          side;   (c) infinite;   (d) virtual image 30 cm on same side
44–5   (a) 6.2×10^{-4};   (b) same;   (c) no;   (d) zero
44–7   More shallow region
44–9   At focal length, 1.7 cm off axis
44–11   13 cm
44–13   106 cm
44–23   (a) virtual image 24 cm on same side as object;   (b) virtual image 40 cm
          on same side as object
44–25   (a) 80 cm on opposite side of object;   (b) 160 cm on opposite side of
          object;   (c) 80 cm on same side as object

44–27 $s'/n_{21}s$
44–29 5.8 cm
44–31 67 cm
44–33 1.6

CHAPTER 45

45–1 (a) zero, zero, 4.0×10^{-3} watt/m², 4.0×10^{-3} watt/m²; (b) 4.0×10^{-3} watt/m², 4.0×10^{-3} watt/m², zero, zero; (c) zero, 4.0×10^{-3} watt/m², 2.0×10^{-3} watt/m², 2.0×10^{-3} watt/m²

45–3 (a) at odd ($\lambda/4$) from either end; (b) at even ($\lambda/4$) from either end

45–5 14°

45–7 (a) $P/2\pi R$, $P/2\pi R$, $P/2\pi R$; (b) 0, $4P/2\pi R$, $2P/2\pi R$; (c) $4P/2\pi R$, 0, $2P/2\pi R$; (d) $2P/2\pi R$, $2P/2\pi R$, $2P/2\pi R$

45–11 76°

45–13 4.2 cm

45–15 1.1×10^3 m

45–17 7.5×10^{-4} m

45–19 9.0×10^{-6} m

45–21 1.1×10^{-7} m

CHAPTER 46

46–5 0.45 mm
46–7 Pattern reduced in size; by factor n for small angles
46–9 (a) 2.9°; (b) 3.8°; (c) 5.7°
46–13 0.038 mm
46–15 3.5°
46–17 1.0×10^3
46–19 (a) 7.0×10^{-4} mm; (b) 55°
46–21 982
46–23 (a) 0°, 5.7°, 12°, 17°, 24°, 30°, 37°, 44°, 53°, 64°, 90° with respect to east-west line; (b) 0.96°; (c) same as part a; (d) 0.48°

CHAPTER 47

47–1 22.5° above X-axis
47–3 Vertical
47–5 East-west
47–7 48°
47–11 21 sec
47–13 Elliptical, same sense as larger
47–15 1.6×10^{-5} m
47–17 (a) 1.0; (b) $2P/\omega$

INDEX

Snell's law, 1069, 1079, 1099
Solenoid, 837
  inductance, 872
Sonar, 1005
Sound waves, 990
  intensity, 993
Spectrometer:
  diffraction-grating, 1182
  prism, 1082
Spectrum:
  acoustic, 1003
  electromagnetic, 1032
  zero-order, 1181
Speed, electromagnetic wave, 1013
Speed of light, 1013
  measurement, 1033
  microwave interferometer, 1155
  vacuum, 1038
  water, 1080
Speed, wave, 988
  string, 943, 946
Spherical aberration, 1111
Spin angular momentum, 1204
Standing waves, 965, 995
Stationary wave, 965
Stellar aberration, 1035
Strength:
  electric field, 632
Superconductor, 746
Superposition, 618, 776, 948, 995
  polarized waves, 974
  simple harmonic motion, 1190
  sinusoidal waves, 960
  two and three dimensions, 1134
Surface integral:
  current, 732
  electric, 656
  gravitational, 673
  magnetic, 784
Surface waves, 1001
Susceptibility, 885, 891
Synchrocyclotron, 797

T

Tandem Van de Graaff generator, 695
Telescope:
  astronomical, 1113
  Galilean, 1116
Temperature coefficient of resistivity, 745
Thin lens, 1099, 1105, 1125
  sign conventions, 1128
Thomson, J. J., 793
  atomic model, 666
Threshold of feeling, 994
Threshold of hearing, 994
Time constant:
  LR circuit, 873
  RC circuit, 747
Tonal quality, 1002
Tone, 970
Toroid, 842, 885
  inductance, 872

Torque:
  magnetic, 801
Torsional waves, 999
Torsion pendulum, 615, 629
Total internal reflection, 1085
Tourmaline, 1195
Townes, C. H., 1146
Transverse waves:
  solid, 998
  string, 944
Traveling wave, 942

U

Ultraviolet light, 1033

V

Van Allen radiation belt, 788
Van de Graaff generator, 614, 694, 797
  tandem, 695
Velocity selector, 790
Virtual wave, 952
Visible light, 1033
Volt, 684
Volta, A., 684
Voltage divider, 773
Voltmeter, 769

W

Wave energy, string, 959
Wave equation, 947
Wave fronts, 1044
Wavelength, 954
Wave number, 955
Wave optics, 1067
Wave pulse, 942
  interference, 949
  reflection, 951
Waves:
  bending, 1000
  electromagnetic, 1010
  equation, 947
  frequency, 954
  gas, 990
  interference, 950
  longitudinal, 984
  membrane, 1001
  nodes, 965
  optical reversibility, 1058
  period, 954
  reciprocity principle, 1058
  reflection, 950, 953
  shock, 1056
  sinusoidal, 953
  speed, 943, 946, 957, 988, 991
  standing, 965
  superposition, 948, 960
  surface, 1001
  torsional, 999
  transmission, 953
  transverse, 944, 998

CONVERSION
FACTORS

(See also Appendices II *and* III)